# MODERN FICTION ABOUT SCHOOLTEACHING

## AN ANTHOLOGY

*edited by*

**JAY S. BLANCHARD**

**AND**

**URSULA CASANOVA**

*Arizona State University*

**Foreword by Robert Coles, MD**

**ALLYN AND BACON**

*Boston   London   Toronto   Sydney   Tokyo   Singapore*

Executive Editor: Virginia Lanigan
Editorial Assistant: Nihad Farooq
Executive Marketing Manager: Kathy Hunter
Editorial-Production Service: Susan McNally
Composition Buyer: Linda Cox
Manufacturing Buyer: Aloka Rathnam
Cover Administrator: Suzanne Harbison

Copyright © 1996 by Allyn & Bacon
A Simon & Schuster Company
Needham Heights, MA 02194

**Library of Congress Cataloging-in-Publication Data**

Modern fiction about schoolteaching : an anthology / edited by Jay S.
  Blanchard and Ursula Casanova.
    p.   cm.
  Includes bibliographical references and index.
  ISBN 0-205-15250-3
  1. Education—Fiction.  2. Teachers—Social life and customs—
Fiction.  3. Teacher-student relationships—Fiction.  4. Teaching—
Fiction.  5. American fiction.  I. Blanchard, Jay S.
II. Casanova, Ursula.
PS648.E33M63    1995
813'.0108355—dc20                    95-36930
                                       CIP

Printed in the United States of America

10  9  8  7  6  5  4  3  2  1    00  99  98  97  96  95

*This book is dedicated to all teachers: those who taught us in the past, those who teach our children today, and those who will teach our grandchildren in the future.*

# TABLE OF CONTENTS

# FOREWORD

William Carlos Williams, the poet and writer of fiction, also happened to be a pediatrician who worked for many years as a school doctor, much interested not only in the health of the students he met, but their educational experience and progress. I wrote my college thesis on his work, got to know him, did a number of formal interviews with him (when tape-recorders were a mammoth presence, indeed!), and heard him talk often about "school-teaching," a phrase he, like the editors of this book, very much favored: "I've watched the kids in the classroom—they're different there, than when they come to see me in the 'sick room.'... The teachers try hard, and the kids know that, and they're grateful, and so they try to pay attention and do their work. Of course, like in every line of work, some teachers are better than others!... I'm talking better prepared: they've...got themselves some good stuff for those kids to read, and for *themselves* to read, and so when you go in their rooms, there's electricity in the air, and kids' arms are waving, and the teacher is working overtime to keep the traffic orderly, so only one person is speaking at a time. The excitement is there—you feel it, you see it, you hear it: they've read a good story, and they're wide awake, because the energy in it is now in them."

Vintage Dr. Williams—his blunt, vigorous, earthy way of getting to the heart of things. He himself wrote short stories and in them tried to do what a writer of fiction can do so wonderfully, tellingly well: convey life's complexities, its ambiguities and ironies, its inevitable inconsistencies and outright contradictions. These days, many of us who teach have, alas, little patience with such a point of view—we prefer the categorizations, the formulations (that become reifications) of the social sciences—the either/or mentality of multiple choice tests. Williams used to insist, however, that there was a lot he didn't know, only suspected, thought about, and wondered about: "Answers can be too pat—and how we look for them!" I fear we have become even hungrier for such "pat answers"—a contrast, indeed, with the attitude fostered by a solid, suggestive, well-told tale: stop and think about this world; be ready for its surprises—the turns of fate, of luck and chance, that await all of us, around this or that corner.

In that regard, the novelist and short story writer Flannery O'Connor threw down the gauntlet over a generation ago when she declared that "it is the business of fiction to embody mystery through manners, and mystery is a great embarrassment to the modern mind." She meant, thereby, to remind us of what she called "our position on this earth." We are the creature of awareness: through language, we can ask questions; we know that time is given us, and time runs out on us; we understand that accidents and incidents, expected and unforeseen, can slowly shape our lives or suddenly alter them—or end them. Such knowledge is the very stuff of fiction, of art imitating life. The reverse can also happen: we read a story, and its magic, its moral energy, its persuasiveness, its capacity to stir our thoughts and our imaginations make it a real force within us, a means by which we contemplate our past experiences and prepare for those awaiting us.

The stories about schoolteaching that follow are very much in the tradition given voice by Williams and O'Connor—they remind us that a classroom is part of that well-known "stage" that Shakespeare mentioned: "all the world" is forever taking part in the human drama that occurs when people come together, try to get on, speak their various parts, depart. A classroom is a daily scene in this drama, wherein the coming and going of human beings—teachers, students, parents, and others—prompts a wide range of responses, depending upon who the characters are, where they come from, and what they bring to that time spent listening, speaking, assigning tasks, and doing them. The schoolteaching that occurs there takes various forms: lessons given and learned are intermingled with memorable moments that leave their impression not only on the mind, but on the heart, even the soul—moments when something said or done sticks fast to a teacher, a student, a room full of students.

"I was sitting at my desk," a child once told me, "and I saw the teacher crying, and I wondered why, why she was crying." The child didn't continue, so I asked him what had moved the teacher to tears: "She was reading us a story, and I guess it got to her, so she had to use her handkerchief. I don't think I'll ever forget her being like that." In this instance, the story being read was not a "classic" included in a collection such as this. Rather, the teacher had chosen to read to her class a report from the daily newspaper, concerning a child's brave, year-long struggle against a fatal disease—a struggle the teacher herself had witnessed a decade earlier, waged by her own daughter. The teacher's sharing of stories—one from her own life, one that she had read—had profoundly impressed this eleven-year-old child; the experience had become a thread in his own story.

So it will be for the readers who encounter the stories in the pages that follow, at the behest of their teachers in their own classroom situations: readings that especially touch them will become a part of their own lives. In turn, their stories—their lives—embody an aspect of the "mystery" that is at the heart of our existence, which narrative excursions, whether written or spoken (the daily accounts we offer one another) evoke so compellingly. Stories, then, are what we have, what we seek, and what we very much need—thus this book will wonderfully fill the appetites of its readers, quench their thirst.

Robert Coles, M.D.

Robert Coles is a child psychiatrist and Pulitzer Prize-winning author. He is presently a Research Psychiatrist for Harvard University Health Services in Cambridge, Massachusetts. He is the author of *Children in Crisis* (five volumes), *The Moral Life of Children, The Political Life of Children, The Call of Stories,* and *The Story of Ruby Bridges.*

# INTRODUCTION

People live in a world of stories. They are born into a world full of stories, their lives are stories and so are their deaths. Everyone listens to and tells stories—short ones and long ones—simple ones and complex ones—tragic ones and happy ones. Stories have been used throughout history to organize and communicate meaning, as well as to ponder the mysterious, the magical, and the unexplainable. Whether fictional or factual, whether spoken, written, or drawn, stories help us to remember, to understand, to explain, and to find intellectual, social, and spiritual meaning.

In the opening dialogue of the novel *Ceremony* by Leslie Silko, a character describes the compelling importance of stories in people's lives: "Let me tell you something about stories, they aren't just entertainment, don't be fooled. They are all we have, you see, all we have to fight off illness and death. You don't have anything if you don't have stories." Expanding on this view, the writer Ursula K. Le Guin notes that "stories are important because they're where we learn most of our real working skills: what we expect of life, what we expect to give to living. Our myths, our movies, our comics, and horror stories aren't mere wishful fictions of what we want to pretend was once upon a time. Story is our nearest and dearest way of understanding our lives and finding our way onward."

This is an anthology of fictional stories about schoolteaching. We believe these stories can enrich the lives of readers and teach as well.[1] We are not alone in suggesting that stories can be used for teaching. And, we are not alone in trying to make fictional stories on teaching and learning more accessible. Others have preceded us.[2] For instance, Elliott Landau, Sherrie Epstein, and Ann Stone address the role fiction can play in learning about child development:

> *The art of literature has its power to elicit emotion, and we hope that literature will add a personal, emotional dimension to the usual intellective approach to the subject [child development]. The principles of child development may be gleaned in many ways and through the many authoritative traditional texts, but to step into the moccasins of a child or of a parent (or of a teacher) requires more than the statement of the problem and the tabulation of data. Emotional involvement other than that attained though firsthand experience is possible only through the perceptions and narration of the literary artist.*

## Fictional Stories and Schoolteaching

Fictional stories consist of imagined plots, events, characters, actions, and settings. The students, teachers, and schools in this anthology exist only in the minds of the authors and the readers. Although the authors have done the writing, it is the readers that "imagine" the stories, and as J. Hillis Miller has noted:

> *With fiction we investigate, perhaps, invent the meaning of human life. In fiction we reorder the givens of experience. We give experience a form and a meaning, a linear order with a shapely beginning, middle and end, and central theme. The human capacity to tell stories is one way men and women collectively build a significant and orderly world around themselves.*

Fictional stories are especially powerful tools for teaching and learning. Detached enough from the actual life of the reader, they allow unbiased exploration of a particular situation, and yet, at the same time, they evoke empathizing responses. Iris Tiedt notes that fiction offers "an opportunity to engage in life with other human beings, to empathize, to understand, and to share responses with others. This involvement with the complexities of life and the willingness to admit human frailty and vulnerability provide a kind of learning . . . that is not available in any pedagogical textbook." Consider this excerpt about a school teacher named Mrs. Womble from the "The Second Grade Mind" by Frances Gray Patton:

> *Carol Nelson met Mrs. Womble, who was to be her son Tommy's teacher, the Saturday before school opened. Mrs. Womble was a broad-beamed, middle-aged lady with incongruously small feet upon which she bustled into the office of the school principal. She had a fleshy face, out of which her somewhat slanting eyes surveyed Carol with a martyred, and even contemptuous, patience, as if the younger woman's presence had torn their gaze rudely—though only temporarily—away from its fast hold upon Mrs. Womble's own inner virtues.*

In the two past decades, stories and other forms of narrative have sparked interest among social scientists studying the human condition. A common term for this study is *naturalistic inquiry.* Unfortunately, there has been less interest in using fictional stories, or what Robert Coles calls the literary documentary tradition, in naturalistic inquiry.[3]

Well then, why fictional stories? How can they help teachers, those who want to be teachers, and readers in general? For example, how might stories make a difference in teachers' personal lives, their relationships with others, and, perhaps most important, their views of what it means to be teachers? The answers to these questions lie in an examination of certain social and intellectual functions of fictional stories: entertainment, reflection, evaluation, and direction.[4] Before discussing each of these functions, two caveats are in order. First, these are not the *only* functions of fiction, nor are these functions mutually exclusive. They are in fact intertwined. Second, reader responses to the stories will differ, depending upon a great many variables. Good fictional stories seem naturally to resist a single interpretation. For instance, experienced teachers might find a teacher-student exchange in a story to be a familiar experience offering an opportunity for critical reflection. For aspiring and novice teachers as well as non-educators, the same exchange might provide an opportunity to imagine more fully what it is like to be a teacher. It also might help them to evaluate their expectations for teachers and to think about the complexity of teaching.

### *Entertainment*

As Robert Penn Warren notes, we read fictional stories because we like them. The special, most immediate motivation that takes us to fiction is always our interest in a story. Stories render life experiences in compelling, often pleasurable ways and they provide more enjoyment than lectures, note taking, and textbooks. There is no denying that entertainment, or "fun," attracts us to these narratives. This element of fun does not suggest a lack of seriousness; as with any learning experience, the value of studying stories does not lie in the amount of pain or pleasure sustained, but in the knowledge gained and the effect that knowledge has on one's thoughts and actions.

### Reflection

Much has been written, in both the fields of the humanities and the social sciences, about the ways in which fiction and other narratives shed light on the human condition. Images of teachers and students in fiction provide excellent opportunities for fruitful personal reflection. For example, reflection allows teachers to see their own familiar behaviors and challenges in the themes, plots, actions, characters, and settings of the stories. Reflection also allows teachers to see themselves as others—students, parents, and other teachers—see them. What all this means is that reflection may bring both affirmation and a healthy critical attitude about oneself.

Fictional stories also provide an opportunity to reflect on the teaching profession itself. For all types of readers, including teachers and aspiring teachers, this reflection might reawaken excitement in teaching, illuminate the art of teaching, portray the inescapable diversity among teachers and students, and highlight the sometimes quirky aspects of schoolteaching.

### Evaluation

A study of schoolteaching stories can yield insights for the evaluation of classroom management, methodologies, materials, interpersonal relationships and communication. Unfortunately, history indicates that the impact of stories on these variables, especially relative to educational and psychological theories, has been minimal. But that situation is slowly changing. Today, some educational and psychological theorists are beginning to abstract views of these variables from stories.

A study of schoolteaching stories can also yield insights in the evaluation of attitudes, opinions, and stereotypes. Stories, especially fictional ones, can provide nonthreatening scenarios in which the governing attitudes, opinions, and stereotypes of a culture can be examined, demystified, and critiqued. J. Hillis Miller amplifies this point:

> Narratives are a relatively safe or innocuous place in which the reigning assumptions of a given culture can be criticized. In a novel, alternative assumptions can be entertained or experimented with—not as in the real world, where such experimentations might have dangerous consequences, but in the imaginary world where, it is easy to assume, 'nothing really happens' because it happens only in the feigned world of fiction.

### Direction

The use of fictional stories to provide direction or guidance is a worldwide phenomenon that has continued from generation to generation especially in ethical and moral development.[5] It seems to be one of the few traditions that exist in diverse cultures regardless of literacy sophistication. Again, J. Hillis Miller notes that:

> A story is a way of doing things with words. It makes something happen in the real world: for example, it can propose . . . ways of behaving that are then imitated in the real world. Seen from this point of view, fictions may be said to have a tremendous importance not as the accurate reflectors of a culture but as the makers of that culture. . . . If this is true, then changes in the rise and fall in popularity of different genres over time or changes in the dominant medium—first from oral storytelling to print, then from printed books to cinema and television—will have an incalculable importance for the shape of that culture.

Robert Coles recounts a conversation with William Carlos Williams, the physician, writer, and poet, about the power of stories. "The more palpable the connection between the story and the reader's story, the better the chance that something is going to happen. Look, these novels or short stories are not meant to save the world. But a story can engage a reader—not every reader, and some readers only somewhat, but plenty of readers a lot, a whole lot."

Consider this excerpt from "Death in the Fifth Grade" by Marjorie Marks. It just begins to hint at the ethical and moral power of stories. A student in Miss Steineck's class has just died and the students have questions. Miss Steineck's answers and the rest of this story reveal much about ethical and moral direction as well as the power of stories:

> Quietly Miss Steineck shut the roll book and squared her shoulders. "You know, Norma has been very, very ill," she said. That was the way she had planned. So far, so good. The bell rang. There was a little flutter through the class. Evie and Carolyn exchanged nervous glances over Norma's empty desk. Miss Steineck wished now that she'd had the janitor take it away before school. She had debated during the night the wisdom of this and decided it would be less of a shock this way. But now, her sensibilities heightened by this situation, its emptiness accused her.
>
> Jane, the youngest in the class, who hadn't much sense, piped up from the front row, "We all know she's dead, Miss Steineck, you don't need to tell us."
>
> A snicker which was half a shudder passed through the group.
>
> Rosanne mouthed sanctimoniously, lifting her eyes for approval from the teacher, "You mustn't say she's dead. She's gone to heaven to be an angel. That's what my mother says. It's true, isn't it, Miss Steineck?"
>
> The eyes of twenty-six implored her for an answer. But how could she answer? She had left heaven behind with high button shoes for Sunday and a dime inside her glove for the collection. How could she tell them what she really believed . . . ?

### Summary

We believe the fictional stories in this anthology can direct and change lives. As Freema Elbaz has noted:

> Story is the very stuff of teaching, the landscape within which we live as teachers and researchers and within which the work of teachers can be seen as making sense. This is not merely a claim about the aesthetic or emotional sense of story with our intuitive understanding of teaching, but an epistemological claim that teachers' knowledge in its own terms is ordered by story and can best be understood in this way.

But a gnawing irony persists: before such stories can affect readers, before they can excite them, cause them to make connections, or see themselves more clearly, they must be read. If they are read, perhaps then they will have power to direct and change lives.

### Selection of the Stories

Modern stories on schoolteaching in large numbers do not exist and the authors of those that are available appear to favor nonfiction for describing schoolteaching. Among these modern stories, a few have become widely known (for example, *Up the Down Staircase* by Bel Kaufman, *To Sir with Love* by Edward Braithwaite, *Among School Children* by

Tracy Kidder, *Blackboard Jungle* by Evan Hunter, *Small Victories* by Samuel Freedman, *The Water Is Wide* by Pat Conroy). We looked instead for less familiar stories.

Despite an exhaustive bibliographic search involving thousands of titles that seemed to suggest a schoolteaching focus, we found that most of the stories were not about schoolteaching, and of the few we could find, most lacked sufficient depth and breadth of content. Simply put, very few authors have focused their fictional efforts on themes related to schoolteaching. This seems somewhat surprising since most people in the world share school experiences. In our search we could find no more than a few hundred that met our content requirements which were as follows:

- Evidence of strong character development in teachers and students
- Evidence that the characters are pursuing goals of teaching and learning
- Evidence that while pursuing these goals the relationships of the characters (both teachers and students) are revealed
- Evidence of problems and themes that currently confront kindergarten through twelfth grade teaching and learning
- Evidence that schoolteaching is of prime importance to the story
- Evidence that the story is fictional[6]

We also sought a wide representation of schoolteaching situations hoping to introduce new writers and stories to the relatively small canon of modern fiction on schoolteaching. To accomplish this, we searched not only through established literature collections but also through less known specialized collections from authors and publishers across the world.[7] We have gathered a diverse collection. The 51 stories of this anthology should provide ample opportunities for comparison among characters, settings, themes and pedagogical issues. The time period in which these stories were published (approximately 1940s–1990s) can also allow comparisons across a range of time. Although some of the stories were written many years ago, the situations described in them are still relevant and continue to recur in today's classrooms.

Interestingly, despite this diversity, we found more similarities than differences among the stories we selected for the anthology. For example, we found similarities in the stories about the Jewish American girl in Frances Silverberg's "Rebecca by Any Other Name," the Mexican American boy in Hugo Martínez-Serros's "Ricardo's War," and the Muslim African boy in Abioseh Nicol's "As the Night the Day."

Some readers may feel that there are too many unpleasant images of schoolteaching in this anthology; this partly reflects the choices available in the literature. Perhaps writers are more likely to write about unhappy school experiences, or alternatively, those who have unhappy experiences are more likely to write about them. Also, it's a simple fact of storytelling that conflicts and difficulties tend to build interesting stories. Unquestionably, the writers' own experiences are evident in stories. For example, Zenna Henderson, as a teacher first, a writer second, depicts teachers who are sympathetic, multidimensional human beings in stories such as "You Know What, Teacher?" and "The Anything Box." The authors of some of the darker stories speak from marginalized groups in North America as well as other parts of the world. Their school experiences are likely to have been painful, a fact that is reflected in their fiction. We have also included some stories that contain themes, characters, images, and language some readers may find objectionable or offensive because, unfortunately, they describe situations that students and teachers actually encounter. But we have tried to balance cold and threatening scenarios with warm and encouraging images of schoolteaching.

## Organization of the Stories

The reader will notice that the stories are arranged in chapters; each begins with an introduction that briefly comments on the chapter theme and the individual stories. The stories in each chapter share characteristics that support cross-story inquiries and discussions. However, the categorization of the stories is not meant to be inflexible; stories from various chapters often share a theme and may be fruitfully studied in groupings that overstep chapter boundaries.

For the editors, the search for stories on schoolteaching turned up an unexpected and pleasant discovery—her name is Zenna Henderson. Her stories are unusual in their ability to capture images of classrooms and the voices of children. She was a gifted writer and, we suspect, a gifted teacher as well. We delighted in every one of her stories; she has enriched this collection. Unfortunately Zenna Henderson passed away in 1983, so we were unable to share our delight with her.

## Endnotes

Publication information for all sources listed in the endnotes is given in the bibliography.

1. For references to narratives used in the examination of the human experience known as schoolteaching, see for example, Benjet, 1994; Cardarelli, 1992; Dyson and Genishi, 1994; Hansen-Krening, 1992; Nissman, 1965; Smith, Thomas and Nicholas, 1993; Tama and Peterson, 1991; Tiedt and Tiedt, 1967.
2. For examples, see Bower, *The Handicapped in Literature*; Coles, *The Call of Stories*; Coser, *Sociology through Literature*; Dyson and Genishi, *The Need for Story*; Dietrich and Sundell, *The Art of Fiction*; Fernández, *Social Psychology through Literature*; Gregory, *Juvenile Delinquency in Literature*; Spradley and McDonough, *Anthropology through Literature.*
3. See Lincoln and Guba, 1985, for a discussion of naturalistic inquiry.
4. For references to the social and intellectual functions of narrative see Martin, 1986; Mitchell, 1981; Miller, 1990; Scholes and Kellogg, 1966; Walsh, 1959. For references to the importance of fiction and other narratives as a reflection of the human condition from the perspective of the humanities, see Martin, 1986; Mitchell, 1981; Scholes and Kellogg, 1966; Valance, 1995; Walsh, 1959. For such references from the perspective of social sciences see Barone, 1992; Britton and Pellegrini, 1990; Brooks and Warren, 1959; Bruner, 1985, 1986; Carter, 1993; Coles, 1989; Connelly and Clandinin, 1990; Eisner, 1991; Egan, 1988; Grumet, 1988; Gudmundsdottir, 1991; Jackson, 1968; Joseph and Burnaford, 1994; Lightfoot, 1983; Polkinghorne, 1988; Sarbin, 1986; Tiedt, 1992.
5. For a discussion on the use of stories in moral development, see Vitz, 1990.
6. We made a decision to avoid selecting stories that were from the romance story, pulp fiction, and private boarding school story genres. Previous research on these genres indicates that one-dimensional views of schoolteaching in theme, plot, action, and characters predominate. For instance, they tend to portray teachers as embittered spinsters; absent-minded, hoodwinked, nervous incompetents; stern and pernicious taskmasters; pretty young schoolmarms; and lecherous predators. We felt these simplistic unidimensional portrayals were simply too limited for inclusion. For references to opinions, attitudes and stereotypes in literature about schoolteaching, students, and teachers, see Benjet, 1994; Biklen,

1986; Briggs, 1962; Charles, 1950; Deegan, 1951; Enger, 1974; Foff, 1958; Furness, 1960; Griffin, 1961; Kauffman, 1962; Jones, 1957; Manke, 1994; Mills, 1977; Nissman, 1965; Trabue, 1962.

On a few occasions it was difficult to determine if a title was fictional or autobiographical: author notes or reviews provided no clues. In these cases, we made the best judgment we could.

7. Despite, the realization that we were dealing with a small canon of fiction on modern schoolteaching to choose from for the anthology, we were especially disappointed in our inability to locate fictional stories by Native Americans (Leslie Silko's *Ceremony* is an exception). An extensive bibliographic search using the resources of Labriola National American Indian Center (Arizona State University Libraries) could not locate any fictional schoolteaching stories by Native Americans that fit our criteria.

# Acknowledgments

The editors are only the most visible contributors to this anthology. There are many others who have contributed generously of their time and effort. First, we want to thank Bill Barke for his support. It seems both notable and rare to find a college textbook publisher interested in the power of stories. Second, we want to thank Arizona State University, College of Education for their financial support. On two different occasions, the College of Education provided support for our large interlibrary loan research efforts. Third, we want to thank Jane Conrow of the Arizona State University libraries. She found library office space for us and our assistants when none was available. Fourth, we want to thank our editors at Allyn & Bacon, Virginia Lanigan, Susan McNally, and Susanna Brougham. All were genuinely supportive. Fifth, we also want to thank Sheri Dunbar and Lisa Olson who used their interlibrary loan reference skills to help us locate the stories, as well as Laurie Frankenthaler and Carlos Rodríguez Fraticelli who helped us track down the stories' authors and publishers. Sixth, we owe a debt of gratitude to our colleagues who participated in the 1994 AERA session entitled Teaching Tales; namely, Thomas Barone, David Berliner, Madeline Grumet, Rosalind Wu, John Carey, and Alfredo Benavides. The following reviewers provided valuable suggestions and encouragement during the revision process: John Nevius, Texas Tech; Andrea Karlin, Lamar University; Thomas Barone, Arizona State University; Robert Donmoyer, Ohio State University; and Herman S. García, New Mexico State University. Finally, we want to thank our ever patient and helpful spouses, Nikki and David Berliner, who know the stories of this anthology as well as we do.

# CHAPTER 1

## TEACHING AND LEARNING

Donald Gropman, "The Heart of This or That Man"
Abelardo Díaz Alfaro, "Peyo Mercé: English Teacher"
Lao Hsiang, "A Country Boy Withdraws from School"
Jon Hassler, Excerpt from *Staggerford*
Jacqueline Wilson, "The Boy Who Couldn't Read"
Frances Gray Patton, "Grade 5B and the Well-Fed Rat"

The curriculum, broadly conceived, plays an important role in each of the stories included in this chapter. The first three stories illustrate problems that can arise when a particular curriculum does not suit the students; the next three portray the tension between tradition and innovation in the classroom.

In Donald Gropman's story "The Heart of This or That Man," Mr. Shapiro is a caring teacher who knows that his lessons are mostly irrelevant to the lives of his high school students. They are poor, urban children concerned with basic survival who have little time for the less immediate, lofty concerns of their school curriculum. Aware of this incompatibility, Mr. Shapiro dares to break the norms. Once a week he encourages his students to express themselves by producing, on paper, visual responses to the poetry he reads to them. He knows he is risking his job in doing this. English teachers are not supposed to work in art; they have a literary curriculum to follow. But with the help of materials provided by an understanding art teacher, he succeeds in gaining his students' attention at least one day per week.

Mr. Shapiro's effort is more than rewarded when, in response to one of the poems, Jaime produces a striking painting. There is no doubt in his mind that this formerly distant boy is the winner of the day's prize for the best painting. But Jaime does not behave like a winner; in fact, he appears sad and worried. At Mr. Shapiro's prodding the boy eventually discloses the reason for his reaction as well as the source of his inspiration.

Abelardo Díaz Alfaro, in "Peyo Mercé: English Teacher," employs a lighter tone. The author allows us to peek into a classroom and watch how the imposition of English on Peyo's rural school is sabotaged by the lack of compatibility between the students' experiences and the content of the textbook. This humorous story takes place in Puerto Rico in the early part of this century when policymakers in the United States decided that Spanish-speaking islanders had to learn English in order to become "Americans."

In the story Peyo Mercé will lose his teaching job if he does not comply with the required English instruction mandate, even though he is not an accomplished speaker of that language. And so he tries to find a familiar topic to help his students embark on this difficult task. But even common barnyard animals seem foreign and a little ridiculous when presented in English, turning the language lesson into a joke shared by a good-natured teacher and his students.

Lao Hsiang's story "A Country Boy Withdraws from School" clearly demonstrates the misunderstandings that can result when a curriculum is chosen without considering a community's culture. As in Díaz Alfaro's story, the setting is rural, and an important educational message is wrapped in a humorous story. In this rural Chinese community, tradition rules and the distance between the people's lives and the Western style classroom is wide. In the story a young country boy is forced to go to school by the authorities. But, after the first day, the family of the boy believes the school's instruction is violating traditional family values, and they begin to perceive the school environment as a threat.

The family's suspicions about the school are first aroused by the illustrations in the books: "The people in the pictures are not Chinese!" The way they dress, their household equipment, and even how they stand, shows them to be foreigners and, added to the unfamiliarity of the content, poses a threat to the child's parents and forces the father to act to protect the family. Once again, the lack of compatibility between the beliefs and values of the community and those presented in the textbook have negative consequences for the student.

The next three stories illustrate in various ways the tension between tradition and innovation in education. In the excerpt from Jon Hassler's *Staggerford,* Miss McGee is represented as a proper woman with strong convictions. At first she is gratified that a well-known poet is going to be visiting the school; she harbors a love of poetry nurtured years ago by an elementary school teacher, and she still remembers, and teaches, a poem she learned as a child in that classroom. Poets occupy a lofty position in her mind; therefore she has a strong reaction to Herschel Mancrief, a somewhat unkept and decidedly modern poet who literally brings poetry down to the toilet for her students.

With verve and alacrity Miss McGee takes drastic action, violating her own notions of propriety to save poetry from the defilement perpetrated by the young poet.

Jaqueline Wilson, in "The Boy Who Couldn't Read," dramatically illustrates the lengths to which a teacher might go to resist change. The boy in this story has to withstand cruel treatment from his teacher, Mr. Croft, who resents the demands placed on him by a bright but dyslexic student in his classroom.

David Bates is well-behaved and eager to learn, but when he needs individual attention, Mr. Croft denigrates and ridicules him in front of his classmates. In his classroom everyone does what he says regardless of the appropriateness of the task. His resentment gradually turns into stubborness as he forces the boy to remain after class until the task assigned is completed. The tension between teacher and student builds until it is tragically resolved.

Frances Gray Patton's tale of the well-fed rat is a little different. The teaching methods of Miss Oates, the teacher in this story, appear at first glance to be innovative, but later we realize that she is a traditional teacher who adopts innovative techniques without fully understanding their purpose. She undertakes an experiment in her classroom designed to show how good nutrition contributes to longer life spans in rats. When the experimental evidence fails to support the stated hypothesis, Miss Oates' commitment to "discovery learning" is challenged and the science lesson is compromised.

The stories in this chapter illustrate how the curriculum is more than the printed wishes of educators. Not only does it have important consequences for students, it can also be a restraining but comfortable anchor for teachers who are afraid of change.

# The Heart of This or That Man

## DONALD GROPMAN

Mr. Shapiro fumbled with the window pole. Nine C would be here in a few minutes for its weekly session and he was not prepared. Open the window, remove his jacket, set out the jars of paint and the brushes he argued for each week.

"Now, Allan," Miss Katz would say, "I don't know if this request is covered by any rule. After all, I'm the art teacher and you teach English."

"Well, Miss Katz," he would say, "if you don't tell anyone, and I don't tell anyone, it will be our little secret. You know," and here he would smile, a little less broadly each week, "it's like giving an anonymous donation to the CJA or Red Feather. You and I help these kids, but we don't brag about it. Inside we know we are doing something good."

"Well, all right, Allan, what somebody doesn't know won't hurt him. Now remember to have them wash the brushes and wipe down the jars. Your boys are awfully messy. And by the way, do you really need so much paper?"

He still fumbled to fit the metal hook into the slot at the top of the window. He had read somewhere that an open window provides fresh air and inspiration. Through the high many-paned window he could see the street below him. The pale lemon light of a two o'clock winter afternoon drifted down from a silent and spent sky, but did not seem to fall on the brown heaps of snow and slush.

A policeman walked by, and Mr. Shapiro noticed that he could not see the small balloons of breath puff out over the policeman's shoulder. Was it warmer, what was it, March? Or April already? Snow on the streets in April? No matter. He liked to watch the breath balloons and fill them in. For policemen he inserted things like: *I am a policeman, sometimes I'm your friend; I like to find robbers 'cause I'm partners with them.* The policeman crossed the street. Mr. Shapiro looked over and saw Jaime sitting in a doorway. He was looking up at the empty sky and started up when the policeman burst into his sight. The po-

liceman leaned over and Jaime waved his arms, shook his head, and pointed at Mr. Shapiro. No, Mr. Shapiro thought, he is pointing at the whole school. The policeman now shook his head and crossed back to the school side of the street with Jaime. The policeman disappeared at the side of the window and Jaime disappeared beneath it. Did the policeman invoke me, Mr. Shapiro thought, to make Jaime come to class and stop being truant?

The bell rang to start the last class as Mr. Shapiro was folding his suit jacket over the back of his chair. He had read somewhere that a teacher in shirtsleeves provokes less resistance in these students. The students started to drift into the room, singly or in twos. Mr. Shapiro had a moment of panic. What am I doing here? I should be home reading, getting my Ph.D., getting laid, getting money. What good can I do, help these poor underprivileged bastards become privileged so they can assimilate, have appliances and not live on welfare, and use toilet paper to wipe their asses instead of *El Diario de Nueva York,* so that in the final end they'll fill me with loathing like all the rest of the smug, consuming bastards. Shapiro's law of human nature, not too romantic I hope, says, a human being evinces more interesting manifestations while being consumed than while consuming. A contemporary aesthetic: What is the most beautiful thing in the world, the ultimate perfection? A young girl dying of consumption? No. A whole ethnic group being consumed.

Am I merely stupid, or expiating guilt? Anyway, why do these kids call me Mr. Shapiro? Everyone else calls me Allan, in the army they called me kike, my wife calls me *schmouk,* my professors call me dummy, although I never heard them.

*Hey Al baby, what's shakin'? Man, this is a wise scene and you a real wig. Catch some pot Al, it's just a fifty pinney joint, but like it's all I carry. You not like those other teachers, they hard bastards, but you okay man, you go it everywhere,* and the boy would use his index finger as a wand to touch his own temple, his chest, and his sex. The monologue elated Mr. Shapiro even though he could not recognize the student in the daydream.

On Friday afternoon the class with Nine C always went well. Four times a week Mr. Shapiro tried to teach them English. They wrote compositions and read *Silas Marner.* They had spelling quizzes and tried to parse sentences on the board. Whenever his wife, or anyone else not connected with the school, asked him about the class, Mr. Shapiro had one stock answer, "They just don't give a shit." But one thing did seem to interest them and that was the Friday session.

Mr. Shapiro had decided it would be a good idea to read them poems and let them paint what the poems meant to them. This would serve several functions: they will hear some poetry, they will express themselves in the paintings and, maybe, Mr. Shapiro hoped, I can get through to them. In September he had found a box of gold stars in his desk, the only trace left of the teacher before him. Each week he pasted a star on a painting, trying to give the star where he felt it would do the most good.

He tried to select poetry from the high school reader that would appeal to them. This afternoon he was going to read some Robert Frost. He felt it would make sense to them, offer them images they could instinctively grasp.

While he sat on his desk thinking, the students took paper and jars of paint. Two of them went into the hall to fill the water pitchers, for they had finally accepted the fact that the paints worked better if they were thinned. Most of the class was busy mixing paint when Jaime walked in. He didn't look at Mr. Shapiro. He went to his seat and sat down.

Mr. Shapiro leafed through the reader, but he watched Jaime. The boy was probably older than he looked, perhaps, fifteen or sixteen, but he was no bigger than a twelve-year-old. He always left the two top buttons of his shirt open and he wore no undershirt, so Mr. Shapiro could see the middle of his pale honey-colored chest, the skin pulled taut across the knobby clavicles.

Jaime didn't move. He sat staring at his desk, his thin fingers buried themselves in his matted black hair.

Mr. Shapiro walked up the aisle. "Don't you have any paints, Jaime?"

Jaime looked up at him. Mr. Shapiro saw a bleached face. The black eyes seemed gray, the hirsuteness on the upper lip seemed white. Mr. Shapiro's legs felt suddenly weak, he felt a large parching knot in his throat.

"What's wrong?" he asked, his voice much softer than he had intended.

"Nothing, Mr. Shapiro. There's nothing is wrong."

"Come with me, I'll help you to get some paints and a piece of paper." He felt foolish mouthing these words, silly words about bottles of paint and empty paper, but he could think of nothing else.

Jaime was seated again, his paints before him on his desk. Mr. Shapiro waited until he was ready, smiled at him and began to read. As he read the first words of "Mending Wall" they too sounded silly to his ears. He felt embarrassed and knew that his face was turning red. The volume of his voice dropped from the pitch it started at, he mouthed the words as quickly as he could, droning them out like some primitive and unyielding chant. He looked up from the book while mouthing familiar phrases and saw the class looking at him strangely.

"Am I reading too quickly?" he asked, trying to control his fluster, restraining himself from hurling the high school reader through one of the many-paned windows and leaving the high school and the students forever. "Am I reading too quickly for you to follow me?" He despised himself for the touch of condescension in his voice, but he would have augmented it if a student hadn't answered.

"Yes, Mr. Shapiro, much too fast." It was Jaime. He was still sitting with his elbows on his desk and his fingers buried in his matted black hair.

"Sounds like the IRT," another student said, and there was general laughter, even from Mr. Shapiro.

"I guess you're right, I was going a little fast. I'll begin again."

*Something there is that doesn't love a wall,*
*That sends the frozen-ground-swell under it,*
*And spills the upper boulders in the sun;*
*And makes gaps even two can pass abreast.*

Mr. Shapiro read the whole poem, slowly and with emotion. Now that the poem was fresh in his mind he recited most of it from memory. Before him at the rows of desks he could see the pale honey-colored faces, some with their dark eyes on his face, others staring at the book in his hands. Jaime had not changed his position. Mr. Shapiro could still see where the boy's fingers started to disappear into his black hair. He repeated the last line twice.

*He says again, "Good Fences make good*
*neighbors."*

The class stirred itself, Mr. Shapiro had an ephemeral sense of accomplishment. Maybe there was a contact, he thought, maybe I had their attention, that is the start of a dialogue. "Any questions?" he asked.

One boy asked why the wall was there anyway if it didn't do any good, and Mr. Shapiro started to answer. He started to explain the significance of New England stone walls, how they originated when the farmers had to pick the stones out of the soil in order to plant a crop, and how they have become a tradition in that part of the country. He started to explain further the irony of the dialogue between the two farmers, and felt he was losing the class again, so he cut it short, "Any other questions?"

"Yes, Mr. Shapiro." It was Jaime again. "Can you read that part again where they carry rocks like wildmen?"

Mr. Shapiro picked up the book:

*I see him there*
*Bringing a stone grasped firmly by the top*
*In each hand, like an old-stone savage armed.*
*He moves in darkness, as it seems to me,*
*Not of the woods only and the shade of trees.*

"What did you want to know about them, Jaime?"

"Nothing, Mr. Shapiro, I just wanted to hear you read them again."

"All right. All right, class, we'll begin painting now. It wasn't a long poem and it didn't take up much time. Maybe there will be time enough for two paintings."

It was Mr. Shapiro's practice not to bother the students while they were painting, he felt his looking over their shoulders might inhibit or intimidate them. He took his jacket and went to the teacher's room for a cigarette. It was not the standard procedure, leaving a class alone, especially Nine C, but he had done it before on Fridays and there were never any complaints from the adjoining rooms.

The lounge for male teachers was next to that for female teachers. At the door he saw Miss Katz. He didn't want to talk to her. He didn't even want her to see him.

"Allan, you naughty, have you left your class unattended? And with poster paints yet! I hope you don't have any trouble," Miss Katz said, walking up to him. She had an empty cup in her hand. Mr. Shapiro knew that if it was wet she was leaving the lounge and if it was dry she was just arriving. But Miss Katz held the cup upside down and he couldn't tell. At first he didn't hear her words. He was convinced she was holding the cup that way just to keep him from knowing if it was wet or dry. "I hope you've never left them before, this could raise a problem for you."

"No," Mr. Shapiro said, "I haven't. I had to go to the bathroom." He had wanted to say *I had to take a wicked leak,* or *I suddenly, for no reason at all, felt like puking,* but he only said, and repeated, "I had to go to the bathroom." He hated himself again, for not saying what he wanted to say, for putting the bathroom excuse in some vague past tense, as if everyone didn't have to empty out at least once a day. He thought of the kids in the room, their honey-colored faces screwed up over their paintings, dreaming in their heads of orchards and fields, and he blurted out, "Do you know, Miss Katz, they are really more ginger-colored than honey-colored," and he leaped into the male lounge.

When he returned to the classroom it was just as he'd imagined. He saw rows of heads, almost every one of the heads covered with very black hair, bent over the desks. He felt pleased, he forgot all about Miss Katz and the probability that she was at that moment telling some other faculty member what he had said to her. When Mr. Shapiro thought about this in the lounge he tried to re-create Miss Katz's language. "You know, Louise, we were talking about his leaving his class unattended, and he was looking strange to begin with, staring at my teacup, and suddenly he shouted at me something about ginger and honey. Then he flew into the men's lounge and slammed the door. Don't you think he's disturbed?" He had ground his cigarette out on the floor of the lounge, and Miss Katz with it.

He stood at the window looking out. The sun was still shining, but it really wasn't shining, he thought, that is too active a description. The sunlight is drifting down, it is settling like a cloud of pale dust, it is falling because of gravity. He glanced at the students and saw Jaime. His head was bent over his desk, but both his hands were buried in his hair. Mr. Shapiro walked over to him. "What's wrong, Jaime, don't you feel like painting today?"

"Yes, Mr. Shapiro, I'm all done."

Mr. Shapiro looked at the painting on Jaime's desk. There were two huge figures, man-like but inanimate, facing each other. Both figures had their arms raised above their heads and in their hands held stones. There were bright carmine streaks on their heads, faces and shoulders. Between them was a black wall that began in the absolute foreground of the painting and ran right through the depth and off the paper. Mr. Shapiro looked more closely and saw a third figure, a smaller one, crouched in a blob of gray on the wall. He felt the same weakness in his legs and the knot in his throat that he had when he looked into Jaime's face at the start of the class.

"What does it mean?" His voice was gruff, almost angry. Two or three of the other students looked up at him, then turned back to their paintings.

"Nothing."

"It can't mean nothing. Everything means something. It has to mean something." His voice was more insistent, hatred for himself ran through his body like a chill. "What does it mean?"

"Nothing," Jaime said, looking up at him with the gray eyes and white hirsuteness on his upper lip. "It don't mean nothing."

Mr. Shapiro straightened up, he looked at the painting again from his new and more distant perspective. The two large figures were both all green. He hadn't noticed that before. And the sky was watery yellow. The ground, where there was grass in the poem, was grape-purple. His eyes were drawn to the small blotted figure crouched on the wall. He leaned over again to have a closer look at it. "Who is that little figure supposed to be, the one on the top of the wall?"

Jaime looked up at him for a moment, then slid his fingers back into his hair and started to look at his painting again.

Mr. Shapiro looked at the clock over the door. There were only ten minutes left to the class. Ten minutes and the day was over, and the week. "All right, class, let's start cleaning up. While you clean the brushes and wipe off the jars I'll come around and pick the star winner for today."

Most of the paintings tried to show the two farmers standing by the wall, and most of them had green grass and blue skies. But Mr. Shapiro could not think about any of them. He looked at them all, made a comment here, gave a word of encouragement there, but his imagination wasn't in it.

He walked up the aisle Jaime sat in. He paused a little longer at each painting as he got closer to Jaime. When he got to him he walked right by.

The brushes were all washed and standing in a jar, the bottles of paint were all cleaned on the outside, the empty water pitchers stood beside them. Mr. Shapiro looked at the clock. The bell would ring in two minutes. He had to announce a winner. "All right, class, the best painting today was done by Jaime Morales. Come up, Jaime, and I'll give you your gold star." The usual practice was to exhibit the best painting at the front of the room, and explain why it was the best. But today Mr. Shapiro didn't do this. He only announced the winner, and when Jaime didn't come forward he repeated, "Jaime, come up and I'll give you your star."

He looked at Jaime. The boy was still sitting as he had sat for all the time Mr. Shapiro saw him in class. He saw the top of his head, the thin fingers buried in the thick black hair. But now the fingers were clutching at Jaime's scalp. He was crying.

A few of the students around him looked at him, and then looked at Mr. Shapiro. Mr. Shapiro looked back at them vacantly. Jaime started to cry louder. Mr. Shapiro saw the bony clavicles in Jaime's pale honey-colored chest jerk in and out, he saw the boy's forehead and cheek muscles clench up to hold back the tears.

"What the hell is wrong?" he shouted, running up the aisle. "What's wrong now, what did I do?" The whole class was staring at them now, at Jaime and Mr. Shapiro. "What's wrong? Answer me!" he shouted. He didn't care that he was shouting, or that the whole class was watching him. Jaime looked up at him. Now his gray eyes were flecked with red. He stopped crying. "Nothing is wrong, ever."

The bell rang. Mr. Shapiro was still standing over Jaime. Some of the class got up, others waited for Mr. Shapiro to dismiss them. 'Okay," he said, his voice cracking and weary, "you can all go now."

Mr. Shapiro was still leaning over Jaime. He was looking at the painting. He was still drawn to the small gray figure.

"What's wrong, Jaime, you can tell me now, everyone is gone."

"There's nothing wrong."

"Come on," Mr. Shapiro said, his confidence returning, "you can tell me."

"I have nothing to tell."

"Well, in that case, how about helping me carry the supplies back to the art room?"

Mr. Shapiro felt that he had suppressed whatever it was that made his legs weak and made him

shout. Together, in two trips, they returned all the supplies. Now the week was over, but Mr. Shapiro knew something in it was unfinished. He wanted to know why Jaime had cried. He wanted to know because he wanted to help the boy. He wanted to understand him, to communicate with him and thereby comfort and help him. He could be honest with himself again, now that he had himself in control, and he could admit that he also wanted to know just for the sake of knowing.

"C'mon, Jaime, I go your way, I'll walk you home." They started out the door. "Wait a minute, you forgot your painting." Jaime went back to get it. Mr. Shapiro remembered the open windows and began to close them. The pale lemon light of an hour ago had turned to grayish-yellow. The sun seemed to be drawing into itself, absorbing its light back from the world.

He turned from the window and saw that Jaime was crying.

The slush had hardened on the sidewalk. Mr. Shapiro could see breath balloons when Jaime exhaled, but he could think of no words to fill them. "I'll buy you a Coke, or a hot chocolate," he said, and they went into a Nedick's. Jaime had his painting rolled up, and he put it on the floor beside him. They both ordered hot chocolates and Jaime put two teaspoons of sugar into his. They blew into their cups without talking. Jaime took a sip of his chocolate and smacked his lips. It was too hot.

"Do you want to know why I cried?"

"Yes, if you want to tell me."

"I want to tell you, Mr. Shapiro, but it's not easy. It's hard."

"Start at the beginning, then, take it slow." Mr. Shapiro felt very comfortable sitting at the counter in Nedick's on a Friday afternoon with one of his students. Before Jaime started to talk, he already felt a sense of accomplishment.

"It's account of my painting."

Mr. Shapiro was mildly disappointed. "How could that painting make you cry? And anyway, you won the star this week. It was the best painting. You should be proud of it." Mr. Shapiro had not yet tasted his chocolate, but he felt warm inside. He said again, "You should be proud of it."

"I am, I am, I wanted to win a star, but now I don't have anything to do with it."

Mr. Shapiro was hardly listening. He felt expansive inside himself. The questions that had nagged at him earlier in the day seemed resolved. He knew why he was here, why he was teaching and not doing something else, why he was teaching in this particular school. He knew why he was teaching students like Jaime. He was helping them. He would never despise them for assimilating or becoming bourgeois. He was their friend, not their critic. He understood them. They needed him.

"What did you say, Jaime?"

"I don't have anything to do with it now, nothing at all."

"Why don't you keep it in your wallet as a memento, so you can look at it and feel good when you want to."

"What do you mean, Mr. Shapiro, it can't fit in my wallet, it's too big."

"Oh, you're talking about the painting. I thought you meant my gold star."

"The painting, that's what I can't do anything with," Jaime said, his voice cracking, and he started to cry again.

Mr. Shapiro was upset. "What is it, Jaime, you're not telling me everything. What is it? I have a right to know."

"I'm proud of my painting, Mr. Shapiro, I'm glad I got the star today." Jaime huddled up on his stool, he crouched over his hot chocolate and held the cup in both his hands. "We live in a room with four other families," he said, and he looked at Mr. Shapiro. Mr. Shapiro didn't want to hear what Jaime was saying. He looked at the boy's eyes. They were black now, and shining. Tears rolled like pebbles down his smooth face. Mr. Shapiro blew into his chocolate. He drank some, it scalded and stuck in his throat. "Would you like a doughnut?" he sputtered.

"We live in a room with four other families. Every month we change places in the room. This month is our turn in the middle. I want to hang my painting but I have no wall." Jaime stopped. He was still looking at Mr. Shapiro. "I have no wall!" he shouted into Mr. Shapiro's face, and ran out of the Nedick's.

Mr. Shapiro sat at the counter. He looked down and saw Jaime's painting on the floor. He picked it up. A chill ran up his arm and down his back. He pushed his cup of chocolate aside and unrolled the painting. One end of the black stone wall drilled into Nedick's countertop, the wider end thrust at him.

When he first saw the painting in the classroom he knew what it was about, but he had tried to fool himself. Now his eyes fell on the green figures planted on the grape-purple grass. So, he thought, so I've come to this.

He glanced around Nedick's, but nothing seemed as real as the green men stiffly raging on the purple lawn beneath the streaked and watery sky.

He folded the painting and stuffed it into his coat pocket. He lit a cigarette and sipped some chocolate. Miss Katz's teacup, dry or wet, what was the difference? Why had he let it matter?

He felt sorry.

Mr. Shapiro slapped the edge of the countertop with his fingers. The countergirl asked what he wanted, but he did not look up. It has always been walls, he thought. Hearts of men sometimes pushed against walls. But the heart of this or that man, he thought, is the heart of this or that man ever strong enough to force the issue, to burst the walls and let the outside pour in?

He did not know. He was sorrier now, for his brains had failed him. *Kike* they called him, *schmouk, dummy.* They may be right. He nestled deeper into his shame. But it was more bitter than that. He knew now, with a fierce hatred for all mankind, that he did not have the heart to reject his own sorrow.

# Peyo Mercé: English Teacher

## ABELARDO DÍAZ ALFARO

After the story about Santa Claus' debut in the *barrio* of La Cuchilla made the rounds, the animosity between Peyo Mercé and Rogelio Escalera, the school supervisor, grew worse. Escalera ordered the old teacher, by means of a virulent and drastic letter, to emphasize at once the teaching of English, or else he would be forced to resort to methods that were not to his taste, "but that would prove healthful for the development of progressive education." That oft-repeated letter-ending of the supervisor, Peyo already knew by heart; scornfully, he threw aside the wretched message. The unusual thing about the whole matter was that, along with the letter, he received some books with white-plastered covers and glaring landscapes adorned with well-fed, neatly dressed children.

Peyo grabbed one of the books. It read *Primer,* in black letters. He thought for a while and then, scratching an ear, said to himself, *"Primer* must come from *'primero,'* which means that with this book I must start my new trip to the Calvary. One more headache. Peyo Mercé to teach English in English! And I'll have to—my job depends on it. Cuchilla style, it will be. If I myself don't chew it right, how am I going to make the kids digest it? But Mr. Escalera wants English and English it will be." He then went quickly through the book pages, which smelled brand-new.

The children's gabble, as they entered the shabby schoolroom, began to pull him out of his pondering. Funny-looking skirts and pants held by cloth-suspenders which had been tarnished by plantain, hair straight and faded, tiny feet covered by the red clay of the rural trails, and the soft glow of hungry eyes on withered faces.

The indignation that the supervisor's letter had stirred up in him diminished as all his children began to fill the room. He loved them because they were his own kind and because for each of them he envisioned a destiny as dark as the night becomes just before a storm. Good

morning, *Don* Peyo, they said, and with a light movement of the head approached the benches nailed to tabletops. Peyo did not like to be addressed as *Mister.* "I'm a hick from La Cuchilla and I feel honored to be so. That *mister* thing tastes to me just like Kresto and 'chewing-gaw' and the other stuff they sell us now. I bear within me the stain of the plantain and can turn whichever way, just like the bushleaf."

He looked out the lopsided window as if to collect his breath. Over the grayish-green of the hills spotted by the swaying tobacco groves, white clouds raised their swollen sunlight sails. Against the red blaze of some shade trees, crackles burnt their black wings. And he felt a lack of interest, a weakening of the will, come over him, driving his attention rather to a class study of the land—the fertile land that yielded so much light, so many ruby-colored clots. To return to everyday chores on such a sunny day was something that he could not help but lament. And painful it was to have to teach as dry a thing as *Primer English.*

He walked slowly to the front of the class. His cracked lips hinted at the laughter that would damn it all. A bitter thought put away the laughter from his thoughts and wrinkled his forehead. Once again he turned the pages of the meddlesome book. There was not a single thing in it that could arouse his students' interest, nothing that related to the environment. He joyfully came upon a print of a bigcrest rooster that displayed its luxuriant tail. The proud rooster had long, bent spurs in which an Isabela game-cock could well spend the night. "That's it; today the kids will have rooster in English." In better spirits now, Peyo decided to face his class most calmly.

*"Well, children . . . We are goin' to talk in Englis' toooday."* While these gaspingly bespattered words came out of his mouth, his eyes went fleetingly over the astonished faces of his children.

And in order to make the best of his approach, he asked in a high pitch, *"Under-es-stan'?"*

Complete silence was the answer they gave him. And Peyo felt like reprimanding them, but— how could he manage that in English? He moved over again to the window in search of courage. A lark cut through the bluish expanse—a black petal in the wind. And he felt loaded with misery. With a deep longing for freedom.

He availed himself of the moment to re-hearse the pronunciation of the word he would be teaching next. And with a wry face followed by a sort of sneezing sound, he muttered, *"Cock …Cock…Cock…"* And scolded, "Language of the devil."

He decided to try out a method that was not ex-actly what the tedious pedagogical lectures of the experts advised.

Silence came over the classroom. Peyo was loved and respected by his students. That was something that Rogelio Escalera could not understand! Peyo did not know anything about the latest studies conducted on the teacher's personality traits and even less about child psychology. He did not like to attend the "fixed model classes," something that the supervisor took very much to heart.

A spurt of light came through the small win-dow, red-spotting the wan faces and white-cap-ping the loose, long hair.

"Well, children, today we're going to gad about in English for a while—straight English." His words coming out laboriously, he was inclined to give out with a little speech concerning the goodness of what he was about to deal with. But his main fault as a teacher was sincerity.

Feeling a lump in his throat, he loosened the knot of his faded tie with nervous fingers. Out in the farthest corner of his mind, he cursed a few things—among them, the supervisor who wanted him to swim in deep-sea waters where only the best fish can keep alive. With full resignation, he said to himself, "You can spike and lash any old

mare into making a move." And the *jíbaro* saying acquired in his own mind all of its painful reality.

Peyo tried to think about the "devices" suggested in the books that had to do with the teaching of English. His mind, however, was as gloomy as a night that threatened stormy weather. "A shortcut, a footpath, a trick—anything that can lead me out to the road," he implored. And shaking his dis-tressed head with rough fingers, while his students stared with surprise, he said, "What paradise this would be if it were not for the supervisor and his nonsense."

Convinced that his efforts to conduct the class in English would prove futile, he again re-sorted to a method all his own, "a cut-through" as he called it. He would mix it, concoct it, graft it. And whatever would come out of it, duck or wid-geon, would be all right.

He raised the book over the head of his stu-dents. With a tobacco-stained finger, he pointed at the illustration of the superb rooster.

"Look, *this is a cock*. Repeat that."

And the students sang way out of tune, *Cock, cock, cock.*"

Peyo, all excited, head stuffed up, shouted, "Whoa! Easy. These brats are setting up a cockpit right here!" The dissonant voices died down. Peyo was stifling. Once again he walked to the window. Sweat soaked his many-colored shirt. He needed air, a lot of air. And he held himself there for a while, hands stuck like hooks on the slanted win-dow-frame.

He stared unconsciously at the neighboring stream—a fresh tear sliding through the rocks. And he envied Petra's son, who was dunking his face in the sunlit water.

Disgusted, he decided to get out of the mess he had gotten into. And nervously he walked back to the front of the room.

"All right, *cock* is rooster in English, in American." Again he pointed the tobacco-stained finger at the luxurious rooster. "This is *cock* in English, *cock* is rooster. Now let's go easy, 'cause that's the way to tame a stallion. Otherwise, he runs wild. What's this in English, Teclo?"

Teclo, who had been staring at the strange rooster, answered timidly, "That's a turkey gamecock." And the children's laughter made the shabby room rattle. Peyo frowned, pretending not to be moved by the funny remark, and said maliciously, "I knew it, he walks on the sly into *Don* Cipria's cockpit. Turkey gamecock, indeed! Child, this is a tame rooster, a respectable rooster, not one of those shaved ones that fight around."

And again he asked, "What's this in English?" And the students went into the monotonous singsong, "*Cock, cock, cock.*" And Peyo felt pretty good. Out of that bloody encounter, he had emerged unharmed. He distributed some books and ordered the students to turn to the page that told all about that bragging rooster. "Let's read a little in English." The children looked surprised at the page and could hardly hold back the roars of laughter.

Peyo's face changed colors. A chill ran through his body. He even thought of handing the supervisor his most definite resignation. "The pig's tail is curling for sure now." And by fits and starts, stuttering, with a heavy tongue and lips tasting of thorny *maya* leaves, he read, "*This is the cock. The cock says cock-a-doodle-do.*" He then told himself, "Either that rooster has distemper or else Americans don't hear too good." That was really the last straw. But he gave a moment's thought to his everyday bread.

"Read with me. *The cock says cock-a-doodle-do.*" The voices shimmered on the morning wind. "That's good."

"Now, Tellito, how does the rooster sing in English?"

"I don't know, *Don* Peyo."

"But you just read it, boy."

"No," Tellito whimpered, looking at the print.

"Look, you dumb-bell, the rooster says *cock-a-doodle-do.*"

And Tellito, as though apologizing, said, "*Don* Peyo, that American Manila rooster may go like that, but the black and white one we got home goes caw-caw-raw-caw."

Peyo forgot all his pain and let out a boisterous laugh that was accompanied by the children's own titter.

Alarmed by the noise, *Don* Cipria's own *camagüey* cock shook his iridescent wings and wove into the sky's blue silk his own clean, metallic caw-caw-raw-caw.

*Translated by Pedro Juan Soto*

# A Country Boy Withdraws from School

## LAO HSIANG

A boy in the country gets to be at least half as useful as a grown-up by the time he is eight or nine years old. He can weed in the spring or tie up harvest bundles in summer; he is able to pass bricks when a house is built or open and shut the furrows to the irrigation ditches. That being the case, who'd want to send him to school? But an official proclamation has been issued in the city to the effect that unless a boy over six years of age is sent to school, some adult in the family will have to go to jail. This was how it happened that the Country Boy of our story went to school.

On his first day at school the Boy came back with eight books. His grandparents and his father and mother all gathered around him and marveled at the pictures in the books. Said Grandfather: "The *Four Books* and the *Five Classics* never had any pictures like these."

"The people in the pictures are not Chinese!" Father suddenly exclaimed. "Look carefully and you'll see that none of them wear the kind of clothes we do. See, these are leather shoes, this is a foreign costume, this is what is called a dog stick. They remind me of the old missionary that preaches at the cross street in the city."

"This woman at the spinning wheel is also a foreigner," Grandmother said. "We use the right hand to spin but she uses her left."

"If that makes her a foreigner, then this driver is not Chinese either. Look, have you ever seen a Chinese driver standing on this side of the cart?" commented Grandfather.

"The teacher says that the books cost a dollar and twenty cents," the Boy suddenly said, taking courage in their absorption in the books. The statement stunned everyone like a sudden clap of thunder.

Grandmother was the first to speak: "They certainly have nerve to make us pay for the books after we give up the boy for them! He's gone to

school hardly a day and it's cost us over a dollar already. Who can afford such schools? We can't save that much money if we go without light for half a year, and we'll have to sell at least eight bushels of corn to raise that much money."

"I should think one book ought to be enough to start with. They can get another after they have finished that," Grandfather said.

"Moreover, why should it cost so much when there are only three or four characters on a page?" Grandmother continued. "The almanac has both large and small characters and is closely printed and it cost only five coppers. How could these be worth more than a dollar?"

The books which they had marveled at a few minutes ago had suddenly become a cause for depression. The family discussed the matter at supper and all through the rest of the evening and finally decided that they would accept this calamity and pay the amount required since it was the first time. In order to make up the sum, the Boy's mother had to contribute the proceeds from two pairs of earrings that she had recently sold. His father gave him a solemn lecture, saying, "You are now nine, no longer so young. We're sparing you from work and sending you to school, though we can't afford it in our circumstances. You'll be very ungrateful if you don't study hard and learn something."

The Boy took his father's instruction to heart and set out for school the next day at dawn. When he got there, however, the porter said to him in a low voice: "Classes don't start till nine. It's now only five-thirty. You are too early. The teacher is asleep and the class room isn't unlocked. You had better go home now." The Boy looked around the yard and found that he was indeed the only student there; he listened outside the teacher's window and heard him snoring; he walked around the lecture room and found no open door. There was nothing for him to do but run back home. Grandfather was sweeping the yard when he suddenly caught sight of the Boy. He threw down his broom and said, "What is the use of trying to make a scholar of a boy whom Heaven has intended for the hoe? Look at him, it's only the second day and he is playing truant already!" The Boy was just about to explain when his mother gave him two resounding slaps and made him tend the fire for breakfast. Needless to say, the price of the books that they had to buy had a great deal to do with their tempers.

When the Boy went to school again after breakfast, the teacher was already on the platform and was holding forth on the subject of being late to school. To illustrate his point he told a story about a little fairy that waited by the wayside with a bag of gold to reward the earliest boy. Our Boy was enchanted with the story and the words "fairy" and "gold" but he could not figure out just what was meant by "earliest."

In the afternoon our young hero came back from school at three-thirty, just as his father was going back to work after his midday nap. Luckily his father happened to see the other boys also coming home from school and the teacher taking a stroll with his "dog stick" and concluded that his son was not playing truant. He kept wondering, however, about the strange ways of these foreign schools.

The first six days of school was taken up with the first lesson in the Reader, with the text "This is mama." It couldn't be said that the Boy was not diligent. He reviewed his lesson every day after school, reading over and over again "This is mama" until dusk. With his left hand holding the book open and his right following the characters he read on faithfully and conscientiously, as if afraid that the characters would fly away if he did not fix his entire attention on them.

But every time he read "This is mama" his mother's heart would jump. On the sixth day of school, she could stand it no longer. She snatched the book from him and said, "Let me see who your mama is!" Thinking that his mother was re-

ally eager to learn, the Boy pointed to the accompanying picture and said, "This is mama, the lady with leather shoes, bobbed hair, and long dress." One glance at the picture and Mother burst out crying. Grandfather, Grandmother, and Father were frightened, thinking that she might have become possessed by some evil spirits. At first she only cried and would not say anything when they asked her what the matter was, but when they persisted, she said, "Where did the boy get that vampirelike mama?"

When they found the cause of her distress, Father said, "We'll have the boy ask his teacher whose mama this really is. Maybe it is the teacher's mama."

The next morning before dawn Mother woke up her son and made him go to school and ask the teacher for a solution of the problem that had bothered her all night. Arriving at school the Boy found that it was Sunday and that there would be no school. Moreover, the teacher had drunk more wine than was good for him the night before and was still sound asleep. The Boy told Mother the circumstances, which made her curse the institution of Sunday.

At general assembly on Monday the teacher said gently to his charges: "One who wants to learn must not be afraid to ask questions. Anyone who has any question should raise it at once, to his teacher at school or to his parents at home." Thereupon our hero stood up and asked: "The Reader says 'This is mama.' Whose mama is she really?" The teacher answered even more gently than before. "It is the mama of anyone who happens to read the book. Do you understand now?"

"No," the Boy said. This embarrassed the teacher a little but he said patiently: "Why don't you understand?"

"Baldy is also reading this, but his mama is not like this lady," the Boy said.

"Baldy's mother is lame in one arm and has only one eye," Hsiao Lin said.

"And you have no mama at all. She died a long time ago," Baldy said in self-defense.

"Don't talk among yourselves!" the teacher said, knocking on the blackboard with his ferrule. "We are going to have the second lesson today: 'This is papa.' Look, everyone. This is papa, the man with spectacles and parted hair."

After school Mother was still worried about who the picture woman was but when she heard her son reiterating "This is papa," she did not dare to pursue the question, being afraid that her husband might want to know when she'd found a new papa for their son. She was puzzled more than ever and wondered why the book insisted on presenting people with papas and mamas when they had them already.

A few days later the Boy learned two new sentences: "The ox tends the fire; the horse eats noodles." He read the text over thousands of times but he could not get over the feeling that there was something queer about the assertions. They had an ox and a horse and he had himself taken them out to graze in the hills but he had never once seen a horse eat noodles and he was sure that their ox could not tend the fire. But could the book be wrong? Since he could not answer these questions, he obeyed his teacher's injunction of the week before and asked his father about it. Father said: "I once went to a foreign circus in the city and saw a horse that could ring a bell and fire a gun. Perhaps the book is talking about such horses and oxen."

Grandmother, however, did not agree with Father's explanation. She said: "The ox must be the Ox-Head Devil King and the horse must also be a demon. Don't you see that they all wear human clothing? They haven't changed their heads for human heads yet, but that alone will take five hundred years." The old lady then went on to tell stories about demons that could command the wind and summon rain; the result was that the Boy dreamed that night of being seized by a winged wolf demon and woke up crying.

The following day the Boy asked his teacher: "Is this ox that can tend the fire a foreign ox?"

The teacher laughed and said: "You are too literal! The book has only made those things up. It is not true that oxen can really tend the fire or that horses really eat noodles."

The explanation cleared up at one stroke many things in the book that had puzzled the Boy. He had read about such things as "bread," "milk," "park," "ball," and the like which he had never seen and which had made him wonder. It dawned upon him that the book dealt only with make-believe things.

One day the Boy and his schoolmates decided that they would play "tea party" as they had read about it in their Reader. They agreed that each would contribute twenty cents so that they could send to the city for oranges, apples, chocolate, and things. Our Boy knew, of course, that he would be only inviting a beating to ask money for buying sweetmeats. Grandmother always mumbled that school would bankrupt them yet whenever he had to buy a sheet of writing paper. But he could not resist the glowing picture that his book gave of the "tea party" and decided to help himself to the money that his mother had just got from selling more of her jewels and which she had set aside for buying cabbage seedlings.

Grandfather had been suffering for a long time from a chronic cough, and someone had told him that orange peels would give him relief. He kept on asking what orange peels were like and where they could be gotten. Thinking that this was a chance for him to ingratiate himself into his grandfather's favors, the Boy said, "We are getting some oranges."

"You are getting some oranges?" Grandfather asked. "What are you getting oranges for?"

"We want to hold a tea party," the Boy said.

"What is a tea party?"

"It means to get together and eat things and drink tea," the Boy said. "It is in the book."

"What kind of book is this that is either making animals talk or teaching people to eat and play? No wonder the boys have become lazy and choosy about their food since they went to school!" Grandmother said.

"And it is always about foreign food. There doesn't seem to be any corn wowotou or bean curd with onions in it," Grandfather said.

"Remember, son, to bring back some orange peels for your grandfather's cough," said Mother.

"Where did you get the money to buy oranges?" asked Father.

"The teacher..." but before the Boy had finished making up his story, Baldy, who lived to the east, suddenly began to cry. Then they heard his father shout: "We can't even afford salt, and yet you want to buy candy...."

This was followed by the voice of Hsiao Lin's uncle, who lived to their west: "I let you buy books with my hard-earned money because it is for your good, but I haven't any money for you to buy sweetmeats. You can ask whoever wants you to hold tea parties for it."

The truth came out. The Boy's father aimed a kick at him, but fortunately the table intervened. He only upset the table and broke a few rice bowls. Grandfather was of the opinion that it might be better to take the Boy out of school, but Grandmother did not want her son to go to jail.

After long arguments it was decided that they would let the Boy try school for a few more days.

After this humiliation, our young scholar vowed to study harder and to recover his lost prestige in the family. Everyday after school he read without stopping until it was dark. He did not realize that the source of his troubles lay in the textbook itself.

For Grandmother had been feeling that her son was no longer as close to her as before his marriage and that her position in the family had been gradually slipping. Now as she listened to the Boy reading aloud his latest lessons she heard him say, "In my family I have a papa, a mama, a didi and a meimei," but nothing about Grandfather and Grandmother; she became very indignant and shouted: "So this house is now all yours and I have no longer a share in it!" She was mad with fury. She picked up a brick and broke their iron pot into pieces.

"Don't be angry any more!" the Boy's father said. "We won't let him read this kind of book any longer. I would rather go to jail.'

And so the next day Father discharged a day laborer and the teacher marked the Boy's absence in the record book at school.

# Excerpt from *Staggerford*

## JON HASSLER

Few could remember a time when Miss McGee—slight and splay-footed and quick as a bird—was not teaching at St. Isidore's. This was her forty-first year in the same classroom, her forty-first year of flitting and hovering up and down the aisles in the morning when she felt fresh, and perching behind her walnut desk in the afternoon when fatigue set in. In the minds of her former students, many of whom were now grandparents, she occupied a place somewhere between Moses and Emily Post, and when they met her on the street they guarded not only their speech but also their thoughts.

They knew of course—for she had been telling the story for over half a century—that when she was a girl she had met Joyce Kilmer, but who would have guessed the connection between that meeting many years ago and the fire alarm this afternoon? Standing in the garden among her cabbages, she decided that she would never tell a soul—not even Miles—about the cause of the fire alarm. She could not lie, but she could keep a secret.

Agatha McGee met Joyce Kilmer when she was six. She was a first grader at St. Isidore's. The year was 1916 and her teacher, Sister Rose of Lima, primed the first grade for months, leading them in a recitation of "Trees" every morning between the Apostles' Creed and the Pledge of Allegiance; and then on the last day of school before Christmas break, Joyce Kilmer stepped through the classroom door at the appointed hour, casting Sister Rose of Lima into a state of stuttering foolishness and her students into ecstasy. Miss McGee remembered it like yesterday. Mr. Kilmer was handsome, cheery, and a bit plump. He wore a black suit and a red tie. With a playful sparkle in his eye he bowed to Sister Rose of Lima, saying he was delighted to meet her, and then he walked among her students, asking their names. The children's voices were suddenly undependable, and

they told their names in tense whispers and unexpected shouts. Jesse Farnham momentarily forgot who he was, and the silence was thick while he thought. When he finally said, "Jesse," Mr. Kilmer told him that he has known a girl by that name, and the first grade exploded with more laughter than Sister Rose of Lima permitted on ordinary days. (Priests and poets melted her severity.) The laughter, ending as suddenly as it began, was followed by a comfortable chat, the poet telling stories, some without lessons. Before Mr. Kilmer left, his admirers recited "Trees" for him. For Agatha McGee his visit was, like Christmas in those years, a joy undiminished by anticipation.

But that was long ago. Nowadays poetry, among other things, wasn't what it used to be. Yesterday at St. Isidore's as Miss McGee sat at the faculty lunch table she overheard Sister Rosie tell Sister Judy in an excited whisper that Herschel Mancrief was coming to town. He was touring the Midwest on a federal grant, and would arrive at St. Isidore's at ten the next morning. The two sisters were huddled low over the Spanish rice, trying to keep the news from Miss McGee. She wasn't surprised. She was well aware that the new nuns, although pranked out in permanents and skirts up to their knees, were still a clandestine sorority. How like them to plan an interruption in the schoolday and not let her know.

"About whom are you speaking?" she asked.

"Oh, Miss McGee," said Sister Rosie, the lighthearted (and in Miss McGee's opinion, lightheaded) principal of St. Isidore's. "We were discussing Herschel Mancrief, and we were not at all sure you would be interested." Sister Rosie was twenty-six and she had pierced earlobes.

"I will be the judge of my interests, if you please. Who is Herschel Mancrief?"

"He's a poet the younger generation is reading," said Sister Judy, blushing behind her acne. "We studied him in the novitiate."

"His credentials are super," said Sister Rosie.

"And he's coming to St. Isidore's? I might have been told. Will he visit classes or speak to an assembly?"

"He will visit classes. But of course no one is obliged to have him in. I know what a nuisance interruptions can be."

"Poets are important to children. I was visited by Mr. Joyce Kilmer when I was a girl, and I treasure the memory. Please show Mr. What's-his-name to my classroom when the time comes. What's his name?"

"Herschel Mancrief. He can give you twenty minutes at quarter to twelve."

So this morning Miss McGee announced to her sixth graders that they were about to meet Herschel Mancrief. They looked up from their reading assignment, a page headed "Goths and Visigoths," and as a sign of their undivided attention they closed their books. Divided attention was among the things Miss McGee did not permit. Slang and eye shadow were others.

"Meeting a poet is a memorable experience," she said. "When I was a girl, my class was visited by Mr. Joyce Kilmer, who wrote 'Trees,' the poem every child carries in his heart from the primary grades, and to this day I can recall what Mr. Kilmer said to us. He came to Staggerford a mere two years before giving his life for his country in World War One." She tilted her head back, in order to read her twenty-four sixth graders through her bifocals—difficult reading these days, for they lurked, boys and girls alike, behind veils of hair.

"The poet, you understand, is a man with a message. His mission is to remind us of the beauty God has made. He writes of the good and lasting things of life. His business is beauty. Are there any questions?"

There was one, and several students raised their hands to ask it: "How does 'Trees' go?"

"Heavens, surely you remember."

But it was discovered that no one in the class had heard it. As Miss McGee began reciting, "'I think that I shall never see,'" a frightening sensation crept up her spine and gripped her heart—an invisible tremor like the one she had felt in 1918 when her third-grade teacher said that Joyce Kilmer was dead in France. An imperceptible shudder that moved out along her nervous system and left her nauseous. Her name for it was the Dark Age dyspepsia, because it struck whenever she came upon a new piece of alarming evidence that pointed to the return of the Dark Ages.

Dark Age evidence had been accumulating. Last month at Parents' Night, Barbara Betka's father and mother told Miss McGee they would see her fired if she did not lift her prohibition against the wearing of nylons by sixth-grade girls. They were standing in the assembly room where coffee was to be served. Mr. Betka, fidgeting and averting his eyes, did most of the talking while Mrs. Betka, having called the tune, stood at his side and fingered his arm like a musical instrument. "Fired indeed!" said Miss McGee, turning on her heel and snatching up her purse in a single motion of amazing agility, like a move in hopscotch, and she flew from the assembly room oefore coffee was served. She was followed home by the Dark Age dyspepsia and scarcely slept that night, haunted by the specter of a man in his fifties sent out by his wife to do battle for nylons. "The craven ninny," she said to herself at dawn, rising to prepare the day's lessons.

And that was the day Dr. Murphy from the State Department of Education came to town to address a joint meeting of public and parochial school faculties. Both Miles and Miss McGee attended his lecture. "Never," Dr. Murphy said at the end of a tedious address on language arts, "never burden a child with a book written earlier than the child's date of birth. That way you can be confident that you and your students are in tune with each other, that you are moving with them on a contemporary plane." This harebrained proposal proved to Miss McGee that not even the State Department of Education was immune from the spreading plague of dark and crippling ignorance.

Nor were the sisters immune. More than once, for their spring picnic, Sister Judy had taken her fourth graders to a hippie farm. When Miss McGee first heard about that, she went to the pastor, Father Finn, and warned him about the return of the Dark Ages. Father Finn, ordinarily a man of understanding, did not understand Miss McGee's anxiety. If the Dark Ages were coming back, he had not yet caught sight of them. He told Miss McGee that she was an alarmist.

This morning as she concluded with the line, "But only God can make a tree," the door opened and Herschel Mancrief appeared. He was led into the classroom by Sister Rosie. He was untidy. That was Miss McGee's first impression of him. Under his wrinkled suitcoat he wore a T-shirt and under his nose a thicket of hair that curled around the corners of his mouth and ended in a stringy gray beard.

Miss McGee said, "I am pleased to meet you," and she gracefully offered her hand.

"Groovy," said the poet, tapping her palm with the tip of one finger. Up close she saw that his neck and his T-shirt were unmistakably unwashed. His asymmetrical sideburns held lint. She hopped silently backward and slipped into an empty desk halfway down an aisle, and Sister Rosie introduced the visitor, training a spit curl as she spoke.

"Mr. Mancrief has already been to three rooms and he has another one to visit after yours, class, and he has to leave by twelve thirty, so when his time is up please don't bug him to stay." On her way out the door, Sister Rosie added, "Room 102 is next, Herschel. It's just across the hall."

The sixth grade regarded the poet.

"I am here to make you childlike," he began, blinking as he spoke, as though his words gave off too much light. "I am here to save you from growing up." His voice was deep and wheezy, and his frown was fixed. "You see, grownups aren't sensitive. They get covered over with a kind of crust. They don't *feel.* It is only through constant effort that I am able to maintain the wonder, the joy, the capacity for feeling that I had as a

child." He quit blinking and inserted a hand under his suitcoat to give his ribs a general and thoughtful scratching. "Do you understand what I am saying?"

The class looked at Miss McGee. She nodded and so did they.

"Good. Now here's a poem of mine called 'What I Envied.' It's an example of what I'm saying." He closed his eyes and spoke in an altered voice, a chant:

> *"I envied as a child*
> *the clean manikins in store windows*
> *because their underwear fit*
> *their toes were buried in thick carpet*
> *their happy smiles immutable,*
> *until my father driving us home*
> *past midnight after a day in the country*
> *passed a window full of manikins*
> *and then I knew*
> *the trouble it must be*
> *to smile all night!"*

After a silent moment the poet opened his eyes signaling the end of the poem.

Miss McGee had heard worse. Except for the reference to underwear, it came as close to poetry as most of the verse she had read lately, and she set the class to nodding its approval.

Herschel Mancrief shed his suitcoat and revealed that his pants were held up by a knotted rope. It was not the white, carefully braided rope of the Franciscans, who were Miss McGee's teachers in college, but a dirty length of frazzled twine.

"Good," said the poet, laying his suitcoat across Miss McGee's walnut desk. "You remember how heroic those manikins used to seem when you were small and they were larger than life. You would see one in a store window and it was close enough to make you salute. The pity is that you gradually lose your sense of wonder for things like that. Take toilets, for example. My poem 'So Tall' is about a toilet."

He recited with his eyes shut. Miss McGee shut hers as well.

*"How tall I seem to be these days*
*and how much I am missing,*
*things at ground level escape my notice*
*wall plugs wastebaskets heat registers,*
*what do I care for them now I am so tall?*
*I was once acquainted with a toilet*
*when it and I were eye to eye,*
*it would roar and swallow and scare me half*
    *to death.*
*What do I care for that toilet now,*
*now I am so tall?"*

There was the sound of a giggle, stifled.

"You are surprised I got a toilet into a poem?" He was asking Miss McGee, who had not giggled. "But poetry takes all of life for her domain. The beautiful and the unbeautiful. Roses and toilets. Today's poet seeks to represent the proportions of life. You don't very often pick a rose, but you go to the bathroom several times a day."

Certain now that he had taken the measure of Miss McGee's tolerance for the unbeautiful (color was rising in her face) the poet announced his third selection, "In My End of Town."

*"In my end of town*
*like a cathedral against the sky*
*stands the city sewage plant,*
*the direction of the wind*
*is important to us,*
*in my end of town*
*man disposes."*

He opened his eyes to study Miss McGee's reaction, but the desk she had been sitting in was empty. She was at his side, facing the class.

"Students, you will thank Mr. Mancrief."

"Thank you, Mr. Mancrief." They spoke the way they prayed, in unison and without enthusiasm.

She handed the poet his coat and, not wishing to touch his hairy arms, she steered him to the door as if by remote control. "There"—she pointed—"is Room 102."

Nothing in his government-sponsored travels had prepared Herschel Mancrief for the brush-off.

"Actually," he said, blinking as he backed into the corridor, "I hadn't finished."

"I regret we can spare you no more time. We recite the Angelus at twelve."

Looking more surprised than offended, he raised a hand as though to speak, but then thought better of it and stepped across the corridor and knocked on the door of 102. It opened instantly and Sister Judy put her head out.

Miss McGee, afraid now that her treatment of the man had been too delicate, said, "Another thing, Mr. Mancrief. Your poetry is…" She searched for the word. The poet and Sister Judy listened for it.

"Your poetry is undistinguished."

Sister Judy rolled her eyes and the poet chuckled into his hand. Miss McGee turned back to her class, pulling the door shut behind her. "Entirely undistinguished, class. You will rise now for the Angelus."

Later, entering the lunchroom, Miss McGee saw at the far end of the faculty table Herschel Mancrief and Sister Judy ignoring their beans and tuna and laughing like ninnies.

"I thought he was to have been on his way by this time."

"We asked him to stay for lunch," said Sister Rosie. "He has agreed to stay a while longer. Isn't he super?"

"He's horribly dated. He said 'groovy.' I haven't heard anyone say 'groovy' for at least three years."

"Oh, Miss McGee, he's super. Admit it."

"Pass the relish, if you please."

Two hours later, after putting her class to work on equilateral triangles, Miss McGee opened her door for a change of air. From behind the closed door of 102 she heard raucous laughter alternating with the excited voice of Herschel Mancrief. The man evidently could not bring himself to leave St. Isidore's. She stepped closer and listened through the door.

"Acquainted with a toilet," said the poet.

The fourth grade laughed.

"It would roar and swallow and scare me half to death."

More laughter.

"There, now you've caught the spirit of the poem. Now repeat it after me."

They did so, briskly, line by line.

"Now let's try another one—a poem I wrote just the other day called 'Be Careful Where You Grab Me.'"

Fierce laughter.

Miss McGee hurried to the nearest fire alarm and with a trembling hand she broke the seal and set off an ear-splitting jangle of horns and bells that emptied the building in forty-five seconds.

Two ladder trucks pulled up to the front door and while the fire chief, a former student of Miss Mc-Gee's, gave the building a thorough inspection, Herschel Mancrief drove off in his rented car, the fourth grade throwing him kisses from the curb.

"A false alarm," declared the fire chief, emerging from the front door of the school in his yellow rubber coat.

"Someone set off the alarm near your room," he said to Miss McGee as she led her sixth grade up the steps and back into the building. "Did you notice anything suspicious, Miss McGee?"

"Goths and Visigoths," she said.

# The Boy Who Couldn't Read

## JACQUELINE WILSON

Mr Croft worked the children hard for most of the day. He believed in getting straight down to it, first day of term or not. But he'd relented by the last lesson. He was a little worried by their sullen obedience. They gathered round the other teachers in the playground and laughed and chatted without any inhibitions but no one ever came and talked to him now. Perhaps he was too hard on them?

He decided to give them a little treat. He'd read to them for twenty minutes and then let them draw a picture. He fumbled in the back of the cupboard and found his old copy of *The Mountain of Adventure*. You couldn't beat a good Enid Blyton adventure story, no matter what all these trendy educationalists said. Let them read obscure fantasies or sordid kiddie kitchen sink. He knew what the children liked.

But one child didn't like *The Mountain of Adventure*. Mr Croft looked up after a couple of pages and saw David Bates hunched up over his own book. He stopped reading aloud and the children held their breath. It took David a few seconds before he noticed the expectant silence.

"What are you doing, David Bates?"

"I'm sorry," said David snapping his book shut.

"Let me see that."

David sighed and handed the book over. It was a book on astronomy. Mr Croft thumbed through it and then gave it back.

"Why were you looking at that instead of listening to the story?"

"I—I'm interested in astronomy."

"Oh yes? And I take it you're not interested in *The Mountain of Adventure*?"

"Not really."

"Why, may I ask?"

"Well, I think it's a bit infantile, if you really want to know."

Someone tittered.

"Infantile. Oh, I see. The boy wonder prefers to read an adult book on astronomy, correct?"

"Yes."

"What tosh! You silly little boy. We all know you can't even read properly. Of course you can't manage to read that astronomy book, you're just showing off."

"I can read it," said David, his face getting red.

"I've heard you read, boy. You have to have your special coaching, don't you?"

"I *can* read."

"Very well. Demonstrate. Come out to the front of the class. You're always trying to tell me my job. Well, you take over altogether. Here's *The Mountain of Adventure*. Very infantile, right? Well, read it then. Read it loud to the class."

David stood up, burning. He took the book and cleared his throat. He read, stumbling, hesitating, with little expression. Another child giggled nervously, but most were still and silent, their own faces red.

"That's enough, lad. A five-year-old could do better," said Mr Croft. "You can hardly read at all. Sit down then."

Mr Croft read on to the end of the chapter. David Bates sat motionless throughout. Then Mr Croft handed round pieces of paper and told the children to do a drawing to illustrate the story. There were only ten minutes left of the lesson but they passed very slowly. The bell rang at last and the children stretched and sighed. One stood up, several disappeared behind their desk lids.

Mr Croft rapped on his own desk with the blackboard eraser.

"What are you doing? I didn't say that the lesson is over," he said, although he had also sagged with relief. He decided he was too exhausted to make an issue of it. It was the first day of term after all. They always took a few days to simmer down, especially after Christmas.

"Very well. Off you go," he said, in a kindlier fashion. "Hand in your drawings as you go."

They handed in their efforts. Some were hastily scribbled and coloured with school wax crayon. Others were lovingly embellished with privately owned felt-tip pen. Gideon Symons handed in a masterpiece worthy of a gold star, his artistic ability enormously aided by his huge tin of forty Caran D'Ache.

David Bates passed Mr Croft's desk without pausing.

"David?"

The child's face was still unusually red but he maintained his irritating composure.

"Yes, Mr Croft?"

"Hand in your drawing, David."

"There's little point," said David, and he handed in a blank sheet of paper. He waited.

Mr Croft looked at the blank paper, wanting to crumple it.

"I suppose you think you're being clever," he said eventually.

David chose not to reply. Mr Croft looked at his peaky face and spiky hair and round spectacles. A sparrow of a child with owl eyes. There'd been other kids equally bright. Disturbing kids. Kids who wet themselves or couldn't sit still or had epileptic fits on the woodblock floor. Kids with nits, kids with knives. Kids like Gideon Symons with his Caran D'Ache crayons and his yellow Kickers boots. All sorts of kids, but he'd never hated one the way he hated David Bates.

It was hard keeping the hatred out of his voice.

"You're being very silly, David. Now take your paper, go back to your desk, and do me a drawing."

The few remaining children raised their eyebrows and nudged each other. Mr Croft glared at them and they whisked out of the classroom. David looked at the door, swinging open. For a moment Mr Croft thought he was going to ignore him and walk straight out after them. But David merely sighed elaborately and did as he was told.

At least, he took the sheet of paper and sat down at his desk. He did not draw.

"Come along, lad. Get on with it," said Mr Croft.

David did nothing.

Mr Croft decided to ignore him for five minutes. He picked up his briefcase and took out the compositions 2A had written that morning.

"'What I did at Christmas.'" Everyone must fill at least two sides of paper. Neat writing, don't forget punctuation and watch that spelling."

Well, what did they do over Christmas? He gave the first few a glance.

"Mum let me stay up to see Morecambe and Wise it was smashing."

"My mum and dad and my aunties and uncles all had a few and got ever so tiddly and my Auntie Vi did a cancan and we did have a laugh."

"I didn't get what I wanted. I really wanted a poodle nightdress case. I got lovely presents and Mum and Dad gave me a Bionic Woman but I really did want a poodle nightdress case."

Mr Croft leafed through the compositions until he found David's. It was untidy and hopelessly misspelt. He tried to follow the general gist but it became impossible. He wanted to put a savage red line through the incomprehensible essay, but Maple, the headmaster, insisted that David had to be handled sensitively. Mr Croft wondered what Maple would say if he got to hear about this afternoon's little contretemps and his armpits prickled with anxiety. Reluctantly he picked out a handful of misspelt words in David's composition and wrote out the correct spellings, leaving space for David to copy each word ten times. Dyslexia! Once upon a time if a kid couldn't read properly by the time it was nearly nine it was thick and that was that. Well, all right, David Bates was no fool, although he wasn't necessarily another Einstein. His Stanford Binet assessment might be up in the 160s, but that only meant he was good at puzzles. That was all these I.Q. tests really were when you got down to it. And what was the use of being able to do silly puzzles when you could barely write your own name?

He glanced at the child. David returned his stare calmly. The piece of paper was still blank.

"I've just about had enough of this behaviour, Bates, Now get drawing. Go on, do as you're told."

David remained motionless.

"Pick up that pencil and *draw*!"

Mr Croft marched to the desk and wrapped the child's small cold hand round the pencil.

"Now draw," he said, giving him a hard prod in the back.

David leant on one elbow and let the pencil slide out of his hand back on to the desk.

"I'm warning you, Bates," said Mr Croft. "Stop this silly act. You're not impressing me at all. Just get on with drawing, do you hear?" He waited. *"Pick up that pencil!"*

David jumped but didn't obey. Mr Croft wanted to hit the boy so badly that he went back to his own desk, scared of losing control altogether. David watched him, his small face impassive.

"All right," said Mr Croft. "You want to play silly games, we'll play silly games. We shall sit it out. You are not leaving this classroom until you have done me a drawing. Do you understand? We shall sit here until breakfast if necessary."

"Then may I phone my mother?" David asked.

"No, you may not."

"But she will be worried about me. She always worries if I'm late. It isn't very fair on her," said David reasonably.

"I'm afraid I can't help that. It's you choosing to worry her, laddie, not me. Do me a drawing and you can be home in no time."

"Why do you want me to do a drawing so badly?" said David.

"Don't be so damn impertinent! Just remember who you are. You're not here to ask clever-dick questions. You're here to do as you're told. Now *do* as you're told."

Mr Croft longed to loosen his tie. His shirt was sticking to him. The central heating was turned up ridiculously high. He went to open a few windows. He had to use the window pole, although his hands were shaking badly so that the pole nudged useless against the glass many times before connecting. But he persevered, determined not to be defeated.

And he wasn't going to let this supercilious little twerp defeat him either. There wouldn't have been any problem in the old days. One swish of the cane and there wouldn't be any further argument. Not that he was one of these sadistic perverts getting some kind of kick out of caning kiddies. The cane had grown dusty in the cupboard, its very presence serving enough purpose.

He was sure he'd been popular with children then. The boys looked up to him and the little girls had all giggled at his jokes. They'd called him Sir and opened the door for him and worked hard. But now that some of their own children were at the school things were very different. 2A were a lost cause anyway after Jeff Priestly's influence. They spent a whole year in his form without learning how to write a decent sentence or any of their times tables. All they seemed to do was mess around with egg-boxes and toilet rolls. It seemed modern education was literally a load of old rubbish.

But it was no use complaining any more. Jeff Priestly was well in with Maple, thought to be a fine teacher, for God's sake. What sort of influence was he on the kids, with his shoulder-length hair and his tattered jeans and his cock-eyed Marxist theories? He wasn't even clean: he'd obviously been wearing that ridiculous Cambridge University sweatshirt for days. Cambridge University! Jeff Priestly was probably lucky to scrape five O-levels. Yet the way things were going he'd probably end up a headmaster. He wouldn't stay an underpaid and unappreciated junior school teacher.

But even Jeff Priestly had had a bit of bother with David Bates.

"He's the sort of kid who gets up my nose," he'd said once in the staff room, in his usual unprepossessing way. "He seems to have been born middle-aged. He's got this way of peering through his specs at you like a little professor."

David was peering through his glasses now, arms folded.

"You're obviously intending to spend the night here, my boy," said Mr Croft. "Well, it's no skin off my nose. I've got a lot of work here to be getting on with. I'm in no hurry to get home."

He pretended to mark the children's compositions. He wasn't really bluffing. The Christmas holidays seemed to have gone on for ever, a horrible reminder that this was what it was going to be like all the time when he retired. Only another year and two terms to go.

He hadn't thought he'd mind when Elaine finally moved out. They'd never really got on well together. He thought it would be a relief to be free of her whining. But the house was unpleasantly silent nowadays and although he kept it reasonably clean there was a dead atmosphere to the place, as if it had been sealed up for years.

"What I did at Christmas." Mr Croft had cooked his small oven-ready chicken and his mini Christmas pudding, but halfway through his meal he'd pushed his plate away, put his head down on the checked tablecloth, and wept.

He found his eyes were stinging now and he blinked quickly, horrified. Perhaps he was going to pieces, heading for a breakdown? No, he was just feeling a bit seedy, that was all. Perhaps he was starting 'flu, there was a bug going around at the moment. Maybe that was why he was so hot.

He loosened his tie after all and yawned several times. He was tired too, of course. He hadn't been sleeping well. He'd spent most of last night tossing about under his Marks and Spencer duvet, the double bed growing larger and more lonely by the minute. At least you could tuck yourself in tightly with good old-fashioned sheets and blankets. He'd tried wrapping the duvet round him until he felt like a giant Swiss roll but it still didn't help him to sleep. He'd grown so used to Elaine's warm brushed nylon bulk that he'd lost the knack of sleeping without her.

Funny how you could miss a woman you didn't even like. He hadn't thought much of her right from the start. A silly little shopgirl with painted lips, not his sort at all. She was all right for a bit of messing about, but that was all. Messing about was an accurate description too. Elaine might sport a blonde rinse and lipstick but she knew as little about sex as he did. It was a wonder their Betty ever managed to get herself conceived, her parents' coupling was so brief and inadequate.

Betty had been another disappointment. She'd appalled him as a red-faced shrieking baby, but she'd been an enchanting little girl, with her mother's fluffy good looks and a quick wit that took him by surprise. He had her whizzing through the Beacon Readers by the time she was four. She was top of the class all the way up her junior school and passed to the grammar without any bother. When she was twelve she was on Junior Criss Cross Quiz and did very well for herself too. But everything went wrong when she reached puberty. She wouldn't do her homework, went out dancing, sat around coffee bars. Her mother all over again. He tried pleading with her, slapping her, even locking her out of the house, but she wouldn't see reason.

She was three months pregnant when she took her O-levels. She only passed Domestic Science and Art and didn't seem to give a damn, because she had a wedding ring safe on her finger now. His Betty, swollen with the child of a greasy little garage mechanic who'd been in the lowest stream of a tough Secondary Modern.

The marriage had lasted, much to his surprise, and Betty's husband had his own garage now. Elaine had gone to live with them in their four bedroomed neo-Georgian house on a posh new estate in Surrey. Betty had tried to keep in touch. She'd even invited him for Christmas too, not wanting to appear to take sides, but he wasn't having any.

"Can we come in and do you now?"

Mr Croft looked around, startled. It was a couple of cleaning women, looking impatient.

"We've left you till last, you know. We really ought to be off now."

David sat up properly. Oh no, you little bugger, thought Mr Croft, I'm not giving up yet.

"I'm afraid you'll have to give this classroom a miss this afternoon, ladies," he said, in his most authoritative tones.

They tutted a little but went off with their brushes and brooms. The school was very still. It began to get much colder. The heating had obviously gone off for the night. David started shivering. Mr Croft was cold too now, but he decided to put up with his own discomfort.

"We seem to be the only ones left in the school," he said. "What a silly boy you are, Bates. Isn't it time you came to your senses?"

David said nothing.

Mr Croft said nothing.

They stared at each other and then both started when they heard the door slam at the end of the corridor. Maple's door. Oh God, he's forgotten Maple.

David's eyes glinted behind his glasses. There was going to be hell to pay with Maple. He was never keen on any kind of punishment. He hated the idea of children being kept after class. And it would be a hundred times worse because it was his precious David Bates.

There had been a bit of a barney last term. Mr Croft had made a slip when he was chalking some arithmetic on the board and David Bates immediately pointed out the mistake. He did it in such an offensive way, sighing heavily, eyebrows raised, that Mr Croft couldn't let it go at that. So he blustered, pretending that the mistake had been deliberate. He thought he sounded reasonably convincing, but David Bates gave a tight smile of contempt. Mr Croft sent the boy out of the room for insolence. Maple was indulging in one of his little tours of inspection and found the kid stuck outside the classroom.

Maple was angry but he handled it tactfully enough, saying nothing in front of the children. He waited and had a little chat with Mr Croft after school was over.

"Please don't think I'm interfering, Arthur," he said, taking pains to sound matey. "I know just how tiresome these gifted children can be. Maybe I'd have done the same myself. But I don't feel it's quite the right way of coping with the situation. Young David's a highly sensitive child and he needs careful handling. He got off to a very bad start at that other school. His mother assures me he could read fluently before he went to school, but when they started messing him about, insisting he start at the Look, Janet, Look stage, and in i.t.a. too, it confused and frustrated him so much that he became mildly dyslexic. Thank heavens we seem to be winning though. His reading age is only slightly below par now, and when he gets a bit of confidence I'm sure he'll make even greater progress. Can't you see why he badly needs to show off a bit in the lessons he's good at? If I were you'd I'd praise him as much as possible, Arthur. Thank God we've got rid of the poisonous gold star and form prize competitive claptrap, but kids still need a pat on the back at times."

Mr Croft shook his head and nodded at the appropriate moments because he had no other choice, but inwardly he burned with resentment. Maple thought he knew it all because he'd done a course in child psychology but he knew nothing. The kids had liked getting their gold stars for good work. When there weren't any more stars they stopped working. It was as simple as that. And mollycoddling insolent little sods like David Bates made them cockier than ever.

Mr Croft remembered his own schooldays. Miss Jennings at his little village school had been a wonderful woman, but she was a stickler for discipline. The tinies had to sit with their hands on their heads if they were naughty, and the older children got a stinging slap on the back of their legs if they dared to get up to mischief. No one would have dreamed of pointing out a mistake to Miss Jennings.

Mr Croft had been a polite little boy, neat and well-scrubbed, his hair smarmed oilily into submission. He had been top of the school and Miss Jennings' favourite. He'd sat the scholarship and passed to the big boys' Grammar in the town.

"You're destined to go far, my boy," Miss Jennings said, but she had been wrong. Mr Croft had expected to be top of the big boys' Grammar school too but to his shame and horror he was nearer the bottom of the form. He didn't give up. He worked even harder. He passed his school certificate and stayed on in the sixth form and spent every spare minute studying, but it wasn't enough. Boys like David Bates hardly worked at all but they got their scholarships to Oxford and Cambridge. Mr Croft didn't manage university at all. He did well enough at his Teacher Training College and after a while he thought he'd got over his disappointment. He decided to make a go of things and end up a headmaster, but it hadn't worked out that way.

Now he was only hanging on to his job by the skin of his teeth. Maple had already made a few hints about an early retirement. Oh God, this was the very opportunity Maple was looking for.

Mr Croft clenched his fists, waiting for the soft pad of Maple's Hush Puppies along the corridor, come to see why there was still a light in 2A long after everyone else had gone home.

But he didn't come. He couldn't have spotted the light. They heard him go outside, the slam of his car door, the splutter of his ignition key. They heard him drive away.

"Draw me a picture, David," said Mr Croft.

"I'm not going to," said David, and for the first time he sounded childish and defiant. "I'm going home."

He stood up but Mr Croft was by his side in an instant.

"Sit down again. At once!"

"You can't keep me here by force," said David, but he didn't sound sure. Mr Croft wasn't a very big man but David was small and slight for his age.

"Draw, David." Mr Croft put his face very close to the child's. Their breaths mingled. *"Draw!"*

David's face crumpled. He bit his lips, fighting for control, but tears spilled behind his glasses.

"Aah! Poor little diddums," said Mr Croft.

"You shut up!" David sobbed furiously.

"Don't use that tone with me."

"You keep making these threats but you can't do anything," David said. "I'm going home now. My mother will be ever so worried."

"Poor little Mumsie's crybaby, eh?"

"You're mad. You're a real nutcase," David shouted, and he made a run for it.

Mr Croft caught him at the classroom door. David struggled and kicked but Mr Croft had his spindly arms in a pincer grip. David's feet barely touched the ground as Mr Croft pulled him back to his desk. He pushed him down so hard that the child's head juddered with shock.

"There! Now draw, you little runt, draw!"

"I can't! I don't know what to draw," David wailed.

"Every other child in the class drew me a picture, David Bates. I told them to draw me a scene from *The Mountain of Adventure*. That's what you're going to do, boy. You're no different from the others. You're not getting preferential treatment from me. You're going to draw, do you understand?" He was shouting, spittle shining on his chin.

"But I wasn't—I didn't listen to it," David sobbed. "I don't know what it's about. You know I wasn't listening. I *can't* draw."

"Can't even draw, eh? Can't read. Can't write. Now it turns out the boy wonder can't even draw. Well, you'd better learn fast," said Mr Croft. "I'm going to count to five, David Bates. One. Two. Three. Four."

David picked up the pencil. He drew one jagged uncontrolled line and the lead broke.

"You did that on purpose!" Mr Croft shouted, and he slapped the boy hard across the face.

Mr Croft had caned children in the past. He'd prodded them and pulled them, he'd thrown blackboard chalk at them and rapped their knuckles with his ruler. But he'd never once struck a child across the face. His hand was trembling, wanting to hit again and again. He clenched it, panting.

"Find another pencil," he said, his voice high-pitched.

David fumbled in his satchel, whimpering, his nose running into his mouth.

"I—I haven't got one."

Mr Croft felt in his breast pocket for his own ballpoint pen.

"Use this then. Draw with it, draw, draw, *draw.*"

Sudden pain flared in his chest. Mr Croft stared at the child and then doubled up. Red-hot agony. Chest, arm, everywhere. He couldn't draw breath. Couldn't talk, Christ Almighty, the pain.

He swayed in front of David, still holding the ballpoint pen.

"Help! Get help! I'm ill! I'm having a heart attack!" he screamed, but he could only gurgle and drool in the grip of the pain. He clutched the pen and stabbed at the piece of drawing paper.

"P-h-o-n-e 999," he scrawled desperately. *"Heart."*

David Bates looked at the piece of paper and then he looked at Mr Croft.

"I can't read, can I?" he said.

Mr Croft slumped to his knees. David walked round him, crumpling the paper and stuffing it into his pocket. He switched off the light, walked along the corridor and out of the silent school.

He met his mother hurrying along the road.

"David, where on earth have you been? I've been so worried."

"Sorry, Mum. That hateful Croft man kept me in again."

"This is getting ridiculous. I think I'd better go and see him, David. Come on, we'll go back to the school and have it out with him."

"No, he'll have gone by now," David said quickly. "Don't fuss, Mum. Things will work out. You'll see."

David tucked his hand in her arm and they went straight home.

# Grade 5B and the Well-Fed Rat

## FRANCES GRAY PATTON

"Dear Parent," said the mimeographed letter from the Parent-Teacher's Association of the Oaklawn School, "In this atomic age the future safety of civilization depends upon a truly scientific atmosphere. The boys and girls of today will be the men and women of tomorrow. At our meeting, Wednesday November 14, Miss Oates' grade, 5B-1, will take over the program to show we parents how our little folk are progressing in this direction."

Mrs. Potter sighed when she read it. Her daughter, Elinor, was in grade 5B-1.

Mrs. Potter made a point of staying away from schools. They depressed her. The very odor of their halls was an undertow to her spirits. It sucked her back into that nervous dullness of childhood from which she, by the grace of time, had thankfully escaped.

Her first two children were boys. They seemed fond of their mother, and not abnormally ashamed of her. They accompanied her on bird-walks in the woods, and sometimes even to a movie—though they did not sit with her there because, they explained, they could see better from the front row. They talked openly to her about sex and tropical fish and airplane motor frequency. But they did not discuss their school affairs. And on the rare occasions when she was obliged to come to their school (to bring forgotten note-books, for instance, or raincoats when the weather had changed unexpectedly), their embarrassment was pathetic. They greeted her vaguely, like peo-ple who "know the face, but can't recall the name." It suited Mrs. Potter.

But Elinor was different. To Elinor school was the stuff of life, and she brought it home with her. She remembered in detail the appearance of her teachers. She discovered, somehow, their pri-vate histories and philosophies. She recounted ev-erything at the dinner table.

"Miss Oates had lipstick on her teeth again today," Elinor would remark. "It was probably her mother's fault. Miss Oates lives with this old, old mother, and sometimes she beats Miss Oates to the bathroom in the morning and she stays in there so long—you know how old people are!—that Miss Oates doesn't have time to fix herself up be-fore school. Poor Miss Oates! I don't like lipstick on teeth."

Or she would lean forward, pudding spoon halfway to her mouth, and announce solemnly:

"Miss Bangs, our new music teacher, loves God. She really *loves* Him."

Elinor liked, also, to share her homework with her family. Her eyes shone as she recited the multiplication table or the trials of the Jamestown Colony. Her voice was full of proud emotion when she read her compositions aloud. One of these ended with a fine, confident flourish:

"After reading this chapter in *Tales of Distant Lands,*" declared Elinor, "I know that if I woke up tomorrow morning in the middle of the Desert of Sahara, I would feel perfectly at home."

(She probably would at that, thought Mrs. Potter. Anybody who feels at home in a public school would feel at home anywhere.)

It was entertaining. It might have been entire-ly charming if Elinor had not begun urging her mother to visit the school. Other mothers came all the time; wasn't her mother interested in educa-tion?

"Miss Oates thinks the school and the home should co-operate," said Elinor. "And besides," she added, "everybody wants to see you. I've told them you look like a pin-up girl."

This bit of flattery was irresistible. Mrs. Pot-ter, though well-preserved, was plumpish and close to forty. She promised Elinor that next time her class was on the program she would attend the P.T.A. meeting. It had seemed then something far-away and rather unlikely to happen.

Now, with the letter in her hand, she knew she was caught.

On the morning of the appointed Wednesday Mrs. Potter awoke with a heaviness, like a cold, undigested pancake, on her stomach. Then she heard her husband gargling in the bathroom and she took heart. Maybe, she thought, he was coming down with a strep throat, and she would have to stay home and nurse him. But he said he was all right—he was just gargling as a precaution because there were some colds in the office.

"I guess this is it," she said bleakly, and went down to the kitchen to start the cereal.

Elinor was too excited to eat much breakfast. She was to make the longest speech of all. She had not said the speech at home because she wanted it to be a surprise for her mother, and now she was afraid she didn't know it. She stared down at her plate and kept mumbling something about rats.

"Mama," one of the boys said at last, "don't let her go crazy right here at the breakfast table. She takes my appetite away."

"Suppose I forget something," said Elinor, trembling, "before those thousands of people!"

"I don't suppose there'll be many people," murmured Mrs. Potter soothingly.

It was the wrong thing to say.

"You mean we won't have a good audience?" demanded Elinor. In a gesture of despair she clapped her hand to her head. "My hair!" she moaned, holding out a yellow wisp in her fingers. "Oh, I wish I had some glamour. I have to get up there on that stage—without any glamour!"

She moaned again as she gathered up her books. But it was a moan, Mrs. Potter knew, made half of ecstasy.

"Wear your new girdle, Mama," said Elinor, "and use enough lipstick. Don't get it on your teeth."

Before the meeting Mrs. Potter went downtown for a shampoo and a manicure. She disliked painted fingernails, but this time she permitted the manicurist to give her a brilliant polish called *Frozen Flame*. She was not going to let Elinor down.

Then she went to a department store where she bought a red rayon carnation to pin on her coat. She thought she looked very nice. She almost believed she was going to enjoy the meeting.

After all, she told herself, her attitude of aloofness toward her children's education was self-indulgent and anti-social. More than that, it was ignorant; it was based upon some infantile fixation of her own. Times had changed. The public school must have changed with them, and—witness Elinor's enthusiasm—for the better.

But when she went into the school it did not smell very different. It did not look different, either. The walls were painted the same pale tan—a faintly nauseating color—and on the wall the same peasant girl still listened to her lark. As she walked down the concrete hall Mrs. Potter heard the echo of her own footsteps tapping behind her, like some hopeless monotony that would shadow her all her life.

At the door of the auditorium she was welcomed by Miss Oates. Her teeth, Mrs. Potter saw with relief, were clean as the proverbial hound's. Miss Oates, when Mrs. Potter introduced herself, exclaimed in evident surprise: "Are you *Elinor's* mother?" She gave her a long look, equally appraising and disappointed.

Mrs. Potter found a seat among the score of other mothers who were, she saw, as carefully coifed, as resolutely complacent as she herself. There was time only for the briefest interchange of compliments on one another's "darling children" before Miss Bangs began playing the piano. (Mrs. Potter found herself thinking irreverently that God might have rewarded that lady's devotion with the gift of greater talent!) Thirty children filed out upon the stage, singing "We march, we march, to vic-to-ree," in fresh, tuneless voices.

The children all looked healthy and clean. The boys wore white shirts and dark knickers. The bright, starched dresses of the girls belled out like field flowers. Their eyes were steady and serious, as if some transcendent emotion arose to sweep the least trace of frivolity from them. They made a touching picture.

Her Elinor, Mrs. Potter observed, was pale. She looked as if she had been crying and had just washed her face. But she seemed composed. She stood primly, with her hands crossed, like little limp fish, over her middle. When she caught her mother's glance, she shot her a swift, tremulous smile.

Miss Oates mounted the rostrum. She was a thin, tall woman. She curved her body a little from the waist, as if to reduce the impression of its length. She fingered her pearls as she talked, and her features assumed the languid lines of patronizing whimsy. But her prominent blue eyes were coy and restless. Mrs. Potter felt sorry for her, and sorry, too, that she did not like her.

"*Ave!*" said Miss Oates cheerfully. "In this day of racial unrest and the atom bomb—"

Mrs. Potter shivered. Suddenly the pretty children on the platform looked unsubstantial, doomed, like the overbright figures in a nightmare. What earthly relevance had the race problem to the matter in hand, and why drag in the bomb at this juncture? The woman was a plain fool. Mrs. Potter bowed her head in vicarious shame.

"In this atomic age," Miss Oates continued, "this time of changing val-yews, we must dare to change our methods also. Therefore, when the fifth graders took up the study of nutrition, we did not give them dead books, but live, vibrant material. The Health Department kindly donated two white rats. We named one of them Wiffles, and the other one Squiffles."

She paused, smiling graciously. The audience made a sound that Mrs. Potter supposed might be called "an appreciative titter."

"Wiffles," said Miss Oates, "had his private cage, and Squiffles had his. But while Wiffles was fed milk and eggs and vegetable stew, Mr. Squiffles received only cookies and coca-cola. At first we thought Squiffles was the lucky rat, but we soon changed our minds. Wiffles began to look like a great big Marine sergeant, and Squiffles was just a poor little 4-F. But I'm going to let our young scientists tell you the rest. I know you want to hear, in their own little words, just what they've learned with their honest, inquiring little minds.

So, ladies and gentlemen," here she dimpled at the principal, a bald, sleepy-looking man, "and mothers of the fifth grade, I want to introduce somebody you already know—The Class of Five B One."

Miss Oates retired into the wings. Everybody clapped. A stout, pink-cheeked boy came forward. He gave his bulging pants a hitch, and began to talk in challenging, uninflected tone.

"In this atomic age," he said, "we must all be scientists."

Mrs. Potter did not listen closely to him. She did not pay much attention, either, to the girl who maintained that, since the discovery of the airplane and the atom bomb, it was necessary to learn the rules of health. Mrs. Potter was waiting for Elinor.

Elinor, whose job was to sum up the results of the class experiment, was the last to speak. Mrs. Potter thought she was infinitely better than the others. In the first place, she looked exactly the way a ten-year-old girl ought to look. Even her straight hair, with its bothersome cowlick, had all the weedy grace of childhood; it made the ringlets of the other girls look artificial. And she spoke her piece in a rapid, businesslike way, without any hesitation or any fancy frills.

"The characteristics of the well-fed rat," said Elinor, "are different from the characteristics of the poorly-fed rat. The well-fed rat is heavier. The fur of the well-fed rat is soft and creamy. The poorly-fed rat has sore eyes, and his fur is very ratty. The poorly-fed rat is maladjusted, and he also has a bad disposition. He is ready to dart out of his cage whenever the door is opened. The well-fed rat has a calm, kind disposition. He is contented with his surroundings and does not wish to leave his cage. His tail is pink and waxy."

After the program was over Mrs. Potter stayed to congratulate Miss Oates upon the performance of her pupils. The children were marching off the stage through a back door, but Elinor darted from the line (like the poorly-fed rat, thought Mrs. Potter), and bounced over the footlights to her mother's side. Miss Oates came down, too, but by the steps.

"We're glad to see Mummy, aren't we, Elinor?" she said. There was something subtly menacing in her tone.

"It was really remarkable, Miss Oates," said Mrs. Potter. "I'm sure *we* were never so poised in the fifth grade." Then, in an attempt to add a friendly, adult note to the conversation, she added flippantly: "But it's sad, isn't it, that the well-fed rat liked his cage. Is the desire for freedom only the desire for food?"

Miss Oates curved her lips slightly. It was the sort of smile, Mrs. Potter remembered, that teachers kept for parents who tried to be funny.

"That's what the chart told us," Elinor said. "It said the well-fed rat liked his cage. It wasn't that way with our Wiffles."

She gulped on the last word. Miss Oates gave her an uneasy look.

"But, Elinor," said Mrs. Potter, "I thought you said in your report—"

"You see, Mrs. Potter," said Miss Oates, "the Health Department furnished us with a chart on rat nutrition to help us find our facts, but the rats didn't always cooperate. Squiffles, *our* poorly-fed rat, just cowered in a corner—"

"With a blank expression on his face," said Elinor contemptuously.

"—while Wiffles, who was supposed to feel all comfy, was forever trying to get out. Once he did escape, didn't he, Elinor?"

"Yes, Miss Oates," said Elinor, "and bit the blood out of Randy Adams when he caught him."

"We disinfected Randy's finger with iodine," Miss Oates said quickly.

Mrs. Potter was honestly puzzled.

"I thought," she said, "that the class just observed the rats first-hand, and drew its own conclusions."

"That's right," said Miss Oates patiently, "we observed them for a month. We fed and weighed them every day. Then, with the chart as a guide, we made out our reports."

"I see," said Mrs. Potter. But she wondered if she did.

"But," said Miss Oates, "when we compared our findings with those on the chart we saw that something, somewhere, had gone wrong. Maybe there was something funny about the rats to begin with. Or maybe we didn't follow directions properly. I don't know." She shrugged helplessly. "Frankly, I've never been good at science. I was always more the esthetic type."

"I know," said Mrs. Potter vaguely.

"Anyhow," said Miss Oates, "our results weren't exactly what we'd expected. We had promised to give this program and we simply didn't have time to do the experiment all over again. But we know from the Health Department what facts we *ought* to have found, so—well, we just decided to take the bull by the horns and go ahead and find them! In this atomic age, we can't afford to be narrow about facts, can we? I mean we have to realize their broader implications. And after all," she finished, on a note of inspiration, "things often don't turn out right the first time— even at Oak Ridge."

"Indeed they don't," agreed Mrs. Potter.

"Now," said Miss Oates briskly, "I've dissipated long enough. I must go see what my class is doing. I believe in trusting children, you know. In times like these they have to learn self-reliance. And then I check up on them. Elinor, would you like to spend five whole minutes alone with Mummy? Be sure to ask her to come again."

"Maybe Elinor could show me the rats," suggested Mrs. Potter.

A glint of something like exasperation shone in Miss Oates' eyes.

"I do wish she could," she said, "but the truth is we've had a minor tragedy in our midst. When we took the covers off the cages this morning we found something that made us all feel dreadfully blue." She pursed her mouth ruefully and dropped her voice. "The well-fed rat was dead."

She began to back off with her eyes fixed warily on Elinor.

"Bye-bye," she said, and was gone.

"I hate her," said Elinor, grinding her words between her teeth. "She is a cold, black-hearted woman."

Mrs. Potter was dismayed.

"Oh no, darling—you don't!" she cried. "You don't *hate* anybody."

"I hate Miss Oates," said Elinor flatly. "She wouldn't even let us have a funeral for him."

"But she was so busy," said Mrs. Potter. "And she has that poor old mother!"

"I feel sorry for Miss Oates' mother," said Elinor. "Imagine thinking you were going to have a nice baby, and it turning out to be Miss Oates! She has no feeling for children or rats or anything. Mama, I loved Wiffles. He was a sweet rat."

"Maybe he's happy somewhere," said Mrs. Potter. It seemed the only thing to say.

"He didn't look happy," said Elinor. "He looked awful dead. He was lying on his back with his feet up in the air. His body was still warm." She began to sob quietly. "We wanted to cremate him like we read in the paper Jerome Kern was cremated. We were going to build a funeral pyre on the playground, and dance around it singing hymns. But ole Quaker Oats wouldn't let us. Do you know what she said?"

"What did she say?" asked Mrs. Potter, aware of an ignominious sympathy for Miss Oates.

"She said: 'In this atomic age we have no time to play funeral with rats.' And then—" Elinor's voice shook with grief and scorn—"she picked him up, by his pink, waxy tail, and gave him to the janitor."

Mrs. Potter kissed Elinor and patted her on the shoulder. She wiped her wet cheeks with a handkerchief.

"I guess you'll have to go now, baby," she said. "It was a lovely program, anyhow." She fished a nickel out of her purse. "After school get yourself an ice-cream cone—or a coca-cola."

As she saw Elinor's face brighten, Mrs. Potter felt like crying. The quick shift of a child's mood, like sunlight running up the beach on the heels of a cloud, had always been a thing to move her deeply. She had an impulse to snatch Elinor out of these borogoves of pious confusion and set her free in the simple light of day. But of course she did no such thing. She only smiled and watched her little girl skip jauntily off to Miss Oates' home room.

And a minute later when she, herself, walked down the hall, Mrs. Potter felt comforted. The old smell of chalk and peanuts, the hollow, reverberating sound of her own shoes, the pastoral rapture—expressed in sepia—of Millet's rustic, all managed to put reality smugly in its place. Life seemed inept and innocent and debonair. Even the split atom lost its terrors for the moment and became just something people talked about at P.T.A. meetings.

# CHAPTER 2

## CONNECTIONS AND RELATIONSHIPS

Lucia Berlin, "El Tim"
Ruth Moose, "Rules and Secrets"
Spiro Zavos, "Class Wars"
Richard Yates, "Doctor Jack-o'-Lantern"
Brian James, "Untimely Aid"
Stanley Ellin, "Robert"

Connections and relationships are the grassroots business of classrooms. They are at the very heart of successful teaching and learning. These stories depict attempts to make and sustain contact with others in the midst of disorder, diversity and conflict. Establishing connections and relationships often involves a complex balancing act, requiring the subtle skills of listening and properly interpreting verbal and nonverbal communication, and a tough, persistent faith in building meaningful relationships. In these stories, some teachers and students succeed in these efforts; others fail.

In Lucia Berlin's "El Tim," a new junior high teacher finds that one student can entirely change the climate of the classroom. Mrs. Lawrence is in her first year of teaching, and she is also the first lay teacher at San Marcos, a Catholic school. Her classes seem productive and manageable until Timothy Sánchez (El Tim) shows up accompanied by Sister Lourdes, the school principal.

> The room became still. "El Tim!" someone whispered.
> ...He was dressed in black, his shirt open to the waist, his pants low and tight on lean hips. A gold crucifix glittered from a heavy chain. He was half-smiling, looking down at Sister Lourdes, his eyelashes creating jagged shadows down his gaunt cheeks. His black hair was long and straight. He smoothed it back with long slender fingers, quick, like a bird.
> I watched the awe of the class. I looked at the young girls, the pretty young girls who whispered in the rest room not of dates or love but of marriage and abortion. They were tensed, watching him, flushed and alive.

Tim has been out of school because of trouble with the police, and the court has allowed him to return as a term of probation. Too old for ninth grade and too smart, he takes control of the class, a forbidding tyrant to some and to others an exciting devil. Mrs. Lawrence appeals to Sister Lourdes for help but the sister wants only to cajole and placate him. Finally, Tim's actions force a climax to the story.

Connections and relationships succeed beautifully in "Rules and Secrets" by Ruth Moose. Miss McLean, a new teacher, breathes openness and awareness into a rural North Carolina elementary class. She compliments and encourages her students, bringing their achievements and their lives into the limelight. They grow more alert to their surroundings, less dependent on their teacher, and more confident in themselves. But, the changes

Miss McLean has inspired in the students are not welcomed by everyone, and the students' new awareness fails to prepare them for the day when the school year ends, and she leaves.

In "Class Wars," Spiro Zavos humorously shows what happens to a school where connections and relationships have failed at all levels. Henry Cown is a first-year teacher at a boy's high school. He soon discovers that everyone in the school has lost faith in teaching and learning. The following excerpt (during Henry's initial employment interview he has asked for a "better" class) alerts Henry to the principal's opinions about the school's teachers and students:

> *"Let me tell you something about teachers," he said finally, "they're so interested in the easy life they'd eat their mothers to get a good class. I'm afraid," he continued, his face assuming the look of a sympathetic centurion sending a Christian to the lions, "that in your earlier years as a teacher it's the tough classes for you. There's one comforting thing about it though," he rose and waved his left arm casually towards the door, an indication that the interview was nearly over, "if you survive this you'll survive anything."*

The story continues to chronicle Henry's less than inspiring journey through his first teaching experiences in a school where meaningful connections and relationships are few and far between.

In Richard Yates's "Doctor Jack-o'-Lantern" stillborn student-teacher connections result when a teacher tries to satisfy the needs of a new student only to end up hindering his adjustment and reinforcing misunderstanding among other students. A city boy (Vincent Sabella) resettles in the suburbs and begins attending an elementary school. Vinny feels out of place in this suburban classroom. He looks different, and his classmates know he is different. Vinny's teacher, Miss Price, unwittingly subverts Vinny's chances to lower the barriers and fit in through her special treatment of Vinny.

> *All Vincent Sabella's errors in homework were publicly excused, even those having nothing to do with his newness, and all his accomplishments were singled out for special mention. Her campaign to build him up was painfully obvious, and never more so than when she tried to make it subtle; once, for instance, in explaining an arithmetic problem, she said, "Now suppose Warren Berg and Vincent Sabella went to the store with fifteen cents each, and candy bars cost ten cents. How many candy bars would each boy have?" By the end of the week he was well on the way to becoming the worst possible kind of teacher's pet, a victim of the teacher's pity.*

The other students recognize the preferential treatment right away; Vinny is doomed to be an outcast and responds accordingly.

"Untimely Aid" by Brian James is a parody on connections, pointing out how fragile, fleeting, and vulnerable to illusion our ties to others can be. Mr. Beresford is deaf and his students know it; therefore they say just about anything they want to during his class. As a result, a certain chumminess has flourished between the teacher and students—the teacher likes the students and he thinks they enjoy his classes. This equilibrium is knocked off balance when he gets a hearing aid, leading him to lament not only the loss of silence but also his loss of innocence as well.

Stanley Ellin's "Robert" is a story about a teacher and student who never do establish a relationship. Miss Gildea, an experienced sixth-grade teacher, is locked in a contest of wills with Robert, a student with a subversive agenda. The story escalates in intensity as the final days of the school year approach. Robert wins, and his victory extracts a terrible price from the teacher—and in the final paragraphs the reader discovers that Robert has paid a high price, too.

Connections and relationships drive successful teaching and learning. Both are fostered by communication, yet challenges must be overcome to establish communication in classrooms. Through characters like El Tim, Mrs. Lawrence, Vinny, and Miss Price these stories serve to document some of these challenges and how they determine success and failure in classrooms.

# El Tim

## LUCIA BERLIN

A nun stood in each classroom door, black robes floating into the hall with the wind. The voices of the first grade, praying, *Hail Mary, full of grace, the Lord is with Thee.* From across the hall, the second grade began, clear, *Hail Mary, full of grace.* I stopped in the center of the building, and waited for the triumphant voices of the third grade, their voices joined by the first grade, *Our Father, Who art in Heaven,* by the fourth grade, then, deep, *Hail Mary, full of grace.*

As the children grew older they prayed more quickly, so that gradually the voices began to blend, to merge into one sudden joyful chant . . . *In the name of the Father and of the Son and of the Holy Ghost. Amen.*

I taught Spanish in the new junior high which lay at the opposite end of the playground like a child's colored toy. Every morning, before class, I went through the grade school, to hear the prayers, but also simply to go into the building, as one would go in a church. The school had been a mission, built in 1700 by the Spaniards, built to stand in the desert for a long time. It was different from other old schools, whose stillness and solidity is still a shell for the children who pass through them. It had kept the peace of a mission, of a sanctuary.

The nuns laughed in the grade school, and the children laughed. The nuns were all old, not like tired old women who clutch their bags at a bus stop, but proud, loved by their God and by their children. They responded to love with tenderness, with soft laughter that was contained, guarded, behind the heavy wooden doors.

Several junior high nuns swept through the playground, checking for cigarette smoke. These nuns were young and nervous. They taught "underprivileged children," "borderline delinquents," and their thin faces were tired, sick of a blank stare. They could not use awe or love like the grade school nuns. Their recourse was impregnability, indifference to the students who were their duty and their life.

The rows of windows in the ninth grade flashed as Sister Lourdes opened them, as usual, seven minutes before the bell. I stood outside the initialed orange doors, watching my ninth-grade students as they paced back and forth in front of the wire fence, their bodies loose and supple, necks bobbing as they walked, arms and legs swaying to a beat, to a trumpet that no one else could hear.

They leaned against the wire fence, speaking in English-Spanish-Hipster dialect, laughing soundlessly. The girls wore the navy blue uniforms of the school. Like muted birds they flirted with the boys, who cocked their plumed heads, who were brilliant in orange or yellow or turquoise pegged pants. They wore open black shirts or V-neck sweaters with nothing under them, so that their crucifixes gleamed against their smooth brown chests . . . the crucifix of the pachuco which was also tattooed on the back of their hand.

"Good morning, dear."

"Good morning, Sister." Sister Lourdes had come outside to see if the seventh grade was in line.

Sister Lourdes was the principal. She had hired me, reluctantly having to pay someone to teach, since none of the nuns spoke Spanish.

"So, as a lay teacher," she had said, "the first one at San Marco, it may be hard for you to control the students, especially since many of them are almost as old as you. You must not make the mistake that many of my young nuns do. Do not try to be their friend. These students think in terms of power and weakness. You must keep your power . . . through aloofness, discipline, punishment, control. Spanish is an elective, give as many F's as you like. During the first three weeks you may transfer any of your pupils to my Latin class. I have had no volunteers," she smiled, "you will find this a great help."

The first month had gone well. The threat of the Latin class was an advantage; by the end of the second week I had eliminated seven students. It was a luxury to teach such a relatively small class, and a class with the lower quarter removed. My native Spanish helped a great deal. It was a surprise to them that a "gringa" could speak as well as their parents, better even than they. They were impressed that I recognized their obscene words, their slang for marijuana and police. They worked hard. Spanish was close, important to them. They behaved well, but their sullen obedience and their automatic response were an affront to me.

They mocked words and expressions that I used and began to use them as much as I. "La Piña," they jeered, because of my hair, and soon the girls cut their hair like mine. "The idiot can't write," they whispered, when I printed on the blackboard, but they began to print all of their papers.

These were not yet the pachucos, the hoods that they tried hard to be, flipping a switch blade into a desk, blushing when it slipped and fell. They were not yet saying: "You can't show me nothing." They waited, with a shrug, to be shown. So what could I show them? The world I knew was no better than the one they had the courage to defy.

I watched Sister Lourdes whose strength was not, as mine, a front for their respect. The students saw her faith in the God, in the life that she had chosen; they honored it, never letting her know their tolerance for the harshness she used for control.

She couldn't laugh with them either. They laughed only in derision, only when someone revealed himself with a question, with a smile, a mistake, a fart. Always, as I silenced their mirthless laughter, I thought of the giggles, the shouts, the grade-school counterpoint of joy.

Once a week I laughed with the ninth grade. On Mondays, when suddenly there would be a banging on the flimsy metal door, an imperious BOOM BOOM BOOM that rattled the windows and echoed through the building. Always at the tremendous noise I would jump, and the class would laugh at me.

"Come in!" I called, and the knocking would stop, and we laughed, when it was only a tiny first grader. He would pad in sneakers to my desk. "Good morning," he whispered. "May I have the cafeteria list?" Then he would tiptoe away and slam the door, which was funny, too.

"Mrs. Lawrence, would you come inside for a minute?" I followed Sister Lourdes into her office and waited while she rang the bell.

"Timothy Sánchez is coming back to school." She paused, as if I should react. "He has been in the detention home, one of many times—for theft and narcotics. They feel that he should finish school as quickly as possible. He is much older than his class, and according to their tests he is an exceptionally bright boy. It says here that he should be 'encouraged and challenged.'"

"Is there any particular thing you want me to do?"

"No, in fact. I can't advise you at all...he is quite a different problem. I thought I should mention it. His parole officer will be checking on his progress."

The next morning was Halloween, and the grade school had come in costume. I lingered to watch the witches, the hundreds of devils who trembled their morning prayers. The bell had rung when I got to the door of the ninth grade. "Sacred Heart of Mary, pray for us," they said. I stood at the door while Sister Lourdes took the roll. They rose as I entered the room, "Good morning." Their chairs scraped as they sat down.

The room became still. "El Tim!" someone whispered.

He stood in the door, silhouetted like Sister Lourdes from the skylight in the hall. He was dressed in black, his shirt open to the waist, his pants low and tight on lean hips. A gold crucifix glittered from a heavy chain. He was half-smiling, looking down at Sister Lourdes, his eyelashes creating jagged shadows down his gaunt cheeks. His black hair was long and straight. He smoothed it back with long slender fingers, quick, like a bird.

I watched the awe of the class. I looked at the young girls, the pretty young girls who whispered in the rest room not of dates or love but of marriage and abortion. They were tensed, watching him, flushed and alive.

Sister Lourdes stepped into the room. "Sit here, Tim," she motioned to a seat in front of my desk. He moved across the room, his broad back stopped, neck forward, tssch-tssch, tssch-tssch, the pachuco beat. "Dig the crazy nun!" he grinned, looking at me. The class laughed. "Silence!" Sister Lourdes said. She stood beside him. "This is Mrs. Lawrence. Here is your Spanish book." He seemed not to hear her. Her beads rattled nervously.

"Button your shirt," she said. "Button your shirt!"

He moved his hands to his chest, began with one to move the button in the light, with the other to inspect the buttonhole. The nun shoved his hands away, fumbled with his shirt until it was buttoned.

"Don't know how I ever got along without you, Sister," he drawled. She left the room.

It was Tuesday, dictation. "Take out a paper and pencil." The class complied automatically. "You too, Tim."

"Paper," he commanded quietly. Sheets of paper fought for his desk.

"Llegó el hijo," I dictated. Tim stood up and started toward the back of the room. "Pencil's broken...," he said. His voice was deep and hoarse, like the hoarseness people have when they are about to cry. He sharpened his pencil slowly, turning the sharpener so that it sounded like brushes on a drum.

"No tenían fé." Tim stopped to put his hand on a girl's hair.

"Sit down," I said.

"Cool it," he muttered. The class laughed.

He handed in a blank paper, the name "EL TIM" across the top.

From that day everything revolved around El Tim. He caught up quickly with the rest of the class. His test papers and his written exercises were always excellent. But the students responded only to his sullen insolence in class, to his silent, unpunishable denial. Reading aloud, conjugating on the board, discussions, all of the things that had been almost fun were now almost impossible. The boys were flippant, ashamed to get things right; the girls embarrassed, awkward in front of him.

I began to give mostly written work, private work that I could check from desk to desk. I assigned many compositions and essays, even though this was not supposed to be done in ninth-grade Spanish. It was the only thing Tim liked to do, that he worked on intently, erasing and recopying, thumbing the pages of a Spanish dictionary on his desk. His compositions were imaginative, perfect in grammar, always of impersonal things... a street, a tree. I wrote comments and praise on them. Sometimes I read his papers to the class, hoping that they would be impressed, encouraged by his work. Too late I realized that it only confused them for him to be praised, that he triumphed anyway with a sneer... *"Pues, la tengo..."* I've got her pegged.

Emiterio Pérez repeated everything that Tim said. Emiterio was retarded, being kept in the ninth grade until he was old enough to quit school. He passed out papers, opened windows. I had him do everything the other students did. Chuckling, he wrote endless pages of neat formless scribbles that I graded and handed back. Sometimes I would give him a B and he would be very happy. Now even he would not work. *"Para qué, hombre?"* Tim whispered to him. Emiterio would become confused, looking from Tim to me. Sometimes he would cry.

Helplessly, I watched the growing confusion of the class, the confusion that even Sister Lourdes could no longer control. There was not silence now when she entered the room, but unrest...a brushing of a hand over a face, an eraser tapping, flipping pages. The class waited. Always, slow and deep, would come Tim's voice. "It's cold in here, Sister, don't you think?" "Sister, I got something the matter with my eye, come see." We did not move as each time, every day, automatically the nun buttoned Tim's shirt. "Everything all right?" she would ask me and leave the room.

One Monday, I glanced up and saw a small child coming toward me. I glanced at the child, and then, smiling, I glanced at Tim.

"They're getting littler every time...have you noticed?" he said, so only I could hear. He smiled at me. I smiled back, weak with joy. Then with a harsh scrape he shoved back his chair and walked toward the back of the room. Halfway, he paused in front of Dolores, an ugly shy little girl. Slowly he rubbed his hands over her breasts. She moaned and ran crying from the room.

"Come here!" I shouted to him. His teeth flashed.

"Make me," he said. I leaned against the desk, dizzy.

"Get out of here, go home. Don't ever come back to my class!"

"Sure," he grinned. He walked past me to the door, fingers snapping as he moved...tsch-tsch, tsch-tsch. The class was silent.

As I was leaving to find Dolores, a rock smashed through the window, landing with shattered glass on my desk.

"What is going on!" Sister Lourdes was at the door. I couldn't get past her.

"I sent Tim home."

She was white, her bonnet shaking.

"Mrs. Lawrence, it is your duty to handle him in the classroom."

"I'm sorry, Sister, I can't do it."

"I will speak to the Mother Superior," she said. "Come to my office in the morning. Get in your seat!" she shouted at Dolores, who had come in the back door. The nun left.

"Turn to page 93," I said. "Eddie, read and translate the first paragraph."

I didn't go to the grade school the next morning. Sister Lourdes was waiting, sitting behind her desk. Outside the glass doors of the office, Tim leaned against the wall, his hands hooked in his belt.

Briefly, I told the nun what had happened the day before. Her head was bowed as I spoke.

"I hope you will find it possible to regain the respect of the boy," she said.

"I'm not going to have him in my class," I said. I stood in front of her desk, gripping the wooden edge.

"Mrs. Lawrence, we were told that this boy needed special attention, that he needed 'encouragement and challenge.'"

"Not in junior high. He is too old and too intelligent to be here."

"Well, you are going to have to learn to deal with this problem."

"Sister Lourdes, if you put Tim in my Spanish class, I will go to the Mother Superior, to his parole officer. I'll tell them what happened. I'll show them the work that my pupils did before he came and the work they have done since. I will show them Tim's work, it doesn't belong in the ninth grade."

She spoke quietly, dryly. "Mrs. Lawrence, this boy is our responsibility. The parole board turned him over to us. He is going to remain in your class." She leaned toward me, pale. "It is our duty as teachers to control such problems, to teach in spite of them."

"Well, I can't do it."

"You are weak!" she hissed.

"Yes, I am. He has won. I can't stand what he does to the class and to me. If he comes back, I resign."

She slumped back in her chair. Tired, she spoke, "Give him another chance. A week. Then you can do as you please."

"All right."

She rose and opened the door for Tim. He sat on the edge of her desk.

"Tim," she began softly, "will you prove to me, to Mrs. Lawrence and to the class that you are sorry?" He didn't answer.

"I don't want to send you back to the detention home."

"Why not?"

"Because you are a bright boy. I want to see you learn something here, to graduate from San Marco's. I want to see you go on to high school, to..."

"Come on, Sister," Tim drawled. "You just want to button my shirt."

"Shut up!" I hit him across the mouth. My hand remained white in his dark skin. He did not move. I wanted to be sick. Sister Lourdes left the room. Tim and I stood, facing each other, listening as she started the ninth grade prayers.... *Blessed art Thou amongst women, Blessed is the fruit of thy womb, Jesus...*

"How come you hit me?" Tim asked softly.

I started to answer him, to say, "Because you were insolent and unkind," but I saw his smile of contempt as he waited for me to say just that.

"I hit you because I was angry. About Dolores and the rock. Because I felt hurt and foolish."

His dark eyes searched my face. For an instant the veil was gone.

"I guess we're even then," he said.

"Yes," I said, "let's go to class."

I walked with Tim down the hall, avoiding the beat of his walk.

# Rules and Secrets

## RUTH MOOSE

Miss Melody McLean was from Virginia. No one knew how she came to teach that one year in a small town in the North Carolina mountains, but there she was the first day of school sitting on her desk, rollbook in hand, checking us off as if we were a shipment of rare goods she had waited a long time for. Her red-orange hair waved and curled with a mind of its own and her green eyes always saw something to smile about. She wore a plaid skirt, white organdy blouse, green vest, and swung her long freckled legs. She had more freckles than anyone I'd ever seen. Arms, legs, face—more freckles even than Vaden Stringer, who had a million. One time Miss McLean hugged Vaden and said, "If there was a freckle-counting contest, Vaden and I would tie for first place." He smiled wider than anyone had ever seen him. Maybe because nobody had hugged him before. Most of the teachers tried to stay as far away from him as possible and nobody wanted to be the one in front of or directly behind him in line. He usually smelled. Like car motors or oil or grease. His father ran the local garage, the family lived above it, and Vaden must have played in and around the grease pits. Teachers gave up long ago when they inspected his nails. Vaden was always passed over. Except by Miss McLean. Vaden began to come to school with cleaner shirts, sometimes ironed and free of grease spots, and he started combing his hair. He worked on his hands and they were cleaner. Not as clean as anybody else's hands, but wonderfully clean for Vaden.

Miss McLean always noticed when anyone wore anything new—scarf, blouse, shirt, jeans, sweater, socks—and commented "That's a pretty new dress, Lucy," she'd say. Lucy Estridge looked down to see what dress she was wearing and said, "It's just one my mother made."

"How wonderful to have such a talented mother." Miss McLean touched the collar. "Not everyone can sew and it means you can have so many more clothes."

Lucy looked like she'd never thought about it like that before. And began to say when she had something new, before anyone could comment, "My mother made me this dress." Or blouse, or skirt. Her mother even made Lucy a coat and jumper of soft green wool. We envied Lucy now and wished our mothers could sew.

Lucy was pretty that year. Maybe she always was and we'd never really looked at her before. The way no one had ever listened to Carolyn sing. We didn't know she could sing until Miss McLean picked her for the part of Dinah Shore for the Friday assembly. And Kenny Stone. "Crooner," we called him for weeks afterward, and he looked it. All the fifth-grade girls got his autograph and used to follow him on the playground. Skinny Kenny Stone with the thick glasses and pointed nose. Miss McLean took the glasses off, combed his hair back like Bing Crosby, and put him behind the broomstick microphone. He had a wonderful, deep voice. There was swooning in assembly that Friday. Carolyn wore her older sister's pink satin evening gown with the sweetheart neckline and borrowed her grandmother's fox fur piece. She was glamorous, she was Hollywood, after Miss McLean made her up, swept back her hair on one side, and pinned in a silk carnation. Bing—er—Kenny was clear and strong. The rest of the year Carolyn and I sang as we walked home from school.

But Miss McLean wasn't all play and music. She said a lot, "Work when you work, play when you play." We worked when we worked. But it was fun. Arithmetic problems became real when she substituted our names for the ones in the book, or the names of businesses in town. History was acted out—if you read your assignment and knew what to do. Spelling was always two teams chosen for six weeks at a time, with the winners receiving certificates Miss McLean made. She had two shelves of her own books, brought from home, for us to read, check out, and take home. We'd read all the good ones in the library and I loved books with her name in them in that fancy, curling handwriting.

"I don't know what that teacher's doing," Mama said one night, "but your math grades are improving. She's got you really interested and working like you should for the first time."

Miss McLean had us working in partners. We switched every week, graded each other's papers and studied together. It was fun every week but the one I had with Sylvia Hurley. She cried when you marked one of her answers wrong, begged you not to. How was she going to learn if you didn't mark wrong answers? And she missed a lot of them. She copied over every paper and put in the right answers. I had to mark 100 on it so she could show her mother.

Sylvia was the only one unhappy that year. She'd always come to school looking like she'd been crying. Sometimes there were bruise marks on her arms or legs. She was last in line to everything and nobody wanted her on their team for softball. Most of the time she wouldn't play anyway, but sat on the bank by herself and didn't even watch. If the ground was damp, Miss McLean spread her jacket or sweater for Sylvia to sit on. That was one of the few times Sylvia smiled, looked even a little happy.

We were on the playground the day Sylvia's mother came to school and argued at Miss McLean. We couldn't hear everything she said, but she kept jerking Sylvia by the collar of her dress, pulling her arms, and Sylvia cried. "My child wouldn't steal your handkerchief," Mrs. Hurley yelled. "She's not a thief."

"Of course not," Miss McLean said. "Nobody ever thought she was."

Mrs. Hurley yelled some more things that didn't make sense and Miss McLean kept saying, "I *gave* Sylvia my handkerchief. She had a cold and didn't have one."

That seemed to make Mrs. Hurley even more angry and she started yelling a lot of things about taking care of her own child's needs and Miss McLean kept saying she knew she did and Sylvia was such a well-behaved student, tried so very hard on every subject and so on. Miss McLean's voice was sweet and nice. Once she reached to put her arm around Sylvia but Mrs. Hurley jerked her away. Finally, more upset than ever, yelling and screaming things, she grabbed Sylvia's elbow and jerked her away. We watched them walk off the playground. When we grouped around Miss McLean to return to class, tears had dried on her cheeks and she excused herself to stop by the teacher's lounge.

Nobody could understand what the fuss had been about. Of course Miss McLean had given Sylvia the handkerchief. She was always doing things like that, loaning her books, pencils...to all of us. Whatever we needed. And when we finished, we returned them. Sylvia must have kept the handkerchief, wanted it, because Miss McLean was so special, and everything that belonged to her was special. Her handkerchiefs had monograms in the corners and were trimmed with lace. Miss McLean wouldn't have cared if Sylvia had stolen the handkerchief. She would have let her keep it, if she'd ask. What was one handkerchief? Who would steal one? Who would accuse anyone of stealing something so silly? Something at all. Not Miss McLean. But why did she cry?

We were all in our seats and strangely quiet when Miss McLean, face washed and lipstick freshened, came in. She still looked pale, moved some books and papers to sit on the corner of her desk. "I wish that you had not had to witness the incident on the playground a few minutes ago. And I hope you won't feel or act any differently toward Sylvia because of it. Except to be more understanding with her and toward her. She can't change the way things are in her life, not yet— maybe not ever—and we can help by being more patient, less critical. We won't mention this again." She picked up the geography book, turned to the chapter on "African States," pulled down the pink and green map, got down to business.

On the way home Carolyn and I talked. Last year, other years, Sylvia had been called "Bird

Legs" or "Bird Brain" or "Feather Face"—ugly names—and she'd shrugged them off, even smiled. I was glad we'd never called her things, but I remembered times I'd giggled when somebody else did, and felt terrible. Times when I got to choose teams and waited until last to pick her, hoping the other captain would, then yelled at her when she dropped a fly ball on the third out and we lost.

Carolyn and I invited Sylvia to the church Halloween party, offered to give her a ride. At five-thirty she called, said her mother was going out and she had to go with her. Sylvia sounded like she'd been crying.

"I'd cry too," Carolyn said, "if my mother made me miss the Halloween party."

Lights were on at Sylvia's house, the car in the drive, when we drove past at nine, taking Benny Cushman home. "I bet she didn't go out at all," Carolyn said. We didn't mention it to Sylvia—the party or anything. Some things are better left unsaid, Miss McLean had said a long time before about anger and retaliation. We liked the sound of that word, new words, but she didn't write it on the board as she usually did any new word we heard or asked about.

Anger was like a shade pulled over her face the day she read aloud—according to instructions—the new school policy toward Christmas, against gifts and "any said and possibly planned parties" at school. This was the word sent down from the superintendent's office. The law of the red brick land. "No student shall give any teacher a Christmas present. Due to the differences in circumstances, since all students are not able to give gifts of equal value, none shall be given. And consequently, no teacher shall give students gifts of any kind. There will be no Christmas parties allowed in any classroom in the system. To facilitate janitorial and maintenance services, holiday decorations should be kept to a minimum." Miss McLean's face got darker and darker as she read the notice. We didn't understand it. In the past, I'd given teachers gifts, small gift-wrapped boxes with the bow the biggest thing about them. Usually earrings, lotion or perfumed soap, a scarf. Caro-

lyn and I spent hours in the dime store picking out the perfect gift for our teachers. The day we left school for our holidays was always party day. With cupcakes and punch, games (how many words can you make out of the words "Merry Christmas"?) and carols, listening to the *Nutcracker Suite* or a teacher reading Dickens's "Christmas Carol." We could have none of that this year? It wouldn't be Christmas. Who was the superintendent of schools? Scrooge? There were cries of protest around the room, *Oh no's* and *How could anyone be so mean?* At Christmastime? It was awful.

Miss McLean thought so too, but she didn't say much. "In Virginia, I gave my class a party. I was planning—"

She was going to give us a party? No teacher had ever done that before. Room mothers came in and gave parties with cupcakes and candy canes, Santa napkins, but a teacher giving her class a party was something else. "Please, Miss McLean," we begged, "isn't there any way we can still have the party? We won't invite the superintendent. We won't tell the principal. We'll be so quiet no one will know."

She grinned with a small shake of her head. "I wish I could."

"Why can't you?" Kenny Stone stood at his desk. "No one would have to know. We can keep it a secret."

Miss McLean laughed, looked at us in a warm, sad way. "Oh my little dears...it would never work."

"And if she went against the rules, she'd be fired," said Bruce Stern. His daddy was a deputy for the sheriff's department, wore a uniform with a badge, carried a gun. Sometimes he picked Bruce up at school in the county car. "Using taxpayers' gas," Daddy said. "I don't think it's right." But he did it anyway and nobody said anything.

Miss McLean's giving the class a party herself was not using taxpayers' money, nor school funds. Why couldn't she do it? Carolyn and I discussed it walking home. Life was unfair, school was unfair, and whoever was superintendent wanted to make Christmas miserable for us.

The next day, Miss McLean asked everyone to stay for a few minutes after final bell. We would have stayed forever for her.

"This class *is* going to have a Christmas party," she announced, her eyes sparkling.

We looked at each other, mouthed *oh boy, oh boy*. Then remembered "How?" asked Carolyn. "The rule made by the superintendent. You'll—"

"Maybe not," Miss McLean smiled. "I'll have the party at my apartment, on my own time, and that shouldn't get anybody in trouble." She wrote the time on the board. An open house, six until eight o'clock, and her address.

She never told us not to tell. Somehow we knew. We were breaking a rule and keeping a secret about it. That made the party even more special, exciting. But what to tell our parents?

I solved that by spending the night with Carolyn. We did that on Friday nights often. And we simply told Carolyn's mother we were going to an open house at Miss McLean's.

Carolyn wore her blue velvet dress with lace collar and cuffs, her new coat with the white rabbit collar, and both of us wore our Sunday slippers, white ankle socks and matching charm bracelets we exchanged for Christmas, opening them early to wear to the party.

The streets had been scraped dry of snow that frosted yards, shrubbery, and rooftops and made the world look like a Christmas card. Chimneys ballooned out plumes of smoke and we stopped every block or so to admire our bracelets or try to puff out a perfect ring of breath.

Miss McLean had a wreath of fresh balsam on her door with holly, pine cones, and a soft red bow. Christmas music and the smell of something hot, orange, and spicy met us at the door, opened by Kenny Stone in sport coat and tie. Sylvia took our coats, hung them in the closet.

Miss McLean, with a moss-green bow in her hair, matching long skirt and red gingham blouse, poured punch, gave us small sandwiches and decorated cookies.

We stood around like strangers. Everyone looked so dressed up and so pretty—even Sylvia.

I wondered what she'd told her mother, and if she came alone? Probably Miss McLean would take her home, though none of us lived more than six blocks or so from school.

I'd walked by this apartment building every school day for six years and had never seen inside. Four teachers lived in four apartments. Sometimes we saw wash on the line and guessed what belonged to who. Sometimes we giggled when we recognized a blouse or shirtwaist dress of the second-grade teacher or Miss Beal, the librarian.

The living room had bookshelves on each side of the fireplace that reached the ceiling, all painted white, as were the walls; green wool carpet, matching drapes, and an armchair of the same color. There was a small desk by the window, a yellow lamp with a shade of different kinds of birds. I decided Miss McLean graded my homework papers there. Unless she used the kitchen table, my favorite place at home rather than the kneehole desk in my bedroom. There was a mirror above the fireplace and I looked at all of us framed there, the lights, laughter, and Miss McLean lifting red punch from a crystal bowl, candles reflecting in her cheeks, her eyes. Sylvia, by the door, important, collecting coats, placing them carefully on hangers. And Kenny Stone by the fireplace, Burce Stern putting on another log.

Later we sang carols around the piano, Miss McLean playing softly, as she sometimes did on rainy days when we could get the music room off the auditorium. Carolyn sang "Silent Night" as a solo, then "O Little Town of Bethlehem" as a duet with Bruce. Everyone sang "We Three Kings" last as we left Miss McLean gave us gifts—two new red pencils apiece, saying "I don't want to hear anyone say they don't have a pencil next time I announce a spelling test."

We laughed, gave mock groans. Then she gave us each an envelope with our names written in red ink, said, "Merry Christmas."

Carolyn and I didn't open the envelopes until we were outside. Under the streetlights we dug from the envelope three movie passes, "Admit

One" to the Center Theater. We hugged each other, dancing in the cold. Movies! Three free passes. Nothing could have been as wonderful. She was giving us the world for three Saturday afternoons: Tom Mix, Superman, Wonder Woman, Roy Rogers and Dale Evans, Lash LaRue... the Pan-a-View News, popcorn and Cokes. Each other. No teacher had ever given us a party before, certainly not at her home, with gifts. Pencils, because she was serious about school and learning and wanted us to be too. Movie passes because she believed life should have some fun in it.

Fun was movies on Saturdays, but it was also school five days a week. I denied colds, sore throats, and low fevers that year, to keep my mother from keeping me home. Missing a day would have meant missing everything, seeing everybody, Miss McLean. Almost nobody was absent, even Sylvia, who last year had been on the absent list several days a week, looked bluish, pale, and thin shivering in her chair when she was there. She moved that spring, an oddity for the town and our lives. Each year we had the same people, from first grade on. You knew who you wanted to sit beside, be on your relay, dodgeball, softball team. Sylvia didn't say goodbye. No one knew until the Monday morning Miss McLean, with a firm mouth, made the announcement and started the day's work. We wondered where she moved? Why would anyone move before school was out? And especially since we were planning a May Day. Lucy's mother was making costumes, Carolyn's blue and mine yellow. A long dress with the skirt a complete circle. We couldn't wait.

My father grumbled behind his newspaper that he was "paying good money for a dress that will only be worn once. Somebody in this town has big ideas."

A seventh-grade girl, Sarah Grambling, was May Queen. She was beautiful, blond with round blue eyes, the longest dark lashes in the world, and a different angora sweater for each day of the week.

Three of us were chosen for the May Court. We were to wear lacy picture hats, carry bouquets of real daisies. Daddy said it was too much for a little elementary school in a small town.

Mother said it was going to be beautiful and she hoped he could get off work to come.

He didn't answer.

Mother kept rolling my hair on leather curlers, twisting them tight to my head. "I try," she sighed, "even if it doesn't stay in."

I thought of Miss McLean who never had to roll her hair at all, how it waved, curled, and did things by itself. Like she did. All energy and sparkle and fun. She suggested the May Day, planned and directed it. And it was beautiful, more beautiful than even my mother thought.

The whole town turned out to see the king and queen crowned, the throne Miss McLean borrowed from one of the churches set atop a platform covered with red felt. There was a red runner on the front lawn and a processional for the presentation of the court. I bobbed and bowed, didn't spill flowers from my basket. Court jesters did card tricks and juggled. Toby Simpson rode his unicycle and Kenny Stone's black and white dog did tricks.

Fathers took pictures, some movies of it all. The Maypoles were braided to music, unbraided, then woven again. Everyone said it was beautiful, and parents kept repeating this to the principal, superintendent, who stood stiff and out of place in dark suits, narrow ties. They didn't smile much, complained about the heat "so early in the year," and brushed playground dust from their polished shoes.

Summer vacation and the end of the school year came too fast. The last day nobody wanted to leave. We stayed to stack books, rewash boards, put chairs on tables, take down decorations, divide up the plants, discard dead science projects, and clean out closets. Anything to linger. Miss McLean shushed us when we said there would never be another teacher we'd love as much as her, another year that would be more fun. "Go on with all of you." She headed us toward the door.

"Get on with the business of growing up." She hugged everybody, touseled Bruce Stern's hair and told Carolyn to keep singing.

What was she going to do this summer? "Going back to Virginia," she said.

"See you next year," we called, feeling light-headed to leave the classroom without an armload of books, homework assignments.

The next week Carolyn and I went to her apartment to visit. We promised ourselves we wouldn't go in—or maybe only for a glass of iced tea—if she invited us. For an excuse we carried potholders we'd woven on a lap loom Carolyn got for her birthday.

There was no answer at the door. We heard it ring when we rang again. It was working. Surely she hadn't packed and left so soon. Not for the whole summer. We weren't tall enough to peer in the door glass, so we had to find a low window, one that looked in the living room. The empty, empty living room. And kitchen and bedroom.

We couldn't believe it. "Maybe she found a better apartment," Carolyn said.

"In this town?" It wasn't possible.

Or moved to a house? My daddy would have said something. He sold real estate—but not lately. I heard him tell people, "I *used* to sell real estate."

She had moved. Disappeared, left our lives. We would never see her again. Carolyn and I said it must have been Sylvia who told. Or Sylvia's mother.

Bruce Stern said once at the swimming pool he had gotten a letter from Miss McLean. But he never showed it to anyone and he liked to tell lies.

# Class Wars

## SPIRO ZAVOS

The right-arm sleeve of the headmaster's baggy grey suit flapped slightly when he shifted his body into the seat behind the cluttered desk. The interview had not started, but Henry Cown, Master of Arts (second class honours), author of a thesis entitled "Raven Images in Late Edwardian Rustic Poetry," beer drinking intervarsity runner-up 1972, former insurance company clerk (death claim section), and now a hopeful teacher, was uneasy. How would he shake hands with the headmaster at the end of it? Would they bow to each other like Japanese? Perhaps a friendly tap on the back like the Americans was in order?

The measured, carefully enunciated words of Mr. Crick, the headmaster, broke through to his consciousness putting a brake on this train of thought. "Of course," the headmaster was saying, gazing at a point some feet above Henry's head, "being untrained will have its difficulties for you. Even experienced teachers have problems in this area. I know you're slightly older than the ordinary run of first year teachers and I know you've had experience in what I'd like to call the commercial world, but ..." Mr. Crick lowered his head as if searching for something. He examined his fingers intently. Somewhere in the empty school building a door banged. The silence in the headmaster's room became an oppressive presence, a real thing. Suddenly it was broken. Mr. Crick raised his gaze again at the target above Henry's head. "The fact is this is a farming area. The kids can be pretty tough. We've had a number of people leave in the past year. Young teachers won't touch us with a barge pole. They'd rather teach in Otara and places like that where the kids have knives than come to Waiapa College."

"I was rather hoping," said Henry, determined to grab the receding initiative, "that I'd be given some of the better class to start off with. Give me a chance to play myself in, as it were."

Mr. Crick found the comment highly amusing. For some moments he sniggered convulsively, his body making little jumps of pleasure.

"Let me tell you something about teachers," he said finally, "they're so interested in the easy life they'd eat their mothers to get a good class. I'm afraid," he continued, his face assuming the look of a sympathetic centurion sending a Christian to the lions, "that in your earlier years as a teacher it's the tough classes for you. There's one comforting thing about it though," he rose and waved his left arm casually towards the door, an indication that the interview was nearly over, "if you survive this, you'll survive anything."

Henry was just about to set off down the corridor when he remembered something he'd wanted to ask the headmaster. He opened the door to the office. Mr. Crick had his head in hands, his body was shaking with laughter.

"What do I do if I can't control a class," Henry asked.

"Chorale speaking. Chorale speaking," replied the headmaster.

The staff room smelt of stale tobacco and chalk, a sour smell that seemed to lodge itself in the nostrils of the nose and the caverns of the mouth. Requests for books to be returned to the office and out-of-date class lists were pinned to the notice board. The room was unkept like an unshaved face. Chairs lay on their sides, books were strewn across the red formica-covered tables. A voice came out of a sofa which had its back to the door. "Been to see the one-armed bandit," the voice asked.

"As a matter of fact, yes," Henry replied.

"Put you onto chorale speaking I suppose."

"Well, yes," Henry said, embarrassed. He had tried to remember if any of the teachers had tried chorale speaking in classes he'd been in as a student. The only time the classes spoke out loud and clear was when teachers had specifically called for silence, he'd recalled.

The voice from behind the sofa rose to greet Henry. From his size Henry guessed that the man standing in front of him with the slightly apish grin on his tanned, weather-lined face was the phys-ed teacher. He had a tartan woollen shirt on with the buttons undone to reveal a thick grey mat of hair on his chest. The hand he extended for Henry to shake was as brown as treacle. The fingers on his hand were thick sausages.

"Morris. Head of maths," the voice said. "Let me give you a piece of advice. Don't make the mistake, the fatal mistake, of trying to teach the little wretches anything. You'll come a terrible cropper if you do this. Self-protection is the name of the game. Forget about any great ideas you might have to put a bit of culture in their heads. You're a lion-tamer, nothing more, nothing less. If one of them gets out of line, give them a crack of the cane."

"I left the insurance firm," Henry said wedging his words into the break in Morris's flow of conversation, "because I felt there was more to life than selling death claims. I've done a bit of re-vue acting and I think I can inject a bit of culture into their miserable little lives." He laughed nervously at his own attempt at adopting Morris's callous attitude to the students.

Morris shook his head "Culture. You've got to be kidding. It's only second hand stuff from America anyway. It's like the waves coming all the way down the Pacific and after years finally lapping up, a spent force, on Porirua beach, with no one there. Forget culture, my boy. There's only two things the boys in this school know: draw a naked woman on the black board and that'll keep them quiet for a while, otherwise," and he raised his eyebrows dramatically, "take one of them outside, preferably one of the smaller boys in the class, and give him a good hiding."

He sank back into the sofa again "Never forget, my boy, that the greatest educator of them all remains—the cane."

For a few minutes the class listened attentively to what Henry had to say. He would treat them like adults, if they behaved like adults, Henry told the intently staring faces. Some of the things he'd ask them to do would seem at the time perhaps too hard or uninteresting, or indeed both; but there would be a reason for it and if they bore with him throughout the year, he hoped they wouldn't be too bored.

Henry smiled at his own witticism. "In the last sentence I used a figure of speech," he continued, "can anyone tell me what it was."

A small boy in the back row, golden hair brushed neatly in contrast with the straggly locks of his classmates, put up his hands.

"Yes," Henry demanded eagerly.

"Sir," replied the angelic-faced boy, "the only figures we know have nothing to do with speech."

While Henry was trying to work out what this meant—he suspected the worst—a fight broke out in the front row near the door. Henry marched across to put an end to it. While his back was turned he heard the sound of other fights in different parts of the room. Boys were jumping over desks pummelling each other's bodies, yelling. He was losing control. "Silence," he roared. "Silence."

The silence that followed was almost as frightening as the previous mayhem. Catching his breath, Henry went on with what he wanted to say. "We'll be exploring all aspects of expression. Prose…" Sniggers greeted this last word. Henry raised an eyebrow in puzzlement. A boy in the far corner, bigger than the rest, explained the cause of the merriment. "We want to know all about pros, Sir."

"What's your name, boy," Henry asked in his sharpest voice.

"Bennett," the boy replied. The rest of the class burst into laughter. With beaming smiles on their faces, boys turned around and grinned their approval of what the boy had said.

Henry had no idea what the joke was about, if indeed it was a joke. He determined to push on forward. "As I said, we'll be looking at prose, drama, and even a bit of poetry." This last produced a chorus of groans. "What's the matter with poetry," Henry asked. The groaning continued. Bennett was leading the chorus. "You, Bennett," Henry asked, his voice edgy, "what's so horrible about poetry."

The boy stared back, with a defiant look on his face. The class was silent again. Henry was finding the lulls and then the storms a nerve-wracking experience. Someone had told him, some time when he'd informed his friends he was thinking of going teaching, that unless you got on top of a class right from the beginning, the class would get on top of him. He could see clearly enough that this latter prospect was well in train. He'd had to make a stand now or forever be lost.

He fixed Bennett with the iciest look he could place upon his face. "I asked, what's so horrible about poetry." He measured his words, enunciating them slowly. His heart was beating fiercely. He felt his hands clenching and unclenching. He had a desire to hit the sullen, scowling face that stared at him from across the length of the room. The rest of the class sensed that a private and intense battle for supremacy was in progress. Not a chair creaked. Not a shuffle of shoes on the floor could be heard.

Finally Bennett replied. "Because," he spoke slowly and softly. "Because, poetry doesn't milk the cows."

Henry did not know how to respond.

The last word was with Bennett, "Sir," he said defiantly.

Henry's mind was in a turmoil, although outwardly he remained standing rigidly fixed in front of the desk. Should he take the boy outside and give him a good caning? Would it be a better way of playing the situation to laugh and congratulate Bennett on saying something genuinely humorous? Should he give him a warning that if . . .

The bell resounded. Amid the clatter of banging desk lids, flailing arms, and one shoe being thrown against the back room, the boys fled past Henry out into the corridor.

13.3.77

Dear Mary,

One month, nine days and twenty-eight minutes—see how I've adopted the school child mentality already—after my first class I'm still in a state of shock and still wondering what I've let myself in for. Me and my ideals. If school continues the way it has since the start I'll join most other teachers in a mad rush for the asylum. The headmaster has one arm. Yesterday I opened the door for him as he left the staff room after a meeting. It was as if I'd attacked his virility. He seized the door handle out of my hand, yanked the door open and strode off in high dudgeon down the corridor. He calls me his untrained teacher—no training college, you see—and has taken to prowling the corridors outside my rooms. It was embarrassing for a time but I've devised a scheme to thwart him. The last time he came snooping around I managed to get some silence in the room by yelling out, "Everyone look at Mr. Crick who is looking at us." I pointed out the headmaster to them. He fled as the heads turned like spectators at a tennis match to the window he was gazing through.

The kids are awful. It's not the farting or the blobbing my coat with ink as I walk up and down the rows trying to keep order. It's their terrible lack of humour. Someone—a tough but bright kid called Bennett, (I think)—handed in an essay that had, as Winston Churchill once said, every cliché in it "except God is love and gentlemen will please adjust their clothing before leaving the toilet." At the bottom of the essay, in a flash of what I thought was genuine wit, I wrote: "Avoid clichés like the plague." When I handed the book back to Bennett, he took one look at my comment and said: "But Sir, that's a cliché." He's in Four Ag, the tough farming kids. It's one of the worst classes in the school, but my best. I take the bottom third form for French, which is a nightmare. They can't speak, write or spell English, let alone another language. Teaching them French is akin to loading the ignorant with the unintelligible. Then there's my core maths class. You have to remember that a number of these kids come from the hill country around here. Inbreeding is the norm. The kids emerge from all this thicker than concrete. They can only count by using their fingers, for instance. We spend most of the class working out the answer to a multiplication sum, something like 1999976 multiplied by 67894. This keeps them happy although no one ever gets the answer correct. Strangely though, if you look at the back of their school books you find meticulous and neat lists of all the top pop songs. The front of the book, where they're supposed to do their work, is splotchy, untidy, incorrect and incomplete. I suppose there's a moral in this somewhere.

The staff confirm all the things people say about teachers. They must be the most boring breed of humanity—after death claims clerks—in the whole world. As soon as the last bell is sounded they're out of the building as fast as wharfies half an hour before smoke time. I've made a bit of a friend with one of them, Morris, the head of maths. He just plays the system for all it's worth. Inspectors are coming, for instance, next week, and Morris has put his classes through a pre-arranged class so that when the inspectors walked into his room, he automatically goes into his prepared lesson with the kids answering back the responses they've been rehearsing for weeks. He also told me he puts the kids with the best books on the outside of the rows because inspectors usually only look at the outside books. The man is obviously headed for the director-general of education's chair.

The one other teacher who I've come in contact with is Bennett, (is this why the kids laugh at the other Bennett's name?) a teacher of geography. Bennett's got a degree in psychology actually and is forever hectoring the younger teachers like myself on the necessity of never using the cane or speaking loudly in class. I happened to walk into one of his classes by mistake one day to find a group of boys at his table trying to tie him up. The whole room was in uproar and chaos reigned. At morning tea he made no explanation except to

say: "Things weren't as out of hand as they seemed." Morris told me that Bennett had adopted the pacifist attitude to kids after a bad experience he had once when he threatened that anyone coming late to his class would get caned. This was in his early days as a teacher. A boy came in late. Bennett marched him outside into the corridor and prepared to cane him. The boy tried to say something, but Bennett would have nothing of it. "No excuses, no excuses," he kept on saying. "Take your medicine like a man." Bennett eventually caned him only to find out that the boy was not a member of his class but the lad bringing around the roll . . .

Henry was giving some instructions to his French class when the inspector sidled into the room. The eyes of the students swivelled towards the lean-faced, grey-suited, thin man who had intruded into their presence. "Take no notice of me, just continue with what you're doing," the inspector said. Their eyes continued to be fastened onto him. "Please just pretend I'm not even in the room. I want to watch and observe like a fly on the wall." His face creased with a barest hint of smile. The inspector began to walk up and down the rows looking at books. He studied each for several seconds, flicking through the few pages of work in them, and placing them back enigmatically on the desk. He worked his way to the back of the room and looked expectantly at Henry as if to tell him to continue with whatever it was he was doing.

"Well," said Henry to the class. "Where were we before we were so . . . so . . ." he looked at the inspector who was staring straight ahead. The inspector had a pad opened in front of him. Henry saw him suddenly bend down and begin to write. "Before we were pleasantly interrupted. I want you to do questions One, Two, Three, Six, Seven, and Nine."

A pupil towards the back of the hall put his hand in the air.

"No questions. Markham," Henry said authoritatively. "Just get on with the work please."

"What page, Sir," Markham asked plaintively.

He noticed however that the inspector started to write again following this exchange.

"Page thirty-three as I told you previously Markham."

"But Sir you didn't."

"You must have been asleep, then."

Another hand was raised. "There's only a picture on page Thirty-three, Sir."

Henry looked at the book, terror flooding in on him. The inspector was writing away onto his pad presumably about what was happening in front of him.

"Page Forty-three was what I meant. Didn't I say that before?"

The inspector finally stopped writing and came down the row from the back to the front of the room. "You don't speak to the children in English like this normally do you," he asked in a loud voice.

Henry nodded.

The inspector's face fell. "Never, never," he said. "Only speak French. How in heaven's name will they ever learn an accent or, to speak the language, which is the object really of what you are about, unless you do this."

Henry's accent was decidedly un-French. He did not relish trying to read in front of the class with what was obviously a fluent French speaking inspector listening to his pathetic efforts. He had a brain-wave. With all the meekness and false humility he could muster, assuming the cringing, attitude of a beggar, he asked, "Would it be possible, Sir, to please kindly give a demonstration." Perhaps he had laid on the fawning a shade too thick. The request however was granted.

"Enchanté," the inspector said. He grabbed the textbook from Henry's hand and began to pace the platform. "Page quarante-trois, s'il vous plait," he said, speaking slowly but with a finely turned accent. The class was mesmerized. They looked to Henry for guidance. "Not me," Henry said and then, remembering, continued, "regardez l'inspecteur."

The inspector was now well launched into his performance. "Écoutez et puis traduisez." He began to read in French from the textbook. Markham looked at Henry and tapped his head. The boy had a worried look on his face. Henry shook his head and nodded gravely towards the inspector.

"Qu'est-ce que, je plonge," the inspector was asking. There was a dazed look in the faces of the children. "Je plonge, je plonge," the inspector said. The class was clearly not going quite the way it had with the better classes he had tried it on. He was showing signs of becoming rattled. His voice, initially so calm and rotund, was gaining a shrill edge to it. "Je plonge, je plonge." He was shouting now.

Henry saw with a feeling of dread the inspector climbing onto the teacher's chair. He was obviously going to climb onto the table and do something or other. The table Henry noticed was balanced, as it always was, so that the slightest pressure on it, would send it tumbling off the platform. Henry was going to bark out a warning when he remembered the injunction about speaking English. He racked his brains for the appropriate French words. They came at last. "Defense..." he started to call out. Too late. The inspector was on the table. "Je plonge, je plonge," he said, his arms making diving motions. The table started to wobble. The inspector fought like a logroller to keep it stable. For some seconds it looked as if he might succeed. But the bell for the end of class rang breaking his concentration. The table fell over, taking the inspector with it. As he lay on the floor, the textbook still clutched in his hand, the pupils trampled over him in their rush to the door.

From the staff room window the inspectors could be seen climbing into their cars. In their long grey gaberdine overcoats they looked like a Russian trade mission about to go home.

The staff room throbbed with a feeling of release. Teachers forgot their waistlines and devoured the cooking classes' rock cakes. The bell rang for the commencement of classes but no one moved towards the door. To gossip about what had happened was a necessity.

"...Did you hear about Bennett...Morris had them trained up for days...as soon as the beaks came in...best books on the outside, that sort of thing...he froze up, couldn't say a word...but the woodwork man and not the maths man came in...appears it was terrible...woodwork man asked the sort of questions a maths teacher would never dream of...he ran out in the end...the kids were all confused...appears he'd been telling the kids that the inspectors were inspecting them not us...being energetic he scrambled across the desks and got some of the books...believe he's already been offered a job in the Department in the psychological services..."

There was a knock on the door. A small boy handed Henry a note from the headmaster. It was in Mr. Crick's handwriting, painfully scribbled with his left hand in large kindergarten-sized letters. Henry was to be congratulated, it said, for impressing the inspectors to the degree he did, especially the French inspector.

Henry nodded to the boy to stay where he was. He wrote his first note to the headmaster. "Who are the lunatics in this asylum?" the note asked. The boy hurried away with his message while Henry put on his coat and made his way to the door.

# Doctor Jack-o'-Lantern

## RICHARD YATES

All Miss Price had been told about the new boy was that he'd spent most of his life in some kind of orphanage, and that the grey-haired "aunt and uncle" with whom he now lived were really foster parents, paid by the Welfare Department of the City of New York. A less dedicated or less imaginative teacher might have pressed for more details, but Miss Price was content with the rough outline. It was enough, in fact, to fill her with a sense of mission that shone from her eyes, as plain as love, from the first morning he joined the fourth grade.

He arrived early and sat in the back row—his spine very straight, his ankles crossed precisely under the desk and his hands folded on the very center of its top, as if symmetry might make him less conspicuous—and while the other children were filing in and settling down, he received a long, expressionless stare from each of them.

"We have a new classmate this morning," Miss Price said, laboring the obvious in a way that made everybody want to giggle. "His name is Vincent Sabella and he comes from New York City. I know we'll all do our best to make him feel at home."

This time they all swung around to stare at once, which caused him to duck his head slightly and shift his weight from one buttock to the other. Ordinarily, the fact of someone's coming from New York might have held a certain prestige, for to most of the children the city was an awesome, adult place that swallowed up their fathers every day, and which they themselves were permitted to visit only rarely, in their best clothes, as a treat. But anyone could see at a glance that Vincent Sabella had nothing whatever to do with skyscrapers. Even if you could ignore his tangled black hair and gray skin, his clothes would have given him away; absurdly new corduroys, absurdly old sneakers and a yellow sweatshirt, much too small, with the shredded remains of a Mickey Mouse de-

sign stamped on its chest. Clearly, he was from the part of New York that you had to pass through on the train to Grand Central—the part where people hung bedding over their windowsills and leaned out on it all day in a trance of boredom, and where you got vistas of straight, deep streets, one after another, all alike in the clutter of their sidewalks and all swarming with gray boys at play in some desperate kind of ball game.

The girls decided that he wasn't very nice and turned away, but the boys lingered in their scrutiny, looking up and down with faint smiles. This was the kind of kid they were accustomed to thinking of as "tough," the kind whose stares had made all of them uncomfortable at one time or another in unfamiliar neighborhoods; here was a unique chance for retaliation.

"What would you like us to call you, Vincent?" Miss Price inquired. "I mean, do you prefer Vincent, or Vince, or—or what?" (It was purely an academic question; even Miss Price knew that the boys would call him "Sabella" and that the girls wouldn't call him anything at all.)

"Vinny's okay," he said in a strange, croaking voice that had evidently yelled itself hoarse down the ugly streets of his home.

"I'm afraid I didn't hear you," she said, craning her pretty head forward and to one side so that a heavy lock of her hair swung free of one shoulder. "Did you say 'Vince'?"

"Vinny, I said," he said again, squirming.

"Vincent, is it? All right, then, Vincent." A few of the class giggled, but nobody bothered to correct her; it would be more fun to let the mistake continue.

"I won't take time to introduce you to everyone by name, Vincent," Miss Price went on, "because I think it would be simpler just to let you learn the names as we go along, don't you? Now we won't expect you to take any real part in the work for the first day or so; just take your time, and if there's anything you don't understand, why, don't be afraid to ask."

He made an unintelligible croak and smiled fleetingly, just enough to show that the roots of his teeth were green.

"Now then," Miss Price said, getting down to business. "This is Monday morning, and so the first thing on the program is reports. Who'd like to start off?"

Vincent Sabella was momentarily forgotten as six or seven hands went up, and Miss Price drew back in mock confusion. "Goodness, we do have a lot of reports this morning," she said. The idea of the reports—a fifteen-minute period every Monday in which the children were encouraged to relate their experiences over the weekend—was Miss Price's own, and she took a pardonable pride in it. The principal had commended her on it at a recent staff meeting, pointing out that it made a splendid bridge between the worlds of school and home, and that it was a fine way for children to learn poise and assurance. It called for intelligent supervision—the shy children had to be drawn out and the show-offs curbed—but in general, as Miss Price had assured the principal, it was fun for everyone. She particularly hoped it would be fun today, to help put Vincent Sabella at ease, and that was why she chose Nancy Parker to start off; there was nobody like Nancy for holding an audience.

The others fell silent as Nancy moved gracefully to the head of the room; even the two or three girls who secretly despised her had to feign enthrallment when she spoke (she was that popular), and every boy in the class, who at recess liked nothing better than to push her shrieking into the mud, was unable to watch her without an idiotically tremulous smile.

"Well—" she began, and then she clapped a hand over her mouth while everyone laughed.

"Oh, *Nancy,*" Miss Price said. "You *know* the rule about starting a report with 'well.'"

Nancy knew the rule; she had only broken it to get the laugh. Now she let her fit of giggles subside, ran her fragile forefingers down the side seams of her skirt, and began again in the proper way. "On Friday my whole family went for a ride in my brother's new car. My brother bought this new Pontiac last week, and he wanted to take us all for a ride—you know, to try it out and everything? So we went into White Plains and had dinner in a restaurant there, and then we all wanted to go see this movie, 'Doctor Jekyll and Mr. Hyde,' but my brother said it was too horrible and everything, and I wasn't old enough to enjoy it—oh, he made me so mad! And then, let's see. On Saturday I stayed home all day and helped my mother make my sister's wedding dress. My sister's engaged to be married, you see, and my mother's making this wedding dress for her? So we did that, and then on Sunday this friend of my brother's came over for dinner, and then they both had to get back to college that night, and I was allowed to stay up and say goodbye to them and everything, and I guess that's all." She always had a sure instinct for keeping her performance brief—or rather, for making it seem briefer than it really was.

"Very good, Nancy," Miss Price said. "Now, who's next?"

Warren Berg was next, elaborately hitching up his pants as he made his way down the aisle. "On Saturday I went over to Bill Stringer's house for lunch," he began in his direct, man-to-man style, and Bill Stringer wriggled bashfully in the front row. Warren Berg and Bill Stringer were great friends, and their reports often overlapped. "And then after lunch we went into White Plains, on our bikes. Only we *saw* 'Doctor Jekyll and Mr. Hyde.'" Here he nodded his head in Nancy's direction, and Nancy got another laugh by making a little whimper of envy. "It was real good, too," he went on, with mounting excitement. "It's all about this guy who—"

"About a *man* who," Miss Price corrected.

"About a man who mixes up this chemical, like, that he drinks? And whenever he drinks this chemical, he changes into this real monster, like? You see him drink this chemical, and then you see his hands start to get all scales all over them, like a reptile and everything, and then you see his face start to change into this real horrible-looking face—with fangs and all? Sticking out of his mouth?"

All the girls shuddered in pleasure. "Well," Miss Price said, "I think Nancy's brother was probably wise in not wanting her to see it. What did you do *after* the movie, Warren?"

There was a general "*Aw-w-w!*" of disappointment—everyone wanted to hear more about the scales and fangs—but Miss Price never liked to let the reports degenerate into accounts of movies. Warren continued without much enthusiasm: all they had done after the movie was fool around Bill Stringer's yard until suppertime. "And then on Sunday," he said, brightening again, "Bill Stringer came over to *my* house, and my dad helped us rig up this old tire on this long rope? From a tree? There's this steep hill down behind my house, you see—this ravine, like?—and we hung this tire so that what you do is, you take the tire and run a little ways and then lift your feet and you go swinging way, way out over the ravine and back again."

"That sounds like fun," Miss Price said, glancing at her watch.

"Oh, it's *fun,* all right," Warren conceded. But then he hitched up his pants again and added, with a puckering of his forehead, "'Course, it's pretty dangerous. You let go of that tire or anything, you'd get a bad fall. Hit a rock or anything, you'd probably break your leg, or your spine. But my dad said he trusted us both to look out for our own safety."

"Well, I'm afraid that's all we'll have time for, Warren," Miss Price said. "Now, there's just time for one more report. Who's ready? Arthur Cross?"

There was a soft groan, because Arthur Cross was the biggest dope in class and his reports were always a bore. This time it turned out to be something tedious about going to visit his uncle on Long Island. At one point he made a slip—he said "botormoat" instead of "motorboat"—and everyone laughed with the particular edge of scorn they reserved for Arthur Cross. But the laughter died abruptly when it was joined by a harsh, dry croak-

ing from the back of the room. Vincent Sabella was laughing too, green teeth and all, and they all had to glare at him until he stopped.

When the reports were over, everyone settled down for school. It was recess time before any of the children thought much about Vincent Sabella again, and then they thought of him only to make sure he was left out of everything. He wasn't in the group of boys that clustered around the horizontal bar to take turns at skinning-the-cat, or the group that whispered in a far corner of the playground, hatching a plot to push Nancy Parker in the mud. Nor was he in the larger group, of which even Arthur Cross was a member, that chased itself in circles in a frantic variation of the game of tag. He couldn't join the girls, of course, or the boys from other classes, and so he joined nobody. He stayed on the apron of the playground, close to the school, and for the first part of the recess he pretended to be very busy with the laces of his sneakers. He would squat to undo and retie them, straighten up and take a few experimental steps in a springy, athletic way, and then get down and go to work on them again. After five minutes of this he gave it up, picked up a handful of pebbles and began shying them at an invisible target several yards away. That was good for another five minutes, but then there were still five minutes left, and he could think of nothing to do but stand there, first with his hands in his pockets, then with his hands on his hips, and then with his arms folded in a manly way across his chest.

Miss Price stood watching all this from the doorway, and she spent the full recess wondering if she ought to go out and do something about it. She guessed it would be better not to.

She managed to control the same impulse at recess the next day, and every other day that week, though every day it grew more difficult. But one thing she could not control was a tendency to let her anxiety show in class. All Vincent Sabella's errors in schoolwork were publicly excused, even those having nothing to do with his newness, and all his accomplishments were singled out for special mention. Her campaign to build him up was painfully obvious, and never more so than when she tried to make it subtle; once, for instance, in explaining a arithmetic problem, she said, "Now, suppose Warren Berg and Vincent Sabella went to the store with fifteen cents each, and candy bars cost ten cents. How many candy bars would each boy have?" By the end of the week he was well on the way to becoming the worst possible kind of teacher's pet, a victim of the teacher's pity.

On Friday she decided the best thing to do would be to speak to him privately, and try to draw him out. She could say something about the pictures he had painted in art class—that would do for an opening—and she decided to do it at lunchtime.

The only trouble was that lunchtime, next to recess, was the most trying part of Vincent Sabella's day. Instead of going home for an hour as the other children did, he brought his lunch to school in a wrinkled paper bag and ate it in the classroom, which always made for a certain amount of awkwardness. The last children to leave would see him still seated apologetically at his desk, holding his paper bag, and anyone who happened to straggle back later for a forgotten hat or sweater would surprise him in the middle of his meal—perhaps shielding a hard-boiled egg from view or wiping mayonnaise from his mouth with a furtive hand. It was a situation that Miss Price did not improve by walking up to him while the room was still half full of children and sitting prettily on the edge of the desk beside his, making it clear that she was cutting her own lunch hour short in order to be with him.

"Vincent," she began, "I've been meaning to tell you how much I enjoyed those pictures of yours. They're really very good."

He mumbled something and shifted his eyes to the cluster of departing children at the door. She went right on talking and smiling, elaborating on her praise of the pictures; and finally, after the door had closed behind the last child, he was able to give her his attention. He did so tentatively at first; but the more she talked, the more he seemed

to relax, until she realized she was putting him at ease. It was as simple and as gratifying as stroking a cat. She had finished with the pictures now and moved on, triumphantly, to broader fields of praise. "It's never easy," she was saying, "to come to a new school and adjust yourself to the—well, the new work, and new working methods, and I think you've done a splendid job so far. I really do. But tell me, do you think you're going to like it here?"

He looked at the floor just long enough to make his reply—"It's awright"—and then his eyes stared into hers again.

"I'm so glad. Please don't let me interfere with your lunch, Vincent. Do go ahead and eat, that is, if you don't mind my sitting here with you." But it was now abundantly clear that he didn't mind at all, and he began to unwrap a bologna sandwich with what she felt sure was the best appetite he'd had all week. It wouldn't even have mattered very much now if someone from the class had come in and watched, though it was probably just as well that no one did.

Miss Price sat back more comfortably on the desk top, crossed her legs and allowed one slim stockinged foot to slip part of the way out of its moccasin. "Of course," she went on, "it always does take a little time to sort of get your bearings in a new school. For one thing, well, it's never too easy for the new member of the class to make friends with the other members. What I mean is, you mustn't mind if the others seem a little rude to you at first. Actually, they're just as anxious to make friends as you are, but they're shy. All it takes is a little time, and a little effort on your part as well as theirs. Not too much, of course, but a little. Now for instance, these reports we have Monday mornings—they're a fine way for people to get to know one another. A person never feels he has to make a report; it's just a thing he can do if he wants to. And that's only one way of helping others to know the kind of person you are; there are lots and lots of ways. The main thing to remember is that making friends is the most natural thing in the world, and it's only a question of time until you have all the friends you want. And in the meantime, Vincent, I hope you'll consider *me* your friend, and feel free to call on me for whatever advice or anything you might need. Will you do that?"

He nodded, swallowing.

"Good." She stood up and smoothed her skirt over her long thighs. "Now I must go or I'll be late for *my* lunch. But I'm glad we had this little talk, Vincent, and I hope we'll have others."

It was probably a lucky thing that she stood up when she did, for if she'd stayed on that desk a minute longer Vincent Sabella would have thrown his arms around her and buried his face in the warm gray flannel of her lap, and that might have been enough to confuse the most dedicated and imaginative of teachers.

At report time on Monday morning, nobody was more surprised than Miss Price when Vincent Sabella's smudged hand was among the first and most eager to rise. Apprehensively she considered letting someone else start off, but then, for fear of hurting his feelings, she said, "All right, Vincent," in as matter-of-fact a way as she could manage.

There was a suggestion of muffled titters from the class as he walked confidently to the head of the room and turned to face his audience. He looked, if anything, too confident: there were signs, in the way he held his shoulders and the way his eyes shone, of the terrible poise of panic.

"Saturday I seen that pitcha," he announced.

"Saw, Vincent," Miss Price corrected gently.

"That's what I mean," he said; "I sore that pitcha. 'Doctor Jack-o'-lantern and Mr. Hide.'"

There was a burst of wild, delighted laughter and a chorus of correction: "Doctor *Jekyll!*"

He was unable to speak over the noise. Miss Price was on her feet, furious. "It's a *perfectly natural mistake!*" she was saying. "There's no reason for any of you to be so rude. Go on, Vincent, and please excuse this very silly interruption." The laugher subsided, but the class continued to shake their heads derisively from side to side. It hadn't, of course, been a perfectly natural mistake at all; for one thing it proved that he was a hopeless dope, and for another it proved that he was lying.

"That's what I mean," he continued. "'Doctor Jackal and Mr. Hide.' I got it a little mixed up. Anyways, I seen all about where his teet' start comin' outa his mout' and all like that, and I thought it was very good. And then on Sundy my mudda and fodda come out to see me in this car they got. This Buick. My fodda siz, 'Vinny, wanna go for a little ride?' I siz, 'Sure, where yiz goin'?' He siz, 'Anyplace ya, like.' So I siz, 'Let's go out in the country a ways, get on one of them big roads an make some time.' So we go out—oh, I guess fifty, sixty miles—and we're cruisin' along this highway, when this cop starts tailin' us? My fodda siz, 'Don't worry, we'll shake him,' and he steps on it, see? My mudda's gettin' pretty scared, but my fodda siz, 'Don't worry, dear.' He's tryin' to make this turn, see, so he can get off the highway and shake the cop? But just when he's makin' the turn, the cop opens up and starts shootin', see?"

By this time the few members of the class who could bear to look at him at all were doing so with heads on one side and mouths partly open, the way you look at a broken arm or a circus freak.

"We just barely made it," Vincent went on, his eyes gleaming, "and this one bullet got my fodda in the shoulder. Didn't hurt him bad—just grazed him, like—so my mudda bandaged it up for him and all, but he couldn't do no more drivin' after that, and we had to get him to a doctor, see? So my fodda siz, 'Vinny, think you can drive a ways?' I siz, 'Sure, if you show me how,' So he showed me how to work the gas and the brake, and all like that, and I drove to the doctor. My mudda siz, 'I'm prouda you, Vinny, drivin' all by yourself.' So anyways, we got to the doctor, got my fodda fixed up and all, and then he drove us back home." He was breathless. After an uncertain pause he said, "And that's all." Then he walked quickly back to his desk, his stiff new corduroy pants whistling faintly with each step.

"Well, that was very—entertaining, Vincent," Miss Price said, trying to act as if nothing had happened. "Now, who's next?" But nobody raised a hand.

Recess was worse than usual for him that day; at least it was until he found a place to hide—a narrow concrete alley, blind except for several closed fire-exit doors, that cut between two sections of the school building. It was reassuringly dismal and cool in there—he could stand with his back to the wall and his eyes guarding the entrance, and the noises of recess were as remote as the sunshine. But when the bell rang he had to go back to class, and in another hour it was lunchtime.

Miss Price left him alone until her own meal was finished. Then, after standing with one hand on the doorknob for a full minute to gather courage, she went in and sat beside him for another little talk, just as he was trying to swallow the last of a pimento-cheese sandwich.

"Vincent," she began, "we all enjoyed your report this morning, but I think we would have enjoyed it more—a great deal more—if you'd told us something about your real life instead. I mean," she hurried on, "for instance, I noticed you were wearing a nice new windbreaker this morning. It *is* new, isn't it? And did your aunt buy it for you over the weekend?"

He did not deny it.

"Well then, why couldn't you have told us about going to the store with your aunt, and buying the windbreaker, and whatever you did afterwards. That would have made a perfectly good report." She paused, and for the first time looked steadily into his eyes. "You do understand what I'm trying to say, don't you, Vincent?"

He wiped crumbs of bread from his lips, looked at the floor, and nodded.

"And you'll remember next time, won't you?"

He nodded again. "Please may I be excused, Miss Price?"

"Of course you may."

He went to the boys' lavatory and vomited. Afterwards he washed his face and drank a little water, and then he returned to the classroom. Miss Price was busy at her desk now, and didn't look up. To avoid getting involved with her again, he wandered out to the cloakroom and sat on one of the long benches, where he picked up someone's discarded overshoe and turned it over and over in his hands. In a little while he heard the chatter of returning children, and to avoid being discovered there, he got up and went to the fire-exit door. Pushing it open, he found that it gave onto the alley he had hidden in that morning, and he slipped outside. For a minute or two he just stood there, looking at the blankness of the concrete wall; then he found a piece of chalk in his pocket and wrote out all the dirty words he could think of, in block letters a foot high. He had put down four words and was trying to remember a fifth when he heard a shuffling at the door behind him. Arthur Cross was there, holding the door open and reading the words with wide eyes. "Boy," he said in an awed half-whisper. "Boy, you're gonna get it. You're really gonna *get* it."

Startled and then suddenly calm, Vincent Sabella palmed his chalk, hooked his thumbs in his belt and turned on Arthur Cross with a menacing look. "Yeah?" he inquired. "Who's gonna squeal on me?"

"Well, nobody's gonna *squeal* on you," Arthur Cross said uneasily, "but you shouldn't go around writing—"

"Arright," Vincent said, advancing a step. His shoulders were slumped, his head thrust forward and his eyes narrowed, like Edward G. Robinson. "Arright. That's all I wanna know. I don't like squealers, unnastand?"

While he was saying this, Warren Berg and Bill Stringer appeared in the doorway—just in time to hear it and to see the words on the wall before Vincent turned on them. "And that goes fa you too, unnastand?" he said. "Both a yiz."

And the remarkable thing was that both their faces fell into the same foolish, defensive smile that Arthur Cross was wearing. It wasn't until they had glanced at each other that they were able to meet his eyes with the proper degree of contempt, and by then it was too late. "Think you're pretty smart, don'tcha, Sabella?" Bill Stringer said.

"Never mind what I think," Vincent told him. "You heard what I said. Now let's get back inside."

And they could do nothing but move aside to make way for him, and follow him dumbfounded into the cloakroom.

It was Nancy Parker who squealed—although, of course with someone like Nancy Parker you didn't think of it as squealing. She had heard everything from the cloakroom; as soon as the boys came in she peeked into the alley, saw the words and, setting her face in a prim frown, went straight to Miss Price. Miss Price was just about to call the class to order for the afternoon when Nancy came up and whispered in her ear. They both disappeared into the cloakroom—from which, after a moment, came the sound of the fire-exit door being abruptly slammed—and when they returned to class Nancy was flushed with righteousness, Miss Price very pale. No announcement was made. Classes proceeded in the ordinary way all afternoon, though it was clear that Miss Price was upset, and it wasn't until she was dismissing the children at three o'clock that she brought the thing into the open. "Will Vincent Sabella please remain seated?" She nodded at the rest of the class. "That's all."

While the room was clearing out she sat at her desk, closed her eyes and massaged the frail bridge of her nose with thumb and forefinger, sorting out half-remembered fragments of a book she had once read on the subject of seriously disturbed children. Perhaps, after all, she should never have undertaken the responsibility of Vincent Sabella's loneliness. Perhaps the whole thing called for the attention of a specialist. She took a deep breath.

"Come over here and sit beside me, Vincent," she said, and when he had settled himself, she looked at him. "I want you to tell me the truth. Did you write those words on the wall outside?"

He stared at the floor.

"Look at me," she said, and he looked at her. She had never looked prettier: her cheeks slightly flushed, her eyes shining and her sweet mouth pressed into a self-conscious frown. "First of all," she said, handing him a small enameled basin streaked with poster paint, "I want you to take this to the boys' room and fill it with hot water and soap."

He did as he was told, and when he came back, carrying the basin carefully to keep the suds from spilling, she was sorting out some old rags in the bottom drawer of her desk. "Here," she said, selecting one and shutting the drawer in a business-like way. "This will do. Soak this up." She led him back to the fire exit and stood in the alley watching him, silently, while he washed off all the words.

When the job had been done, and the rag and basin put away, they sat down at Miss Price's desk again. "I suppose you think I'm angry with you Vincent," she said. "Well, I'm not. I almost wish I could be angry—that would make it much easier—but instead I'm hurt. I've tried to be a good friend to you, and I thought you wanted to be my friend too. But this kind of thing—well, it's very hard to be friendly with a person who'd do a thing like that."

She saw, gratefully, that there were tears in his eyes. "Vincent, perhaps I understand some things better than you think. Perhaps I understand that sometimes, when a person does a thing like that, it isn't really because he wants to hurt anyone, but only because he's unhappy. He knows it isn't a good thing to do, and he even knows it isn't going to make him any happier afterwards, but he goes ahead and does it anyway. Then when he finds he's lost a friend, he's terribly sorry, but it's too late. The thing is done."

She allowed this somber note to reverberate in the silence of the room for a little while before she spoke again. "I won't be able to forget this, Vincent. But perhaps, just this once, we can still be friends—as long as I understand that you didn't mean to hurt me. But you must promise me that you won't forget it either. Never forget that when you do a thing like that, you're going to hurt people who want very much to like you, and in that way you're going to hurt yourself. Will you promise me to remember that, dear?"

The "dear" was as involuntary as the slender hand that reached out and held the shoulder of his sweatshirt; both made his head hang lower than before.

"All right," she said. "You may go now."

He got his windbreaker out of the cloakroom and left, avoiding the tired uncertainty of her eyes. The corridors were deserted, and dead silent except for the hollow, rhythmic knocking of a janitor's push-broom against some distant wall. His own rubber-soled tread only added to the silence; so did the lonely little noise made by the zipping up of his windbreaker, and so did the faint mechanical sigh of the heavy front door. The silence made it all the more startling when he found, several yards down the concrete walk outside, that two boys were walking beside him: Warren Berg and Bill Stringer. They were both smiling at him in an eager, almost friendly way.

"What'd she do to ya, anyway?" Bill Stringer asked.

Caught off guard, Vincent barely managed to put on his Edward G. Robinson face in time. "Nunnya business," he said, and walked faster.

"No, listen—wait up, hey," Warren Berg said, as they trotted to keep up with him. "What'd she do, anyway? She bawl ya out, or what? Wait up, hey, Vinny."

The name made him tremble all over. He had to jam his hands in his windbreaker pockets and force himself to keep on walking; he had to force his voice to be steady when he said "Nunnya *business,* I told ya. Lea' me alone."

But they were right in step with him now. "Boy, she must of given you the works." Warren Berg persisted. "What'd she say, anyway? C'mon, tell us, Vinny."

This time the name was too much for him. It overwhelmed his resistance and made his soften-

ing knees slow down to a slack, conversational stroll. "She din say nothin'," he said at last; and then after a dramatic pause he added, "She let the ruler do her talkin' for her."

"The *ruler?* Ya mean she used a *ruler* on ya?" Their faces were stunned, either with disbelief or admiration, and it began to look more and more like admiration as they listened.

"On the knuckles," Vincent said through tightening lips. "Five times on each hand. She siz, 'Make a fist. Lay it out here on the desk.' Then she takes the ruler and *Whop! Whop! Whop!* Five times. Ya think that don't hurt, you're crazy."

Miss Price, buttoning her polo coat as the front door whispered shut behind her, could scarcely believe her eyes. This couldn't be Vincent Sabella—this perfectly normal, perfectly happy boy on the sidewalk ahead of her, flanked by attentive friends. But it was, and the scene made her want to laugh aloud with pleasure and relief. He was going to be all right, after all. For all her well-intentioned groping in the shadows she could never have predicted a scene like this, and certainly could never have caused it to happen. But it was happening, and it just proved, once again, that she would never understand the ways of children.

She quickened her graceful stride and overtook them, turning to smile down at them as she passed. "Goodnight, boys," she called, intending it as a kind of cheerful benediction; and then, embarrassed by their three startled faces, she smiled eve wider and said, "Goodness, it *is* getting colder, isn't it? That windbreaker of yours looks nice and warm, Vincent. I envy you." Finally they nodded bashfully at her; she called goodnight again, turned, and continued on her way to the bus stop.

She left a profound silence in her wake. Staring after her, Warren Berg and Bill Stringer waited until she had disappeared around the corner before they turned on Vincent Sabella.

"Ruler, my eye!" Bill Stringer said. "Ruler, my eye!" He gave Vincent a disgusted shove that sent him stumbling against Warren Berg, who shoved him back.

"Jeez, you lie about *everything,* don'tcha, Sabella? You lie about *everything!*"

Jostled off balance, keeping his hands tight in the windbreaker pockets, Vincent tried in vain to retain his dignity. "Think *I* care if yiz believe me?" he said, and then because he couldn't think of anything else to say, he said it again. "Think *I* care if yiz believe me?"

But he was walking alone. Warren Berg and Bill Stringer were drifting away across the street, walking backwards in order to look back on him with furious contempt. "Just like the lies you told about the policeman shooting your father," Bill Stringer called.

"Even *movies* he lies about," Warren Berg put in; and suddenly doubling up with artificial laughter he cupped both hands to his mouth and yelled, "Hey, Doctor Jack-o'-lantern!"

It wasn't a very good nickname, but it had an authentic ring to it—the kind of a name that might spread around, catch on quickly, and stick. Nudging each other, they both took up the cry:

"What's the matter, Doctor Jack-o'-lantern?"

"Why don'tcha run on home with Miss Price, Doctor Jack-o'-lantern?"

"So long, Doctor Jack-o'-lantern!"

Vincent Sabella went on walking, ignoring them, waiting until they were out of sight. Then he turned and retraced his steps all the way back to school, around through the playground and back to the alley, where the wall was still dark in spots from the circular scrubbing of his wet rag.

Choosing a dry place, he got out his chalk and began to draw a head with great care, in profile, making the hair long and rich and taking his time over the face, erasing it with moist fingers and reworking it until it was the most beautiful face he had ever drawn: a delicate nose, slightly parted lips, an eye with lashes that curved gracefully as a bird's wing. He paused to admire it with a lover's solemnity; then from the lips he drew a line that connected with a big speech balloon, and in the balloon he wrote, so angrily that the chalk kept breaking in his fingers, every one of the words he had written that noon. Returning to the head, he gave it a slender neck and gently sloping shoulders, and then, with bold strikes, he gave it the body of a naked woman: great breasts with hard little nipples, a trim waist, a dot for a navel, wide hips and thighs that flared around a triangle of fiercely scribbled pubic hair. Beneath the picture he printed its title: "Miss Price."

He stood there looking at it for a little while, breathing hard, and then he went home.

# Untimely Aid

## BRIAN JAMES

"Look out! Here comes the silly old bastard!" The "muck-up" in 4B died down at this announcement. Every day it went like that, as every day Mr. Beresford came into 4B and, after a long pause, greeted it with "Good morning, boys!" He was genuinely delighted at taking 4B. Such a fine lot of lads. Indeed, yes, all boys were fine, but the 4B were particularly so, and Mr. Beresford felt the warmth in the responsive chorus of "Good morning, Mr. Beresford!" Felt it all the more that his poor deaf old ears sensed rather than heard. It filled him with more delight than he would have been willing to own to. He was not a vain man; but a human craving for affection was his for all that. And 4B went out of its way to supply it.— "The poor, silly, deaf old bastard!"

4B was actually proud of Mr. Beresford's deafness. It would be very hard to explain why— that is, to give any satisfactory explanation. Under cover of it they could say all manner of disgraceful things and he be totally unaware of them. Undoubtedly that was very funny. Perhaps there is a degree of cruelty in humour, in boys' humour most of all. Often nothing malicious in it, either. Just some twisted interest and distorted pleasure in difference and abnormality. The unfortunately fat boy is funny; and so is the long, thin streak of misery. The boy with no eyebrows, or with ears like bats' wings, or with a nose like a snout, or, again, with no nose to speak of—all these are extremely funny. With unerring precision nicknames are bestowed accordingly.

The boys of 4B liked Mr. Beresford. Deep down somewhere was an appreciation of his so patient goodness, his absurd enthusiasm for the dry-as-dust classics of English Literature, his patience, his earnestness. They liked his tall, well-groomed figure and the well-preserved M.A. gown that he persisted in wearing right into an age that had no time for such flummery. They liked his dignity that was so in accord with his gown—

and no less absurd. They liked his big clear face, so smooth and unwrinkled, with that almost unearthly goodness upon it that is only found on the countenance of celibacy. In short, there was much more of liking than illegitimacy in their crude, but unheard, announcement of his arrival.

And every morning, after greeting and response, it had always gone to the regular pattern: a long beaming look at the boys. His boys. The dear young things who so soon—ah, dear me! all too soon—would be men in a wide, wild, rough, disillusioning world. In the full false light of common day. It was a saddening thought, a sobering reflection. And so the beaming look was tempered, as it were, by two brief, scarce audible sniffs. Such peculiar little sniffs—with no physical need for them. Sniffs that came from the very heart of sympathy and understanding. Sniffs that were followed by two peculiar little sounds that can nearest be rendered by kuk-kuk.

It was a solemn moment—that of the sniff-sniff. It was gracious relief—that of the kuk-kuk. Then followed the ceremony of enthronement on the brief classroom dais. Other men sat down; or flopped into a chair; or put a left foot on the chair and leaned on the knee to support an inclined body; or stood more or less upright and said, "Now, give your full attention," or yanked down the top board to fill it with figures of history notes, or something, with the harsh command, "Get this down!" But Mr. Beresford did none of these things. He enthroned himself, and twenty-four pairs of eyes helped him do it, what time his own beamed all the brighter. But first there was an ever so little hitch of the shoulders so that there would be no tightening, no undue strain, put upon the long black gown. Then the pile of books lovingly held by the left hand, and steadied by the right, would be placed at an exact and pre-ordained distance from the right edge of the table. Such a pile of books, too: the book of the moment and its immediate needs—Lamb's *Essays.* Then some Shakespeare ... and an Isaak Walton, for purposes of reference ... and Herrick's *Hesperides,* also for reference, and Long's *History of Literature.* And a few widely separated volumes—a bound copy of *Household Words,* maybe, and *Sir Roger de Coverley,* and *Tales from Chaucer.* Indeed, well worn books, but neat, as if Time had fingered them as carefully as Mr. Beresford himself had done. The pile always amused the boys, for as often as not Mr. Beresford did not open half of them during a lesson. More often but a quarter of them. Somehow, in a way not to be explained the boys could almost divine, at least the more discerning almost could, that Mr. Beresford lived away up on the North Shore line with two maiden sisters who worshiped him. That his cottage was a smother in wisteria and honeysuckle and climbing roses, and bore withal as chaste appearance as his own and that of his unworldly sisters. That there was an English garden for gilly-flowers and hollyhocks, for oxlips and nodding violets, for the wild thyme and rosemary and rue. And an Australian garden for boronia and all its relations, for epacris, for mint bush, Geraldton wax and indigofera. That there was a yew tree—*not* cut into peacock or any such absurd shape—a holly bush, a flowering gum or two, and the most religious looking of all trees—the lemon scented gum beneath whose half shade revelled some azaleas. A rockery, too, in the sun's full glare, filled with succulent and spiny things that few could rightly name. And, inside, behind the wide curtained windows were cool spacious rooms with books everywhere and pictures, and good taste and gracious living.... Well, perhaps no boy could quite see all these things, but they were there for sensitive deduction.

"This morning, boys, we shall have spread before us a grand feast—nothing less than *Old China.*"

"Holy Moses, and stone the bloody crows, what's the old bastard saying?"

That was Johnson in the back row, quite loud, and not to anyone in particular. Johnson was the class humorist, a cherubic looking youth with

great unhidden powers of acting. Eagleson, in the next row, took it upon himself to answer what was really a rhetorical question: "Aw, he's opening his Lamb—something about Old China. Or an old Chinaman."

Johnson saw fit to seize on Lamb; in a bright conversational tone, "Lamb is it? Unmitigated blush from beginning to end."

"Look out, he'll hear you," warned Thimble, surnamed the Maggot as a compliment to his diminutive size, and not so reasonably on account of a large ingredient of low cunning in his make-up.

"Fiddlesticks!" replied Johnson in louder key—just to show. "The poor old bastard's as deaf as a post, and getting more so every day."

A thrill of real delight went through 4B. The dear fellows!

And so the lesson proceeded. It was more than a lesson—a zestful meandering by the pleasant river Lea (hence the presence of *Compleat Angler*); the excited homecoming with a print of Leonardo (hence *The Merchant of Venice*); the triumph of that dusty Beaumont and Fletcher (hence the *Long*); the wild scramble to the rough-and-ready top shelf of the theatre; the luxury of a dish of early peas—and on and on, from the quiet humour of Chinese mandarins and artists to the quieter pathos of youth turning into age, and the reflection that the days that are gone are indeed gone for ever.... Charles and his sister Mary (an explanation here of his persisting in calling her his cousin Bridget).... Time itself, more elusive than a half-forgotten dream, became a tangible and ponderable quantity, from the tedious minutes and leaden hours to the fleeting years ... and out came *Macbeth,* and Shakespeare's grand sadness over the inexorable passage of time and the unrelenting of fate: "Time and the hour runs through the roughest day"; "Light thickens and the crow makes wing to the rooky wood"; "Now spurs the lated traveller apace to gain the timely inn" ... On to "the last syllable of recorded time".....

He knew it all by heart, but he persisted in reading the quotations, or pretending to—such was his innate modesty—for the words belonged to a greater than he, no matter how much he had made them his own.

It was a grand piece of English teaching, deeply lasting, unforgettable. Dull would he have been of soul who was not touched by it. Duller still he who could not have guessed a little of that house and garden on the North Shore line—so clear and yet so vague—with the quaint old gentleman and his two absurdly ancient sisters. One or other of them, as like as not, speaking into a long, flexible tube—detached from the vacuum cleaner—what time the old gentleman had the other end glued to his ear.

The staff had for long been giving Mr. Beresford good advice about his deafness. How foolish it was to put up with it when it was so easy to get rid of it. Had he seen a specialist now about it? Wax! That's what it was—hadn't he thought of having his ears syringed out?... Look at the Head—deaf as a politician to the mournful cries of the old-age pensioners—and see what he had done about it? Simply installed upon himself one of those hearing-aids. Neat, natty little things, hardly showing at all, and wonderfully effective.

The staff, as well as 4B, derived amusement out of Mr. Beresford's deafness. It said outrageous things and laughed and winked over their misinterpretation. It took sides over the gadgets put forth by rival firms. It persisted and persuaded. Even the Head came into it—rather broadly, and not too gently—intimating that a deaf teacher was for all intents and purposes more or less useless. That was from the practical and common-sense viewpoint.

No one, however strong or mulish, can stand out for ever against the reasoned and unanimous decision of his fellows. Came the day then that Mr. Beresford entered a new world with all manner of strange roarings and cracklings in his head and the almost painful exaggerations of the human voice. It was a wonderful Aid and the distress of it showed on his troubled and bewildered face. But the staff cheered and congratulated, and Mr. Beresford forced a smile and said he would no

doubt get used to it in time. Such a nifty little affair it was, too, a small pearl iridescing in his ear, an unobtrusive black cord, and a small battery hidden in a vest pocket.

He donned his M.A. gown, picked up his pile of books, and proceeded towards 4B.

What was wrong with those model boys? Such noise, such din coming from that sober room! Then he remembered his hearing-aid—his latest vanity. That was it, of course. His impulse was to pull the thing out of his ear—he was not modern enough to think of switching off the battery.

The long corridor itself was noisy enough, but the classrooms that led from it were all "attended" by now. He had been unduly delayed this morning in the staffroom and he was the last therefore to reach his class.... Teachers teaching all along that corridor. How unlovely the human voice can be, unmuffled and overamplified. Trust him to recall some apt allusion—Gulliver and the Brobdingnagian beauty, and how repulsive was the texture of her skin. Ugh!... How those teachers were roaring. As he passed by one of them bellowed "Madagascar." What an ugly word! Another, more gritting and grating, was declaiming, "In the triangle XYZ...."

4B at last and its unwonted din. At the very threshold a remark, nay an exhortation, struck like a blow. One boy to another—and the sort of thing that one gentleman does not say to another. Nowadays there are so very few things that one gentleman cannot say to another—but this, apart from the syntactical crudity of its short verbs, and the very horror of its demand, was most certainly one of them.... No, no, he hadn't heard aright. The infernal Aid was lying grossly, carrying him into a new and awful world of imagination....

And then, "Look out, here comes the silly old bastard!" This was no imagining, but the solid impact of reality.

Twenty-four pairs of eyes watched him totter to his table. Twenty-four pairs of eyes, friendly and welcoming. That was the biggest illusion of all. For no god in his anger struck down the utter-er of the words and all those who heard them unmoved.

The concerted smile of the twenty-four faded as Mr. Beresford let fall his pile of books on the table, where they scattered in confusion. In a new wonder they watched Mr. Beresford fall into his chair. Then, with a wrench and effort sit bolt up-right. But there was no soothing salutation of "Good morning, boys!" Instead there were two sniffs, not those little idiosyncratic ones, but loud and full of meaning. And the kuk-kuks followed, not the perfunctory ones so much in keeping and character, but louder and full of sorrow edged with anger.

Then still life—a tableau that lasted the whole eternity of silent seconds. The silence beat upon the hearing-aid more unbearably than any vast noise could do, nor was it broken by the sounds that drifted down the corridor. *They* were unheard, or unnoticed, across the oceans of time and space. . . .

The silly old bastard! Himself! Silly—possibly. Old—undoubtedly. But—Bastard! And this was 4B! His boys! The dear fellows! . . . It couldn't be true. And yet it was true. And that dreadful ex-hortation that one gentleman does not make to an-other—that was true too. . . .

All silence is too awful to sustain. Broken it was now by a sniff-sniff and a kuk-kuk as loud and as fateful as the first sound that broke the Original Silence. Then a drumming of fingers on the table, more terrible that it was unconsciously done. More terrible than Despair hanging itself on a hook and tapping its heels on a wooden wall.

The drumming stopped. Again the sniff-sniff and a kuk-kuk. And the twenty-four, fascinated, saw two clear, bright tears roll slowly down the stricken face.

"Boys!" in a voice they had never heard be-fore, so husky with emotion, so plumbing all the depths of sadness. "Boys!" sniff-sniff, kuk-kuk. "Boys, I would have you know," sniff-sniff, "that I"—kuk-kuk—"am as well born"—sniff-sniff—"as any one of you"—kuk-kuk.

Then, with a dignity born of an anger that only the angels feel, he gathered up his pile of books, swept his M.A. gown about him, and marched out of the room.

But the silence in 4B remained, a pondering silence and a sense of unnamed guilt. Eyes turned to each other asking the question—"What was it? What happened?" Then Thimble—who but the "Maggot" would have the ready wit to see the cause, and who so earthly as to voice it so?— "Gawd—but didn't you see! He's got one of those bloody gadgets in his ear! He heard you, Johnson!"

Well, well. Fancy a man going on like that over a harmless remark! But 4B, as the full real-ization came, would have wept—if it hadn't been for the public unmanliness of doing so.

On his way to the staff room Mr. Beresford suddenly wrenched something out of his ear and something out of his pocket and in a fury hurled them both out the window. But it was too late.

# Robert

## STANLEY ELLIN

The windows of the Sixth-Grade classroom were wide open to the June afternoon, and through them came all the sounds of the departing school: the thunder of bus motors warming up, the hiss of gravel under running feet, the voices raised in cynical fervour.

*"So we sing all hail to thee,*
*District Schoo-wull Number Three..."*

Miss Gildea flinched a little at the last high, shrill note, and pressed her fingers to her aching forehead. She was tired, more tired than she could ever recall being in her thirty-eight years of teaching, and, as she told herself, she had reason to be. It had not been a good term, not good at all, what with the size of the class, and the Principal's insistence on new methods, and then her mother's shocking death coming right in the middle of everything.

Perhaps she had been too close to her mother, Miss Gildea thought; perhaps she had been wrong, never taking into account that some day the old lady would have to pass on and leave her alone in the world. Well, thinking about it all the time didn't make it any easier. She should try to forget.

And, of course, to add to her troubles, there had been during the past few weeks this maddening business of Robert. He had been a perfectly nice boy, and then, out of a clear sky, had become impossible. Not bothersome or noisy really, but sunk into an endless daydream from which Miss Gildea had to jar him sharply a dozen times a day.

She turned her attention to Robert, who sat alone in the room at the desk immediately before hers, a thin boy with neatly combed, colorless hair bracketed between large ears; mild blue eyes in a pale face fixed solemnly on hers.

"Robert."

"Yes, Miss Gildea."

"Do you know why I told you to remain after school, Robert?"

He frowned thoughtfully at this, as if it were some lesson he was being called on for, but had failed to memorize properly.

"I suppose for being bad," he said, at last.

Miss Gildea sighed.

"No, Robert, that's not it at all. I know a bad boy when I see one, Robert, and you aren't one like that. But I do know there's something troubling you, something on your mind, and I think I can help you."

"There's nothing bothering me, Miss Gildea. Honest, there isn't."

Miss Gildea found the silver pencil thrust into her hair and tapped it in a nervous rhythm on her desk.

"Oh, come, Robert. During the last month every time I looked at you your mind was a million miles away. Now, what is it? Just making plans for a vacation, or, perhaps, some trouble with the boys?"

"I'm not having trouble with anybody, Miss Gildea."

"You don't seem to understand, Robert, that I'm not trying to punish you for anything. Your homework is good. You've managed to keep up with the class, but I do think your inattentiveness should be explained. What, for example, were you thinking this afternoon when I spoke to you directly for five minutes, and you didn't hear a word I said?"

"Nothing, Miss Gildea."

She brought the pencil down sharply on the desk. "There must have been *something*, Robert. Now, I insist that you think back, and try to explain yourself."

Looking at his impassive face she knew that somehow she herself had been put on the defensive, that if any means of graceful retreat were offered now she would gladly take it. Thirty-eight years, she thought grimly, and I'm still trying to play mother-hen to ducklings. Not that there wasn't a bright side to the picture. Thirty-eight years passed meant only two more to go before retirement, the half-salary pension, the chance to putter around the house, tend to the garden properly. The pension wouldn't buy you furs and diamonds, sure enough, but it could buy the right to enjoy your own home for the rest of your days instead of a dismal room in the Country Home for Old Ladies. Miss Gildea had visited the Country Home once, on an instructional visit, and preferred not to think about it.

"Well, Robert," she said wearily, "have you remembered what you were thinking?"

"Yes, Miss Gildea."

"What was it?"

"I'd rather not tell, Miss Gildea."

"I insist!"

"Well," Robert said gently, "I was thinking I wished you were dead, Miss Gildea. I was thinking I wished I could kill you."

Her first reaction was simply blank incomprehension. She had been standing not ten feet away when that car had skidded up on the sidewalk and crushed her mother's life from her, and Miss Gildea had neither screamed nor fainted. She had stood there dumbly, because of the very unreality of the thing. Just the way she stood in court where they explained that the man got a year in jail, but didn't have a dime to pay for the tragedy he had brought about. And now the orderly ranks of desks before her, the expanse of blackboard around her, and Robert's face in the midst of it all were no more real. She found herself rising from her chair, walking toward Robert, who shrank back, his eyes wide and panicky, his elbow half lifted as if to ward off a blow.

"Do you understand what you've just said?" Miss Gildea demanded hoarsely.

"No, Miss Gildea! Honest, I didn't mean anything."

She shook her head unbelievingly. "Whatever made you say it? Whatever in the world could make a boy say a thing like that, such a wicked, terrible thing!"

"You wanted to know! You kept asking me!"

The sight of that protective elbow raised against her cut as deep as the incredible words had.

"Put that arm down!" Miss Gildea said shrilly, and then struggled to get her voice under control. "In all my years I've never struck a child, and I don't intend to start now!"

Robert dropped his arm and clasped his hands together on his desk, and Miss Gildea, looking at the pinched white knuckles, realized with surprise that her own hands were shaking uncontrollably. "But if you think this little matter ends here, young-feller-me-lad," she said, "you've got another thought coming. You get your things together, and we're marching right up to Mr. Harkness. He'll be very much interested in all this."

Mr. Harkness was the principal. He had arrived only the term before, and but for his taste in eyeglasses (the large, black-rimmed kind which, Miss Gildea privately thought, looked actorish) and his predilection for the phrase "modern pedagogical methods" was, in her opinion, a rather engaging young man.

He looked at Robert's frightened face and then at Miss Gildea's pursed lips. "Well," he said pleasantly, "what seems to be the trouble here?"

"That," said Miss Gildea, "is something I think Robert should tell you about."

She placed a hand on Robert's shoulder, but he pulled away and backed slowly toward Mr. Harkness, his breath coming in loud, shuddering sobs, his eyes riveted on Miss Gildea as if she were the only thing in the room beside himself. Mr. Harkness put an arm around Robert and frowned at Miss Gildea.

"Now, what's behind all this, Miss Gildea? The boy seems frightened to death."

Miss Gildea found herself sick of it all, anxious to get out of the room, away from Robert. "That's enough, Robert," she commanded. "Just tell Mr. Harkness exactly what happened."

"I said the boy was frightened to death, Miss Gildea," Mr. Harkness said brusquely. "We'll talk about it as soon as he understands we're his friends. Won't we, Robert?"

Robert shook his head vehemently. "I didn't do anything bad! Miss Gildea *said* I didn't do anything bad!"

"Well then!" said Mr. Harkness triumphantly. "There's nothing to be afraid of, is there?"

Robert shook his head again. "She said I had to stay in after school."

Mr. Harkness glanced sharply at Miss Gildea. "I suppose he missed the morning bus, is that it? And after I said in a directive that the staff was to make allowances..."

"Robert doesn't use a bus," Miss Gildea protested. "Perhaps I'd better explain all this, Mr. Harkness. You see..."

"I think Robert's doing very well," Mr. Harkness said, and tightened his arm around Robert, who nodded shakily.

"She kept me in," he said, "and then when we were alone she came up close to me and she said, 'I know what you're thinking. You're thinking you'd like to see me dead! You're thinking you'd like to kill me, aren't you?'"

Robert's voice had dropped to an eerie whisper that bound Miss Gildea like a spell. It was broken only when she saw the expression on Mr. Harkness's face.

"Why, that's a lie!" she cried. "That's the most dreadful lie I ever heard any boy dare—"

Mr. Harkness cut in abruptly. "Miss Gildea! I *insist* you let the boy finish what he has to say."

Miss Gildea's voice fluttered. "It seems to me, Mr. Harkness, that he has been allowed to say quite enough already!"

"Has he?" Mr. Harkness asked.

"Robert has been inattentive lately, especially so this afternoon. After class I asked him what he had been thinking about and he dared to say he was thinking how he wished I were dead! How he wanted to kill me!"

"Robert said that?"

"In almost those exact words. And I can tell you, Mr. Harkness, that I was shocked, terribly shocked, especially since Robert always seemed like such a nice boy."

"His record...?"

"His record is quite good. It's just..."

"And his social conduct?" asked Mr. Harkness in the same level voice.

"As far as I know, he gets along with the other children well enough."

"But for some reason," persisted Mr. Harkness, "you found him annoying you."

Robert raised his voice. "I didn't! Miss Gildea said I didn't do anything bad. And I always liked her. I like her better than *any* teacher!"

Miss Gildea fumbled blindly in her hair for the silver pencil, and failed to find it. She looked around the floor distractedly.

"Yes?" said Mr. Harkness.

"My pencil," said Miss Gildea on the verge of tears. "It's gone."

"Surely, Miss Gildea," said Mr. Harkness in a tone of mild exasperation. "This is not quite the moment..."

"It was very valuable," Miss Gildea tried to explain hopelessly. "It was my mother's." In the face of Mr. Harkness's stony surveillance she knew she must look a complete mess. Hems crooked, nose red, hair all dishevelled. "I'm all upset, Mr. Harkness. It's been a long term and now all this right at the end of it. I don't know what to say."

Mr. Harkness's face fell into sympathetic lines.

"That's quite all right, Miss Gildea. I know how you feel. Now, if you want to leave, I think Robert and I should have a long friendly talk."

"If you don't mind..."

"No, no," Mr. Harkness said heartily. "As a matter of fact, I think that would be the best thing all around."

After he had seen her out, he closed the door abruptly behind her, and Miss Gildea walked heavily up the stairway and down the corridor to the Sixth-Grade room. The silver pencil was there on the floor at Robert's desk, and she picked it up and carefully polished it with her handkerchief. Then she sat down at her desk with the handkerchief to her nose and wept soundlessly for ten minutes.

That night, when the bitter taste of humiliation had grown faint enough to permit it, Miss Gildea reviewed the episode with all the honesty at her command. Honesty with oneself had always been a major point in her credo, had, in fact, been passed on through succeeding classes during the required lesson on The Duties of an American Citizen, when Miss Gildea, to sum up the lesson, would recite: "This above all: To thine own self be true..." while thumping her fist on her desk as an accompaniment to each syllable.

*Hamlet,* of course, was not in the syllabus of the Sixth Grade, whose reactions over the years never deviated from a mixed bewilderment and indifference. But Miss Gildea, after some prodding of the better minds into a discussion of the lines, would rest content with the knowledge that she had sown good seed on what, she prayed, was fertile ground.

Reviewing the case of Robert now, with her emotions under control, she came to the unhappy conclusion that it was she who had committed the injustice. The child had been ordered to stay after school, something that to him could mean only a punishment. He had been ordered to disclose some shadowy, childlike thoughts that had drifted through his mind hours before, and, unable to do so, either had to make up something out of whole cloth, or blurt out the immediate thought in his immature mind.

It was hardly unusual, reflected Miss Gildea sadly, for a child badgered by a teacher to think what Robert had; she could well remember her own feelings toward a certain pompadoured harridan who still haunted her dreams. And the only conclusion to be drawn, unpleasant though it was, was that Robert, and not she, had truly put into practice those beautiful words from Shakespeare.

It was this, as well as the sight of his pale accusing face before her while she led the class through the morning session next day, which prompted her to put Robert in charge of refilling the water pitcher during recess. The duties of the water pitcher monitor were to leave the playground a little before the rest of the class and clean and refill the pitcher on her desk, but since the task was regarded as an honour by the class, her gesture, Miss Gildea felt with some self-approval, carried exactly the right note of conciliation.

She was erasing the blackboard at the front of the room near the end of the recess when she heard Robert approaching her desk, but much as she wanted to she could not summon up courage enough to turn and face him. As if, she thought, he were the teacher, and I were afraid of him. And she could feel her cheeks grow warm at the thought.

He re-entered the room on the sound of the bell that marked the end of recess, and this time Miss Gildea plopped the eraser firmly into its place beneath the blackboard and turned to look at him. "Thank you very much, Robert," she said as he set the pitcher down and neatly capped it with her drinking glass.

"You're welcome, Miss Gildea," Robert said politely. He drew a handkerchief from his pocket, wiped his hands with it, then smiled gently at Miss Gildea. "I bet you think I put poison or something into this water," he said gravely, "but I wouldn't do anything like that, Miss Gildea. Honest, I wouldn't."

Miss Gildea gasped, then reached out a hand toward Robert's shoulder. She withdrew it hastily when he shrank away with the familiar panicky look in his eyes.

"Why did you say that, Robert?" Miss Gildea demanded in a terrible voice. "That was plain impudence, wasn't it? You thought you were being smart, didn't you?"

At that moment the rest of the class surged noisily into the room, but Miss Gildea froze them into silence with a commanding wave of the hand. Out of the corner of her eye she noted the cluster of shocked and righteous faces allied with her in condemnation, and she felt a quick little sense of triumph in her position.

"I was talking to you, Robert," she said. "What do you have to say for yourself?"

Robert took another step backward and almost tumbled over a schoolbag left carelessly in the aisle. He caught himself, then stood there helplessly, his eyes never leaving Miss Gildea's.

"Well, Robert!"

He shook his head wildly. "I didn't do it!" he cried. "I didn't put anything in your water, Miss Gildea! I told you I didn't!"

Without looking, Miss Gildea knew that the cluster of accusing faces had swung toward her now, felt her triumph turn to a sick bewilderment inside her. It was as if Robert, with his teary eyes and pale, frightened face and too large ears, had turned into a strange jellylike creature that could not be pinned down and put in its place. As if he were retreating further and further down some dark, twisting path, and leading her on with him. And, she thought desperately, she had to pull herself free before she did something dreadful, something unforgivable.

She couldn't take the boy to Mr. Harkness again. Not only did the memory of that scene in his office the day before make her shudder, but a repeated visit would be an admission that after thirty-eight years of teaching she was not up to the mark as a disciplinarian.

But for her sake, if for nothing else, Robert had to be put in his place. With a gesture, Miss Gildea ordered the rest of the class to their seats and turned to Robert, who remained standing.

"Robert," said Miss Gildea, "I want an apology for what has just happened."

"I'm sorry, Miss Gildea," Robert said, and it looked as if his eyes would be brimming with tears in another moment.

Miss Gildea hardened her heart to this. "*I apologize, Miss Gildea, and it will not happen again,*" she prompted.

Miraculously, Robert contained his tears. "I apologize, Miss Gildea, and it will not happen again," he muttered and dropped limply into his seat.

"Well!" said Miss Gildea, drawing a deep breath as she looked around at the hushed class. "Perhaps that will be a lesson to us all."

The classroom work did not go well after that, but, as Miss Gildea told herself, there were only a few days left to the end of term, and after that, praise be, there was the garden, the comfortable front porch of the old house to share with neighbors in the summer evenings, and then next term a new set of faces in the classroom, with Robert's not among them.

Later, closing the windows of the room after the class had left, Miss Gildea was brought up short by the sight of a large group gathered on the sidewalk near the parked buses. It was Robert, she saw, surrounded by most of the Sixth Grade, and obviously the centre of interest. He was nodding emphatically when she put her face to the window, and she drew back quickly at the sight, moved by some queer sense of guilt.

*Only a child,* she assured herself, *he's only a child,* but that thought did not in any way dissolve the anger against him that stuck like a lump in her throat.

That was on Thursday. By Tuesday of the next week, the final week of the term, Miss Gildea was acutely conscious of the oppressive atmosphere lying over the classroom. Ordinarily, the awareness of impending vacation acted on the class like a violent agent dropped into some inert liquid. There would be ferment and seething beneath the surface, manifested by uncontrollable giggling and whispering and this would grow more and more turbulent until all restraint and discipline was swept away in the general upheaval of excitement and good spirits.

That, Miss Gildea thought, was the way it always had been, but it was strangely different now. The Sixth Grade, down to the most irrepressible spirits in it, acted as if it had been turned to a set of robots before her startled eyes. Hands tightly clasped on desks, eyes turned toward her with an almost frightening intensity, the class responded to her mildest requests as if they were shouted commands. And when she walked down the aisles between them, one and all seemed to have adopted Robert's manner of shrinking away fearfully at her approach.

Miss Gildea did not like to think of what all this might mean, but valiantly forced herself to do so. Can it mean, she asked herself, that all think as Robert does, are choosing this way of showing it? And, if they knew how cruel it was, would they do it?

Other teachers, Miss Gildea knew, sometimes took problems such as this to the Teacher's Room, where they could be studied and answered by those who saw them in an objective light. It might be that the curious state of the Sixth Grade was being duplicated in other classes. Perhaps she herself was imagining the whole thing, or, frightening thought, looking back, as people will when they grow old, on the sort of past that never really did exist. Why, in that case—and Miss Gildea had to laugh at herself with a faint merriment—she would just find herself reminiscing about her thirty-eight years of teaching to some bored young women who didn't have the fraction of experience she did.

But underneath the current of these thoughts, Miss Gildea knew there was one honest reason for not going to the Teachers' Room this last week of the term. She had received no gifts, not one. And the spoils from each grade heaped high in a series of pyramids against the wall. The boxes of fractured cookies, the clumsily wrapped jars of preserves, the scarves, the stockings, the handkerchiefs, infinite, endless boxes of handkerchiefs, all were there to mark the triumph of each teacher. And Miss Gildea, who in all her years at District School Number Three had been blushingly proud of the way her pyramid was highest at the end of each term, had not yet received a single gift from the Sixth Grade class.

After the class was dismissed that afternoon, the spell was broken. Only a few of her pupils still loitered in the hallway near the door, Miss Gildea noticed, but Robert remained in his seat. Then, as she gathered together her belongings, Robert approached her with a box outheld in his hand. It was, from its shape, a box of candy, and, as Miss Gildea could tell from the wrapping, expensive candy. Automatically, she reached a hand out, then stopped herself short. He'll never make up to me for what he's done, she told herself furiously; I'll never let him.

"Yes, Robert?" she said coolly.

"It's a present for you, Miss Gildea," Robert said, and then, as Miss Gildea watched in fascination, he began to strip the wrappings from it. He laid the paper neatly on the desk and lifted the cover of the box to display the chocolates within. "My mother said that's the biggest box they had," he said wistfully. "Don't you even want them, Miss Gildea?"

Miss Gildea weakened despite herself. "Did you think I would, after what's happened, Robert?" she asked.

Robert reflected a moment, "Well," he said at last, "if you want me to, I'll eat one right in front of you, Miss Gildea."

Miss Gildea recoiled as if at a faraway warning. *Don't let him say any more,* something inside her cried; *he's only playing a trick, another horrible trick,* and then she was saying, "Why would I want you to do that, Robert?"

"So you'll see they're not poison or anything, Miss Gildea," Robert said. "Then you'll believe it, won't you, Miss Gildea?"

She had been prepared. Even before he said the words, she had felt her body drawing itself tighter and tighter against what she knew was coming. But the sound of the words themselves only served to release her like a spring coiled too tightly.

"You little monster!" sobbed Miss Gildea and struck wildly at the proffered box which flew almost to the far wall, while chocolates cascaded stickily around the room. "How dare you!" she cried. "How dare you!" and her small bony fists beat at Robert's cowering shoulders and back as he tried to retreat.

He half turned in the aisle, slipped on a piece of chocolate, and went down to his knees, but before he could recover himself Miss Gildea was on him again, her lips drawn back, her fists pummelling him as if they were a pair of tireless mallets. Robert has started to scream at the top of his lungs from the first blow, but it was no more than a remote buzzing in Miss Gildea's ears.

"Miss Gildea!"

That was Mr. Harkness's voice, she knew, and those must be Mr. Harkness's hands which pulled her away so roughly that she had to keep herself from falling by clutching at her desk. She stood there weakly, feeling the wild fluttering of her heart, feeling the sick churning of shame and anguish in her while she tried to bring the room into focus again. There was the knot of small excited faces peering through the open doorway. They must have called Mr. Harkness, and Mr. Harkness himself was listening to Robert, who talked and wept alternately, and there was a mess everywhere. Of course, thought Miss Gildea dazedly, those must be chocolate stains. Chocolate stains all over my lovely clean room.

Then Robert was gone, the faces at the door were gone, and the door itself was closed behind them. Only Mr. Harkness remained, and Miss Gildea watched him as he removed his glasses, cleaned them carefully, and then held them up at arm's length and studied them before settling them once more on his nose.

"Well, Miss Gildea," said Mr. Harkness as if he were speaking to the glasses rather than to her, "this is a serious business."

Miss Gildea nodded.

"I am sick," Mr. Harkness said quietly, "really sick at the thought that somewhere in this school, where I tried to introduce decent pedagogical standards, corporal punishment is still being practiced."

"That's not fair at all, Mr. Harkness," Miss Gildea said shakily. "I hit the boy, that's true, and I know I was wrong to do it, but that is the first time in all my life I raised a finger against any child. And if you knew my feelings..."

"Ah," said Mr. Harkness, "that's exactly what I would like to know, Miss Gildea." He nodded to her chair, and she sat down weakly. "Now just go ahead and explain everything as you saw it."

It was a difficult task, made even more difficult by the fact that Mr. Harkness chose to stand, facing the window. Forced to address his back this way, Miss Gildea found that she had the sensation of speaking in a vacuum, but she mustered the

facts as well as she could, presented them with strong emotion, and then sank back in the chair quite exhausted.

Mr. Harkness remained silent for a long while, then slowly turned to face Miss Gildea. "I am not a practicing psychiatrist," he said at last, "although as an educator I have, of course, taken a considerable interest in that field. But I do not think it needs a practitioner to tell what a clear-cut and obvious case I am facing here. Nor," he added sympathetically, "what a tragic one."

"It might simply be," suggested Miss Gildea, "that Robert..."

"I am not speaking about Robert," said Mr. Harkness soberly, quietly.

It took an instant for this to penetrate, and then Miss Gildea felt the blood run cold in her.

"Do you think I'm lying about all this?" she cried incredulously. "Can you possibly..."

"I am sure," Mr. Harkness replied soothingly, "that you were describing things exactly as you saw them, Miss Gildea. But—have you ever heard the phrase "persecution complex"? Do you think you could recognize the symptoms of that condition if they were presented objectively? I can, Miss Gildea. I assure you, I can."

Miss Gildea struggled to speak, but the words seemed to choke her. "No," she managed to say, "you couldn't! Because some mischievous boy chooses to make trouble..."

"Miss Gildea, no child of eleven, however mischievous, could draw the experiences Robert has described to me out of his imagination. He has discussed these experiences with me at length; now I have heard your side of the case. And the conclusions to be drawn, I must say, are practically forced on me."

The room started to slip out of focus again, and Miss Gildea frantically tried to hold it steady.

"But that means you're taking his word against mine!" she said fiercely.

"Unfortunately, Miss Gildea, not his word alone. Last weekend, a delegation of parents met the School Board and made it quite plain that they were worried because of what their children told them of your recent actions. A dozen children in your class described graphically at that meeting how you had accused them of trying to poison your drinking water, and how you had threatened them because of this. And Robert, it may interest you to know, was not even one of them.

"The School Board voted your dismissal then and there, Miss Gildea, but in view of your long years of service it was left for me to override that decision if I wished to on my sole responsibility. After this episode, however, I cannot see that I have any choice. I must do what is best."

"Dismissal?" said Miss Gildea vaguely. "But they can't. I only have two more years to go. They can't do that, Mr. Harkness; all they're trying to do is trick me out of my pension!"

"Believe me," said Mr. Harkness gently, "they're not trying to do anything of the sort, Miss Gildea. Nobody in the world is trying to hurt you. I give you my solemn word that the only thing which has entered into consideration of this case from first to last has been the welfare of the children."

The room swam in sunlight, but under it Miss Gildea's face was grey and lifeless. She reached forward to fill her glass with water, stopped short, and seemed to gather herself together with a sudden brittle determination. "I'll just have to speak to the Board myself," she said in a high breathless voice. "That's the only thing to do, go there and explain the whole thing to them!"

"That would not help," said Mr. Harkness pityingly. "Believe me, Miss Gildea, it would not."

Miss Gildea left her chair and came to him, her eyes wide and frightened. She laid a trembling hand on his arm and spoke eagerly, quickly, trying to make him understand. "You see," she said, "that means I won't get my pension. I must have two more years for that, don't you see? There's the payment on the house, the garden—no, the garden is part of the house, really—but without the pension..."

She was pulling furiously at his arm with every phrase, as if she could drag him bodily into a

comprehension of her words, but he stood unyielding and only shook his head pityingly. "You must control yourself, and its impossible..."

"No!" she cried in a strange voice. "No!"

When she pulled away he knew almost simultaneously what she intended to do, but the thought froze him to the spot, and when he moved, it was too late. He burst into the corridor through the door she had flung open, and almost threw himself down the stairway to the main hall. The door to the street was just swinging shut and he ran toward it, one hand holding the rim of his glasses, a sharp little pain digging into his side, but before he could reach the door he heard the screech of brakes, the single agonized scream, and the horrified shout of a hundred shrill voices.

He put his hand on the door, but could not find the strength to open it. A few minutes later, a cleaning woman had to sidle around him to get outside and see what all the excitement was about.

Miss Reardon, the substitute, took the Sixth Grade the next day, and, everything considered, handled it very well. The single ripple in the even current of the session came at its very start, when Miss Reardon explained her presence by referring to the "sad accident that happened to dear Miss Gildea." The mild hubbub which followed this contained several voices, notably in the back of the room, which protested plaintively, "It was *not* an accident, Miss Reardon, she ran right in front of that bus," but Miss Reardon quickly brought order to the room with a few sharp raps of her ruler, and after that, classwork was carried on in a pleasant and orderly fashion.

Robert walked home slowly that afternoon, swinging his schoolbag placidly at his side, savoring the June warmth soaking into him, the fresh green smell in the air, the memory of Miss Reardon's understanding face so often turned toward his in eager and friendly interest. His home was identical to all the others on the block, square white boxes with small lawns before them, and its only distinction was that all its blinds were drawn down. After he had closed the front door very quietly behind him, he set his schoolbag down in the hallway and went into the stuffy half-darkness of the living room.

Robert's father sat in the big armchair in his bathrobe, the way he always did, and Robert's mother was bent over him holding a glass of water.

"No!" Robert's father said. "You just want to get rid of me, but I won't let you! I know what you put into it, and I won't drink it! I'll die before I drink it!"

"Please," Robert's mother said, "please take it. I swear it's only water. I'll drink some myself if you don't believe me." But when she drank a little and then held the glass to his lips, Robert's father only tossed his head from side to side.

Robert stood there watching the scene with fascination, his lips moving in silent mimicry of the familiar words. Then he cleared his throat.

"I'm home, Mama," Robert said softly. "Can I have some milk and cookies, please?"

# CHAPTER 3

# FAMILIES

Zenna Henderson, "You Know What, Teacher?"
Abraham Rodríguez, Jr., "The Boy without a Flag"
Bernard MacLaverty, "The Exercise"
Frances Gray Patton, "The Second-Grade Mind"
Elizabeth Spencer, "The Bufords"
R. K. Narayan, "Father's Help"

The simple and much-used word *families* hides much—and each of these stories sheds light on facets of this private world. Nothing that happens in any of the stories is unimaginable or exaggerated; in fact, most seem only too familiar. The inextricable ties that bind families to teachers and schools are explored showing how impossible it is to contemplate educating students without considering these ties.

"You Know What, Teacher?" by Zenna Henderson portrays a family's crushing emotional hardships and their impact on a child and a teacher. Miss Peterson, a first-grade teacher, discovers through her student Linnet's innocent words and actions the seriousness of her family's dysfunction.

> *"You know what, teacher?" Linnet's soft little voice spoke at her elbow. "You know what my mother thinks?"*
> *..."My mother thinks my daddy is running around with another woman."*
> *Miss Peterson's startled eyes focused on Linnet's slender little face.*
> *"She does?" she asked, wondering what kind of answer you were supposed to give to a statement like that from a six-year-old.*

The story continues to chronicle the slow disintegration of Linnet's family through Miss Peterson's interactions with Linnet, culminating in a frightening conclusion.

In both "The Boy Without a Flag" by Abraham Rodríguez, Jr. and "The Exercise" by Bernard MacLaverty, adolescents struggle to come of age under difficult circumstances.

In "The Boy Without a Flag," the young man's father is a frustrated Puerto Rican nationalist full of contempt for and diatribes against anything American. The boy hopes to gain the admiration of his father by refusing to salute the American flag at school. In the confusion and chaos that follow, school authorities clash with the boy, resulting in a confrontation with his father that unsettles the boy's assumptions about his father's desires and ideas.

"The Exercise" takes place in a Catholic grammar school in Ireland. A boy's confidence in his father's infallibility is undermined by his teacher whose methods exemplify how a demanding sharp-tongued, sarcastic teacher may carelessly use his power to a student's detriment; in a few short minutes he impresses on Kevin a view of his father, his family and his social class that withers his sense of innocence.

In "The Second-Grade Mind," Frances Gray Patton explores issues surrounding the normal tensions that crop up between families and schools when children leave home for the first time to start school. The story begins as Carol Nelson insists that her son Tommy skip the first grade and start school in the second grade. She thinks he is "too smart for first grade." Tommy gets into the second grade, but his mother is convinced that his teacher, Mrs. Womble, does not have his best interests at heart, citing her own unhappy childhood memories of school and the peculiarities of Mrs. Womble's teaching style as evidence. Throughout the story Mrs. Nelson wavers between her efforts to protect her son and her emerging confidence that he'll be fine at school.

Elizabeth Spencer chronicles the struggles between a fourth-grade teacher, Miss Jackson, and a family, the Bufords. This poor, proud, headstrong family from rural Mississippi does not have much respect for formal schooling and teachers. The Bufords consider "a schoolteacher a sort of challenge. A teacher hung in their minds like the deep, softly pulsing, furry throat in the collective mind of a hound pack. They hardly thought of a teacher as human." Miss Jackson finds Dora Mae Buford to be frustrating work. One day, pushed to the breaking point, Miss Jackson loses her temper and hits Dora Mae. She has never hit a student before. Miss Jackson is more hurt and bewildered than Dora Mae. The incident sparks a climax to the story; one that seems to leave the Bufords just as bewildered as Miss Jackson.

In the parable "Father's Help," R. K. Narayan shows what happens when a young boy, Swami, tries to pit his family against his teacher, Mr. Samuel. The setting of the story is the Albert Mission School in India. Swami does not want to go to school and claims to have a headache, spinning an elaborate lie about conditions at the school to make his case for staying home more convincing. When his father decides to take action in response to Swami's story, Swami struggles to maneuver himself out of the corner he has painted himself into. The effects of lies—both on the perpetrator and possible innocent victims—weave a moral for this story about a student, a teacher, and a parent.

The stories in this chapter are about the need to consider families as the most immediate and instinctive factor in school teaching. Each story, in very different ways, captures the contradictions and fractures that abound in families: No one in school teaching can escape their influence, which is precisely what the authors intended.

# You Know What, Teacher?

## ZENNA HENDERSON

Miss Peterson looked resignedly around the school yard. Today was a running day. The children swept ceaselessly from one side of the playground to the other, running madly, sometimes being jet planes, sometimes cowboys, but mostly just running. She shifted a little as an angle of the wire fence gouged into her hip, sighed, and for the fourth time looked at her watch. Two minutes less of noon recess than the last time she had looked.

"You know what, teacher?" Linnet's soft little voice spoke at her elbow. "You know what my mother thinks?"

"What does your mother think?" asked Miss Peterson automatically as she weighed the chances of getting across the grounds to one of the boys—who was hanging head down from the iron railing above the furnace-room stairs—before he fell and broke his neck.

"My mother thinks my daddy is running around with another woman."

Miss Peterson's startled eyes focused on Linnet's slender little face.

"She does?" she asked, wondering what kind of answer you were supposed to give to a statement like that from a six-year-old.

"Yes," said Linnet; and she was swept away by another running group that left its dust to curl around Miss Peterson's ankles.

Miss Peterson passed the incident along to Miss Estes in the brief pause between loading the school buses and starting afternoon duties.

"Piquant detail, isn't it?" said Miss Estes. "It might do some of these parents good if they knew just how much of their domestic difficulties get passed on to us."

"It's a shame," said Miss Peterson. "I've thought for some time that something was wrong at home. Linnet hasn't been doing well in her work and she's all dither-brained again. She'd be in my upper group if she could ever feel secure long enough."

Rain swept the closed windows with a rustly, papery sound. Miss Peterson tapped her desk bell and blessed the slight lull that followed. Rainy days were gruesome when you had to keep the children in. They were so accustomed to playing outdoors that the infrequent rainy-day schedules always meant even more noise-making than usual. In a few minutes she would call the class to order and then have a wonderful five-minute Quiet Time before the afternoon activities began.

"Teacher, Wayne keeps breaking down what I build!" protested Henry, standing sturdily before her, his tummy pushing through the four-inch gap between his blue jeans and his T-shirt.

"Well, he knocked down my garage and he keeps taking all my spools," Wayne defended, trying to balance the sixth spool at the top of his shaky edifice.

"You got more'n I have," retorted Henry as the towering structure fell, exploding spools all over the corner.

"You both know we're supposed to share," said Miss Peterson. "We don't fight over things like that. You'd better begin to put the spools away, anyway. It's almost Put-Away Time."

"You know what, teacher?" Linnet's voice was soft by her shoulder.

"W-h-a-t, that's what," laughed Miss Peterson, hugging Linnet's fragile body against her.

Linnet considered for a moment and then smiled.

"I mean, you know what happened at our home last night?"

"No, what?" The memory of the previous report from the domestic front sobered Miss Peterson.

"My mother and my daddy had a big fight," said Linnet, "Not a hitting fight—a holler fight."

"Oh?" Miss Peterson, still holding Linnet in the circle of her arm. reached for the bell and tapped the double Put-Away signal. The clatter crescendoed as puzzles, blocks, books, spools, and scissors were all scrambled into their respective storage spots.

"Yes," persisted Linnet. "I listened. Daddy said Mother spent too much money and Mother said she spent it for food and rent and not on women and she got so mad she wouldn't sleep in the bedroom. She slept all night on the couch."

"That's too bad," said Miss Peterson, hating battling parents as she looked into Linnet's shadowed face.

"I took her one of my blankets," said Linnet. "It was cold. I took her my blue blanket."

"That was nice of you," said Miss Peterson. "Honey, would you help Lila get the doll house straightened out? It's almost Quiet Time."

"Okay, teacher." Linnet flitted away as soundlessly as she had come, one diminutive oxford trailing an untied lace.

Miss Peterson gnawed reflectively on a thumbnail.

"Parents!" she thought in exasperation. "Selfish, thoughtless, self-centered—I thank Heaven most of mine are fair-to-middling!"

For the next few months the state of affairs at Linnet's house could have been charted as exactly as the season's temperatures. When she came hollow-eyed to school to fall asleep with a crayon clutched in one hand, it was either that Daddy had come home and they'd gone to the Drive-In Theater to celebrate, or Daddy had gone away again after a long holler fight the night before.

The school year rounded the holiday season and struggled toward spring. One day the children in Group Two sat in the reading circle studying a picture in their open primers.

"How is this bus different from ours?" asked Miss Peterson.

"It's got a upstairs," said Henry. "Ours don't got—" he caught Miss Peterson's eye—"don't *have* upstairses."

"That's right," nodded Miss Peterson. "How else is it different?"

"It's yellow," said Linnet. "Ours aren't yellow."

"Our school buses are," said Henry.

"They're really orange," said Linnet. "And when we go downtown, we ride on the great big gray ones."

"Well, let's read this page to ourselves and find out what these children are going to do." said Miss Peterson.

A murmuring silence descended, during which Miss Peterson tapped fingers that pointed and admonished lips that moved. Page by page, the story was gone through. Then tomorrow's story was previewed, and the reading group was lifting chairs to carry them back to the tables.

Linnet lingered, juggling her book under one arm as she held her chair.

"You know what, teacher?" she asked. "Last night we rode on the bus a long ways."

"Downtown?" asked Miss Peterson.

"Farther than that," said Linnet. "We even had to get off our bus and get on another one."

"My!" said Miss Peterson. "You must have had fun!"

"I almost didn't get to go," said Linnet. "Mother was going to leave me with Mrs. Mason, but she couldn't. We knocked on the front door and the back door but she wasn't home."

"So you got to have a pleasant ride after all, didn't you? asked Miss Peterson.

"Mother cried," said Linnet. "All the way home."

"Oh, that's too bad." Miss Peterson's heart turned over at the desolation on Linnet's face.

"She didn't cry till we left the motel," said Linnet, lowering her chair to the floor and shifting her book. "You know what, teacher?" The lady at the motel got mixed up. She told Mother that Mrs. Luhrs was in one of her cabins."

"Oh, did you go to the motel to visit some relatives?" asked Miss Peterson.

"We went to find Daddy. The lady said Daddy wasn't there, but Mrs. Luhrs was. But how could *she* be Mrs. Luhrs when *Mother* is Mrs. Luhrs? *She* wasn't in the cabin."

"Well," said Miss Peterson, wondering, as she had frequent occasion to, how to terminate a conversation with a child unobviously.

"The money went *ding ding* in the box just like in our song," said Linnet.

"The money?"

"Yes, when we got on the bus. It went *ding ding* just like our song."

"Well, how pleasant!" cried Miss Peterson in relief. "Now you'd better get started on your writing or you won't have time for your fun-paper before lunch."

"It makes me so mad I could spit," she said later to Elsie Estes over the kerthump of the ditto machine she was cranking. The machine was spewing out pictures of slightly drunken cows, mooing at lopsided calves. She stopped and examined one of the pictures critically. "Well, they'll know what they're supposed to be—after I tell them."

Miss Peterson started the cranking again. "Why can't that mother manage to keep *something* from the child?" There's no reason to drag Linnet through the nasty mess. Maybe if they had six kids, neither one of them would have time to—Do you want any of these, Elsie?"

"Yes, I guess so," said Miss Estes. "I don't know about that. Look at my Manuelo. He's got six brothers and sisters in school and only Heaven knows how many more at home, and papa turns up *muy borracho* nearly every payday and I get a blow-by-blow account of it next morning. Then Manuelo has a new papa for a while until the old papa beats the new papa up, and then it's all bliss and beans till papa goes on another toot."

"Well, I'm kind of worried. There, I gave you forty-five, just in case. I met Mrs. Luhrs at a PTA meeting several weeks ago. She looks—well, unstable—the mousy-looking kind that gives you a feeling of smoldering dynamite—if dynamite can smolder. Poor Linnet. I see now where she picked up the habit of pressing three fingers to her mouth. But I don't like it at all. Linnet's such a sweet child—"

"You could break your heart over any number of kids," said Miss Estes. "I found out long ago we can't reform parents and it's flirting with termination of contract if we try to. Remember how worried you were over your *Mexicano-Chino* last year? Didn't do either one of you any good, did it?"

"No." Miss Peterson stacked tomorrow's work papers, criss-crossing them. "And he's in the Juvenile Home now and his father's in the insane asylum. Elsie, when my emotional storm signals go up, something's cooking. You wait and see."

Several weeks later, Linnet leaned against Miss Peterson's desk and asked, "How much more until lunch, teacher? I'm hungry."

"Not very long, Linnet. What's the matter, didn't you eat a good breakfast this morning?"

"I didn't eat *any* breakfast," said Linnet, her eyes half smiling as she awaited the expected reaction.

"No breakfast! Why, Linnet, we always eat a good breakfast. Why didn't you eat one this morning?"

"I got up too late. I almost missed the bus."

"You'd better tell your mother to get you up earlier," said Miss Peterson.

"She didn't wake up, either," said Linnet. "The doctor gave her some sleeping stuff so she won't cry at night, and she didn't hear the alarm clock. She said one morning without breakfast wouldn't hurt me. But I'm hungry."

"I should think you would be. It's only fifteen minutes till lunch time, dear. That isn't very long."

Then about a week later, Linnet came to school resplendent in a brand-new dress, carrying a huge box of crayons.

"Even a gold and a silver and a *white* one, teacher!" She was jiggling around excitedly, her newly set curls bobbing with an animation that they hadn't shown in months.

"You know what, teacher?" Daddy came home last night. I woke up and I heard him tell Mother he was through with that double-crossing bitch and he'd never go away again."

Before Miss Peterson could gather her scattered senses to question Linnet's terminology, the child was borne away by an enthusiastic mob of classmates who wanted to try out the gold and silver and white crayons and admire the new dress and the ruffled slip under it . . .

"How long do you suppose it will last?" asked Miss Estes at lunchtime over the Spanish rice at the cafeteria serving table. "The poor kid must feel like a Yo-Yo. Don't look now, but isn't that your Wayne squirtin' milk through his straw? He just made a bull's eye in my Joanie's ear. Who'll do the honors this time—you or me?"

It lasted a month.

Then Linnet crept around again in the schoolroom, not even caring when Henry took her white crayon and chewed it reflectively into a crumbled mess that he had trouble spitting into the wastebasket when discovered. Again her three trembling fingers crept up to cover a quivering mouth. Again she forgot simple words she had known for months, and again she cried before trying new ones.

One day the reading group laughed over the story of Spot dragging covers off Sally to wake her up. They all had wide-eyed stories to tell about how hard *they* were to wake up or how incredibly early they woke up by themselves. Then Miss Peterson was dismissing the group with her automatic, "Lift your chairs, don't drag them."

"You know what, teacher? That's just like Daddy and Mother this morning," said Linnet softly. "They didn't get out of bed, so I fixed my own breakfast and got ready for school, all by myself."

"My, you're getting to be a big girl, aren't you?"

"Yes. When I got up I went into their bedroom but they weren't awake. I pulled the covers up for Mother because her shoulders were cold. Her nightgown hasn't got any sleeves."

"That was thoughtful of you," said Miss Peterson. "Who combed your hair for you if she didn't wake up?"

"I did." Linnet flushed. "I can get me ready."

"You did a pretty good job," acknowledged Miss Peterson, ignoring the crooked part and the tangled back curls.

When Linnet brought up the smudged, straggly writing paper that had again replaced her former neat and legible ones, Miss Peterson wondered why this morning, when Daddy was home, Linnet's work hadn't improved.

"You know what, teacher?" Linnet was saying. "Last night Mother promised she wouldn't cry any more, not ever again. And she said Daddy won't ever go away again."

"Isn't that fine?" asked Miss Peterson. "Now you can have lots of fun together, can't you?"

Linnet turned her head away. "Daddy doesn't like me any more."

"Oh, surely he does," protested Miss Peterson. "All daddies love their little girls."

Linnet looked up at her, her shadowy eyes and pale little face expressionless, "My daddy doesn't. Mother let me take him a cup of coffee last night while she was doing the dishes. He drank it and said, 'Hell, even the coffee around here is enough to turn your stomach. Beat it, brat.' And he pushed me and I dropped the empty cup and it broke."

"But if he isn't going away any more—"

"Mother told me *that*." Linnet's eyes were full of unchildlike wisdom. "She told me lots of times before. But she didn't hear Daddy swear."

"Well, it'll be nice if your mother doesn't cry any more."

"Yes," said Linnet. "When she cries, I cry, too."

Miss Peterson watched Linnet go back to her table and start her fun-paper. Poor cherub, she thought . . .

"Do you suppose I ought to *do* something about it?" she asked Miss Estes in the cafeteria.

"Do what?" asked Miss Estes. "Call the sheriff because a father swore at his child and called her a brat?"

"You know it's more than that. An unwholesome home environment."

"What would you do?" asked Miss Estes, nibbling her square of cheese. "Take her away from them? In that case you'd have to take half the kids in the nation away from their parents. Nope, as long as she's fed and clothed and carries no visible scars, you can't invoke the law."

"Maybe I could talk with her mother."

"My, you are a neck-sticker-outer, aren't you? She'd probably spit in your eye."

"I'm awfully uneasy—"

"It's the beans. They didn't cook them long enough today."

After the buses had gone, Miss Peterson saw a lonely little figure sitting in one of the swings.

"Oh, whirtleberries!" she thought. "Who missed the bus this time?"

"Hi, teacher!"

"Why, Linnet! How did you ever come to miss the bus?"

"I didn't miss it. Mother told me not to come home on the bus today. She said someone would come after me."

"Is she busy somewhere this afternoon?" Miss Peterson dropped into the swing next to Linnet, savoring the quiet of the empty playground.

"I don't know." Linnet was opening and shutting a little blue-and-white box.

"What's that?" asked Miss Peterson.

"It's empty," Linnet's voice defended. "Mother wouldn't care. She lets me play with empty boxes. But not with medicine in them."

"That's right," said Miss Peterson. "We never play with boxes that have medicine in them."

"Mother got this at the drugstore yesterday. It had medicine in it *then*."

"Yesterday?" Miss Peterson was surprised. "But it's all gone."

"It was Mother's sleeping stuff." Linnet snapped the box shut again.

Miss Peterson was curious. "Let me see it, Linnet." She took the box and turned it over in her hand. There was only a prescription number and *Take as directed* on it.

"You know what, teacher? She put an awful lot of sugar in Daddy's coffee before I took it to him, and he doesn't like very much sugar. Maybe *that's* why he got mad last night.*"

"Could be," said Miss Peterson grimly. "Where did you get this box, Linnet?"

"It was on Mother's dresser by her coffee cup. When I went in this morning to see if they were awake, I found it. It was empty. I took her cup back to the kitchen."

Miss Peterson sat eyeing the box for a long minute. Of course it couldn't be. Children so often exaggerate and draw mistaken conclusions. Add to that an overly imaginative teacher and you could dream up some mighty weird situations. But...

"Let's play something while you're waiting," she said. "Let's play What Comes Next. You know, like we do with the picture stories in our workbooks."

"Okay, teacher!" Linnet's eyes lighted with pleasure.

"Now," said Miss Peterson. "Your mother started to wash the dishes last right. What Comes Next?"

"And I got to dry the knives and forks and spoons!" added Linnet.

"Yes. Then your mother poured your daddy's coffee. What Comes Next?"

"Oh, you missed What Comes Next!" laughed Linnet. "Mother put a lot of the sleeping stuff in Daddy's cup. She said Daddy was getting restless. *Then* she poured the coffee."

"Then you took it to your daddy?"

"Uh-uh! First I had to get Mother a hankie because she was crying. *Then* I took it to Daddy."

Miss Peterson massaged the goose bumps over each elbow.

"And then your daddy drank it." Miss Peterson's voice was flat. "What Comes Next?"

Linnet swung herself to and fro without letting her feet move.

"I don't know," she said, her face averted.

"You said you dropped the cup—" half-questioned Miss Peterson, sensing the withdrawal.

"Yes—yes, I dropped the cup when Daddy got mad and pushed me."

"Yes," said Miss Peterson, knowing Linnet was deliberately forgetting. The two sat in silence a while, then Miss Peterson took up the thread again.

"When it got dark, you got ready for bed and your mother and daddy said good night."

"Not Daddy," said Linnet. "He went to bed before I did last night. He yawned and yawned and went to bed. And then I went to bed and Mother woke me up and hugged me and told me she wouldn't ever cry again and that Daddy wouldn't ever leave her again. And then—and then—" Linnet's forehead creased and her three grubby little fingers came up to her soft, dismayed mouth. "Oh, teacher! You know what? She gave me a note to give to you and I wasn't even absent yesterday!"

"Where is it?" Miss Peterson felt her innards sinking into some endless nothingness. "Did you lose it?"

"No," cried Linnet triumphantly. "She put it in my shoe so I wouldn't."

She pulled off the scuffed little oxford and fished inside it. Finally she came up with two grimy pieces of paper.

"Oh!" she was shocked. "It came in two. Is it spoiled?"

"No," said Miss Peterson, taking the two pieces and fitting the folds together. "No, I think I'll be able to read it."

She sat in the swaying swing, watching vagrant papers rise and circle in a sudden whirlwind and then drift lazily to the ground again. And she wished with all her heart that she didn't have to read the note.

Then conscious of Linnet's eyes upon her, she unfolded the halves of paper

> *Please don't let Linnet ride the bus home.*
> *Call AR 2-9276 when school is over. Ask them to keep her for a day or two until her grandmother comes. Thank you,*
>
> *Linnell Luhrs*

Miss Peterson tasted the phone number again with silently moving lips. It tasted of her little Mexicano-Chino—the Juvenile Home.

"What does it say, teacher?" asked Linnet.

"It says for you not to go home on the bus," said Miss Peterson, her thumbnail straightening out a curl of the paper. "You're to wait."

She looked down at the cramped, close-written line that slanted sharply below the signature.

> *God forgive me. I couldn't let him go away again.*

"Well," Miss Peterson stood up, feeling old and tired. "I have to go to the office and make a phone call. You stay here and play. Remember, don't go away. Don't move away from here."

"I won't," Linnet promised. "You know what, teacher?"

Miss Peterson looked down into Linnet's dark eyes. "No, what?"

"It's kinda lonesome here, all alone," said Linnet.

"Yes, it is, dear," said Miss Peterson, blinking against the sting in her eyes. "It is kinda lonesome, all alone."

# The Boy without a Flag

## ABRAHAM RODRÍGUEZ, JR.

Swirls of dust danced in the beams of sunlight that came through the tall windows, the buzz of voices resounding in the stuffy auditorium. Mr. Ríos stood by our Miss Colón, hovering as if waiting to catch her if she fell. His pale mouse features looked solemnly dutiful. He was a versatile man, doubling as English teacher and gym coach. He was only there because of Miss Colón's legs. She was wearing neon pink nylons. Our favorite.

We tossed suspicious looks at the two of them. Miss Colón would smirk at Edwin and me, saying, "Hey, face front," but Mr. Ríos would glare. I think he knew that we knew what he was after. We knew, because on Fridays, during our free period when we'd get to play records and eat stale pretzel sticks, we would see her way in the back by the tall windows, sitting up on a radiator like a schoolgirl. There would be a strange pinkness on her high cheekbones, and there was Mr. Ríos, sitting beside her, playing with her hand. Her face, so thin and girlish, would blush. From then on, her eyes, very close together like a cartoon rendition of a beaver's, would avoid us.

Miss Colón was hardly discreet about her affairs. Edwin had first tipped me off about her love life after one of his lunchtime jaunts through the empty hallways. He would chase girls and toss wet bathroom napkins into classrooms where kids in the lower grades sat, trapped. He claimed to have seen Miss Colón slip into a steward's closet with Mr. Ríos and to have heard all manner of sounds through the thick wooden door, which was locked (he tried it). He had told half the class before the day was out, the boys sniggering behind grimy hands, the girls shocked because Miss Colón was married, so married that she even brought the poor unfortunate in one morning as a kind of show-and-tell guest. He was an untidy dark-skinned Puerto Rican type in a colorful dashiki. He carried a paper bag that smelled like glue. His eyes seemed sleepy, his Afro an uncombed

Brillo pad. He talked about protest marches, the sixties, the importance of an education. Then he embarrassed Miss Colón greatly by disappearing into the coat closet and falling asleep there. The girls, remembering him, softened their attitude toward her indiscretions, defending her violently. "Face it," one of them blurted out when Edwin began a new series of Miss Colón tales, "she married a bum and needs to find true love."

"She's a slut, and I'm gonna draw a comic book about her," Edwin said, hushing when she walked in through the door. That afternoon, he showed me the first sketches of what would later become a very popular comic book entitled "Slut At The Head Of The Class." Edwin could draw really well, but his stories were terrible, so I volunteered to do the writing. In no time at all, we had three issues circulating under desks and hidden in notebooks all over the school. Edwin secretly ran off close to a hundred copies on a copy machine in the main office after school. It always amazed me how copies of our comic kept popping up in the unlikeliest places. I saw them on radiators in the auditorium, on benches in the gym, tacked up on bulletin boards. There were even some in the teachers' lounge, which I spotted one day while running an errand for Miss Colón. Seeing it, however, in the hands of Miss Martí, the pig-faced assistant principal, nearly made me puke up my lunch. Good thing our names weren't on it.

It was a miracle no one snitched on us during the ensuing investigation, since only a blind fool couldn't see our involvement in the thing. No bloody purge followed, but there was enough fear in both of us to kill the desire to continue our publishing venture. Miss Martí, a woman with a battlefield face and constant odor of Chiclets, made a forceful threat about finding the culprits while holding up the second issue, the one with the hand-colored cover. No one moved. The auditori-

83

um grew silent. We meditated on the sound of a small plane flying by, its engines rattling the windows. I think we wished we were on it.

It was in the auditorium that the trouble first began. We had all settled into our seats, fidgeting like tiny burrowing animals, when there was a general call for quiet. Miss Martí, up on stage, had a stare that could make any squirming fool sweat. She was a gruff, nasty woman who never smiled without seeming sadistic.

Mr. Ríos was at his spot beside Miss Colón, his hands clasped behind his back as if he needed to restrain them. He seemed to whisper to her. Soft, mushy things. Edwin would watch them from his seat beside me, giving me the details, his shiny face looking worried. He always seemed sweaty, his fingers kind of damp.

"I toldju, I saw um holdin hands," he said. "An now lookit him, he's whispering sweet shits inta huh ear."

He quieted down when he noticed Miss Martí's evil eye sweeping over us like a prison-camp searchlight. There was silence. In her best military bark, Miss Martí ordered everyone to stand. Two lone, pathetic kids, dragooned by some unseen force, slowly came down the center aisle, each bearing a huge flag on a thick wooden pole. All I could make out was that great star-spangled unfurling, twitching thing that looked like it would fall as it approached over all those bored young heads. The Puerto Rican flag walked beside it, looking smaller and less confident. It clung to its pole.

"The Pledge," Miss Martí roared, putting her hand over the spot where her heart was rumored to be.

That's when I heard my father talking.

He was sitting on his bed, yelling about Chile, about what the CIA had done there. I was standing opposite him in my dingy Pro Keds. I knew about politics. I was eleven when I read William Shirer's book on Hitler. I was ready.

"All this country does is abuse Hispanic nations," my father said, turning a page of his *Post,* "tie them down, make them dependent. It says de-

mocracy with one hand while it protects and feeds fascist dictatorships with the other." His eyes blazed with a strange fire. I sat on the bed, on part of his *Post,* transfixed by his oratorical mastery. He had mentioned political things before, but not like this, not with such fiery conviction. I thought maybe it had to do with my reading Shirer. Maybe he had seen me reading that fat book and figured I was ready for real politics.

Using the knowledge I gained from the book, I defended the Americans. What fascism was he talking about, anyway? I knew we had stopped Hitler. That was a big deal, something to be proud of.

"Come out of fairy-tale land," he said scornfully. "Do you know what imperialism is?"

I didn't really, no.

"Well, why don't you read about that? Why don't you read about Juan Bosch and Allende, men who died fighting imperialism? They stood up against American big business. You should read about that instead of this crap about Hitler."

"But I like reading about Hitler," I said, feeling a little spurned. I didn't even mention that my fascination with Adolf led to my writing a biography of him, a book report one hundred and fifty pages long. It got an A-plus. Miss Colón stapled it to the bulletin board right outside the classroom, where it was promptly stolen.

"So, what makes you want to be a writer?" Miss Colón asked me quietly one day, when Edwin and I, always the helpful ones, volunteered to assist her in getting the classroom spiffed up for a Halloween party.

"I don't know. I guess my father," I replied, fiddling with plastic pumpkins self-consciously while images of my father began parading through my mind.

When I think back to my earliest image of my father, it is one of him sitting behind a huge rented typewriter, his fingers clacking away. He was a frustrated poet, radio announcer, and even stage actor. He had sent for diplomas from fly-by-night companies. He took acting lessons, went into broadcasting, even ended up on the ground floor of what is now Spanish radio, but his family talked him out of all of it. "You should find yourself real work, something substantial," they said, so he did. He dropped all those dreams that were never encouraged by anyone else and got a job at a Nedick's on Third Avenue. My pop the counterman.

Despite that, he kept writing. He recited his poetry into a huge reel-to-reel tape deck that he had, then he'd play it back and sit like a critic, brow furrowed, fingers stroking his lips. He would record strange sounds and play them back to me at outrageous speeds, until I believed that there were tiny people living inside the machine. I used to stand by him and watch him type, his black pompadour spilling over his forehead. There was energy pulsating all around him, and I wanted a part of it.

I was five years old when I first sat in his chair at the kitchen table and began pushing down keys, watching the letters magically appear on the page. I was entranced. My fascination with the typewriter began at that point. By the time I was ten, I was writing war stories, tales of pain and pathos culled from the piles of comic books I devoured. I wrote unreadable novels. With illustrations. My father wasn't impressed. I guess he was hard to impress. My terrific grades did not faze him, nor the fact that I was reading books as fat as milk crates. My unreadable novels piled up. I brought them to him at night to see if he would read them, but after a week of waiting I found them thrown in the bedroom closet, unread. I felt hurt and rejected, despite my mother's kind words. "He's just too busy to read them," she said to me one night when I mentioned it to her. He never brought them up even when I quietly took them out of the closet one day or when he'd see me furiously hammering on one of his rented machines. I would tell him I wanted to be a writer, and he would smile sadly and pat my head, without a word.

"You have to find something serious to do with your life," he told me one night, after I had shown him my first play, eighty pages long. What was it I had read that got me into writing a play? Was it Arthur Miller? Oscar Wilde? I don't remember, but I recall my determination to write a truly marvelous play about combat because there didn't seem to be any around.

"This is fun as a hobby," my father said, "but you can't get serious about this." His demeanor spoke volumes, but I couldn't stop writing. Novels, I called them, starting a new one every three days. The world was a blank page waiting for my words to recreate it, while the real world remained cold and lonely. My schoolmates didn't understand any of it, and because of the fat books I carried around, I was held in some fear. After all, what kid in his right mind would read a book if it wasn't assigned? I was sick of kids coming up to me and saying, "Gaw, lookit tha fat book. Ya teacha make ya read tha?" (No, I'm just reading it.) The kids would look at me as if I had just crawled out of a sewer. "Ya crazy, man." My father seemed to share that opinion. Only my teachers understood and encouraged my reading, but my father seemed to want something else from me.

Now, he treated me like an idiot for not knowing what imperialism was. He berated my books and one night handed me a copy of a book about Albizu Campos, the Puerto Rican revolutionary. I read it through in two sittings.

"Some of it seems true," I said.

"Some of it?" my father asked incredulously. "After what they did to him, you can sit there and act like a Yankee flag-waver?"

I watched that Yankee flag making its way up to the stage over indifferent heads, my father's scowling face haunting me, his words resounding in my head.

"Let me tell you something," my father sneered. "In school, all they do is talk about George Washington, right? The first president? The father of democracy? Well, he had slaves. We had our own Washington, and ours had real teeth."

As Old Glory reached the stage, a general clatter ensued.

"We had our own revolution," my father said, "and the United States crushed it with the flick of a pinkie."

Miss Martí barked her royal command. Everyone rose up to salute the flag.

Except me. I didn't get up. I sat in my creaking seat, hands on my knees. A girl behind me tapped me on the back. "Come on, stupid, get up." There was a trace of concern in her voice. I didn't move.

Miss Colón appeared. She leaned over, shaking me gently. "Are you sick? Are you okay?" Her soft hair fell over my neck like a blanket.

"No," I replied.

"What's wrong?" she asked, her face growing stern. I was beginning to feel claustrophobic, what with everyone standing all around me, bodies like walls. My friend Edwin, hand on his heart, watched from the corner of his eye. He almost looked envious, as if he wished he had thought of it. Murmuring voices around me began reciting the Pledge while Mr. Ríos appeared, commandingly grabbing me by the shoulder and pulling me out of my seat into the aisle. Miss Colón was beside him, looking a little apprehensive.

"What is wrong with you?" he asked angrily. "You know you're supposed to stand up for the Pledge! Are you religious?"

"No," I said.

"Then what?"

"I'm not saluting that flag," I said.

"What?"

"I said, I'm not saluting that flag."

"Why the . . .?" He calmed himself; a look of concern flashed over Miss Colón's face. "Why not?"

"Because I'm Puerto Rican. I ain't no American. And I'm not no Yankee flag-waver."

"You're supposed to salute the flag," he said angrily, shoving one of his fat fingers in my face. "You're not supposed to make up your own mind about it. You're supposed to do as you are told."

"I thought I was free," I said, looking at him and at Miss Colón.

"You are," Miss Colón said feebly. "That's why you should salute the flag."

"But shouldn't I do what I feel is right?"

"You should do what you are told!" Mr. Ríos yelled into my face. "I'm not playing games with you, mister. You hear that music? That's the anthem. Now you go stand over there and put your hand over your heart." He made as if to grab my hand, but I pulled away.

"No!" I said sharply. "I'm not saluting that crummy flag! And you can't make me, either. There's nothing you can do about it."

"Oh yeah?" Mr. Ríos roared. "We'll see about that!"

"Have you gone crazy?" Miss Colón asked as he led me away by the arm, down the hallway, where I could still hear the strains of the anthem. He walked me briskly into the principal's office and stuck me in a corner.

"You stand there for the rest of the day and see how you feel about it," he said viciously. "Don't you even think of moving from that spot!"

I stood there for close to two hours or so. The principal came and went, not even saying hi or hey or anything, as if finding kids in the corners of his office was a common occurrence. I could hear him talking on the phone, scribbling on pads, talking to his secretary. At one point I heard Mr. Ríos outside in the main office.

"Some smart-ass. I stuck him in the corner. Thinks he can pull that shit. The kid's got no respect, man. I should get the chance to teach him some."

"Children today have no respect," I heard Miss Martí's reptile voice say as she approached, heels clacking like gunshots. "It has to be forced upon them."

She was in the room. She didn't say a word to the principal, who was on the phone. She walked right over to me. I could hear my heart beating in my ears as her shadow fell over me. Godzilla over Tokyo.

"Well, have you learned your lesson yet?" she asked, turning me from the wall with a finger on my shoulder. I stared at her without replying. My face burned, red hot. I hated it.

"You think you're pretty important don't you? Well, let me tell you, you're nothing. You're not worth a damn. You're just a snotty-nosed little kid with a lot of stupid ideas." Her eyes bored holes through me, searing my flesh. I felt as if I were going to cry. I fought the urge. Tears rolled down my face anyway. They made her smile, her chapped lips twisting upwards like the mouth of a lizard.

"See? You're a little baby. You don't know anything, but you'd better learn your place." She pointed a finger in my face. "You do as you're told if you don't want big trouble. Now go back to class."

Her eyes continued to stab at me. I looked past her and saw Edwin waiting by the office door for me. I walked past her, wiping my face. I could feel her eyes on me still, even as we walked up the stairs to the classroom. It was close to three already, and the skies outside the grated windows were cloudy.

"Man," Edwin said to me as we reached our floor, "I think you're crazy."

The classroom was abuzz with activity when I got there. Kids were chattering, getting their windbreakers from the closet, slamming their chairs up on their desks, filled with the euphoria of soon-home. I walked quietly over to my desk and took out my books. The other kids looked at me as if I were a ghost.

I went through the motions like a robot. When we got downstairs to the door, Miss Colón, dismissing the class, pulled me aside, her face compassionate and warm. She squeezed my hand.

"Are you okay?"

I nodded.

"That was really a crazy stunt out there. Where did you get such an idea?"

I stared at her black flats. She was wearing tan panty hose and a black miniskirt. I saw Mr. Ríos approaching with his class.

"I have to go," I said, and split, running into the frigid breezes and the silver sunshine.

At home, I lay on the floor of our living room, tapping my open notebook with the tip of my pen while the Beatles blared from my father's stereo. I felt humiliated and alone. Miss Martí's reptile face kept appearing in my notebook, her voice intoning, "Let me tell you, you're nothing." Yeah, right. Just what horrible hole did she crawl out of? Were those people really Puerto Ricans? Why should a Puerto Rican salute an American flag?

I put the question to my father, strolling into his bedroom, a tiny M-1 rifle that belonged to my G.I. Joe strapped to my thumb.

"Why?" he asked, loosening the reading glasses that were perched on his nose, his newspaper sprawled open on the bed before him, his cigarette streaming blue smoke. "Because we are owned, like cattle. And because nobody has any pride in their culture to stand up for it."

I pondered those words, feeling as if I were being encouraged, but I didn't dare tell him. I wanted to believe what I had done was a brave and noble thing, but somehow I feared his reaction. I never could impress him with my grades, or my writing. This flag thing would probably upset him. Maybe he, too, would think I was crazy, disrespectful, a "smart-ass" who didn't know his place. I feared that, feared my father saying to me, in a reptile voice, "Let me tell you, you're nothing."

I suited up my G.I. Joe for combat, slipping on his helmet, strapping on his field pack. I fixed the bayonet to his rifle, sticking it in his clutching hands so he seemed ready to fire. "A man's gotta do what a man's gotta do." Was that John Wayne? I don't know who it was, but I did what I had to do, still not telling my father. The following week, in the auditorium, I did it again. This time, everyone noticed. The whole place fell into a weird hush as Mr. Ríos screamed at me.

I ended up in my corner again, this time getting a prolonged, pensive stare from the principal before I was made to stare at the wall for two more hours. My mind zoomed past my surroundings. In one strange vision, I saw my crony Edwin climbing up Miss Colón's curvy legs, giving me every detail of what he saw.

"Why?" Miss Colón asked frantically. "This time you don't leave until you tell me why." She was holding me by the arm, masses of kids flying by, happy blurs that faded into the sunlight outside the door.

"Because I'm Puerto Rican, not American," I blurted out in a weary torrent. "That makes sense, don't it?"

"So am I," she said, "but we're in America!" She smiled. "Don't you think you could make some kind of compromise?" She tilted her head to one side and said, "Aw, c'mon," in a little-girl whisper.

"What about standing up for what you believe in? Doesn't that matter? You used to talk to us about Kent State and protesting. You said those kids died because they believed in freedom, right? Well, I feel like them now. I wanna make a stand."

She sighed with evident aggravation. She caressed my hair. For a moment, I thought she was going to kiss me. She was going to say something, but just as her pretty lips parted, I caught Mr. Ríos approaching.

"I don't wanna see him," I said, pulling away.

"No, wait," she said gently.

"He's gonna deck me," I said to her.

"No, he's not," Miss Colón said, as if challenging him, her eyes taking him in as he stood beside her.

"No, I'm not," he said. "Listen here. Miss Colón was talking to me about you, and I agree with her." He looked like a nervous little boy in front of the class, making his report. "You have a lot of guts. Still, there are rules here. I'm willing to make a deal with you. You go home and think about this. Tomorrow I'll come see you." I looked at him skeptically, and he added, "to talk."

"I'm not changing my mind," I said. Miss Colón exhaled painfully.

"If you don't, it's out of my hands." He frowned and looked at her. She shook her head, as if she were upset with him.

I re-read the book about Albizu. I didn't sleep a wink that night. I didn't tell my father a word, even though I almost burst from the effort. At night, alone in my bed, images attacked me. I saw Miss Martí and Mr. Ríos debating Albizu Campos. I saw him in a wheelchair with a flag draped over his body like a holy robe. They would not do that to me. They were bound to break me the way Albizu was broken, not by young smiling American troops bearing chocolate bars, but by conniving, double-dealing, self-serving Puerto Rican landowners and their ilk, who dared say they were the future. They spoke of dignity and democracy while teaching Puerto Ricans how to cling to the great coat of that powerful northern neighbor. Puerto Rico, the shining star, the great lap dog of the Caribbean. I saw my father, the Nationalist hero, screaming from his podium, his great oration stirring everyone around him to acts of bravery. There was a shining arrogance in his eyes as he stared out over the sea of faces mouthing his name, a sparkling audacity that invited and incited. There didn't seem to be fear anywhere in him, only the urge to rush to the attack, with his arm band and revolutionary tunic. I stared up at him, transfixed. I stood by the podium, his personal adjutant, while his voice rang through the stadium. "We are not, nor will we ever be, Yankee flagwavers!" The roar that followed drowned out the whole world.

The following day, I sat in my seat, ignoring Miss Colón as she neatly drew triangles on the board with the help of plastic stencils. She was using colored chalk, her favorite. Edwin, sitting beside me, was beaning girls with spitballs that he fired through his hollowed-out Bic pen. They didn't cry out. They simply enlisted the help of a girl named Gloria who sat a few desks behind him. She very skillfully nailed him with a thick wad of gum. It stayed in his hair until Edwin finally went running to Miss Colón. She used her huge teacher's scissors. I couldn't stand it. They all seemed trapped in a world of trivial things, while I swam in a mire of oppression. I walked through lunch as if in a trance, a prisoner on death row waiting for the heavy steps of his executioners. I watched Edwin lick at his regulation cafeteria ice cream, sandwiched between two sheets of paper. I was once like him, laughing and joking, lining up for a stickball game in the yard without a care. Now it all seemed lost to me, as if my youth had been burned out of me by a book.

Shortly after lunch, Mr. Ríos appeared. He talked to Miss Colón for a while by the door as the room filled with a bubbling murmur. Then, he motioned for me. I walked through the sudden silence as if in slow motion.

"Well," he said to me as I stood in the cool hallway, "have you thought about this?"

"Yeah," I said, once again seeing my father on the podium, his voice thundering.

"And?"

"I'm not saluting that flag."

Miss Colón fell against the door jamb as if exhausted. Exasperation passed over Mr. Ríos' rodent features.

"I thought you said you'd think about it," he thundered.

"I did. I decided I was right."

"*You* were right?" Mr. Ríos was losing his patience. I stood calmly by the wall.

"I told you," Miss Colón whispered to him.

"Listen," he said, ignoring her, "have you heard of the story of the man who had no country?"

I stared at him.

"Well? Have you?"

"No," I answered sharply; his mouse eyes almost crossed with anger at my insolence. "Some stupid fairy tale ain't gonna change my mind anyway. You're treating me like I'm stupid, and I'm not."

"Stop acting like you're some mature adult! You're not. You're just a puny kid."

"Well this puny kid still ain't gonna salute that flag."

"You were born here," Miss Colón interjected patiently, trying to calm us both down. "Don't you think you at least owe this country some respect? At least?"

"I had no choice about where I was born. And I was born poor."

"So what?" Mr. Ríos screamed. "There are plenty of poor people who respect the flag. Look around you, damnit! You see any rich people here? I'm not rich either!" He tugged on my arm. "This country takes care of Puerto Rico, don't you see that? Don't you know anything about politics?"

"Do you know what imperialism is?"

The two of them stared at each other.

"I don't believe you," Mr. Ríos murmured.

"Puerto Rico is a colony," I said, a direct quote of Albizu's. "Why I gotta respect that?"

Miss Colón stared at me with her black saucer eyes, a slight trace of a grin on her features. It encouraged me. In that one moment, I felt strong, suddenly aware of my territory and my knowledge of it. I no longer felt like a boy but some kind of soldier, my bayonet stained with the blood of my enemy. There was no doubt about it. Mr. Ríos was the enemy, and I was beating him. The more he tried to treat me like a child, the more defiant I became, his arguments falling like twisted armor. He shut his eyes and pressed the bridge of his nose.

"You're out of my hands," he said.

Miss Colón gave me a sympathetic look before she vanished into the classroom again. Mr. Ríos led me downstairs without another word. His face was completely red. I expected to be put in my corner again, but this time Mr. Ríos sat me down in the leather chair facing the principal's desk. He stepped outside, and I could hear the familiar clack-clack that could only belong to Miss Martí's reptile legs. They were talking in whispers. I expected her to come in at any moment, but the principal walked in instead. He came in quietly, holding a folder in his hand. His soft brown eyes and beard made him look compassionate, rounded cheeks making him seem friendly. His desk plate solemnly stated: Mr. Sepúlveda, PRINCIPAL. He fell into his seat rather unceremoniously, opened the folder, and crossed his hands over it.

"Well, well, well," he said softly, with a tight-lipped grin. "You've created quite a stir, young man." It sounded to me like movie dialogue.

"First of all, let me say I know about you. I have your record right here, and everything in it is very impressive. Good grades, good attitude, your teachers all have adored you. But I wonder if maybe this hasn't gone to your head? Because everything is going for you here, and you're throwing it all away."

He leaned back in his chair. "We have rules, all of us. There are rules even I must live by. People who don't obey them get disciplined. This will all go on your record, and a pretty good one you've had so far. Why ruin it? This'll follow you for life. You don't want to end up losing a good job opportunity in government or in the armed forces because as a child you indulged your imagination and refused to salute the flag? I know you can't see how childish it all is now, but you must see it, and because you're smarter than most, I'll put it to you in terms you can understand.

"To me, this is a simple case of rules and regulations. Someday, when you're older," he paused here, obviously amused by the sound of his own voice, "you can go to rallies and protest marches and express your rebellious tendencies. But right now, you are a minor, under this school's jurisdiction. That means you follow the rules, no matter what you think of them. You can join the Young Lords later."

I stared at him, overwhelmed by his huge desk, his pompous mannerisms and status. I would agree with everything, I felt, and then, the following week, I would refuse once again. I would fight him then, even though he hadn't tried to humiliate me or insult my intelligence. I would continue to fight, until I . . .

"I spoke with your father," he said.

I started. "My father?" Vague images and hopes flared through my mind briefly.

"Yes. I talked to him at length. He agrees with me that you've gotten a little out of hand."

My blood reversed direction in my veins. I felt as if I were going to collapse. I gripped the armrests of my chair. There was no way this could be true, no way at all! My father was supposed to ride in like the cavalry, not abandon me to the ene-

my! I pressed my wet eyes with my fingers. It must be a lie.

"He blames himself for your behavior," the principal said. "He's already here," Mr. Ríos said from the door, motioning my father inside. Seeing him wearing his black weather-beaten trench coat almost asphyxiated me. His eyes, red with concern, pulled at me painfully. He came over to me first while the principal rose slightly, as if greeting a head of state. There was a look of dread on my father's face as he looked at me. He seemed utterly lost.

"Mr. Sepúlveda," he said, "I never thought a thing like this could happen. My wife and I try to bring him up right. We encourage him to read and write and everything. But you know, this is a shock."

"It's not that terrible, Mr, Rodriguez. You've done very well with him, he's an intelligent boy. He just needs to learn how important obedience is."

"Yes," my father said, turning to me, "yes, you have to obey the rules. You can't do this. It's wrong." He looked at me grimly, as if working on a math problem. One of his hands caressed my head.

There were more words, in Spanish now, but I didn't hear them. I felt like I was falling down a hole. My father, my creator, renouncing his creation, repentant. Not an ounce of him seemed prepared to stand up for me, to shield me from attack. My tears made all the faces around me melt.

"So you see," the principal said to me as I rose, my father clutching me to him, "if you ever do this again, you will be hurting your father as well as yourself."

I hated myself. I wiped at my face desperately, trying not to make a spectacle of myself. I was just a kid, a tiny kid. Who in the hell did I think I was? I'd have to wait until I was older, like my father, in order to have "convictions."

"I don't want to see you in here again, okay?" the principal said sternly. I nodded dumbly, my father's arm around me as he escorted me through the front office to the door that led to the hallway, where a multitude of children's voices echoed up and down its length like tolling bells.

"Are you crazy?" my father half-whispered to me in Spanish as we stood there. "Do you know how embarrassing this all is? I didn't think you were this stupid. Don't you know anything about dignity, about respect? How could you make a spectacle of yourself? Now you make us all look stupid."

He quieted down as Mr. Ríos came over to take me back to class. My father gave me a squeeze and told me he'd see me at home. Then, I walked with a somber Mr. Ríos, who oddly wrapped an arm around me all the way back to the classroom.

"Here you go," he said softly as I entered the classroom, and everything fell quiet. I stepped in and walked to my seat without looking at anyone. My cheeks were still damp, my eyes red. I looked like I had been tortured. Edwin stared at me, then he pressed my hand under the table.

"I thought you were dead," he whispered.

Miss Colón threw me worried glances all through the remainder of the class. I wasn't paying attention. I took out my notebook, but my strength ebbed away. I just put my head on the desk and shut my eyes, reliving my father's betrayal. If what I did was so bad, why did I feel more ashamed of him than I did of myself? His words, once so rich and vibrant, now fell to the floor, leaves from a dead tree.

At the end of the class, Miss Colón ordered me to stay after school. She got Mr. Ríos to take the class down along with his, and she stayed with me in the darkened room. She shut the door on all the exuberant hallway noise and sat down on Edwin's desk, beside me, her black pumps on his seat.

"Are you okay?" she asked softly, grasping my arm. I told her everything, especially about my father's betrayal. I thought he would be the cavalry, but he was just a coward.

"Tss. Don't be so hard on your father," she said, "He's only trying to do what's best for you."

"And how's this best for me?" I asked, my voice growing hoarse with hurt.

"I know it's hard for you to understand, but he really was trying to take care of you."

I stared at the blackboard.

"He doesn't understand me," I said, wiping my eyes.

"You'll forget," she whispered.

"No, I won't. I'll remember every time I see that flag. I'll see it and think, 'My father doesn't understand me.'"

Miss Colón sighed deeply. Her fingers were warm on my head, stroking my hair. She gave me a kiss on the cheek. She walked me downstairs, pausing by the doorway. Scores of screaming, laughing kids brushed past us.

"If it's any consolation, I'm on your side," she said, squeezing my arm. I smiled at her, warmth spreading through me. "Go home and listen to the Beatles," she added with a grin.

I stepped out into the sunshine, came down the white stone steps, and stood on the sidewalk. I stared at the towering school building, white and perfect in the sun, indomitable. Across the street, the dingy row of tattered uneven tenements where I lived. I thought of my father. Her words made me feel sorry for him, but I felt sorrier for myself. I couldn't understand back then about a father's love and what a father might give to insure his son safe transit. He had already navigated treacherous waters and now couldn't have me rock the boat. I still had to learn that he had made peace with The Enemy, that The Enemy was already in us. Like the flag I must salute, we were inseparable, yet his compromise made me feel ashamed and defeated. Then I knew I had to find my own peace, away from the bondage of obedience. I had to accept that flag, and my father, someone I would love forever, even if at times to my young, feeble mind he seemed a little imperfect.

# The Exercise

## BERNARD MacLAVERTY

"We never got the chance," his mother would say to him. "It wouldn't have done me much good but your father could have bettered himself. He'd be teaching or something now instead of serving behind a bar. He could stand up with the best of them."

Now that he had started grammar school Kevin's father joined him in his work, helping him when he had the time, sometimes doing the exercises out of the text books on his own before he went to bed. He worked mainly from examples in the Maths and Langauge books or from previously corrected work of Kevin's. Often his wife took a hand out of him, saying "Do you think you'll pass your Christmas Tests?"

When he concentrated he sat hunched at the kitchen table, his non-writing hand shoved down the back of his trousers and his tongue stuck out.

"Put that thing back in your mouth," Kevin's mother would say, laughing. "You've a tongue on you like a cow."

His father smelt strongly of tobacco for he smoked both a pipe and cigarettes. When he gave Kevin money for sweets he'd say, "You'll get sixpence in my coat pocket on the bannisters."

Kevin would dig into the pocket deep down almost to his elbow and pull out a handful of coins speckled with bits of yellow and black tobacco. His father also smelt of porter, not his breath, for he never drank but from his clothes and Kevin thought it mixed nicely with his grown-up smell. He loved to smell his pyjama jacket and the shirts that he left off for washing.

Once in a while Kevin's father would come in at six o'clock, sit in his armchair and say, "Slippers."

"You're not staying in, are you?" The three boys shouted and danced around, the youngest pulling off his big boots, falling back on the floor as they came away from his feet, Kevin, the el-dest, standing on the arm of the chair to get the slippers down from the cupboard.

"Some one of you get a good shovel of coal for that fire," and they sat in the warm kitchen doing their homework, their father reading the paper or moving about doing some job that their mother had been at him to do for months. Before their bedtime he would read the younger ones a story or if there were no books in the house at the time he would choose a piece from the paper. Kevin listened with the others although he pretended to be doing something else.

But it was not one of those nights. His father stood shaving with his overcoat on, a very heavy navy overcoat, in a great hurry, his face creamed thick with white lather. Kevin knelt on the cold lino of the bathroom floor, one elbow leaning on the padded seat of the green wicker chair trying to get help with his Latin. It was one of those exercises which asked for the nominative and genitive of: an evil deed, a wise father and so on.

"What's the Latin for 'evil'?"

His father towered above him trying to get at the mirror, pointing his chin upward scraping underneath.

"Look it up at the back."

Kevin sucked the end of his pencil and fumbled through the vocabularies. His father finished shaving, humped his back and spluttered in the basin. Kevin heard him pull the plug and the final gasp as the water escaped. He groped for the towel then genuflected beside him drying his face.

"Where is it?" He looked down still drying slower and slower, meditatively until he stopped.

"I'll tell you just this once because I'm in a hurry."

Kevin stopped sucking the pencil and held it poised, ready and wrote the answers with great speed into his jotter as his father called them out.

"Is that them all?" his father asked, draping the towel over the side of the bath. He leaned forward to kiss Kevin but he lowered his head to look at something in the book. As he rushed down the stairs he shouted back over his shoulder.

"Don't ever ask me to do that again. You'll have to work them out for yourself."

He was away leaving Kevin sitting at the chair. The towel edged its way slowly down the side of the bath and fell on the floor. He got up and looked in the wash-hand basin. The bottom was covered in short black hairs, shavings. He drew a white path through them with his finger. Then he turned and went down the stairs to copy the answers in ink.

Of all the teachers in the school Waldo was the one who commanded the most respect. In his presence nobody talked, with the result that he walked the corridors in a moat of silence. Boys seeing him approach would drop their voices to a whisper and only when he was out of earshot would they speak normally again. Between classes there was always five minutes' uproar. The boys wrestled over desks, shouted, whistled, flung books while some tried to learn their nouns, eyes closed, feet tapping to the rhythm of declensions. Others put frantic finishing touches to last night's exercise. Some minutes before Waldo's punctual arrival, the class quietened. Three rows of boys, all by now strumming nouns, sat hunched and waiting.

Waldo's entrance was theatrical. He strode in with strides as long as his soutane would permit, his books clenched in his left hand and pressed tightly against his chest. With his right hand he swung the door behind him, closing it with a crash. His eyes raked the class. If, as occasionally happened, it did not close properly he did not turn from the class but backed slowly against the door snapping it shut with his behind. Two strides brought him to the rostrum. He cracked his books down with an explosion and made a swift palm upward gesture.

Waldo was very tall, his height being emphasized by the soutane, narrow and tight-fitting at the shoulders, sweeping down like a bell to the floor. A row of black gleaming buttons bisected him from floor to throat. When he talked his Adam's apple hit against the hard, white Roman collar and created in Kevin the same sensation as a fingernail scraping down the blackboard. His face was sallow and immobile. (There was a rumour that he had a glass eye but no-one knew which. Nobody could look at him long enough because to meet his stare was to invite a question.) He abhorred slovenliness. Once when presented with an untidy exercise book, dog-eared with a tea ring on the cover, he picked it up, the corner of one leaf between his finger and thumb, the pages splaying out like a fan, opened the window and dropped it three floors to the ground. His own neatness became exaggerated when he was at the board, writing in copperplate script just large enough for the boys in the back row to read—geometrical columns of declined nouns defined by exact, invisible margins. When he had finished he would set the chalk down and rub the used finger and thumb together with the same action he used after handling the host over the paten.

The palm upward gesture brought the class to its feet and they said the Hail Mary in Latin. While it was being said all eyes looked down because they knew if they looked up Waldo was bound to be staring at them.

"Exercises."

When Waldo was in a hurry he corrected the exercises verbally, asking one boy for the answers and then asking all those who got it right to put up their hands. It was four for anyone who lied about his answer and now and then he would take spot checks to find out the liars.

"Hold it, hold it there," he would say and leap from the rostrum, moving through the forest of hands and look at each boy's book, tracing out the answer with the tip of his cane. Before the end of the round and while his attention was on one book a few hands would be lowered quietly. Today he was in a hurry. The atmosphere was tense as he looked from one boy to another, deciding who would start.

"Sweeny, we'll begin with you." Kevin rose to his feet, his finger trembling under the place in the book. He read the first answer and looked up at Waldo. He remained impassive. He would let someone while translating unseens ramble on and on with great imagination until he faltered, stopped and admitted that he didn't know. Then and only then would he be slapped.

"Two, nominative. *Sapienter Pater.*" Kevin went on haltingly through the whole ten and stopped, waiting for a comment from Waldo. It was a long time before he spoke. When he did it was with bored annoyance.

"Every last one of them is wrong."

"But sir, Father, they couldn't be wr..." Kevin said it with such conviction, blurted it out so quickly that Waldo looked at him in surprise.

"Why not?"

"Because my..." Kevin stopped.

"Well?" Waldo's stone face resting on his knuckles. "Because my what?"

It was too late to turn back now.

"Because my father said so," he mumbled very low, chin on chest.

"Speak up, let us all hear you." Some of the boys had heard and he thought they sniggered.

"Because my father said so." This time the commotion in the class was obvious.

"And where does your father teach Latin?" There was no escape. Waldo had him. He knew now there would be an exhibition for the class. Kevin placed his weight on his arm and felt his tremble communicated to the desk.

"He doesn't, Father."

"And what does he do?"

Kevin hesitated, stammering,

"He's a barman."

"A barman!" Waldo mimicked and the class roared loudly.

"*Quiet.*" He wheeled on them. "You, Sweeny. Come out here." He reached inside the breast of his soutane and with a flourish produced a thin yellow cane, whipping it back and forth, testing it.

Kevin walked out to the front of the class, his face fiery red, the blood throbbing in his ears. He held out his hand. Waldo raised it higher, more to his liking, with the tip of the cane touching the underside of the upturned palm. He held it there for some time.

"If your brilliant father continues to do your homework for you, Sweeny, you'll end up a barman yourself." Then he whipped the cane down expertly across the tips of his fingers and again just as the blood began to surge back into them. Each time the cane in its follow-through cracked loudly against the skirts of his soutane.

"You could have made a better job of it yourself. Other hand." The same ritual of raising and lowering the left hand with the tip of the cane to the desired height. "After all, I have taught you some Latin." *Crack.* "It would be hard to do any worse."

Kevin went back to his place resisting a desire to hug his hands under his armpits and stumbled on a schoolbag jutting into the aisle as he pushed into his desk. Again Waldo looked round the class and said, "Now we'll have it *right* from someone."

The class continued and Kevin nursed his fingers, out of the fray.

As the bell rang Waldo gathered up his books and said, "Sweeny, I want a word with you outside. Ave Maria, gratia plena..." It was not until the end of the corridor that Waldo turned to face him. He looked at Kevin and maintained his silence for a moment.

"Sweeny, I must apologise to you." Kevin bowed his head. "I meant your father no harm—he's probably a good man, a very good man."

"Yes, sir," said Kevin. The pain in his fingers had gone.

"Look at me when I'm talking, please." Kevin looked at his collar, his Adam's apple, then his face. It relaxed for a fraction and Kevin thought he was almost going to smile, but he became efficient, abrupt again.

"All right, very good, you may go back to your class."

"Yes Father." Kevin nodded and moved back along the empty corridor.

Some nights when he had finished his homework early he would go down to meet his father coming home from work. It was dark, October, and he stood close against the high wall at the bus-stop trying to shelter from the cutting wind. His thin black blazer with the school emblem on the breast pocket and his short grey trousers, both new for starting grammar school, did little to keep him warm. He stood shivering, his hands in his trouser pockets and looked down at his knees which were blue and marbled, quivering uncontrollably. It was six o'clock when he left the house and he had been standing for fifteen minutes. Traffic began to thin out and the buses became less regular, carrying fewer and fewer passengers. There was a moment of silence when there was no traffic and he heard a piece of paper scraping along on pointed edges. He kicked it as it passed him. He thought of what had happened, of Waldo and his father. On the first day in class Waldo had picked out many boys by their names.

"Yes, I know your father well," or "I taught your elder brother. A fine priest he's made. Next."

"Sweeny, Father."

"Sweeny? Sweeny?—You're not Dr. John's son, are you?"

"No Father."

"Or anything to do with the milk people?"

"No Father."

"Next." He passed on without further comment.

Twenty-five past six. Another bus turned the corner and Kevin saw his father standing on the platform. He moved forward to the stop as the bus slowed down. His father jumped lightly off and saw Kevin waiting for him. He clipped him over the head with the tightly rolled newspaper he was carrying.

"How are you big lad?"

"All right," said Kevin shivering. He bumped his shoulders and set off beside his father, bumping into him uncertainly as he walked.

"How did it go today?" his father asked.

"All right." They kept silent until they reached the corner of their own street.

"What about the Latin?"

Kevin faltered, feeling a babyish desire to cry.

"How was it?"

"OK. Fine."

"Good. I was a bit worried about it. It was done in a bit of a rush. Son, your Da's a genius." He smacked him with the paper again. Kevin laughed and slipped his hand into the warmth of his father's overcoat pocket, deep to the elbow.

# The Second-Grade Mind

## FRANCES GRAY PATTON

Carol Nelson met Mrs. Womble, who was to be her son Tommy's teacher, the Saturday before school opened. She was not drawn to the teacher—partly, perhaps, because the teacher was evidently not drawn to her. Mrs. Womble was a broad-beamed, middle-aged lady with incongruously small feet, upon which she bustled into the office of the school principal. She had a fleshy face, out of which her somewhat slanting eyes surveyed Carol with a martyred, and even contemptuous, patience, as if the younger woman's presence had torn their gaze rudely—though only temporarily—away from its fast hold upon Mrs. Womble's own inner virtues.

Those eyes made Carol remember, after twenty years, the atmosphere of a classroom that had laid the first dull blight upon her childhood. She saw paper cutouts of windmills pasted on the window glass and an arithmetic problem chalked on the blackboard; she heard a solitary winter fly buzzing low over the steam radiators; she smelled the old chewing gum stuck under the lids of desks and the odor of little boys' corduroy knickers that were washed only on fair week ends when the weather was good for drying. Those were symbols of the boredom that she had hoped Tommy might escape, and that—to judge from Mrs. Womble's appearance—he would certainly have to endure.

Tommy's birthday came in November, and since the local board of education declared children ineducable until they were six years old and provided no midyear classes for beginners, he'd had to wait until now, when he was almost seven, before he could be entered in public school. He was a bright child, and his mother, wishing to keep him abreast of his general age group, had taught him to read and write and do simple sums at home. It was this that she'd come to the school about: to prevent his being place arbitrarily in a grade where the work would be a repetition of what he had already done.

She'd brought along, as proof of Tommy's ability, a composition that he had written describing the activities of a pair of robins who had built, the spring before, in a maple tree that shaded the Nelson's dining-room window. It was a charming piece, Carol thought. Tommy had done it as a present for his father, an amateur ornithologist, and it reflected the true naturalist's respect for his subject. "The parent birds are nice to their children," Tommy had written in conclusion. "They nurish them with worms and do not push them out of the nest until their wings are big enugh." It was a neat paper, too. It was written legibly in ink and decorated with pretty water-color drawings of maple leaves and winged seeds and birds flying with straws in their beaks.

Whenever Carol looked at it she saw Tommy as he'd sat, putting the final touches on it, at the cleared dining table, his brown head bent above his work; his feet, in soft house slippers, gripping the rung of his chair; and every curve and angle of his body suggesting that marvelous, absorbed happiness of a child who's using all his faculties. But when she'd handed the paper to the principal she had realized that its charms were lost on him.

"Quite the budding artist," he said politely. Then, pulling at the corner of his mustache (he was a meager, old-maidish young man who appeared to find the hair on his upper lip reassuring), he frowned. "But we must face the situation squarely, Mrs. Nelson. A child's nervous system is a risky thing. We find that six-year-olds are naturally first graders. When they aren't first-graders they've been tampered with."

"Tommy'll be seven in a couple of months," Carol said.

"A couple of months is an eon in the growth of a child," said the principal, "and he hasn't had the maturing experience of group life. If you push him ..."

"I'm not pushing him," Carol said. She tried not to let a note of asperity creep into her voice.

"If you push a child," the principal continued, "he may seem undamaged for a while. But eventually—it's like the time bomb—something will explode."

"Yes," Carol said, "but Tommy's really prepared for more than beginner's work. He can read anything, and he's always been—oh, I don't mean he's a genius—but he's always been a little quick for his age."

The principal leaned back in his swivel chair.

"Ah!" he said. "Now we're coming to an important point. We have to reverently consider not only the individual child, but society as a whole. Democracy."

"Democracy?" Carol echoed.

"The public school is the cradle of democracy," said the principal. "In a true democracy all citizens are on an equal footing. Just because a boy, through no merits of his own, has more *brains* than other boys doesn't qualify him for preferential treatment. There are no vested interests in education."

Carol began to feel a trifle dizzy and more than a trifle annoyed. "But—"

"Look at it this way, Mrs. Nelson," the principal said. "Do you have any friends who're financially worse off than you?"

"A few," Carol confessed. "A very few."

"You see!" the principal said, sounding pleased with his dialectics. "And the fact that you have a big bank account doesn't make you feel you should sit higher in church than they do, does it?"

Carol laughed. "Certainly not," she said. "But as for Tommy—"

It was then that the principal had called Mrs. Womble. "Tommy does present a problem," he'd said, "a difficult problem. I'll let you thrash it out with the second-grade teacher."

Carol had said that might be wise.

"You can trust Mrs. Womble," the principal had said. "She wakes the kids up. She understands the second-grade mind."

At this juncture Mrs. Womble had appeared in the doorway, and the principal, after introducing Carol as "a lady who thinks her six-year-old too smart for the first grade," had departed, pleading urgent business with the janitor.

Mrs. Womble smiled in a condescending way that made Carol feel naïve and presumptuous.

"Howdy do, Mrs. Nelson," she said. Her voice sounded spongy. "Pardon me for not shaking hands, but I was getting ready for my first class by writing my first proverb on the board, and"—she spread her pudgy fingers which were powdered with blue-and-red chalk dust—"well, you can see why!"

Carol said she was sorry to have interrupted Mrs. Womble and that she'd make her business brief. Her little boy was entering school Monday. He had been barely underage last year, so she had taught him at home and...

Mrs. Womble appeared deaf to Carol's remarks. "I find my proverbs a great aid in my teaching," she said. "I write a new one on my board every so often and get my little folks to memorize it. That improves their vocabulary. Then I help them relate its moral to their own little world. That makes them think."

"Yes. It would," said Carol.

"You'd be amazed how deep their little thoughts are," Mrs. Womble went on. "And you'd be amazed at what they tell me about their families. There are some grisly skeletons in the closets of this town!" She smacked her lips as if savoring the essence of a hundred scandals. "Now, about your child. What's his name?"

"Tommy," Carol said. "Thomas, really. But we call him Tommy."

"Don't apologize," Mrs. Womble said. "Tommy's a good name. You say *you* taught him to read and write?"

"Yes," Carol said, "he wanted to learn."

"'Tain't what you want that does you good,' as they used to say in olden days," Mrs. Womble observed. "But we won't cry over spilled milk."

"I brought a composition he wrote," Carol said. "It's there on the principal's desk."

Mrs. Womble went around the desk, and, holding her hands carefully away from everything, she scrutinized Tommy's paper about the robins. "He's misspelled two words." she said in an informative tone which implied that Carol, herself, hadn't detected those errors. "But it's not bad for a little fellow who's never been to school. Of course, *birds* are a *first*-grade interest."

"I'll have to tell my husband that," Carol said, wanting to giggle. "They're a passion with him."

"We all have our weak spots," Mrs. Womble said indulgently. "And men are just little boys grown up. Is your husband employed?"

"Oh, yes," said Carol. She wondered uneasily if her old linen dress were shabbier than she'd thought it. "He was in graduate school under the GI bill until year before last"—and why I'm discussing Ned's private affairs with this woman I really don't know, she thought—"but he has a job now with a firm of architects."

"I see," Mrs. Womble said.

"Tommy's just outside the window," Carol said, "taking care of his baby sister."

Mrs. Womble moved, with a lightness oddly at variance with her heft, to the open window. Following her, Carol looked over her shoulder at Tommy. Her heart constricted with a spasm of love, as it always did when she saw him suddenly or from a distance.

Tommy wore a white sweat shirt with a likeness of Hopalong Cassidy stenciled on it in red, and blue jeans that made his legs look long and thin. His brown hair was cropped short, but it curled at his temples, and the summer bloom on his face and arms was as rich as that of a ripe peach. He was bending over the baby's carriage, shaking a rattle very gently. He straightened up, saw the two women at the window, and smiled—not bashfully and not brazenly either, Carol thought, but with just the right mixture of deference and aplomb.

"Immature, isn't he?" said Mrs. Womble.

"We don't think so," Carol said. She longed to tell Mrs. Womble what sort of little boy—what

sort of person—Tommy was: how, from his earliest infancy, in those desolate weeks when Ned, his father, had been listed as missing in Korea, he had seemed a solitary star of hope dancing upon dark waters. And how later, living on a shoestring in two mean rooms in New Haven while Ned studied architecture, Carol hadn't been really lonely because she'd had Tommy's company. But she looked at Mrs. Womble, and, "He's a big help with the baby," she said lamely.

Mrs. Womble wheeled around. "Well," she said, "he should be in the first grade, but we can't put him there. You've already taught him to read, and one fish out of water can spoil a whole class. I'll try him in the second. No use locking the stable door after the horse is gone!"

Meekly, Carol said there wasn't.

"You meant well, Mrs. Nelson," Mrs. Womble said. "And I'll take care of him. After a few months with me he'll be a different child."

The woman's bland assumption that she would welcome the least change in her son sent Carol from the school building in a froth of fury. But once outside, in the mellow September sunshine, she was able to reflect that Mrs. Womble's obtuseness was like that of the girls in the beauty parlors who often promised her that if she'd permit them to pluck her eyebrows and give her a henna rinse, her best friends wouldn't recognize her!

"You're going to be in the second grade," she said cheerfully to Tommy.

"The *second* grade! Gosh!" Tommy said. He walked along, sober and silent, like a man upon whom greatness has been thrust without warning. But when he reached home he fairly flew apart with excitement. He rushed into the house and flung himself upon his father, who was home for Saturday afternoon and relaxing with a can of beer and Peterson's Field Guide to the Birds.

"I saw my teacher, Daddy!" he shouted, sprawling in Ned's lap. "She has a round face like an owl, only her eyes are slanty. And her chest puffs out like a pigeon. She looks nice." He lolled his head against Ned's shoulder. "I'm in the second grade!"

"That's terrific," Ned said. He smiled at Carol as she passed through the room carrying the baby.

"Hi," Carol said. "I'm going to start our lunch and get this infant fed before she goes sound asleep."

In a few minutes Ned joined his wife in the kitchen, where she was arranging strained spinach and a poached egg in a silver porringer. Jane, the baby, was in a high chair in a corner of the room, squirming and making lusty, inarticulate noises.

"I'll see to Jane," Ned said. He took the porringer from Carol.

"Thanks," Carol said. "I'm running behind schedule." She rummaged in the refrigerator for salad ingredients.

Bending from the waist, keeping what distance he could, Ned hand-fed his daughter. She made a game of her dinner. She would receive the spoon demurely and then, clamping her gums tight and squinting and wrinkling her button nose with great archness, she would refuse to release it. Patiently, almost absent-mindedly, Ned kept on scraping food off her chin and replacing it in her mouth.

"Tommy's reviewing arithmetic," he said to Carol. "How were you impressed with the school?"

"Not favorably," Carol said, "but it may be no worse than average. That Mrs. Womble must have been chosen for her propensities as a bore. She's a master of the cliché, and she writes proverbs on the blackboard—to make her little folks think. The principal said—and he's a jerk if I ever saw one—he said Mrs. W. understands the second-grade mind!"

"Poor Tom," said Ned. "But boredom is a part of education, like spelling or catching cold. There are worse things."

Carol, chopping celery and carrots in a wooden bowl, said morosely: "Name three."

"I can't offhand," Ned confessed. "But we've treated Tommy so much as an equal that a letdown may be good for him. Keep his nerves steady. And I'm intrigued with the proverbs. Ev-

eryone should learn some. A penny saved is a penny gained. You can't have your cake and eat it too." He shot a sidewise glance at Carol. "A boy's best friend is his mother."

"Stop there," begged Carol. Her voice was shaky.

"You're going to miss him, aren't you?" said Ned.

Carol groaned.

"I know," Ned said. "I'm not with him as much as you, but I hate to see him fly the nest. It's damn sentimental, but I hate it. I don't want him changed. I don't want anything in my life changed. Not a single thing!"

Carol understood what he meant. Ned, the most amiable and unmilitary of men, had swallowed a heroic dose of war. He had seen his friends killed; he had been wounded; he had been captured and half starved in an enemy prison. When he returned he hadn't been jumpy, as many men had been; he had been simply and calmly determined to shake off the memory of brutality and to live on a sort of private island of tranquility. That retreat he had found in family life. Just as he delighted in the study of birds that, being creatures of instinct, never knew discouragement, so he delighted in household trivia. He liked to help Carol choose the color of curtains, and to polish silver, and to associate with his children. It was an attitude, Carol knew, that was tinged with escapism. But it was an attitude, also, that made him a good father and bestowed a certain grace and dignity and heart upon the small domestic sphere.

"Are you ready for Jane's applesauce?" she asked.

Tommy started school the following Monday. Carol let him go alone (he said that if his mother went with him he might be mistaken for a *first*-grade boy), and when he came home he was in lively spirits. Certainly he hadn't been bored. The procedure of the classroom had been fresh and enchanting to him, and even Mrs. Womble's proverbs had been more entertaining than Carol had expected.

"It said: 'He who kills time commits suicide,'" Tommy reported. "But some of the children didn't know what suicide meant, so this boy named Forrest explained. He said his uncle committed suicide. He put a shotgun in his mouth and pulled the trigger. Do you think Forrest was just bragging?"

"Probably," Carol said.

"Did Daddy ever see anybody killed? In the war, I mean?"

"I suppose he must have," Carol said, elaborately casual.

"I guess he doesn't like to think about it. I wouldn't," said Tommy. "Gosh! A shotgun. He put it in his *mouth!*"

"He must have been a dope," Carol said. "You get yourself a glass of milk and three cookies. Then if you'll go in the back yard and gather some sunflower seed, Daddy will show you how to dry them for the bird's feeding station."

During the next weeks Tommy showed no sign of boredom. He did, however, fulfill Mrs. Womble's prophecy that he would act like "a different child." He wanted to hang about his mother all afternoon, and when she insisted that he play in the open air with the neighborhood children he came back at frequent intervals, ostensibly to go to the bathroom, but obviously to see that nothing was amiss at home. One evening, when his father was late for supper, he went into a panic. He asked to have a night light and to leave his bedroom door ajar. When questioned about school he was apt to assume a transparently blasé expression. "It's O.K.," he would answer. "We had a fire drill today," or "She put a new proverb on the board: 'Curiosity killed the cat!'"

"He's growing up," Ned said, when Carol complained that Tommy was uncommunicative. "He can't stay a chatterbox forever. And I, for one, am a firm believer in the separation of school and home."

"He's so withdrawn," Carol said. "He behaves like you, when you're putting something unpleasant out of your mind."

Ned narrowed his eyes. "Don't explore my subconscious, honey," he said. "And give Tommy time. If anything's troubling him, it'll come out."

A few bits did come out in November, on Tommy's birthday. After a festive supper Carol said that since they had plenty of cake left she might invite Mrs. Womble to tea next day. Tommy was instantly alert. A bright wariness veiled his eyes.

"I wouldn't ask her *here,*" he said. "Not with Jane."

"Why not?" Carol countered, thinking him ashamed of his sister. "Jane's a nice, normal baby."

"I don't think she likes babies," Tommy said. "Not girl babies." He drew a deep breath. "We read this story in Children of Distant Lands. It was about a Chinese family. And afterward Mrs. Womble told us how Chinese people threw girl babies in the river. Right in the muddy river. Maybe she was sad about it, but she didn't sound sad." He paused. "Do you guess she's Chinese?"

"No," Carol said. "Why do you ask?"

"She has those slanty eyes and those little bitty feet. I thought maybe they'd been bound, like Chinese ladies' feet."

"She's plain American," Ned said. "And if she were Chinese that would be fine. Most of them are highly civilized."

"I didn't know that," Tommy said. "She didn't tell us." He seemed relieved. "We have another proverb on the board. 'Pride goeth before a fall.'" (An improvement on the previous two, thought Carol.) "She wrote it today. There's this girl in our room named Phoebe Wilkins. Her daddy's a professor, and she's awfully smart and stuck-up. Mrs. Womble doesn't like her."

"Why not?" Ned asked.

Tommy said, "Because she's stuck-up. Nobody likes her. She told Mrs. Womble she said a word wrong."

"What word?" asked Carol.

"Mrs. Womble said ambul*ance,* and Phoebe raised her hand and said her daddy called it *ambu*lance. Which was right?"

"Phoebe," Ned admitted. "But she shouldn't have corrected the teacher."

"No," Tommy agreed. "Well, today Phoebe walked up to Mrs. Womble's desk to get a spelling paper that had a hundred on it. She was real proud, and she walked real switchy, the way stuck-up ladies walk. And then her panties fell down. Everybody laughed."

"What did Mrs. Womble do?" Carol asked.

"She got up and went to the board and wrote: 'Pride goeth before a fall,'" Tommy said. "I don't like Phoebe, but I feel sorry for her."

"I do, myself," Ned said.

Tommy got up and started out of the room. (He was reliable about keeping track of his bedtime.) At the door he turned. "Daddy," he said, "would you rather sit in an electric chair or a gas chamber?"

Ned looked startled. "The choice is hard," he said.

"The electric chair would be bad," Tommy said, "but Forrest says the first shock knocks you out. The gas chamber is a little glass room. You sit there, and they let in this poison gas—a kind of smoke—and lots of preachers and newspapermen look at you through the glass wall and watch you die." He put his hand to his throat. "It makes me feel like coughing."

Ned assumed a jocular manner. "*You* quit gassing, and make for bed."

"O.K.," Tommy said. "Will you tuck me in? Can I have my door open?"

When he had left them, Ned and Carol eyed each other.

"Kids' talk," Ned said. "They're born morbid. Remember when we were in grammar school how we used to dwell on the possibility of coming alive in our graves?" He lighted a cigarette. He stared at the match before he blew it out. "Still," he said, "a pop call on the school would do no harm."

A day or so later, when the weekly cleaning woman was present to keep an eye on Jane, Carol visited the school.

The second-grade room was empty except for the teacher, who greeted Carol cordially. The children, she said, were having "tiptoe recess" which, Carol gathered, was a euphamism for going to the toilet. They would be back soon.

"We have our literatoor period next," Mrs. Womble said. "I'm glad you'll be able to observe it. You can see my methods—the way I relate literatoor to the little folks' own lives and make them think. I welcome mothers, so long as they don't come too often. There's such a thing as *smother* love."

Carol said she hoped she'd never be guilty of that and asked how Tommy was doing.

"He's a quaint little fellow," Mrs. Womble said, "immature. But I'll fix him. I have another immature child. Phoebe Wilkins. Did Tommy tell you about the proverb?"

"Yes, Mrs. Womble. He told me," Carol said.

"Here they come," said Mrs. Womble as her thirty pupils, rising bouncily on their toes, filed in from the hall. They were clean, brushed children. None of them was much bigger than Tommy, and none of them, with the exception of Phoebe, a thin, angular girl, appeared so intelligent. But Carol could see why Mrs. Womble thought them more mature. Those children had guarded faces. It was as if their actual epidermis had become opaque and tough, concealing their inner lives and resisting outside impressions. Among them Tommy's countenance was as candid and translucent as a peeled grape.

Tommy paled when he saw his mother. She smiled at him. He flushed.

"We have a guest," Mrs. Womble told the class. "Tommy Nelson's mother will sit here beside me and hear us do our literatoor. We must all put our best foot foremost."

The literature lesson consisted of the reading and discussion of a story from the oft-mentioned book about distant lands. It was a stupid story, in Carol's opinion, about a small Canadian girl named Elsie, whose idiotic mother permitted her to venture alone, after nightfall, across frozen, wolf-infested wastes, to deliver kerosene to a lumber camp. Happily, the story was short, and the children, each of whom read a sentence or two aloud, read well. Then Mrs. Womble took over.

"Now we will put on our thinking caps," she said. "Ready. Think!"

The children folded their hands on the desks. They leaned forward, jaws jutting, brows beetling, in the attitude of thought.

"The author tells us that Elsie's mother was afraid for Elsie," Mrs. Womble said. "What was Elsie's mother afraid of?"

"Wolves!" several thinkers cried in unison.

"Elsie might freeze to death," said another.

"She might starve," said a third.

Mrs. Womble nodded. "Those are good answers. Those are the things Elsie's mother, way up in the frozen northland, feared for her little girl. But think. Those aren't the fears *your* mother has when she sends *you* off to school. There are no wolves in this town. Our weather is never cold enough to hurt you. Think. *What is your mother afraid of?*"

The children, without visibly moving a muscle, seemed to draw away from Mrs. Womble. Their faces were closed, incurious. Tommy shot his mother a wild look, a question.

"Well, I'll tell you," Mrs. Womble said. "First of all, she's afraid you'll be run over by a car or a truck and killed or crippled for life." She paused. Silence lay like a trance upon the room. Then there was a faint, nervous rustling among the children. "Second, she thinks of mad dogs who might bite you and give you hydrophobia." The children dropped their eyes as if the possibility embarrassed them. "And last, she's afraid of bad men who might kidnap you and torture you, or keep you for their own wicked purposes." The children looked up. Their eyes glittered. This was real, their faces said; this was what one heard on the radio. "You see," said Mrs. Womble.

Carol left as quickly as she could. She wanted to hurry away before she revealed the rage that quivered in her mind.

Late that evening, she told Ned about the literature lesson. "I wouldn't have believed it if anyone had told me," she said. "The woman sat there, just as calm as you please, talking on in that monotonous, fatuous voice of hers and needling those children with fear!"

"The second-grade mind," said Ned. "She's been exposed to it so long that she's caught it herself."

Next morning was rainy. Carol, knowing she'd have to drive Ned to work and Tommy to school, got up and fixed breakfast earlier than usual. She put her brightest china and a bowl of shiny fruit on the table. By the time the family came down the dining room looked cozy, and the first slices of brown toast were popping up in the toaster.

Ned settled Jane in her high chair beside Carol and took his own place at the head of the table. Tommy slid into his chair and bowed his head to ask grace.

"Come, gentle Lord, and be our guest; what Thou has given, by Thee be blest. Amen," said Tommy.

"Amen," said Jane who was beginning to repeat words.

"Don't laugh at her," said Tommy, seeing the quick smiles on his parents' faces. He reached and patted her hand.

Ned took a swallow of coffee. "Tommy," he said, "I understand Mrs. Womble thinks your mother is afraid when you leave for school."

Tommy toyed with his scrambled eggs. "Isn't she?"

"No," Ned said. "Why should she be? You know how to cross streets, so you won't be run over. There are no rabid dogs in this neighborhood, so you won't be bitten."

"If I was I could take the Pasteur treatment," said Tommy.

"Sure," Ned said, "and you have sense enough not to go off with strangers, so even if there were bad men around—which there aren't—you'd be safe. Your mother would be silly to worry."

"I'm glad she doesn't," Tommy said. "I can take care of myself."

Jane blew out some oatmeal. "Amen," she said. "Amen, amen, amen, amen!"

Ned looked hard at his son. "Tommy," he said, "are you afraid of Mrs. Womble?"

Tommy stuck out his chest. "No!" he almost shouted. "Forrest says she's flabby. If you hit her in the stomach she'd cave in. I'm not scared of anything."

"I am," Ned said. "Lots of things."

"Gosh!" Tommy said. "Well, I'm not scared of Mrs. Womble." He spread jelly on a piece of toast and raised it toward his mouth. He laid it down. "Mr. Womble's dead," he said. "Do you think she killed him?"

"What?"

"Forrest says so. A boy in fourth grade told him Mr. Womble was a little tiny man, and Mrs. Womble rolled on him one night and smothered him to death."

"That's nonsense," Ned snorted. "You know she didn't."

Carol said nothing. She gazed apathetically out the window. The maple tree was bare and gray in the rain. The empty robins' nest hung crooked from a twig, like a wet-weather moon. A few snowbirds, gray too, pecked at the sunflower seed on the feeding station

"I guess not," Tommy said to his father. "I guess if she had, she'd have been sent to the electric chair or the gas chamber. Or the rack."

"The rack?" Ned asked.

"She told us about the rack." Tommy said. "We were reading this story about a boy in Russia. His father had been put to death. Then Mrs. Womble explained how the law put people to death. Gas, you know, and the electric chair, and hanging with ropes, and sometimes the rack. It's a machine that pulls your bones apart. It makes my hips hurt."

"The rack hasn't been used for hundreds of years," Ned said. His voice trembled.

"Oh," Tommy said. "Then there *was* such a thing. I thought Mrs. Womble made it up."

"Made it up?"

"It's the kind of thing she *would* think of," said Tommy. "Look at the juncos eating my sunflower seed. Daddy, did you ever hit a bird with a rock?"

"No," Ned said.

"Did you ever see anybody hit one?"

"No," Ned said. "I can't say I did."

"It would be a mean thing to do," said Tommy.

Carol looked at her wrist watch. "We must go," she said. "You boys get on your raincoats and rubbers. I'll wrap up the baby."

She drove downtown with Jane strapped into an infant's carchair on the front seat, Tommy beside Jane, and Ned in the back. Ned kissed her on the neck before he got out on a corner near his office. As he walked away she saw him lift one shoulder, like a man warding off something colder and more searching than a November wind.

"See the pretty streets!" Tommy said to Jane as they drove on. He pointed to the red and green traffic lights reflected on the wet pavement.

"Amen, amen!" said Jane.

When they stopped in front of the school, Tommy nuzzled the baby. "'By," he said. "Be a good girl." He looked at his mother. "You know," he said, "I *am* afraid of Mrs. Womble. I just didn't like to tell Daddy."

"He would have understood," Carol said. "But she's nobody to be afraid of. She's old and dull and maybe lonesome. She likes to talk about horrors. But deep down I'm sure she's kind."

"No," Tommy said, "she does cruel things."

"Now, Tommy," Carol said, "you've been influenced by boys like Forrest."

Tommy shrugged. "I don't pay attention to Forrest. He brags too much. I don't believe she rolled on her husband. But I know other things she does."

Carol held her breath. She waited to hear.

"The principal knows, too," Tommy said darkly. "I heard her tell him. She was bragging about it."

"What did she tell him?" Carol asked.

"It was yesterday," Tommy said. "We were on the playground having a relay race. Then the principal came and said something to Mrs. Womble, and she went around the building to the front, where we're not allowed to play. The principal stayed with us."

"Yes?" said Carol.

"Then she came back and told him. I heard her. She was rubbing her hands together like she was real proud of herself. She said"—Tommy's face was pinched with outrage and pity—"she said: 'I killed two birds with one stone!'"

"But, darling—" Carol began.

"The birds like the berries on the bushes," Tommy said, pointing to the hedge of ligustrum that hid the foundations of the school building. "Sometimes there's a flock of them, whitethroats and chickadees. Once I saw a cardinal." He sighed a weary, unchildish sigh. "I hunted all around after school, but I couldn't find the dead bodies. Mrs. Womble must have thrown them in the trash can."

"Tommy," Carol said, "you misunderstood her. She was using a figure of speech. She didn't mean . . ."

A bell shrilled through the air. Tommy leaped from the car. "The warning bell!" he gasped.

"Wait!" Carol implored him. "Let me explain!"

"But I'm almost tardy!" Tommy said. He darted up the walk, splashing through puddles. His yellow slicker flapped behind him as he ran. He looked like a little bird himself, Carol thought. Then he pulled open the heavy front door and went inside.

Carol sat staring at the squat brick building. Within its walls her own son—her first-born child for whose sake she would have tossed away her whole life, like yesterday's newspaper—lived with terror in the marrow of his bones. Alone, untutored in cruelty or evil, he was picking his way among bizarre anxieties and fantastic confusions. She took a deep breath. She was being childish, she told herself. She was letting Tommy's irrational fear color her mood just the way Ned had said the second-grade mind affected Mrs. Womble. Where was her sense of proportion, of humor? The child had only made the natural and easily corrected mistake of taking a metaphor for literal fact. She'd explain it to him this afternoon. But afternoon seemed years away and not certain to come at all.

The baby began to rock back and forth, pulling and pushing at her strap. "Go, go" she commanded. "Car go!"

Carol turned to her. "Let's take it easy, Janie. Let's not go home just yet," she said. (She had fallen lately into the habit of addressing the baby as a contemporary.) "Let's go help Tommy."

As she unbuckled Jane's restraining strap and wrapped her in a square of red tarpaulin, Carol had a qualm of misgiving. To rush into a public school, the very citadel of convention and decorum, with an old, damp bandanna on her head and a baby, like a bundle, in her arms! But a sense of urgent haste possessed Carol. She clutched Jane against her right hip. She held her pocketbook in her mouth so as to leave her left hand free for the door. She ran through the rain.

Inside the door Carol paused to turn the tarpaulin back from Jane's head and arms. The corridor was dim-lit and quiet in an eerie way. From behind closed doors came a muffled drone of voices that produced an effect more of vibration than of actual sound in the air. Carol began to run again. Her feet, in their clumsy galoshes, bore her too slowly, she thought, as feet bear a runner in a dream. As she careened around a corner, down the hall toward her destination, she skidded on the slick composition floor. The baby flapped her arms like wings. "Wheeeeeee!" she cried, as Carol recovered her balance.

Without knocking, Carol flung open the door of the second-grade room. What sinister rites she had expected to interrupt, she couldn't have said, but the commonplace serenity of the scene surprised her. Mrs. Womble was standing beside her desk. She looked a trifle weary, more than a trifle complacent and quite human. The children, bent over notebooks, appeared at ease and reasonably cheerful. Tommy, sitting over in the row by the windows, shot Carol a swift, astonished glance. Then he bowed his head as if beneath a weight of shame.

"Good morning, Mrs. Nelson," Mrs. Womble said. She moved lightly to the doorway. "And good morning, little *Miss* Nelson!"

Carol saw Tommy turn in his seat. He leaned forward, muscles flexed, ready to spring to his sister's defense.

The teacher smiled a maudlin, sentimental smile. With a gentle forefinger she prodded the baby's dimpled cheek. "Itsy-bitsy butterball!" she cooed. "Did peshy det all wained on?"

Jane bounced on the crook of Carol's arm. "Amen!" she yelled in her lusty voice. "Amen, amen, amen!"

The pupils roared applause. Jane rewarded them with the coy, ecstatic smile of the successful exhibitionist.

Carol removed her pocketbook from her mouth. "Could I speak to Tommy privately?" she asked Mrs. Womble.

"Why, yes, if it's necessary," Mrs. Womble replied. Her polite tone was flavored with reproach and a hint of *noblesse oblige*. "We run on schedule, you know, and we're in the midst of dictation, but..."

"I'll make it snappy," Carol said.

Tommy's face was blank and stern as he crossed the schoolroom. He didn't speak until he was in the hall with Carol and the door was safely shut behind him. Then he leaned against a wall, limp with fury. "You look like an old peasant woman in our literature book," he said in an outraged whisper. "Like somebody in Siberia!"

Carol was too distraught to be hurt. "Never mind my looks," she said. "I want a serious talk with you."

"Why did you carry your purse in your mouth?" Tommy demanded. He sounded on the verge of tears. "Like a dog!" He shut his eyes for an instant as if the recollection were mortifying beyond endurance. "Oh!" he moaned. "They all know you're kin to *me!*"

Carol set Jane down on the floor. She gave her the chain of car keys to play with. "You must listen to me now, Tommy," she said.

"What about?" Tommy asked.

"About your teacher," Carol said. "I can't have you afraid of her. She's not mean. You saw how nice she was to Jane. She's just—just sort of bored with life, I guess. She talks about dangers and executions and things because they're exciting to her. Like western movies."

Tommy's expression was skeptical and wary.

"And as for what you heard her tell the principal," Carol went on, "she was using an old saying. A kind of proverb. She merely meant..."

Tommy heard her out. At first he preserved a grudging show of reluctance, but gradually—for he was a child who enjoyed ideas and getting at the root of things—his eyes betrayed his interest. "I see," he said when Carol had finished. "But I don't know if Forrest will. It's hard to explain things to Forrest."

"To Forrest?" Carol said.

"I told him what she'd done. What I thought she'd done. He helped hunt for the bodies."

"Oh," said Carol. "You told Forrest." She began to laugh. She was swept by a sense of heady, malicious glee as she relished the poetic justice inherent in the legend that would now attach itself to Mrs. Womble. Generation after generation of second-grade children would preserve and cherish it. Each time she disappeared from their sight, they would imagine her crouched in the shrubbery, teetering on the toes of her ridiculous, undersized feet, shying rocks at songbirds. Knocking them off, *in pairs!*

Tommy stared at her, half puzzled. Suddenly, *he* laughed. His laughter came out in a whoop that echoed against the ceiling. He clapped his hand over his mouth. Jane, always eager for fun and frolic, laughed too. She flung the car keys down the hall. Tommy ran to retrieve them.

"Gosh, I was dumb," he said, as he offered the keys to Carol. "To think that ole sissy could hit two birds at a time!" His upturned face was merry and relaxed. He held his chin at a new angle, cocky and masculine and even a little tough. "I bet she couldn't hit an elephant, if it was standing still in front of her. Why, she couldn't throw as straight as a baby girl!"

# The Bufords

## ELIZABETH SPENCER

There were the windows, high, well above the ground, large, full of sky. There were the child's eyes, settled back mid-distance in the empty room. There was the emptiness, the drowsiness of Miss Jackson's own head, tired from tackling the major problems of little people all day long, from untangling their hair ribbons, their shoelaces, their grammar, their arithmetic, their handwriting, their thoughts. Now there was silence.

The big, clumsy building was full of silence, stoves cooling off, great boxy rooms growing cool from the floor up, cold settling around her ankles. Miss Jackson sat there two or three afternoons a week, after everybody else had gone, generally with a Buford or because of a Buford: It was agreed she had the worst grade this year, because there were Bufords in it. She read a sentence in a theme four times through. Was it really saying something about a toad-frog? Her brain was so weary—it was Thursday, late in the week—she began to think of chipmunks, instead. Suddenly her mouth began to twitch; she couldn't stand it any longer; she burst out laughing.

"Dora Mae, *what* are you doing?"

The truth was that Dora Mae was not doing anything. She was just a Buford. When she was around, you eventually laughed. Miss Jackson could never resist; but then, neither could anyone. Dora Mae, being a Buford, did not return her laugh. The Bufords never laughed unless they wanted to. She drew the book she was supposed to be studying, but wasn't, slowly downward on the desk; her chin was resting on it and came gradually down with it. She continued to stare at Miss Jackson with eyes almost as big as the windows, blue, clear, and loaded with Buford nonsense. She gave Miss Jackson the tiniest imaginable smile.

Miss Jackson continued to laugh. If someone else had been the teacher, she herself would have to be corrected, possibly kept in. It always turned out this way. Miss Jackson dried her eyes. "Sit up straight, Dora Mae," she said.

Once this very child had actually sewed through her own finger, meddling with a sewing machine the high school home-economics girls had left open upstairs. Another time, at recess, she had jumped up and down on a Sears Roebuck catalogue in the dressing room behind the stage, creating such a thunder nobody could think what was happening. She had also shot pieces of broken brick with her brother's slingshot at the walls of the gym, where they were having a 4-H Club meeting. "Head, Heart, Hands, and Health," the signs said. They were inside repeating a pledge about these four things and singing, "To the knights in the days of old, Keeping watch on the mountain height, Came a vision of Holy Grail, And a voice through the waiting night." Some of the chunks of brick, really quite large, came flying through the window.

Dora Mae, of course, had terrible brothers, the Buford boys, and a reputation to live up to— was that it? No, she was just bad, the older teachers in the higher grades would say at recess, sitting on the steps in warm weather or crossing the street for a Coke at the little cabin-size sandwich shop.

"I've got two years before I get Dora Mae," said Miss Martingale.

"Just think," said Mrs. Henry, "I've got four Bufords in my upstairs study hall. At once."

"I've had them already, all but one," said Miss Carlisle. "I've just about graduated."

"I wish they weren't so funny," said Miss Jackson, and then they all began to laugh. They couldn't finish their Cokes for laughing.

Among the exploits of Dora Mae's brothers, there always came to mind the spring day one of them brought a horse inside the school house just before closing bell, leading it with a twist of wire fastened about its lower lip and releasing it to wander right into study hall alone while the principal, Mr. Blackstone, was dozing at his desk.

The thing was, in school, everybody's mind was likely to wander, and the minute it did wander, something would be done to you by a Buford, and you would never forget it. The world you were dozing on came back with a whoosh and a bang; but it was not the same world you had dozed away from, nor was it the one you intended to wake up to or even imagined to be there. Something crazy was the matter with it: a naked horse, unattended, was walking between the rows of seats; or (another day altogether) a little girl was holding her reader up in the air between her feet, her head and shoulders having vanished below desk level, perhaps forever. Had there actually been some strange accident? Were you dreaming? Or were things meant to be this way? That was the part that just for a minute could scare you.

The Bufords lived in a large, sprawled-out, friendly house down a road nobody lived on but them. The grass was never completely cut, and in the fall the leaves never got raked. Somebody once set fire to a sagebrush pasture near their house—one of *them* had done it, doubtless—and the house was threatened, and there were Bufords up all night, stamping the earth and scraping sparks out of the charred fence posts and throwing water into chicken wallows, just in case the fire started again.

When any of the teachers went there to call, as they occasionally had to do, so that the family wouldn't get mad at the extraordinary punishment meted out to one of the children at school—Mr. Blackstone once was driven to give Billy Buford a public whipping with a buggy whip—or (another reason) to try to inform the family just how far the children were going with their devilment and to implore moral support, at least, in doing something about it—when you went there, they all came out and greeted you. They made you sit in a worn wicker rocking chair and ran to get you something—iced tea or lemonade or a Coke, cake, tea cakes, or anything they had.

Then they began to shout and holler and say how glad they were you'd come. They began to say, "Now tell the truth! Tell the truth, now! Ain't Billy Buford the worse boy you ever saw?"... "Did you ever see anybody as crazy as that Pete? Now tell me! Now tell the truth!" ... "Confidentially, Miss Jackson, what on earth are we ever going to do with Dora Mae?"

And Dora Mae would sit and look at you, the whole time, She would sit on a little stool and put her chin on her hands and stare, and then you would say, "I just don't know, Mrs. Buford." And they would all look at you cautiously in their own Buford way, and then in the silence, when you couldn't, shouldn't be serious, one of them would say, very quietly, "Ain't you ever going to eat your cake?"

It was like that.

There had once been something about a skunk that had upset not just the school but the whole town and that would not do to think about, just as it didn't do any good, either, to speculate on what might or could or was about to happen on this or any future Halloween.

Was it spring or fall? Dreaming, herself, in the lonely classroom with Dora Mae, Miss Jackson thought of chipmunks and skunks and toad-frogs, words written into themes on ruled paper, the lines of paper passing gradually across her brow and into her brain, until the fine ruling would eventually print itself there. Someday, if they opened her brain, they would find a child's theme inside. Even now she could often scarcely think of herself with any degree of certainty. Was she in love, was she falling in love, or getting restless and disappointed with whomever she knew, or did she want somebody new, or was she recalling somebody gone? Or: Had someone right come along, and she had said all right, she'd quit teaching and marry him, and now had it materialized or had it fallen through, or what?

Children! The Bufords existed in a haze of children and old people: old aunts, old cousins, grandfathers, friends and relatives by marriage of cousins, deceased uncles, family doctors gone alcoholic, people who never had a chance. What did they live on? Oh, enough of them knew how to make enough for everyone to feel encouraged. Enough of them were clever about money, and everybody liked them, except the unfortunate few who had to try to discipline them. A schoolteacher, for instance, was a sort of challenge. A teacher hung in their minds like the deep, softly pulsing, furry throat in the collective mind of a hound pack. They hardly thought of a teacher as human, you had to suppose. You could get your feelings hurt sadly if you left yourself open to them.

"Dora Mae, let's go," Miss Jackson suddenly said, way too early.

She had recalled that she had a date, but whether it was a spring date (with warm twilight air seeping into the car, filling the street and even entering the stale movie foyer—more excitement in the season than was left for her in this particular person) or whether it was a fall date (when the smell of her new dress brought out sharply by the gas heater she had to turn on in the late afternoon, carried with it the interest of somebody new and the lightness all beginnings have)—which it was, she had to think to say. At this moment, she had forgotten whether she was even glad or not. It was better to be going out with somebody than not; it gave a certain air, for one thing, to supper at the boardinghouse.

Even the regulars, the uptown widows and working wives and the old couple and the ancient widower who came to eat there, held themselves somewhat straighter and took some degree of pride in the matter of Miss Jackson's going out, as going out suggested a progress of sorts and put a tone of freshness and prettiness on things. It was a subject to tease and be festive about; the lady who ran the boardinghouse might even bring candles to light the table. In letting Dora Mae Buford out early, Miss Jackson was responding to that festiveness; she thought of the reprieve as a little present.

She recalled what she had told a young man last year, or maybe the year before, just as they were leaving the movies after a day similar to this

one, when she had had to keep another Buford in, how she had described the Bufords to him, so that she got him to laugh about them, too, and how between them they had decided there was no reason, no reason on earth, for Bufords to go to school at all. They would be exactly the same whether they went to school or not. Nothing you told them soaked in; they were born knowing everything they knew; they never changed; the only people they really listened to were other Bufords.

"But I do sometimes wonder," Miss Jackson had said, trying hard to find a foothold that had to do with "problems," "personality," "psychology," "adjustment," all those things she had taken up in detail at teacher's college in Nashville and thought must have a small degree of truth in them—"I wonder if some people don't just feel obligated to be bad."

"There's something in that," the young man had answered. (He had said this often, come to think of it: a good answer to everything.)

Now the child trudged along beside Miss Jackson across the campus. Miss Jackson looked down affectionately; she wanted a child of her own someday—though hardly, she thought (and almost giggled), one like this. It went along on chunky legs and was shaped like cutout paper-doll children you folded the tabs back to change dresses for. Its face was round, its brow raggedly fringed with yellow bangs. Its hands were plump—meddlesome, you'd say on sight. It wore scuffed brown shoes and navy-blue socks and a print dress and carried an old nubby red sweater slung over its books.

"Aren't you cold, Dora Mae?" said Miss Jackson, still in her mood of affection and fun.

"No, ma'am," said Dora Mae, who could and did answer directly at times. "I'm just tired of school."

Well, so am I sometimes, Miss Jackson thought, going home to bathe and dress in her best dress, and then go to the boardinghouse with the other teachers, where, waiting on the porch, if it was warm enough or in the hall if it was not, sitting or standing with hands at rest against the nice material of her frock, she would already be well over the line into her most private domain.

"I don't really like him all that much," she would have confided already—it was what she always said. "I just feel better, you know, when somebody wants to take me somewhere." All the teachers agreed that this was so; they were the same, they said.

What Miss Jackson did not say was that she enjoyed being *Lelia*. This was her secret, and when she went out, this was what happened: she turned into Lelia, from the time she was dressing in the afternoon until after midnight, when she got in. The next morning, she would be Miss Jackson again.

If it was a weekday.

And if it wasn't a weekday, then she might still feel like Miss Jackson, even on weekends, for they had given her a Sunday School class to teach whenever she stayed in town. If she went home, back fifty miles to the little town she was born in, she had to go to church there, too, and everybody uptown called her "Leel," a nickname. At home they called her "Sister," only it sounded more like Sustah. But Lelia was her name and what she wanted to be; it was what she said was her name to whatever man she met who asked to take her somewhere.

One day soon after she had kept Dora Mae Buford after school, she went back into the classroom from recess quite late, having been delayed at a faculty meeting, and Dora Mae was writing "LELIA JACKSONLELIAJACKSONLELIAJACKSON LELIAJACKSON" over and over in capital letters on the blackboard. She filled one board and had started on another, going like crazy. All the students were laughing at her.

It became clear to Miss Jackson later, when she had time to think about it, that the reason she became so angry at Dora Mae was that the child, like some diabolical spirit, had seemed to know exactly what her sensitive point was and had gone

straight to it, with the purpose of ridiculing her, of exposing and summarizing her secret self in all its foolish yearning.

But at the moment she did not think anything. She experienced a flash of white-faced, passionate temper and struck the chalk from the child's hand. "Erase that board!" she ordered. A marvel she hadn't knocked her down, except that Dora Mae was as solid as a stump, and hitting her, Miss Jackson had almost sprained a wrist.

Dora Mae was shocked half to death, and the room was deadly still for the rest of the morning. Miss Jackson, so gentle and firm (though likely to get worried), had never before struck anyone.

Soon Dora Mae's mother came to see Miss Jackson, after school. She sat down in the empty classroom, a rather tall, dark woman with a narrow face full of slanted wrinkles and eyes so dark as to be almost pitch black, with no discernible white area to them. Miss Jackson looked steadfastly down at her hands.

Mrs. Buford put a large, worn bulging black purse on the desk before her, and though she did not even remove her coat, the room seemed hers. She did not mean it that way, for she spoke in the most respectful tone, but it was true. "It's really just one thing I wanted to know, Miss Jackson. Your first name is Lelia, ain't it?"

Miss Jackson said that it was.

"So what I mean is, when Dora Mae wrote what she did on the blackboard there, it wasn't nothing like a lie or something dirty, was it?"

"No," said Miss Jackson. "Not at all."

"Well, I guess that's about all I wanted to make sure of."

Miss Jackson did not say anything, and Mrs. Buford finally inquired whether she had not been late coming back to the room that day, when Dora Mae was found writing on the board. Miss Jackson agreed that this was true.

"Churen are not going to sit absolutely still if you don't come back from recess," said Mrs. Buford. "You got to be there to say, 'Now y'all get out your book and turn to page so-and-so.' If you don't they're bound to get into something. You realize that? Well, good! Dora Mae's nothing but a little old scrap. That's all she is."

"Well, I know," said Miss Jackson, feeling very bad.

At this point, Mrs. Buford, alone without any of her children around her, must have got to thinking about them all in terms of Dora Mae; she began to cry.

Miss Jackson understood. She had seen them all, her entire class, heads bent at her command, pencils marching forward across their tablets, and her heart had filled with pity and love.

Mrs. Buford brushed her tears away. "You never meant it for a minute. Anybody can get aggravated, don't you know? You think I can't? I can and do!" She put her handkerchief back in her purse and, straightening her coat, stood up to go. "So, I'm just going right straight and say you're sorry about it and you never meant it."

"Oh," said Miss Jackson, all of a sudden, "but I did mean it. It's true I'm sorry. But I did mean it." Her statement, softly made, threw a barrier across Mrs. Buford's path, like bars through the slots in a fence gap.

Mrs. Buford sat back down. "Miss Jackson, just what have we been sitting here deciding?"

"I don't know," said Miss Jackson, wondering herself. "Nothing that I know of."

"Nothing! You call that nothing?"

"Call what nothing?"

"Why, everything you just got through saying."

"But what do you think I said?" Miss Jackson felt she would honestly like to know. There followed a long silence, in which Miss Jackson, whose room this after all was, felt impelled to stand up. "It's not a good thing to lose your temper. But everyone does sometimes, including me."

Mrs. Buford rose also. "Underneath all that fooling around, them kids of mine is pure gold." Drawn to full height, Mrs. Buford became about twice as tall as Miss Jackson.

"I know! I know that! But you say yourselves—" began Miss Jackson. She started to tremble. Of all the teachers in the school, she was

the youngest, and she had the most overcrowding in her room. "Mrs. Buford," she begged, "do please forget about it. Go on home. Please, please go home!"

"You pore child," said Mrs. Buford, with no effort still continuing and even expanding her own authority. "I just never in my life," she added, and left the room.

She proceeded across the campus the way all her dozen or so children went, down toward their lonely road—a good, strong, sincere woman, whose right shoulder sagged lower than the left and who did not look back. From the window, Miss Jackson watched her go.

Uptown a lady gossip was soon to tell her that she was known to have struck a child in a fit of temper and also to have turned out the child's mother when she came to talk about it. Miss Jackson wearily agreed that this was true. She could feel no great surprise, though her sense of despair deepened when one of the Buford boys, Evan, older and long out of school, got to worrying her—calling up at night, running his car behind her on the sidewalk uptown. It seemed there were no lengths he wouldn't go to, no trouble he wouldn't make for her.

When the dove season started, he dropped her. He'd a little rather shoot doves than me, she thought, sitting on the edge of the bed in her room, avoiding the mirror, which said she must be five years older. It's my whole life that's being erased, she thought, mindful that Dora Mae and two of her brothers, in spite of all she could do, were inexorably failing the fourth grade. She got up her Sunday School lesson, washed her hair, went to bed, and fell asleep disconsolate....

Before school was out, the Bufords invited Miss Jackson for Sunday dinner. Once the invitation had come—which pleased her about as much as if it had been extended by a tribe of Indians, but which she had to accept or be thought of as a coward—it seemed inevitable to her that they would do this. It carried out to a T their devious and deceptively simple-looking method of pleasing themselves, and of course what she might feel about it didn't matter. But here she was dressing for them, trying to look her best.

The dinner turned out to be a feast. She judged it was no different from their usual Sunday meal—three kinds of meat and a dozen spring vegetables, hot rolls, jams, pickles, peaches, and rich cakes, freshly baked and iced.

The house looked in the airiest sort of order, with hand-crocheted white doilies sprinkled about on the tables and chairs. The whole yard was shaggy with flowers and blooming shrubs; the children all were clean and neatly dressed, with shoes on as well, and the dogs were turned firmly out of doors.

She was placed near Mr. Tom Buford, the father of them all, a tall spare man with thick white hair and a face burned brick-brown from constant exposure. He plied her ceaselessly with food, more than she could have eaten in a week, and smiled the gentle smile Miss Jackson by now knew so well.

Halfway down the opposite side of the table was Evan Buford, she at last recognized, that terrible one, wearing a spotless white shirt, shaved and spruce, with brown busy hands, looking bland and even handsome. If he remembered all those times he had got her to the phone at one and two and three in the morning, he wasn't letting on. ("Thought you'd be up grading papers, Miss Jackson! Falling down on the job?"..."Your family live in Tupelo? Well, the whole town got blown away in a tornado! This afternoon!") Once, in hunting clothes, his dirt-smeared, unshaven face distorted by the rush of rain on his muddy windshield, he had pursued her from the post office all the way home, almost nudging her off the sidewalk with his front fender, his wheels spewing water from the puddles all over her stockings and raincoat, while she walked resolutely on, pretending not to notice.

From way down at the foot of the table, about half a mile away, Dora Mae sat sighting at her steadily through a water glass, her eyes like the magnified eyes of insects.

"'Possum hunting!" Mr. Tom Buford was saying, carving chicken and ham with a knife a foot long, which Miss Jackson sometimes had lit-

erally to dodge. "That's where we all went last night. Way up on the ridge. You like 'possum, Miss Jackson?"

"I never had any," Miss Jackson said.

Right from dinner they all went to the back yard to see the 'possum, which had been put in a cage of chicken wire around the base of a small pecan tree. It was now hanging upside down by its tail from a limb. She felt for its helpless, unappetizing shapelessness, grizzly gray, with a long snout, its sensitive eyes shut tight, its tender black petal-like ears alone perceiving, with what terror none could know though she could guess, the presence of its captors.

"Don't smell very good, does it?" Billy Buford said. "You like it, Miss Jackson? Give it to you, you want it." He picked up a stick to punch it with.

She shook her head. "Oh, I'd just let it go back to the woods. I feel sorry for it."

The whole family turned from the creature to her and examined her as if she were crazy. Billy Buford even dropped the stick. There followed one of those long, risky silences.

As they started to go inside. Evan Buford lounged along at her elbow. He separated her out like a heifer from the herd and cornered her before a fence of climbing roses. He leaned his arm against a fence post, blocking any possible escape, and looked down at her with wide, speculative, bright brown eyes. She remembered his laughing mouth behind the car wheel that chill, rainy day, careening after her. Oh, they never got through, she desperately realized. Once they had you, they held on—if they didn't eat you up, they kept you for a pet.

"Now, Miss Jackson, how come you to fail those kids?"

Miss Jackson dug her heels in hard. "I didn't fail them. They failed themselves. Like you might fail to hit a squirrel, for instance."

"Well, now. You mean they weren't good enough. Well, I be darned." He jerked his head. "That's a real good answer."

So at last, after years of trying hard, she had got something across to a Buford, some one little thing that was true. Maybe it had never happened before. It would seem she stopped him cold. It would seem he even admired her.

"Missed it like a squirrel!" he marveled. "The whole fourth grade. They must be mighty dumb," he reflected, walking along with her toward the house.

"No, they just don't listen," said Miss Jackson.

"Don't listen," he said after her with care, as though to prove that he, at least, did. "You get ready to go, I'll drive you to town, Miss Jackson. Your name is Lelia, ain't it?"

She looked up gratefully. "That's right," she said.

# Father's Help

## R. K. NARAYAN

Lying in bed, Swami realized with a shudder that it was Monday morning. It looked as though only a moment ago it had been the last period on Friday; already Monday was here. He hoped that an earthquake would reduce the school building to dust, but that good building—Albert Mission School—had withstood similar prayers for over a hundred years now. At nine o'clock Swaminathan wailed, "I have a headache." His mother said, "Why don't you go to school in a *jutka?*"

"So that I may be completely dead at the other end? Have you any idea what it means to be jolted in a *jutka?*"

"Have you many important lessons today?"

"Important! Bah! That geography teacher has been teaching the same lesson for over a year now. And we have arithmetic, which means for a whole period we are going to be beaten by the teacher... Important lessons!"

And Mother generously suggested that Swami might stay at home.

At 9:30, when he ought to have been shouting in the school prayer hall, Swami was lying on the bench in Mother's room. Father asked him, "Have you no school today?"

"Headache," Swami replied.

"Nonsense! Dress up and go."

"Headache."

"Loaf about less on Sundays and you will be without a headache on Monday."

Swami knew how stubborn his father could be and changed his tactics. "I can't go so late to the class."

"I agree, but you'll have to; it is your own fault. You should have asked me before deciding to stay away."

"What will the teacher think if I go so late?"

"Tell him you had a headache and so are late."

"He will beat me if I say so."

"Will he? Let us see. What is his name?"

"Samuel."

"Does he beat the boys?"

"He is very violent, especially with boys who come late. Some days ago a boy was made to stay on his knees for a whole period in a corner of the class because he came late, and that after getting six cuts from the cane and having his ears twisted. I wouldn't like to go late to Samuel's class."

"If he is so violent, why not tell your headmaster about it?"

"They say that even the headmaster is afraid of him. He is such a violent man."

And then Swami gave a lurid account of Samuel's violence; how when he started caning he would not stop till he saw blood on the boy's hand, which he made the boy press to his forehead like a vermilion marking. Swami hoped that with this his father would be made to see that he couldn't go to his class late. But Father's behaviour took an unexpected turn. He became excited. "What do these swine mean by beating our children? They must be driven out of service. I will see...'"

The result was he proposed to send Swami late to his class as a kind of challenge. He was also going to send a letter with Swami to the headmaster. No amount of protest from Swami was of any avail: Swami had to go to school.

By the time he was ready Father had composed a long letter to the headmaster, put it in an envelope and sealed it.

"What have you written, Father?" Swaminathan asked apprehensively.

"Nothing for you. Give it to your headmaster and go to your class."

"Have you written anything about our teacher Samuel?"

"Plenty of things about him. When your headmaster reads it he will probably dismiss Samuel from the school and hand him over to the police."

"What has he done, Father?"

"Well, there is a full account of everything he has done in the letter. Give it to your headmaster and go to your class. You must bring an acknowledgment from him in the evening."

Swami went to school feeling that he was the worst perjurer on earth. His conscience bothered him: he wasn't at all sure if he had been accurate in his description of Samuel. He could not decide how much of what he had said was imagined and how much of it was real. He stopped for a moment on the roadside to make up his mind about Samuel: he was not such a bad man after all. Personally he was much more genial than the rest; often he cracked a joke or two centring around Swami's inactions, and Swami took it as a mark of Samuel's personal regard for him. But there was no doubt that he treated people badly... His cane skinned people's hands. Swami cast his mind about for an instance of this. There was none within his knowledge. Years and years ago he was reputed to have skinned the knuckles of a boy in First Standard and made him smear the blood on his face. No one had actually seen it. But year after year the story persisted among the boys... Swami's head was dizzy with confusion in regard to Samuel's character—whether he was good or bad, whether he deserved the allegations in the letter or not... Swami felt an impulse to run home and beg his father to take back the letter. But Father was an obstinate man.

As he approached the yellow building he realized that he was perjuring himself and ruining his teacher. Probably the headmaster would dismiss Samuel and then the police would chain him and put him in jail. For all this disgrace, humiliation and suffering who would be responsible? Swami shuddered. The more he thought of Samuel, the more he grieved for him—the dark face, his small red-streaked eyes, his thin line of moustache, his unshaven cheek and chin, his yellow coat; everything filled Swami with sorrow. As he felt the bulge of the letter in his pocket, he felt like an executioner. For a moment he was angry with his father and wondered why he should not fling into the gutter the letter of a man so unreasonable and stubborn.

As he entered the school gate an idea occurred to him, a sort of solution. He wouldn't deliver the letter to the headmaster immediately, but at the end of the day—to that extent he would disobey his father and exercise his independence. There was nothing wrong in it, and Father would not know it anyway. If the letter was given at the end of the day there was a chance that Samuel might do something to justify the letter.

Swami stood at the entrance to his class. Samuel was teaching arithmetic. He looked at Swami for a moment. Swami stood hoping that Samuel would fall on him and tear his skin off. But Samuel merely asked, "Are you just coming to the class?"

"Yes, sir."

"You are half an hour late."

"I know it." Swami hoped that he would be attacked now. He almost prayed: "God of Thirupathi, please make Samuel beat me."

"Why are you late?"

Swami wanted to reply, "Just to see what you can do." But he merely said, "I have a headache, sir."

"Then why did you come to school at all?"

A most unexpected question from Samuel. "My father said that I shouldn't miss the class, sir," said Swami.

This seemed to impress Samuel. "Your father is quite right; a very sensible man. We want more parents like him."

"Oh, you poor worm!" Swami thought. "You don't know what my father has done to you." He was more puzzled than ever about Samuel's character.

"All right, go to your seat. Have you still a headache?"

"Slightly, sir."

Swami went to his seat with a bleeding heart. He had never met a man so good as Samuel. The teacher was inspecting the home lessons, which usually produced (at least, according to Swami's impression) scenes of great violence. Notebooks would be flung at faces, boys would be abused, caned and made to stand up on benches. But today Samuel appeared to have developed more tolerance and gentleness. He pushed away the bad books, just touched people with the cane, never made anyone stand up for more than a few minutes. Swami's turn came. He almost thanked God for the chance.

"Swaminathan, where is your homework?"

"I have not done any homework, sir," he said blandly.

There was a pause.

"Why—headache?" asked Samuel.

"Yes, sir."

"All right, sit down." Swami sat down, wondering what had come over Samuel. The period came to an end, and Swami felt desolate. The last period for the day was again taken by Samuel. He came this time to teach them Indian history. The period began at 3:45 and ended at 4:30. Swaminathan had sat through the previous periods thinking acutely. He could not devise any means of provoking Samuel. When the clock struck four Swami felt desperate. Half an hour more. Samuel was reading the red text, the portion describing Vasco da Gama's arrival in India. The boys listened in half-languor. Swami suddenly asked at the top of his voice, "Why did not Columbus come to India, sir?"

"He lost his way."

"I can't believe it; it is unbelievable, sir."

"Why?"

"Such a great man. Would he have not known the way?"

"Don't shout. I can hear you quite well."

"I am not shouting, sir; this is my ordinary voice, which God has given me. How can I help it?"

"Shut up and sit down."

Swaminathan sat down, feeling slightly happy at his success. The teacher threw a puzzled, suspicious glance at him and resumed his lessons.

His next chance occurred when Sankar of the first bench got up and asked, "Sir, was Vasco da Gama the very first person to come to India?"

Before the teacher could answer, Swami shouted from the back bench, "That's what they say."

The teacher and all the boys looked at Swami. The teacher was puzzled by Swami's obtrusive behaviour today. "Swaminathan, you are shouting again."

"I am not shouting, sir. How can I help my voice, given by God?" The school clock struck a quarter-hour. A quarter more. Swami felt he must do something drastic in fifteen minutes. Samuel had no doubt scowled at him and snubbed him, but it was hardly adequate. Swami felt that with a little more effort Samuel could be made to deserve dismissal and imprisonment.

The teacher came to the end of a section in the textbook and stopped. He proposed to spend the remaining few minutes putting questions to the boys. He ordered the whole class to put away their books, and asked someone in the second row, "What is the date of Vasco da Gama's arrival in India?"

Swaminathan shot up and screeched, "1648, December 20."

"You needn't shout," said the teacher. He asked, "Has your headache made you mad?"

"I have no headache now, sir," replied the thunderer brightly.

"Sit down, you idiot." Swami thrilled at being called an idiot. "If you get up again I will cane you," said the teacher. Swami sat down, feeling happy at the promise. The teacher then asked, "I am going to put a few questions on the Mughal period. Among the Mughal emperors, whom would you call the greatest, whom the strongest and whom the most religious emperor?"

Swami got up. As soon as he was seen, the teacher said emphatically, "Sit down."

"I want to answer, sir."

"Sit down."

"No, sir; I want to answer."

"What did I say I'd do if you got up again?"

"You said you would cane me and peel the skin off my knuckles and make me press it on my forehead."

"All right; come here."

Swaminathan left his seat joyfully and hopped on the platform. The teacher took out his cane from the drawer and shouted angrily, "Open your hand, you little devil." He whacked three wholesome cuts on each palm. Swami received them without blenching. After half a dozen the teacher asked, "Will these do, or do you want some more?"

Swami merely held out his hand again, and received two more; and the bell rang. Swami jumped down from the platform with a light heart, though his hands were smarting. He picked up his books, took out the letter lying in his pocket and ran to the headmaster's room. He found the door locked.

He asked the peon, "Where is the headmaster?"

"Why do you want him?"

"My father has sent a letter for him."

"He has taken the afternoon off and won't come back for a week. You can give the letter to the assistant headmaster. He will be here now."

"Who is he?"

"Your teacher, Samuel. He will be here in a second."

Swaminathan fled from the place. As soon as Swami went home with the letter, Father remarked, "I knew you wouldn't deliver it, you coward."

"I swear our headmaster is on leave," Swaminathan began.

Father replied, "Don't lie in addition to being a coward . . ."

Swami held up the envelope and said, "I will give this to the headmaster as soon as he is back . . ." Father snatched it from his hand, tore it up and thrust it into the wastepaper basket under his table. He muttered, "Don't come to me for help even if Samuel throttles you. You deserve your Samuel."

# CHAPTER 4

## SPECIAL CHALLENGES

Barbara Packer, "The Blue Eagle"
Hortense Calisher, "A Wreath for Miss Totten"
Denise Chávez, "Space Is a Solid: Kari Lee"
Lynda Schor, "Class Outing"
Joan O'Donovan, "Little Brown Jesus"

The stories in this chapter contemplate not only especially difficult physical and psychological challenges faced by some children but ethical and social ones as well. The stories raise some troubling themes, most notably the physical, mental, and socioeconomic inequities that prevail in children's lives. Some of the stories address these themes with dignity and grace, but others are imbued with tones of scorn and pity. Prepare yourself for an emotional roller-coaster ride.

In "The Blue Eagle," Barbara Packer provides a classic example of the complexity inherent in the lives of children with special challenges—both inside and outside the classroom. This story chronicles the first year of teaching for Miss McCall and highlights her relationship with one of her students, Caleb McCormick, who is severely retarded. Miss McCall becomes Caleb's protector against the abuses and cruelty of the other students. The story takes place during the early 1930s in rural California amid the hardships of the Great Depression. Caleb collects blue eagles, the sign of the National Recovery Agency (NRA). The blue eagles become a link between Caleb and the teacher—a metaphor for their relationship and a sign of their commitment to each other. Unfortunately, although Miss McCall can protect Caleb from abuses within her classroom, she is powerless to protect him from the world outside.

In "A Wreath for Miss Totten," Hortense Calisher reminds the reader that teachers of students with special challenges can have an impact far beyond the students' time in their classrooms. In this story a narrator reminisces nostalgically about a teacher, Miss Totten, and a student with special challenges, Lilly (Mooley) Davis. Mooley has a speech impairment (a cleft palate) and has spent the past few years in the "ungraded class" of the school.

> *[The ungraded class,] made up of the mute, the shambling, and the oddly tall, some of whom were delivered by bus, was housed in a basement part of the school, with a separate entrance which was forbidden us not only by rule but by a lurking distaste of our own.*

Mooley joins the students of Miss Totten's "graded class" when all the ungraded classes in the New York public schools are "disbanded." Unfortunately, Mooley has fallen far behind the other students and seems doomed to remain there—and the other students know it. Miss Totten's quiet compassion in dealing with Mooley has indelibly etched her image on the mind of the narrator.

Denise Chávez's story "Space Is a Solid: Kari Lee" is set in a rural elementary classroom that contains two students (Arlin and Ginita) who present special challenges. Kari Lee Wembley is another student in the class and seems more hesitant to express herself in physical movement and play than the students with physical challenges. As the students participate in an imaginative activity for Miss Esquibel's Drama Appreciation III class in which everyone is supposed to be a molecule, Kari Lee instead uses the time to reflect upon her classmates, revealing the attitudes that shape one child's understanding of children with special challenges and of her own physical identity:

> Arlin doesn't care about anything but mean boy things, like rough-housing and saying hell and damn. He'll start squawking and flapping around the room, bumping into people and Miss E will say, "Good, Arlin, good! Molecules are like that, they pop and hop!" Everyone laughs but I think he's showing off because he doesn't have arms.
>
> Mama told me, "You mean Arlin Threadgill is in your Drama Appreciation III class, why for land's sakes, Kari Lee, he's a crippled boy! His mama was one of those that took that drug Thalitomite, I think that's what they call it, causing that poor boy that horrible disfigurement for the rest of his born life. God almighty, but ain't I glad you got no stumps like that, Kari Lee Wembley."

In "Class Outing" Lynda Schor provides a sharp-edged and pathetic portrayal of five students with special challenges (Bernadette, Sondra, Marc, Charles, and Laura). The story follows their lives as they try to eke out an existence in the uninspiring classroom to which they are consigned. No lofty goals or aspirations inform teaching and learning; the students' classroom lives are composed of mindless chatter and inane assignments. The excerpt that follows, in which Miss Alba (their teacher) has just returned the students' essays, reveals the classroom's chaos. All students except one were chastised for writing only "a sentence fragment."

> "I'm returning your essays," said Miss Alba.
> "What essays?" Laura asked.
> "Your essays on whether you would die for your beliefs."..."Do any of you know what an essay is?"
> The class was silent except for Charles' version of the takeoff of the Boeing 747 jet. Miss Alba began to weep. Bernadette watched, drooling; the class, nonplussed, sat and stared.

The confusion in the lives of these students seems to make them impossibly resilient—up to a point. In this excerpt, Miss Alba has run out of tissues, a situation that leads her to push a student to the breaking point:

> "Charles, how come there's only one tissue left in this box? I realize I have sinus trouble, but did I use them all up?" Charles looked at the floor.
> "He used them for making airplanes," said Laura.
> "Tattletale," spat Sondra.
> "Charles, for that you go into the closet." Charles began to cry.
> "He's afraid of the dark," said Laura with relish.
> "I'm sorry about your science trouble, Miss Alba," said Charles, trembling.

*"Couldn't we leave the closet door open?" asked Laura, repentant.*

*"No," said Miss Alba. "Charles has to learn not to deface other people's property."*
*She led a slumped and passive Charles into the closet.*

*. . . Bernadette could see his face redden and tears begin to fall as the closet door was*
*shut. For a moment the class was silent. Then a plaintive cry rose eerily from within the*
*metal wardrobe. Miss Alba steeled herself; the others fidgeted.*

The story reaches a sad and disturbing climax during a field trip to the zoo as one of the
students, Bernadette, tries to rescue herself from an increasingly desperate situation. The
story contains sexually explicit content, showing how children can be exploited by the
adults they turn to for protection.

Joan O'Donovan, in "Little Brown Jesus," provides an example of a sympathetic and
understanding teacher and her effect on "backward" elementary students in an "opportunity" school classroom. The story also probes children's views and reactions to cultural
and racial differences. The story's action unfolds as a baby Jesus doll is about to be selected for the Christmas play. Doreen Bax brings in a cute, little black doll, and Heliotrope
Smith brings in a big, white adult female doll—and the debate begins. Nonsense, farce,
and raw-edged feelings about race characterize their interchange:

*"That small one? I don't think that's good enough to be Jesus, miss, that little doll". . .*
*[Heliotrope]*

*"Jesus wasn't a lady!". . . [Doreen]*

*"Jesus could've been anything he liked!" she [Heliotrope] snapped. "He could've*
*been a mouse, or a lion anything! It says so in the Bible."*

*"Well he was a baby in the play, Heliotrope Smith, so there!"*

*"Your doll's black!" she [Heliotrope] said baldly. "The one thing Jesus never was*
*was black. Jesus was real white." She jutted a shoulder contemptuously.*

The teacher's sense of fairness and ability to think on her feet bring humor and cohesive-
ness to a Christmas play that keeps threatening to come apart at the edges.

Each of the stories in this chapter stand as testimony to the amazingly complex
worlds of children with special challenges. As the reader will find, some of the fictional
portraits are brutally honest, unsympathetic and just plain ugly but others are not. Miss
Alba is frightening and students in her classroom must pick their way cautiously. Everything seems awkward. Just the opposite seems true in Miss McCall's and Miss Totten's
classrooms. These fictional teachers are emblematic of those who strive to ensure that students, christened with special challenges, have more to gain than to lose in their classrooms.

# The Blue Eagle

## BARBARA PACKER

It was October already, and still I had received no offers of a job. All through the dismal summer of 1932 I had trekked across the smoldering, somnolent San Joaquin Valley in search of work, but the bright promise of my new-minted teacher's credential tarnished slowly under the hopelessly shaking heads of the administrators who interviewed me. In the end I, too, must have acquired the look of empty apathy I saw in the faces of the transient workers who passed me, drifting in and out of the tinfoil mirages on the long straight country roads. Nothing we did could dent the mute resistance of these squat, identical little towns; they lay shuttered and smug behind a barricade of impenetrable heat. Driving through the streets of a new town, past the dingy frame houses with careless, weedy lawns, to the bulbous pastel stucco of the mock-Spanish school where I was once again rejected, or lying on hot nights in old hotels, listening to the impotent drone of the water coolers, I discovered that despair—romantic novels and tabloid suicide accounts to the contrary—is a silent, sifting emotion that settles like peat dust into all the little corners of the soul.

At home I lived in tacit disgrace. My parents tried to seem sympathetic, but they could not conceal their disappointment that four years of college tuition squeezed from a depression-crippled family budget had netted me nothing—neither husband nor job. Thus, I responded to the call from the County Schools Office one Wednesday with an abject eagerness that must have startled even the Superintendent's secretary. And I was nearly forty-five minutes early for my appointment the following Monday. I bit my fingernails; I watched the huge ball bearings that belched their way to the surface of the hall water cooler. I memorized every curve of the black Roman lettering that stood out against the clouded glass door like enemy airplanes:

## MR. HAROLD LEANDER
## COUNTY SUPERINTENDENT OF SCHOOLS

Finally, a secretary admitted me and, smiling like a doctor's receptionist, gestured me into an inner office.

Mr. Leander peered at me from over the tops of glasses that had slid far down the hump of his formidable nose. He pulled them off with an expansive, reel-casting sideward wave and contemplated them intently as he folded the wings together.

"Good morning, Miss McCall," he said without looking up. "Do sit down."

The chair he indicated was treacherous, overstuffed. I had the feeling, as I moved toward it, that it would envelop me like some sort of predatory plant. "We have a *tentative*—" he paused dramatically, "a *tentative* position for you, Miss McCall. Now, I want you to understand that *I* will understand if you choose to refuse—it might seem a bit too *demanding* for a beginning teacher like yourself."

He glanced down, pawing at a faded desk blotter in a morocco frame, and lifted one side to extract a small folded square of cloth. I had a startling glimpse of the blotter's original hue—a rich, irrigated green.

"You'd be teaching at the Cotton Creek School—you know where that is?—unincorporated, about thirty-eight students, grades one through eight." He opened the glasses again and began wiping an imaginary fingerprint from the left lens. "Thirty-seven, thirty-eight . . . but not forty! Somehow, we can just *never* seem to scrape up forty students, Miss McCall, and that brings us to that *first* hitch I was talking about."

I had the odd, uneasy feeling of being an invisible intruder at a Chautauqua lecturer's drawing-room dress rehearsal. He had not mentioned hitches—to me, at any rate. It was as if the interviewee before me had huffed out in mid-argument, and I had glided soundlessly into place, like a gadget on a conveyor belt, while the even flow of Mr. Leander's rhetoric continued undisturbed.

"Because if there were forty students, the state would allow us to hire two teachers instead of one. As it is, you'd have to handle the whole bunch by yourself." He flashed a row of long brown teeth at me apologetically.

"You may be asking yourself," he switched to the right lens, "—you may be asking yourself *why* we are looking for a teacher nearly *three months* after the beginning of the term." He dismissed the spectacles altogether and leaned suddenly, earnestly across the desk toward me. "I'll be frank. The teacher we *had* hired has quit. And this brings us to our *second* hitch."

He sighed, settled back into his leather chair, which creaked familiarly, and shifted his gaze to the Venetian blinds. "Some of the kids are pretty tough characters. Lots of Italians (he pronounced it "Eye-talians"), Japanese—a few Okies, I think. Well, to make a long story short, your predecessor—or *prospective* predecessor, heh heh—was *struck* by one of the boys when she attempted to discipline him. He has been suspended, of course. Miss Chilcote is not as young as yourself, and she feels she isn't quite up to—well—keeping *up* with the children. But I'm sure if you take a firm stand right from the start—show them you won't stand for any funny business—*you* won't have any trouble. I suggest you turn any discipline problems over to Mr. McAteer—he's on the school board, lives right across the road from the school. Salary is a hundred a month, that's ten months, a thousand a year. And there's twenty dollars extra for cleaning the latrines and things—oh, but of course you'll want to give that to one of the boys. Well, can we count you in?"

His horse's smile widened as I nodded.

The Cotton Creek School looked as though it had been translated bodily from a dimestore oil painting. The yellow frame building was hemmed in by oak trees with rope-and-board swings; there was a hand pump, a pot-bellied stove, and a real school bell whose dangling umbilical I was to yank each morning. I half expected to find, as I approached the door that first nervous Monday, that the knob was nothing but a thick glob of pigment on a façade which would prove impregnably two-dimensional.

But the door and the room behind it turned out to be real, after all. I deposited my things on the desk, went outside again and, feeling faintly foolish, sawed away at the bell rope five or six times. While I waited for the class to assemble, I tried to familiarize myself with the names in the classbook Miss Chilcote had left, but my nervous eyes blurred the column of names beyond deciphering; the twin boundaries of "Areias, A." and "Zannoni, P." were all I could make out.

The class trickled in and settled slowly, the rows of faces grading from oatmeal to creamed-coffee, like spools at a thread counter. Thirty-seven blank bright pairs of eyes regarded me with mild curiosity. I cleared my throat, and rose.

"Good morning, boys and girls, I am your new teacher, Miss McCall."

Good Lord, this was awful! The metallic vibration of my own voice seemed to describe the vague outlines of a sour schoolmarm on the brittle morning air: the reticule, the dressmaker's mouth, a turd of scraggly hair decomposing at neck's nape. For one moment of wild panic I could think of nothing more to say.

"Ah—I—let's see now; I want to make out a temporary seating chart, so that I can begin to learn your names. As I call on you, please give me your name and grade." I gestured to a large brown boy in the back of the classroom.

"Me?" He looked wildly around him, decided I had not meant the wall. "Om Giulio Gianinni." The class tittered. Giulio looked about fourteen.

"And what grade are you in, Giulio?"

He shifted uncomfortably in his chair. "Om inna eighth grade."

A similar hulk in front of him grunted. "Om Eddie Gianinni. Om inna eighth grade, too." "Erwin Grubb, eighth grade." Erwin's pale eyes and muddy hair were repeated around the room, a constellation of drab kin. "Miya Takemoto, seventh grade." Mitsuo Takemoto, sixth grade. Bright eyes, musical syllables. I was reminded of a sign I had seen at the entrance to an orchard—Many Beautiful Fruits for Sale.

"Fronie Grubb, eighth grade." "Ada Simpson, fifth grade." "Joanna Souza, sixth grade." "Tony Areias, fourth grade." I felt a warm glow of friendly recognition. "Ortensia Perez, fourth grade." "Clem Grubb, sixth grade."

There was a pause. I craned to see who was not answering. "Yes? Who's next?" It was a small, fat boy. His oddly shaped head, topped by a mat of red hair, was nodding and jerking like a marionette. "Yes? What's your name?"

Clem nudged him from behind. "Yer *name,* stoop. Tell 'er yer name."

Like a wind-up toy suddenly set in motion, the boy began to wave a fat pink fist. "Duh boo eagow," he said.

The class exploded in riotous laughter; teetering with hilarity, Clem punched the boy's shoulder. "Naw, stoop, yer—haw, haw—*name.* Teacher wantsta—haw—know yer *name.*"

"Duh boo eagow," repeated the boy serenely, regarding with benign approval the outburst he had occasioned. "He ain't real smart, ma'am," offered Clem.

"Well—er, what's his name?"

"Name's—haw—Caleb McCormick."

At the mention of his name, the boy seemed to notice me for the first time. He waved his fist once more, then let the fingers uncurl to show what he was holding—a small, rectangular metal plate with the blue eagle of the National Recovery Act and its motto: We Do Our Part.

"Uh, where did he . . . I mean, what does . . . the eagle?"

"He got it offa Runyon's store. He wanted it, see, an' ole man Runyon let 'im have it. He saves 'em, see?" Clem leaned forward, deftly flipping

up the top of Caleb's desk. A huge pile of scraps—little corners of paper, little blue eagles, torn raggedly off of cigarette cartons, bags of potato chips, bread wrappers, cereal boxes—fluttered like crippled butterflies in the gust. "He ain't real smart," said Clem.

A note I found in the classbook that night explained matters further. "One child in the class, Caleb McCormick, is severely retarded. He should not, properly speaking, be in this school at all, but his parents refuse to admit that he is not normal and, as he is quiet and cooperative, he is allowed to attend. He is 11 years old. Do not leave the desk unlocked; the children will put snakes in it. (Signed) Wilhelmina Chilcote."

Miss Chilcote's parting admonition turned out to be prophetic of things to come. When the children realized that I was not merely another substitute teacher, but a more or less permanent fixture, the pranks began. All the traditional devices were employed—tacks on the chair, worms in the pencil holder—but some of the tactics revealed a fiendish originality, as when someone deposited a small frog in my shoe while I squatted to supervise the first-graders' finger painting. By an effort of sheer will I managed to pretend that I did not notice the slimy green mass crawling up my stocking and to express, when it was pointed out to me, nothing more than mild sympathy for the frog. Luckily, the pump was not visible from the classroom window, or the children could have seen me retching as I washed the squashed viscera from my foot.

My stamina must have impressed them, for eventually the pranks ceased. And I *was* truly eager to succeed at my job. I tried to invent ways to make schoolwork seem interesting. I encouraged classroom contests—spelling bees, historical guessing games, mental arithmetic matches. When we studied Greece and Rome, I draped the children in sheets and had them act out scenes from the history books; for California history we made papier-mâché models of Father Serra's missions.

But at Christmastime I cemented their growing affection once and for all; I wrote a Christmas play in which each child had a part and to which the delighted parents were invited. I wrapped the Gianinnis in bedspreads and cut crowns out of gold paper; the Grubb children were shepherds and the younger children, angels or sheep.

I was curious to see Caleb's parents, but they did not come. He seemed not to mind, though, and sat in his assigned place behind the manager, a sedentary shepherd in my father's bathrobe. Someone had knotted two shoelaces together and run the ends through the holes at either end of his NRA sign; it now hung down around his neck like the breastplate of the Twelve Tribes.

I made real improvements, too. I got permission from the school board to use the small kitchen in the building to make hot chocolate in the morning—at my own cost. Noticing that the Italian children came with lunches bulging with more bread and blood sausage than they could possibly eat, while the Grubbs lurked like hungry cats in the corner, I suggested that we all pool our leftovers and share equally. I encouraged the children to save their blue eagles for Caleb.

The dank, oppressive winter rolled in; the dingy fog crawled up from the river and settled. Then one day I had a revelation.

I was sweeping the classroom before school when Caleb's queer, flat head appeared in the doorway.

"You're a little early today, aren't you, Caleb?"

He nodded, gazing intently at the moving broom. I continued sweeping; suddenly he lumbered across the floor, grabbing at the broom handle with both chubby hands. I did not let go; I suppose I was afraid he wanted to hit me, and so we each tugged fiercely, a couple of grotesque baseball players vying for first-ups. His bovine face registered a hurt look.

"Sweep, O.K.?"

"Caleb, I—"

"O.K.?" He tugged harder; in a moment he would begin to whine. "O.K.?"

"Caleb, it's nice of you to—ugh—want to— ugh—sweep, but I—"

"Duh boo eagow! Duh boo eagow!"

"—don't really think . . ."

I stopped, dumbfounded. "O.K.?" He continued to tug, more gently.

I let him have the broom. He swept the room calmly and carefully, evidently pleased. I retreated to my desk in silence, trying to comprehend the enormity of what he had just said. I was not even sure that I had heard him correctly. When the class was filing out for morning recess I called him back.

"Caleb, I want you to clean the erasers for me. Right now." I demonstrated. "O.K.?"

He stared longingly out at the swings.

"O.K., Caleb?" I had to know. "Caleb . . . the blue eagle?"

He turned; his face beamed radiant comprehension.

"Duh boo eagow," he nodded, and touched his little amulet reverently.

That was all I ever had to say. He began to search out tasks himself when he had exhausted routine classroom chores, each time tapping his token, beaming at me as though we two shared some magnificent private joke, and adding, "Duh boo eagow," by way of explanation.

I do not know when he had taken it into his head to ask, who it was who had explained, what the little motto on his sign *meant;* even less can I hope to understand the dim process of reason by which he had apprehended that motto in such a uniquely personal way. Perhaps he puzzled out the words himself, or heard them on the radio; perhaps his parents simply saw an opportunity to coerce more chore-power from him. He merely believed that his devotion to the blue eagle obligated him to serve everyone, that is all.

And his faith, I think, implied a correlative hope. He would have maintained, I think, that if he, Caleb McCormick, only did his part, he could remedy all the woes of the nation: appease the feral eyes of the hungry children in Hoovervilles, line the pockets of the street-corner apple vendors, reverse the trajectories of falling Wall Street bankers.

Hey, *stoop!* Catch!" Giulio held the scuffed softball out to Caleb, "it" in a recess game of keep-away.

"Hey, *stoopid!* Can't ya even catch a stoopid *ball?*" The boys waited until Caleb was almost upon them, then tossed it just out of reach again. He plodded humbly from one to another, turning clumsily like a poor dancing bear, as they darted around him. "Over here, stoop, *lookit!*"

Suddenly, Eddie reached out and gave a savage jerk on the little tin plate; the frayed shoestring broke. Caleb did not realize his loss, and grubbed happily in the dust for the ball they let drop.

"Hey, stoopid, hey, Caleb, lookit!" Caleb looked up at Eddie, still smiling uncomprehendingly. "Looka *here!*" Eddie shrieked. The rest began to chant: "*Weee gotcher eeeagle, weee gotcher eeeagle!*" Caleb caught sight of the plate in Eddie's outstretched hand. For a second he groped wildly at his chest; then he began to howl.

He stumbled to his feet, wailing—a hoarse, terrified cry—and chased them. They passed the plate, thundering across the yard toward the classroom in a nightmare inversion of brutality—one man chasing a mob. I could not stand it any longer, and when the eagle appeared near me like a quick fish above the sea of hands, I grabbed the wrist that held it.

The normally smooth contours of the brown face Eddie swiveled up at me now betrayed the ravages of a sudden fury. Long furrows of rage deepened as I pried the plate loose from his determined hand, finger by finger. At that moment Caleb caught up with the mob, blundering his way through its outskirts, wailing, wailing. Eddie grimaced up at me for one taut moment longer, then with a violent spasm jerked himself free and ran into the classroom. I had just turned to reach the battered token out to Caleb when the crash came.

A gust of wind was already scattering the scraps. I could not reach Eddie in time to prevent him from throwing two handfuls of paper eagles out the window; I caught him as he turned to run away and slapped him twice, as hard as I could. Behind me the wail widened into a scream.

The scraps still fluttered around the room like dislodged moths, as if the stenciled eagles provided a motive power of their own. Caleb tried vainly to trap one or two, then dropped to his knees in an effort to prevent the wind from eroding the rest of the pile. I tried to press the tin plate into his hand, but he would not be distracted; he held it to his chest, howling a howl into which was compressed all misery, all bereavement, all despair.

We shut the windows and righted the desk; we gathered all the scraps we could find and brought them back to Caleb, but we could not comfort him. All the while Eddie stood motionless in the corner, my red handprints darkening on his face like snapshot negatives.

I was too upset to continue teaching. I dismissed school for the rest of the day and told Miya Takemoto to take Caleb home. I motioned to Eddie to remain behind.

"Eddie, look at me," I said, when the class had gone. The brown hills of his cheeks were smooth, expressionless. "Why did you do it?"

He shrugged.

"Answer me, Eddie. Why did you steal his eagle? A poor boy like that! You should be ashamed."

Eddie continued to stare at the floor.

"I ought to send you to Mr. McAteer for a good strapping. Why did you do it, Eddie? Why?"

"Own't know," he mumbled.

Spring finally exploded, raw and vulgar, like a Mexican movie poster, yellow-green and orange. The harsh Valley wildflowers clawed the fields: scratchy fiddle-neck, angry fists of niggertoes on their wire stalks, poppies that fell apart as soon as they were picked. A scarlet-fever epidemic struck.

Soon I had thirty students; then twenty-eight. One day Caleb, too, came to school ill, his face the color of Indian paintbrush, his eyes glazed by fever. I took his temperature—102—and sent him home. He came back the next day, and I sent him home again, this time with a note. When he returned a third time, I drove him home myself. His mother came out to meet me.

"Good afternoon. I'm Miss McCall, your son's teacher."

"Afternoon," she nodded, "pleased to meet you."

"I sent Caleb home yesterday; didn't he give you the note?"

She eyed me uneasily. "Yes'm, I got it, but we don't believe in that sort a stuff."

"I beg your pardon?"

"We don't believe in that sort a stuff," she repeated.

"In *what* sort of stuff?"

"In doctors, medicine.... We believe in the healing power of the Good Book."

I stared at her in disbelief. "Can't you see, Mrs. McCormick, that Caleb is a very sick boy?"

"The Lord will do as he sees fit."

The set of her jaw made me want to revile, to blaspheme. "He will, will He?" I sputtered. "Well, I'll do as *I* see fit. Scarlet fever is a highly contagious disease ... listen, if you send him to school once more I'll send the sheriff out here with him. He is a menace to the other children."

She stood there dumbly.

"And take him to a doctor—please? Don't you care about your son's life?"

"We're Scientists," she said; "we don't believe in that."

Caleb did not come to school any more. I drove by his house a few days later. I was shocked to find him sitting out under the trees, unattended. I got out of the car and walked over to him. The fever had wasted even his fat round face, and his eyes burned like swollen raisins. He was peeling layers of skin off himself; the dessicated tissue came away like birch bark.

"Caleb, is your mother home?" He looked up, not at me, but somewhere beyond me. "Mrs. McCormick!" I shouted, but no one answered.

"My eagows," said Caleb plaintively, touching the plate that still hung around his neck. Then, "Duh boo eagow," as though it were the revelation of some ultimate truth.

I left him there, still sitting under the trees, and drove straight to the County Schools' nurse. She promised to get a court order to have Caleb hospitalized. It occurred to me that Caleb would want to have the paper eagles from his desk at school. I planned to collect them for him, but I did not have the chance, for three days later the nurse called to say that he had died.

About a week after Caleb's death, a doorbell shattered the thick surface of our after-dinner torpor. My mother vanished quietly and returned with the news that there was a Mr. McCormick to see me.

I immediately felt sorry for the crabbed, beaten little face that seemed somehow stuck in the space framed by the doorway. It was a New England face, with a sour Calvinist flintiness, and it belonged to a countryside where the snow lasted into June. Here, against the rank proliferation of the Valley spring, Mr. McCormick's face looked like the solidification of a chronic whine. I suppose it had never seemed just that a land disgorging truckloads of grain, a land where props were stuck under the blousy boughs of orchard trees to keep them from cracking under the weight of the fruit, could force him to scrabble so hard and unsuccessfully for a living.

He would not come in. "I ain't gonna be but a minute. I come about Caleb." He seemed to be fighting the outbreak of some violent turbulence.

"I—I was deeply shocked—I mean, please let me offer my sympathy—Caleb was very dear—"

"You, you—your *sympathy*!" He blazed up suddenly, and I realized with a shock that the emotion in his washed-out eyes was rage. "You hypocrite! Thou *whited wall*! Scribes and Pharisees! If you hadna took him off to that—that—*hos*pital, that abomination in the sight of the Lord, heda been alive today. If we hadda been able to let the good Lord take care of him, trustin' in the power of the Good Book, like the Lord has advised His servants, but oh, no! Oh, no, don't nobody trust in the Lord no more. Makin' fun of him cause he warnt so smart as other boys, well, I'd like to see 'em on Judgment Day, when he ain't never done no harm and is received into the company of them as has been washed in the Blood of the Lamb!"

He shook his whole body at me defiantly, as if he were demanding a confirmation of some sort. I stood there, nodding stupidly.

"Well, if the Lord see fit to take him unto Himself, His servant will accept this cup, but like I say, if they warnt such abominations in the sight of the Lord...ye of little faith!" He waved a damning finger, not at me, but at the landscape. Suddenly his head dropped, and he trembled. "He was my only child, my only son."

The outburst had drained him of breath, and he looked as though he would suddenly collapse in upon himself, like a paper jack-o'-lantern. I waited helplessly.

"I—I...ain't got nothin' else ta say, I guess, I will pray to the Lord to give you faith." He straightened himself and marched back up the walk.

"Mr. McCormick!" On an impulse, I called out after him. "Ah—I'm sorry...I...do you know what became of Caleb's eagle?"

He looked at me uncomprehendingly.

"You know, the one he used to wear around his neck?"

He shook his head slowly. "I don't know. I don't know what become of it."

I drove out to the school then, past the black hunches of the asparagus fields, with their crop of minuscule sequoias, sentinel stalks springing up like a mythological forest of sown spears, each flanked by the fragile, ephemeral fern that crumbled to the touch; past the brocaded rice paddies, and the penny-colored sorghum, past the truck farms intersected by the arbitrary ramblings of ditches choked with tules. The pall of the peat dirt hung like a catafalque over the chapped hills, and crickets rasped like fingernails on plastic combs.

I unlocked the schoolroom and went in. In the utter quiet of the half-light its emptiness seemed vaguely sinister. I opened Caleb's desk. Nothing was in it but the scraps, fluttering forlornly with the mute sadness of the aftermath of a ticker-tape parade. I emptied them into an out-spread sheet of newspaper and carried them outside to the incinerator. After a few clumsy attempts, I succeeded in lighting the fire, but forgot to cover it with the rusty screen. Dozens of little scraps borne up by the blaze flickered out across the dark furrows. I remembered with horror the roadside warnings: "Do not cast lighted material from your car: Remember, peat land burns." Then I thought: let it burn.

But I did not succeed in exorcising the little eagles. Even long after the NRA no longer functioned, my eyes did not cease to apply the blue birds like invisible decals to shop windows, flour sacks, faces, hearts.

I finished the term. But I did not write for the children any more plays, nor bring hot chocolate, and I did not care, any more, if the Grubb children came away from lunch smelling of Italian blood sausage. I felt somehow cheated, taken in by some brutal and grotesque trick, like the time I had paid a dime at a sideshow to "See A Baby Six Inches Long" and had found, behind the holy secrecy of the tattered velvet curtain, a purpling foetus in a Mason jar.

The cloudy door of Mr. Leander's office held no terrors for me now, nor would his forensics intimidate me. I sat silently while he perused the board report.

"We're *very* pleased with your work, Miss McCall, very pleased indeed."

"Thank you."

"Now then, can we plan to renew your contract for another year? With a raise in salary, of course."

"No, I think not."

"No?—ah, too bad." He began to smile, a knowing, satisfied, pimp's leer. "What—ah—seemed to be the trouble?"

"Oh—pranks, I guess. There were too many things to interfere with the business of teaching. They put a frog in my shoe, a live frog."

"I understand. Well, I'm sure we can find you a place in the city schools. A better class of student."

"I'd appreciate that."

He glanced at the report again. "Then, too, you've had bad luck. There was that incident involving the retarded boy's death—that's always upsetting. Still, in this case, it's probably a blessing."

"Yes," I said, "it's probably all for the best." He nodded sagely, and his long upper lip began to rise slowly, like an opera curtain, over the brown expanse of his teeth. "Glad to have you back with us, Miss McCall."

I returned his smile. The desecration was complete.

# A Wreath for Miss Totten

## HORTENSE CALISHER

Children growing up in the country take their images of integrity from the land. The land, with its changes, is always about them, a pervasive truth, and their midget foregrounds are crisscrossed with minute dramas which are the animalcules of a larger vision. But children who grow in a city where there is nothing greater than the people brimming up out of subways, riveleting in the streets—these children must take their archetypes where and if they find them.

In P. S. 146, between periods, when the upper grades were shunted through the halls in that important procedure known as "departmental," although most of the teachers stood about chatting relievedly in couples, Miss Totten always stood at the door of her "home room," watching us straightforwardly, alone. As, struggling and muffled, we lined past the other teachers, we often caught snatches of upstairs gossip which we later perverted and enlarged; passing before Miss Totten we deflected only that austere look, bent solely on us.

Perhaps, with the teachers, as with us, she was neither admired nor loathed but simply ignored. Certainly none of us ever fawned on her as we did on the harshly blond and blue-eyed Miss Steele, who never wooed us with a smile but slanged us delightfully in the gym, giving out the exercises in a voice like scuffed gravel. Neither did she obsess us in the way of the Misses Comstock, two liverish, stunted women who could have had nothing so vivid about them as our hatred for them, and though all of us had a raffish hunger for metaphor, we never dubbed Miss Totten with a nickname.

Miss Totten's figure, as she sat tall at her desk or strode angularly in front of us rolling down the long maps over the blackboard, had that instantaneous clarity, one metallic step removed from the real, of the daguerreotype. Her clothes partook of this period too—long, saturnine waists and skirts of a stuff identical with that in a good family um-

brella. There was one like it in the umbrella-stand at home—a high black one with a seamed ivory head. The waists enclosed a vestee of dim, but steadfast lace; the skirts grazed narrow boots of that etiolated black leather, venerable with creases, which I knew to be a sign both of respectability and foot trouble. But except for the vestee, all of Miss Totten, too, folded neatly to the dark point of her shoes, and separated from these by her truly extraordinary length, her face presided above, a lined, ocher ellipse. Sometimes, as I watched it on drowsy afternoons, her face floated away altogether and came to rest on the stand at home. Perhaps it was because of this guilty image that I was the only one who noticed Miss Totten's strange preoccupation with "Mooley" Davis.

Most of us in Miss Totten's room had been together as a group since first grade, but we had not seen Mooley since down in second grade, under the elder and more frightening of the two Comstocks. I had forgotten Mooley completely, but when she reappeared I remembered clearly the incident which had given her her name.

That morning, very early in the new term, back in Miss Comstock's, we had lined up on two sides of the classroom for a spelling bee. These were usually a relief to good and bad spellers alike, since it was the only part of our work which resembled a game, and even when one had to miss and sit down, there was a kind of dreamy catharsis in watching the tenseness of those still standing. Miss Comstock always rose for these occasions and came forward between the two lines, standing there in an oppressive close-up in which we could watch the terrifying action of the cords in her spindling gray neck and her slight smile as a boy or a girl was spelled down. As the number of those standing was reduced, the smile grew, exposing the oversize slabs of her teeth, through which the words issued in a voice increasingly unctuous and soft.

On this day the forty of us still shone with the first fall neatness of new clothes, still basked in that delightful anonymity in which neither our names nor our capacities were already part of the dreary foreknowledge of the teacher. The smart and quick had yet to assert themselves with their flying, staccato hands; the uneasy dull, not yet forced into recitations which would make their status clear, still preserved in the small, sinking corners of their hearts a lorn, factitious hope. Both teams were still intact when the word "mule" fell to the lot of a thin colored girl across the room from me, in clothes perky only with starch, her rusty fuzz of hair drawn back in braids so tightly sectioned that her eyes seemed permanently widened.

"Mule," said Miss Comstock, giving out the word. The ranks were still full. She had not yet begun to smile.

The girl looked back at Miss Comstock, soundlessly. All her face seemed drawn backward from the silent, working mouth, as if a strong, pulling hand had taken hold of the braids.

My turn, I calculated, was next. The procedure was to say the word, spell it out, and say it again. I repeated it in my mind: "Mule. M-u-l-e. Mule."

Miss Comstock waited quite a long time. Then she looked around the class, as if asking them to mark well and early this first malfeasance, and her handling of it.

"What's your name?" she said.

"Ull—ee." The word came out in a glottal, molasses voice, hardly articulate, the *l*'s scarcely pronounced.

"Lilly?"

The girl nodded.

"Lilly what?"

"Duh-avis."

"Oh. Lilly Davis. Mmmm. Well, spell 'mule,' Lilly." Miss Comstock trilled out the name beautifully.

The tense brown bladder of the girl's face swelled desperately, then broke at the mouth. "Mool," she said, and stopped "Mmm—oo—"

The room tittered. Miss Comstock stepped closer.

"*Mule!*"

The girl struggled again "Mool."

This time we were too near Miss Comstock to dare laughter.

Miss Comstock turned to our side. "Who's next?"

I half raised my hand.

"Go on." She wheeled around on Lilly, who was sinking into her seat. "No. Don't sit down."

I lowered my eyelids, hiding Lilly from my sight. "Mule," I said. "M-u-l-e. Mule."

The game continued, words crossing the room uneventfully. Some children survived. Others settled, abashed, into their seats, craning around to watch us. Again the turn came around to Lilly.

Miss Comstock cleared her throat. She had begun to smile.

"Spell it now, Lilly," she said. "Mule."

The long-chinned brown face swung from side to side in an odd writhing movement. Lilly's eyeballs rolled. Then the thick sound from her mouth was lost in the hooting, uncontrollable laughter of the whole class. For there was no doubt about it: the long, coffee-colored face, the whitish glint of the eyeballs, the bucking motion of the head suggested it to us all—a small brown quadruped, horse or mule, crazily stubborn, or at bay.

"Quiet!" said Miss Comstock. And we hushed, although she had not spoken loudly. For the word had smirked out from a wide, flat smile and on the stringy neck beneath there was a creeping, pleasurable flush which made it pink as a young girl's.

That was how Mooley Davis got her name, although we had a chance to use it only for a few weeks, in a taunting singsong when she hung up her coat in the morning, or as she flicked past the little dust-bin of a store where we shed our pennies for nigger-babies and tasteless, mottoed hearts. For after a few weeks, when it became clear that her cringing, mucoused talk was getting worse, she was transferred to the "ungraded" class. This group, made up of the mute, the shambling, and the oddly tall, some of whom were delivered by bus, was housed in a basement part of the school, with a separate entrance which was forbidden us not only by rule but by a lurking distaste of our own.

The year Mooley reappeared in Miss Totten's room, a dispute in the school system had disbanded all the ungraded classes in the city. Here and there, now, in the back seat of a class, there would be some grown-size boy who read haltingly from a primer, fingering the stubble of his slack jaw. Down in 4A there was a shiny, petted doll of a girl, all crackling hairbow and nimble wheelchair, over whom the teachers shook their heads feelingly, saying: "Bright as a dollar! Imagine!" as if there were something sinister in the fact that useless legs had not impaired the musculature of a mind. And in our class, in harshly clean, faded dresses which were always a little too infantile for her, her spraying ginger hair cut short now and held by a round comb which circled the back of her head like a snaggle-toothed tiara which had slipped, there was this bony, bug-eyed wraith of a girl who raised her hand instead of saying "Present!" when Miss Totten said "Lilly Davis?" at roll call, and never spoke at all.

It was Juliet Hoffman, the pace-setter among the girls in the class, who spoke Mooley's nickname first. A jeweller's daughter, Juliet had achieved an eminence even beyond that due her curly profile, embroidered dresses, and prancy, leading-lady ways when, the Christmas before, she had brought as her present to teacher a real diamond ring. It had been a modest diamond, to be sure, but undoubtedly real, and set in real gold. Juliet had heralded it for weeks before and we had all seen it—it and the peculiar look on the face of the teacher, a young substitute whom we hardly knew—when she had lifted it from the pile of hankies and fancy notepaper on her desk. The teacher, over the syrupy protests of Mrs. Hoffman, had returned the ring, but its sparkle lingered on, iridescent around Juliet's head.

On our way out at three o'clock that first day with Miss Totten, Juliet nudged at me to wait. Obediently, I waited behind her. Twiddling her bunny muff, she minced over to the clothes closet and confronted the new girl.

"I know you," she said. "Mooley Davis, that's who you are!" A couple of the other children hung back to watch.

"Aren't you? Aren't you Mooley Davis?"

I remember just how Mooley stood there because of the coat she wore. She just stood there holding her coat against her stomach with both hands. It was a coat of some pale, vague tweed, cut the same length as mine. But it wrapped the wrong way over for a girl and the revers, wide ones, came all the way down and ended way below the pressing hands.

"Where you been?" Juliet flipped us all a knowing grin. "You been in ungraded?"

One of Mooley's shoulders inched up so that it almost touched her ear, but beyond that, she did not seem able to move. Her eyes looked at us, wide and fixed. I had the feeling that all of her had retreated far, far back behind the eyes which—large and light, and purposefully empty—had been forced to stay.

My back was to the room, but on the suddenly wooden faces of the others I saw Miss Totten's shadow. Then she loomed thinly over Juliet, her arms, which were crossed at her chest, hiding the one V of white in her garments, so that she looked like an umbrella which had been tightly furled.

"What's *your* name?" she asked, addressing not so much Juliet as the white muff which, I noticed now, was slightly soiled.

"Jooly-ette."

"Hmm. Oh, yes. Juliet Hoffman."

"Jooly-ette, it is." She pouted creamily up at Miss Totten, her glance narrow with the assurance of finger rings to come.

Something flickered in the nexus of yellow wrinkles around Miss Totten's lips. Poking out a bony forefinger, she held it against the muff. "You tell your mother," she said slowly, "that the way she spells it, it's *Juliet.*"

Then she dismissed the rest of us but put a delaying hand on Mooley. Turning back to look, I saw that she had knelt down painfully, her skirt-hem graying in the floor dust, and staring absently over Mooley's head she was buttoning up the queerly shaped coat.

After a short, avid flurry of speculation we soon lost interest in Mooley, and in the routine Miss Totten devised for her. At first, during any kind of oral work, Mooley took her place at the blackboard and wrote down her answers, but later, Miss Totten sat her in the front row and gave her a small slate. She grew very quick at answering, particularly in "mental arithmetic" and in the card drills, when Miss Totten held up large Manila cards with significant locations and dates inscribed in her Palmer script, and we went down the rows, snapping back the answers.

Also, Mooley had acquired a protector in Ruby Green, the other Negro girl in the class—a huge, black girl with an arm-flailing, hee-haw way of talking and a rich, contralto singing voice which we had often heard in solo at Assembly. Ruby, boasting of her singing in night clubs on Saturday nights, of a father who had done time, cowed us all with these pungent inklings of the world on the other side of the dividing line of Amsterdam Avenue—that deep, velvet murk of Harlem which she lit for us with the flash of razors, the honky-tonk beat of the "numbahs," and the plangent wails of the mugged. Once, hearing David Hecker, a doctor's son, declare "Mooley has a cleft palate, that's what," Ruby wheeled and put a large hand on his shoulder, holding it there in menacing caress.

"She ain' got no cleff palate, see? She talk sometime, 'roun' home." She glared at us each in turn with such a pug-scowl that we flinched, thinking she was going to spit. Ruby giggled.

"She got no cause to talk, 'roun' here. She just don' need to bother." She lifted her hand from David, spinning him backward, and joined arms with the silent Mooley. "Me neither!" she added, and walked Mooley away, flinging back at us her gaudy, syncopated laugh.

Then one day, lolloping home after three, I suddenly remembered my books and tam, and above all my homework assignment, left in the pocket of my desk at school. I raced back there. The janitor, grumbling, unlocked the side door at which he had been sweeping and let me in. In the mauve, settling light the long maw of the gym held a rank, uneasy stillness. I walked up the spiral metal stairs feeling that I thieved on some part of the school's existence not intended for me. Outside the ambushed quiet of Miss Totten's room I stopped, gathering breath. Then I heard voices, one of them surely Miss Totten's dark, firm tones, the other no more than an arrested gurgle and pause.

I opened the door slowly. Miss Totten and Mooley raised their heads. It was odd, but although Miss Totten sat as usual at her desk, her hands clasped to one side of her hat, lunch-box, and the crinkly boa she wore all spring, and although Mooley was at her own desk in front of a spread copy of our thick reader, I felt the distinct, startled guilt of someone who interrupts an embrace.

"Yes?" said Miss Totten. Her eyes had the drugged look of eyes raised suddenly from close work. I fancied that she reddened slightly, like someone accused.

"I left my books."

Miss Totten nodded, and sat waiting. I walked down the row to my desk and bent over, fumbling for my things, my haunches awkward under the watchfulness behind me. At the door, with my arms full, I stopped, parroting the formula of dismissal.

"Good afternoon, Miss Totten."

"Good afternoon."

I walked home slowly. Miss Totten, when I spoke to her, had seemed to be watching my mouth, almost with enmity. And in front of Mooley there had been no slate.

In class the next morning, as I collected the homework in my capacity as monitor, I lingered at Mooley's desk, expecting some change, perhaps in her notice of me, but there was none. Her paper was the same as usual, written in a neat script quite legible in itself, but in a spidery backhand which just faintly silvered the page, like a communiqué issued out of necessity, but begrudged.

Once more I had a glimpse of Miss Totten and Mooley together, on a day when I had joined the slangy, athletic Miss Steele who was striding capably along in her Ground Grippers on the route I usually took home. Almost at once I had known I was unwelcome, but I trotted desperately in her wake, not knowing how to relieve her of my company. At last a stitch in my side forced me to stop, in front of a corner fishmongers'.

"Folks who want to walk home with me have to step on it!" said Miss Steele. She allotted me one measuring, stone-blue glance, and moved on.

Disposed on the bald white window-stall of the fish store there was a rigidly mounted eel which looked as if only its stuffing prevented it from growing onward, sinuously, from either impersonal end. Beside it were several tawny shells. A finger would have to avoid the spines on them before being able to touch their rosy, pursed throats. As the pain in my side lessened, I raised my head and saw my own face in the window, egg-shaped and sad. I turned away. Miss Totten and Mooley stood on the corner, their backs to me, waiting to cross. A trolley clanged by, then the street was clear, and Miss Totten, looking down, nodded gently into the black boa and took Mooley by the hand. As they passed down the hill to St. Nicholas Avenue and disappeared, Mooley's face, smoothed out and grave, seemed to me, enviably, like the serene, guided faces of the children I had seen walking securely under the restful duennaship of nuns.

Then came the first day of Visiting Week, during which, according to convention, the normal school day would be on display, but for which we had actually been fortified with rapid-fire recitations which were supposed to erupt from us in sequence, like the somersaults which climax acrobatic acts. On this morning, just before we were called to order, Dr. Piatt, the principal, walked in. He was a gentle man, keeping to his office like a

snail, and we had never succeeded in making a bogey of him, although we tried. Today he shepherded a group of mothers and two men, officiously dignified, all of whom he seated on some chairs up front at Miss Totten's left. Then he sat down too, looking upon us benignly, his head cocked a little to one side in a way he had, as if he hearkened to some unseen arbiter who whispered constantly to him of how bad children could be, but he benevolently, insistently, continued to disagree.

Miss Totten, alone among the teachers, was usually immune to visitors, but today she strode restlessly in front of us and as she pulled down the maps one of them slipped from her hand and snapped back up with a loud flapping roar. Fumbling for the roll book, she sat down and began to call the roll from it, something she usually did without looking at the book and favoring each of us, instead, with a warming nod.

"Arnold Ames?"

"Pres-unt!"

"Mary Bates?"

"Pres-unt!"

"Wanda Becovic?"

"Pres-unt!"

"Sidney Cohen?"

"Pres-unt!"

"L—Lilly Davis?"

It took us a minute to realize that Mooley had not raised her hand. A light, impatient groan rippled over the class. But Mooley, her face uplifted in a blank stare, was looking at Miss Totten. Miss Totten's own lips moved. There seemed to be a cord between her lips and Mooley's. Mooley's lips moved, opened.

"Pres-unt!" said Mooley.

The class caught its breath, then righted itself under the sweet, absent smile of the visitors. With flushed, lowered lids, but in a rich full voice, Miss Totten finished called the roll. Then she rose and came forward with the Manila cards. Each time, she held up the name of a state and we answered with its capital city.

Pennsylvania.

"Harrisburg!" said Arnold Ames.

Illinois.

"Springfield!" said Mary Bates.

Arkansas.

"Little Rock!" said Wanda Becovic.

North Dakota.

"Bismarck!" said Sidney Cohen.

Idaho.

We were afraid to turn our heads.

"Buh...Boise!" said Mooley Davis.

After this, we could hardly wait for the turn to come around to Mooley. When Miss Totten, using a pointer against the map, indicated that Mooley was to "bound" the state of North Carolina, we focused on one spot with such attention that the visitors, grinning at each other, shook their heads at such zest. But Dr. Piatt was looking straight at Miss Totten, his lips parted, his head no longer to one side.

"N-north Cal...Callina." Just as the deaf gaze at the speaking, Mooley's eyes never left Miss Totten's. Her voice issued, burred here, choked there, but unmistakably a voice. "Bounded by Virginia on the north...Tennessee on the west...South Callina on the south...and on the east...and on the east..." She bent her head and gripped her desk with her hands. I gripped my own desk, until I saw that she suffered only from the common failing—she had forgotten. She raised her head.

"And on the east," she said joyously, "and on the east by the Atlannic Ocean."

Later that term Miss Totten died. She had been forty years in the school system, we heard in the eulogy at Assembly. There was no immediate family, and any of us who cared to might pay our respects at the chapel. After this, Mr. Maloney, who usually chose *Whispering* for the dismissal march, played something slow and thrumming which forced us to drag our feet until we reached the door.

Of course none of us went to the chapel, nor did any of us bother to wonder whether Mooley went. Probably she did not. For now that the girl withdrawn for so long behind those rigidly empty eyes had stepped forward into them, they flicked about quite normally, as captious as anyone's.

Once or twice in the days that followed we mentioned Miss Totten, but it was really death that we honored, clicking our tongues like our elders. Passing the umbrella-stand at home, I sometimes thought of Miss Totten, furled forever in her coffin. Then I forgot her too, along with the rest of the class. After all this was only reasonable in a class which had achieved Miss Steele.

But memory, after a time, dispenses its own emphasis, making a *feuilleton* of what we once thought most ponderable, laying its wreath on what we never thought to recall. In the country, the children stumble upon the griffin mask of the mangled pheasant, and they learn; they come upon the murderous love-knot of the mantis, and they surmise. But in the city, although no man looms very large against the sky, he is silhouetted all the more sharply against his fellows. And sometimes the children there, who know so little about the natural world, stumble still upon that unsolicited good which is perhaps only a dislocation in the insensitive rhythm of the natural world. And if they are lucky, memory holds it in waiting. For what they have stumbled upon is their own humanity—their aberration, and their glory. That must be why I find myself wanting to say aloud to someone: "I remember...a Miss Elizabeth Totten."

# Space Is a Solid: Kari Lee

## DENISE CHÁVEZ

"Space is a solid." Miss Esquibel explained this to us at the beginning of Drama Appreciation III class, but I'm not sure what she meant. Miss Esquibel told us to stand in the middle of the room, all of us kids, and "Pretend you are a molecule." Arlin was cutting up and Miss E said, "Cut it out, just cut it. If you want to squirm, wait till you're a worm." Everybody laughed, including me, even though I'm not sure what she meant by that. Anyway, Arlin was cutting up. Now, that's pretty crazy 'cause he doesn't have any arms. All he has are these little stumps which stick out like the gills of a fish. When he gets excited, they flap up and down, up and down, like wings. My friend Deanna Werner has wings too, but they're on her back. I call her The Chicken 'cause she's so skinny. When she has on a bathing suit, she makes her wings go pwaakk, up and down!

Arlin doesn't care about anything but mean boy things, like rough-housing and saying hell and damn. He'll start squawking and flapping around the room, bumping into people and Miss E will say, "Good, Arlin, good! Molecules are like that, they pop and hop!" Everyone laughs but I think he's showing off because he doesn't have arms.

Mama told me, "You mean Arlin Threadgill is in your Drama Appreciation III class, why for land's sakes, Kari Lee, he's a crippled boy! His mama was one of those that took that drug... Thalitomite, I think that's what they call it, causing that poor boy that horrible disfigurement for the rest of his born life. God almighty, but ain't I glad you got no stumps like that, Kari Lee Wembley. No Wembley as far as I can recollect had no disfigurement like that. And it was all on account of that Thalitomite! Drugs are dangerous, Kari Lee, look at your father's aunt, May Ethel, well, she started on some fancy prescribed drugs for her sciatica and wouldn't you know it, but she started growing hair on her face like a man! No sir, Kari Lee, no Wembley can trace their disfigurements to drugs but your Aunt May Ethel, and she was unsuspecting. Well, she stopped those drugs right then and there and endured her pain just like all the Wembleys done. Ain't right to pump your body with any enzodimes or mites, no thank you ma'am. Listen to me, Kari Lee, now if God wants to send down his wrath on you, that's another thing altogether, why, he'll do it, now just don't you go pushing him."

If Mama stood in the middle of a room, she'd be a talking molecule. I was thinking about that when Miss E turned to me and said, "Kari Lee, what are you thinking?"

"Oh, I don't know."

"Quick, tell me, don't stop to think, Kari Lee. You're a molecule, remember."

"I am?" I said, surprised.

"What does a molecule think?"

"What does a molecule think? Oh, about other molecules, I guess, Miss E. Arlin! Don't you be whapping me with those chicken wings of yours," I almost said, but I stopped in time, and said, "Molecules don't think at all, Miss E, they just move."

"Like responding to stimuli," Arlin said.

"Good, Arlin, good!" Miss Michaelson said excitedly. She's the other Drama Appreciation III teacher, Miss E's boss, kinda.

"So molecules don't talk?" questioned Miss E. She was wearing a real neat velour top. She is so pretty and so friendly and so nice and so funny! Everybody likes her except Arlin, and well, he's a pill!

Mama says that sometimes people are pills, and it's because they aren't normal, haven't got normal feelings and such, they're disfigured, and all. They call attention to themselves just like Arlin. They prance and dance around just like little circus horses, showing how much they can do. Mama says, "I don't know what's wrong with

Mrs. Threadgill, showing off Arlin all over town like he was normal. No, Kari Lee, it ain't decent and all account of that Thalitomite!"

Me, I won't have nothing to do with that Arlin Threadgill, and it's not because he's a cripple. Arlin smells!

Arlin is a talking molecule and I'm a quiet molecule. Most of us molecules are quiet. We're just doing what molecules do, bumping off each other and saying excuse me and I'm sorry, did I hurt you, and then hitting someone else. All except Ginita Wall. She's all balled up in a dark corner, not making a sound, just scrunched up with her head facing the floor, and her arms around her knees, like she can smell her crotch. Ginita always does something different. If Miss E or Miss M say, "Pretend you're in an elevator and it's stuck between floors and the ceiling is coming down to you, closer and closer, and there's fifteen people in there. What would you do?" Well, anyone would scream. Not Ginita Wall. She'll climb through the trap door and save everybody. Or suppose you're supposed to be improvising you're at a bus station, and everything starts getting real dull or rowdy, which means that Arlin has started picking a fight with someone, Ginita will throw one of her epileptic fits right there in front of the ticket office. Anyone would notice *that.* So, wouldn't you know it, Arlin will be the one to put something in her mouth so she won't swallow her tongue or choke to death, and then he'll put a coat over her, and then he'll brag about it! Well, I guess that excepting for his wings, Arlin *could* become a doctor.

I guess there's all types of molecules. There's Arlin and me, and Ginita. Mama is like Arlin and Miss E is like Ginita and I'm like me. Only I wish I had a sister. Mama told me one day that it was too late for that foolishness. She didn't seem too interested in giving me a sister. She said that Daddy was too old, and she was too tired and no Wembly woman had business begetting after age forty, and here she went and upset the whole scheme, she, having me at age forty-two. "Well, it's just almost too much, Kari Lee," she always says, "Me, Nita

Wembley, getting ready to go into middle age with a youngster, something sacrilegious about it. Here me and your Daddy tried for so long, and then I gave up and in my forty-second year, you come along, Kari Lee. Thank God you ain't disfigured! It sometimes happens in your later years. Not that I'm that old, Kari Lee! Oh, was Cloyd surprised! And what about me, nearly done with all that female business and looking forward to your Daddy leaving me alone. Yes, it was a shock! I don't know, I wasn't right *prepared!*"

I don't know what Mama means when she says that; maybe she's just talking. She's got nobody to talk to except herself, and me. Daddy doesn't talk much, all he does is work. Mama too, she works and works, cleaning and renting apartments to people, helping Daddy with his plumbing business and taking care of the house. She says *she's* the reason we live in Oak Hills Estates and are rich.

If space is a solid, then you can cut through it. Your arm is like a knife, and your body is a knife, too, and when you walk, not like normal, all slouched and lazy and kicking things, but as if you're aware and conscious and thinking, you're cutting through space. Your body is a knife. "Try walking like that," Miss E says, "all of you walk in a circle and imagine that you are cutting through space."

Oh, and then Arlin starts playing like he's got an imaginary sword in his imaginary hands and he's cutting space. Ginita just looks at him and she keeps walking around in the circle with a kinda strange but dignified walk like I've never seen her walk, like she's really cutting through space, and I can *almost* see what Miss E is talking about. Whether it's mud or ice or if you're walking on glass or on a hot sidewalk in the summer time with bare feet, or even soft, green grass, keep thinking, "Space is a solid, space is a solid."

"Let's walk in molasses," Arlin says. Me and Ginita Wall just look at each other and then at Arlin. Because of that Pill, with a capital P, everyone has to walk in molasses. Yuck. He *would* say molasses!

"What time is it?" Arlin says, 'cause he's bored.

"Half an hour to go," says Miss M. She keeps watching the time too. Miss M looks bored, maybe she's waiting for that man who meets her after class. He's real dark, probably from another country. "If you're American, marry an American. If you're colored, marry a colored. If you're Chinese, marry a Chinese," Mama says. "None of this other stuff now, no Wembley has ever married anyone but they was from good old West Texas stock. That's the reason we ain't had no disfigurements in this family. Wembleys still Wembleys," Mama says. I wonder who Miss E's boyfriend is. She's *so* pretty!

Oh, that Arlin, he's always so bored! If you're crippled, you get bored easier, that's what Mama says.

"Lay down," Miss E says.

"Me lay down, no way in hell," says Arlin.

Arlin never stays after class to talk to anyone. His Mama picks him up for his karate class, golly, and then he practices on us later!

"You ain't gonna get me to lay down like I was sick," says Arlin, "'cause I'm not sick and I ain't never been sick!"

"You *aren't* gonna get me," I correct.

Arlin stands there and flaps whiles me and Ginita lay down on the rug part of the room and giggle when our toes touch.

"Find a space that's all yours," says Miss E, "spread your arms out."

Gosh, I wonder if hearing things like *that* makes Arlin feel like a worm; well, it's not *his* fault, it's his Mama's, and that drug's.

"Spread out, relax and breathe deeply," says Miss E with a hypnotizing voice. Arlin has *finally* laid down on the boy's side and is play-snoring.

"Find a space that's *yours,* belongs to *you,* and close your eyes."

"Aw, Miss Esquibel, do I have to?" Arlin whispers.

"Close your eyes, Arlin, breathe deeply and imagine you are as small as a molecule. You are becoming smaller and smaller and smaller, until you become so small you can enter your body, which is laying on the floor below you. You are at the top of the ceiling, so small and curious that you can go inside your body easily, a molecule. You go through an orifice . . ."

"Orifice!" shrieks Arlin.

"An eye or an ear or any other place you like," says Miss E.

Arlin snickers when somebody says what an orifice is. For a cripple Arlin sure has a dirty mind.

"Now, wander inside and explore the space. What is it like?"

Arlin snickers again, and then he farts! Everyone laughs and says, "EEEEeeeeeeyyyyywwwwwooooo!" But Miss E says, "Now close your eyes and concentrate. C-O-N-C-E-N-T-R-A-T-E. Now starting from where you are, go through your body, exploring it and seeing and feeling it, and smelling and touching. We're on a body journey this afternoon. No space is too small. No space is too strange or too unfamiliar to us. And if it is unfamiliar, or different, remember how it feels and smells and tastes. Is it dark? Crowded? How do you feel? Now move on.

"Isn't it time to go home?" says Arlin. "I got karate lessons," he mumbles.

Arlin is giggling and my right leg is going to sleep and when I open my eyes, I can see Ginita so relaxed and happy like she *really* is on a body journey and is having a wonderful time. I keep trying, I really do, but I just can't concentrate. I feel too itchy and nervous-like. It's Arlin that's bothering me, not Miss E, 'cause her voice is soft and soothing and she makes me think thoughts I've never felt before. But I just can't concentrate. Golly, I can smell Arlin's feet over here on the girl's side. I *really* am trying to think and remember and then move on, inside my body. I guess that's what Miss E means. Concentrate. Concentrate, Kari Lee. I am. I am. Space is a solid. Space is a solid. Space is a solid.

# Class Outing

## LYNDA SCHOR

Miss Alba was speaking. Bernadette looked across the room at her best friend Sondra Greenhood, who wasn't smiling or looking at her but gazing ahead in a daze. Miss Alba's sentences began to distintegrate into words, then syllables, then insects, the drone of which could still be heard above Bernadette's thoughts.

Bernadette's mouth fell open, her head lolled lethargically on her hand, elbow propped on her desk. Her two large upper teeth became visible, a wide space between them, in a sallow face dotted with freckles. Vaguely oriental eyes peered from under lowered eyelids, a line of white showing between the lower lid and her dark iris. Drool began to collect inside her slack lower lip and suddenly slid down the corner of her mouth, then along the palm of her hand, pooling again at the heel, which her teeth had almost sunk into as her head lowered sleepily, almost imperceptibly, and dripped in small drops on her desk, where, with her other hand, Bernadette drew pictures, the saliva mixing with old ink and carbon from layers of student hieroglyphics.

The desk was covered with Bernadette's drawings, which included copies of the Sistine Chapel paintings, with mathematical allowances for differences in perspective. She didn't hear Miss Alba walk up the aisle and stop beside her. The teacher studied Bernadette's desk in surprise.

"Bernadette, have you been drawing on your desk? Do you know what that means, Bernadette, defacing public property?"

Bernadette remained silent, knowing that everything meant something different to everyone.

"This is vandalism," shivered Miss Alba.

Two other children in the class listened to the chilling rebuke. One was Sondra Greenwood who, despite the fact that she hadn't come close to puberty, possessed a faint black mustache. Bernadette caught the mixture of joy and sympathy on Sondra's face; joy that she herself wasn't being scolded, sympathy for her best friend. Miss Alba stared into Bernadette's half-open eyes, one of which appeared orange with the sun shining into it. Bernadette attempted to remain locked in the stare without flinching.

"I'm going to have to send a note home to your mother," said Miss Alba, still staring.

Afraid of her mother, Bernadette looked down quickly. There were rustling sounds from the closet. Laura, short and squat, raised her hand.

"Marc is in the closet, Miss Skim Milk."

"I know Marc is in the closet," Miss Alba said. She sneezed. "Tissue monitor, please—Tissue monitor," she said louder, staring at Charles, who was involved in making paper airplanes which he directed around the room from his seat, emitting sound effects consisting of motors, jets, rockets, and beyond-the-speed-of-sound sounds.

"How come you don't yell at Charles?" Bernadette asked.

"Charles is completely out of it," said Miss Alba.

Bernadette wished she had the courage to be completely out of it, yet she admired Marc Ratner's open rebellion even more. Marc spent a good part of every day in the closet, today for standing in the aisle, his thick lips forming a stupid smile, after Miss Alba told everyone to be seated. Bernadette was in love with Marc, though Marc exhibited no indications of reciprocity. When Miss Alba shouted, "Marc, please sit down, Marc will you sit down, Marc! Marc! I'll give you up to the count of three. One...Two...Three... Okay, Marc! Into the closet!" Bernadette's heart beat fiercely, her face flushed. She felt his resistance with a combination of fear, embarrassment, admiration and envy.

Marc blinked from the light when the closet door was opened, then resumed smiling. He'd never let anyone see whether or not he was upset, but Bernadette felt that she understood his real feelings. He still refused to sit down, though he stood near his seat, in the aisle. Bernadette noticed that he had a slight scratch on his hairless brown muscular forearm. She removed the pink plastic flamingo pin from her blouse and scraped it over the skin of her pale, freckled, hairy little arm in exactly the same place until it bled slightly, imagining that now they were united in some way. She also imagined that Marc not only knew about her feeling for him, but that he possessed an affinity to her which he was only hiding from embarrassment or fear of rejection; that his blank glances and strange smiles meant special things; the doodles on his desk and papers were all messages. Bernadette had no doubt that Marc would notice the scratch on her arm as an unspoken indication of her love for him. She didn't doubt he knew everything she thought, and reciprocated.

"I'm returning your essays," said Miss Alba.

"What essays?" Laura asked.

"Your essays on whether you would die for your beliefs." Miss Alba aspirated deeply, her nostrils flaring slightly, her chest burgeoning somewhere between the neckline and waistband of her gray gabardine dress. Bernadette stared, hoping for a crisp revelation of Miss Alba's physiognomy. "Do any of you know what an essay is?"

The class was silent except for Charles' version of the takeoff of the Boeing 747 jet. Miss Alba began to weep. Bernadette watched, drooling; the class, nonplussed, sat and stared.

"Tissue monitor," whispered Miss Alba, through her stuffed nose. Marc, in the aisle, lowered his head, still smiling. Laura prodded Charles, who rose with Miss Alba's box of Kleenex. He put his hand on Miss Alba's shoulder. "I'm okay," snuffled Miss Alba. "Charles, how come there's only one tissue left in this box? I realize I have sinus trouble, but did I use them all up?" Charles looked at the floor.

"He used them for making airplanes," said Laura.

"Tattletale," spat Sondra.

"Charles, for that you have to go into the closet." Charles began to cry.

"He's afraid of the dark," said Laura with relish.

"I'm sorry about your science trouble, Miss Alba," said Charles, trembling.

"Couldn't we leave the closet door open?" asked Laura, repentant.

"No," said Miss Alba. "Charles has to learn not to deface other people's property." She led a slumped and passive Charles into the closet. "It's your parents' job to teach you morals and manners, but I have to do everything." She pushed Charles slightly, and he slumped down on her boots, near her umbrella.

Bernadette could see his face redden and tears begin to fall as the closet door was shut. For a moment the class was silent. Then a plaintive cry rose eerily from within the metal wardrobe. Miss Alba steeled herself; the others fidgeted.

"Paper monitor," called Miss Alba. Laura rose tentatively, looking questioningly about her. "Yes, Laura, it's you," said Miss Alba, her sarcasm lost on everyone.

Laura couldn't read the names on top of the papers so she stood there with the sheaf in her hand, looking puzzled. Bernadette, who could read, automatically rose to her aid.

"Bernadette," shrieked Miss Alba, "out of order. One more item on your note home." Bernadette was puzzled by her disobedience. Marc knew he was misbehaving; Bernadette, who always meant well, was unfailingly surprised by Miss Alba's adverse reactions.

"Sondra, you give out the papers." Sondra delivered all the papers to the wrong people. It didn't matter much because each paper had a large red D on top, with the exception of Charles, who got an A.

"All of you except Charles wrote a sentence fragment," said Miss Alba. Sondra herself had Charles' paper and thought the A was meant for her, although she did realize that the paper had quite a bit more verbiage than she recalled writing and was, in fact, four papers, stapled together. This sheaf appeared even fatter due to the fact that each page was a recycled, unfolded former paper airplane. The screams from within the closet were now punctuated by the drumming of fists against the metal. Miss Alba gritted her teeth.

"Almost everyone," said Miss Alba, "wrote the sentence fragment 'I woont.'"

Bernadette felt misunderstood. Though she had someone else's paper on her desk, she meticulously recalled having thought the problem out for three hours before writing, "Iwoulddieformybeliefs," an entire sentence, the question inherent in the answer, as she was taught.

"Come up here with your paper," said Miss Alba. Bernadette went up to Miss Alba with her paper quickly, accelerated by the long jump she made tripping on the saddle oxford that Laura had extended into the aisle for that purpose. "This is not your paper." She looked for Bernadette's paper on each desk.

"No one can understand this," explained Miss Alba. "There's no space between each word."

Bernadette stood there stymied. There always seemed to be something wrong that she hadn't thought of. The banging from the closet increased in volume, accompanied by screaming and crying.

"It may be interesting to note," said Miss Alba above the din, thin lips compressed, "that Bernadette is the only person in the entire class with ideals strong enough to die for."

"Bernadette is an asshole," said Marc, smiling.

Bernadette flushed. She covered the cut on her forearm so no one could see it, then rubbed it, wishing it would go away. She felt tears spring into her eyes, regretting her smooth virgin arm.

"Bernadette is an asshole," shrieked Laura.

A sudden barrage of spitballs and paper airplanes came her way. Bernadette ducked, hands over her head, scrunched in her seat, eyes tightly shut. She fantasized Marc coming over to her and sitting next to her at her desk. She can feel his warm, large and slightly sweaty presence. He puts his firm, strong arm around her, his other hand over her hand. His body covers her, his warmth surrounds her. She looks directly into his deep black eyes. She runs her hand through his soft, straight light brown hair. His thick lips, open but not grinning, come closer, closer. She can feel his nose slightly. His lips press ever so gently on hers as his light breath fans over her face. Bernadette opened her eyes and saw Sondra who, having thrown spitballs herself, has, in remorse, come over and wrapped her arms around her.

Sondra and Bernadette had been close ever since they met in Miss Mancewicz' first grade class. Sondra fell in love with Bernadette during a get-acquainted story-telling session and was protective of her since. Miss Mancewicz began the story and everyone took a turn continuing it.

"There was once a little boy named Timothy, who lived with his grandfather," began Miss Mancewicz. "He used to watch birds for most of the day. Either from inside the house, through the windows, or outside the house...he observed birds. One day he said, 'Grandfather, birds can fly.' 'Yes' said the grandfather, wondering that it took his grandson so much time to formulate that observation. 'Can people fly too, Grandfather?' Timothy asked. Your turn, Charles." Charles was holding aloft a paper airplane, intoning, "Whirrr, whirr." He looked up when he noticed the unnatural silence.

"Of course people can fly, Miss Monkey bitch. In airplanes," said Charles. Marc laughed hysterically and couldn't stop.

"Laura," said Miss Mancewicz, "you continue."

Laura looked attentive. One cheek was larger than the other. She made a garbled sound.

"What's in your mouth?" asked Miss Mancewicz.

Laura spat six marbles onto her desk, where they stuck together spit-soaked, then rolled off, bounced off the edge of her seat and onto the floor. Miss Mancewicz angrily strode up the aisle on heavy legs, aided by tannish orange support hose. Nearing Laura's desk she slid on one of the marbles and swung her arms out and around as in their arm exercises, but both legs flew out despite heavy black Enna-Jetticks, and Miss Mancewicz landed in the aisle on her behind. She attempted to rise, but unsuccessfully, she was so neatly wedged. Marc laughed hysterically, saliva dripping down his chin. Bernadette laughed too, hoping Marc would notice.

"Bernadette," cried Miss Mancewicz, "Help me up, you idiot." Bernadette, chastened, and Sondra, who didn't want Bernadette to feel bad, lifted the struggling Miss Mancewicz by her padded armpits to a standing position.

Laura was in her seat, crying.

"Okay, Laura," said Miss Mancewicz, standing forbiddingly over the squat, tear-stained Laura, teeth clenched, eyes bulging and bloodshot. "Continue."

"No ... hic ... said the grand ... hic ... father ... I'm sor ... ry ... hic ... peo ... ple ... hic ... Just then ... hic ... Super ... man ... hic ... came ... flying ... hic ... down ..."

Everyone was paying close attention. Miss Mancewicz indicated Marc's turn with her chin.

"'I knew people could fly,' shouted Timothy. 'Superman ain't people,' says de granpa. 'No, I ain't people,' said Superman, 'but me and de Hulk and Vampirella can show you a good time.'"

"You try, Sondra." Sondra stood and looked around from under her brows. She was so tall already that Miss Mancewicz had to look up at her even though her posture resembled a divining rod always in the presence of water. Bernadette could smell Sondra's breath even before she spoke.

"Timothy's grandfather didn't want to just give a quick, cursory yes or no, or don't-bother-me answer, so he decided to make a big outing of it. 'Tomorrow we'll go into the woods, Timothy, just you and I, together, eat hamburgers we'll take out from McDonald's and discuss the birds and the bees—'"

"Next," said Miss Mancewicz quickly. Sondra, getting involved and nowhere near finished, stood there with her mouth open, her breath wheezing in and out. "Begin, Bernadette."

"Timothy and his grandfather went to Central Park to watch birds and see why they fly. They found a nest with an entire bird family in it, two kids, and a mother and father bird. The bird ba-

bies' names were Alice and Jerry. All of a sudden a bluejay swept down and ate them all, spitting out the bones. The grandfather was so upset he turned purple, had a heart attack and died. Timothy, wearing a Fieldcrest towel as a Superman cape, not having had the benefit of his grandfather's lesson, felt that the quickest way to get help would be to fly for it. He jumped off the high rock they were on and smashed into the brambles below. But he didn't die. His eyes were scratched out and he was blinded, but his life was saved by his landing on an enormous pile of horseshit, as it was the bridle path."

"It could be a 'Scratch 'n Sniff' book," suggested Laura.

By the time they opened the closet it was ominously silent. Charles was rigid and had to be lifted out and placed in his seat. Luckily, from crouching, his legs were bent the correct way, but they had a bit of trouble prying Miss Alba's boot out from where it was stuck between Charles' ankle and the back of his thigh.

"Will Charles be able to go to the zoo with us today?" asked Sondra.

Miss Alba's class and Miss Halac's class were going together. Miss Halac attempted to direct the herd into line formation two by two, like Noah's Ark, with her blackboard pointer, which she appeared to fantasize into a billiard cue, the tip of which she constantly rubbed with chalk, and the heads as billiard balls, only herself comprehending whose head was the eight ball.

It took nearly half an hour for the lining-up arrangements to be completed, after which Miss Alba suggested that it might be too late to go at all. Sondra and Bernadette, always partners, were quick and obedient, fearfully watchful that due to some naughtiness or iniquity on the part of someone else they'd be separated. Someone was absent from Miss Halac's class, but that conveniently left two extra pupils to support the rigid Charles.

They left the classroom, then the school, Miss Halac shouting, "Hup two three four, hup two three four," and keeping them in line with the pointer. "If any one of you dashes out of line and gets hit by an automobile, you shall be painfully punished," she said. "I have a story to tell you that could be amazingly helpful to you in the future. Once, when I was a little girl, I fell off a railway platform. Hup two three four. Do any of you know how I survived?"

"The train wasn't coming," said someone from her own class.

"It was coming, it was," said Miss Halac.

"You were killed and reincarnated, Miss Halitosis," said the boy.

Miss Halac thought for a moment as if that might be a better story. "Not quite," she said, "hup two three four," as they dragged along, the line tight in front, then slackening, Miss Alba keeping the rear up as she assisted with Charles. In a moment's silence she could be heard pleading, "Charles, we're going to see monkeys and elephants. Please put your feet down, Charles."

"I was there on the tracks," continued Miss Halac. "I heard the whistle, then I saw it coming—so fast, so long, so hard—I knew then that I could never get out of its path in time. I lay down directly in the center of the track, my hands at my sides, closed my eyes and sent a prayer up to God. I felt a swoosh of air as the train began to pass over me. Everything became black and there was a great roaring. I counted the cars as each passed over me by the light that came through my eyelids. I counted as many as thirty, waited a moment and sat up. I looked behind me and watched the train going off into the distance."

She looked around. Miss Alba was coming forward, the others lagging, some looking at something at the curb, others admiring a car, two trying to pick Charles up from the sidewalk. Bernadette gave Sondra a piece of chewing gum she'd scraped carefully from the concrete, and she could hear Sondra's teeth grind the grime embedded in it.

"There's a bum," shouted Laura, pointing to an old man dressed like a woman with bare legs, short skirt, old suit jacket topped with a shawl, and a kerchief on his head held in place with two wooden clothespins.

"Don't point," admonished Miss Alba absently, now walking with Miss Halac, deep in conversation.

"That's no bum," said Marc, "that's what Bernadette's gonna look like when she grows up."

There was almost unanimous agreement, and much giggling. Bernadette smiled as if it were a joke she could take. Sondra put her arm around her. Bernadette was touched and didn't know what to say. She was slightly embarrassed and felt she owed Sondra something for her devotion, yet the first thing she could think of to say was, "You have bad breath." There was silence. Sondra removed her arm from Bernadette.

"I have a friend who's going to beat you up," she said. Bernadette looked puzzled. Not only hadn't she meant to say that, she couldn't understand how she could get beaten up for an immutable fact.

"Wait here," said Sondra, who left her place on line and went to speak with an enormous bruiser from Miss Halac's class, who now moved slowly up in Sondra's place to become Bernadette's line partner. Bernadette looked for Miss Alba, but she and Miss Halac, their backs to the class, were conversing. She thought of running away, just getting out of line and running, but she looked up the vast street, at the enormous buildings and large cars, didn't know where she was and was too terrified.

"Does Sondra Greenwood have bad breath?" asked the large girl, whom Bernadette wouldn't look at, but who whistled her s's. "Answer me," she said, giving Bernadette a punch in the arm that sent her reeling out of line.

"You stay in line," ordered the looming aggressor. "If those teachers see anything, you'll get it worse. I'll be waiting for you every day." She gave Bernadette a pinch that brought tears to her eyes; she nearly screamed. She began weeping silently.

"Crybaby," said the girl, punching her again. Bernadette continued weeping unashamedly as she was pinched and punched repeatedly.

"Does Sondra Greenhood have bad breath?" she asked again. Bernadette didn't answer except to tell herself a silent "yes."

Miss Alba and Miss Halac turned to face them as they reached the zoo.

"My name is Madeline," said the girl. "You're right. Sondra Greenhood has bad breath."

"Bernadette, are you crying?" asked Miss Alba.

"Bernadette's a crybaby, Bernadette's a crybaby," chanted Marc.

"Marc, even though we have no closet here, I can shut you in the monkey house," said Miss Alba.

Giggles. Bernadette's smile crinkled her tear-stiffened face. She hoped Marc was only picking on her to smoke-screen his feelings for her, which appeared obvious due to his lack of indifference to her presence.

"Bernadette's a crybaby, Bernadette's a crybaby," they chanted in unison.

"If you want to sing," said Miss Halac, "Let's sing a song by Joyce Kilmer from the poem you were supposed to memorize. 'I think that I shall never see, a poem lovely as a tree, A tree that looks at God all day, . . .' go on, class," Miss Halac's was the only audible voice as the class stood dumbfounded, mouthing syllables silently after Miss Halac had already sung them.

"I'm hungry," said Laura. "Let's eat."

"We didn't come to the zoo to eat," said Miss Alba.

"We didn't come to the zoo to sing either," said Marc.

They surrounded a small concession, a cart displaying fur monkeys, plastic animals, horns, Cracker Jacks. There was a helium tank around which were wrapped many balloon strings. The bright balloons bobbed a few feet above.

"Put him down on the grass gently," said Miss Alba to the two boys who were dragging Charles. "Charles, listen to me. I want you to stretch your legs. Do you hear me, Charles?"

It took a long time for Bernadette to decide what color balloon she wanted. Her quarter smelled metallic in her sweaty palm, as most of the class, more aggressive, made their purchases. Bernadette anxiously watched them line up without her as people crowded in front of her. She finally

shouted "White!" and watched her opaque creamy balloon become large and pale. She gave the man her quarter, which he wiped on his pants leg.

"Thirty cents," he said. Bernadette handed him back the balloon.

"You can owe it to me," said the concessionaire when he realized Bernadette didn't have another nickel.

"We're all going to the bathroom now," said Miss Alba. "Miss Halac will take the boys and wait outside and I'll take the girls." Bernadette wondered when she could get the nickel she owed to the balloon man.

The public toilet was an enormous building, no different in appearance from the animal houses. The girls filed up the steps of one side of the building into a huge cool tiled room. As Bernadette looked around at the sinks along one wall, and the gray stall doors lining two walls, her balloon flew out of her hand, rapidly making its way to the high ceiling. She was staring upward, dismayed, when Miss Alba pushed her into one of the empty toilet stalls.

"We have no time to worry about your balloon," said Miss Alba, shutting the gray door.

"Don't forget we never sit down on public toilet seats," Miss Alba's voice echoed. "We don't want to catch any disease."

Bernadette remembered the white-haired matron sitting in the corner, her hands folded in her lap. After the girls leave she'll probably help me get my balloon back, she thought. It took Bernadette a long time to unbuckle her suspender, but she was determined not to ask anyone in her class to do it for her. She pulled her pants down and straddled the bowl. Recalling Miss Alba's admonition, she tried to urinate without sitting down. She felt like crying when the liquid merely trickled down her leg into her sock. She stopped and tried again, but she had to go very badly, and it wouldn't stop, wetting her overalls, socks and shoes. She remained in the toilet closet crying, listening to her class emerge from the stalls, Miss Alba helping them wash their hands, their leaving. Though she'd planned to wait there till they left, she somehow never thought they'd completely forget about her.

"I hate them," she cried, angrily pulling pieces of toilet tissue from the holder one by one, trying to place them on the seat without touching it as her mother had shown her, but they fell into the bowl. When it was stuffed, one or two pieces stuck on the seat, Bernadette, overalls pulled up and buckled, sat there and wept.

"Bernadette," she heard someone call suddenly. "Bernadette." It echoed coldly through the enormous tiled room. She so much wanted to run outside, be with her class again, but she sat there very still and in a moment it was silent. She sniffled, left the booth. Her balloon, she could see, was still touching the ceiling like a milky cloud, its dirty string vibrating gently, out of reach.

"Please may I stand on your chair so I can get my balloon?" Bernadette asked the attendant politely, feeling safe in the old woman's presence.

"Don't bother me," said the matron. "Why don't you get out with the rest of your class? Get yourself another balloon." She got up, grabbed a mop and swung it, just barely missing Bernadette's arm.

There were few people around outside. Bernadette heard the lion's roar from a distance. All the animals seemed to be indoors. She looked in vain for her class. She heard monkey chattering and ran into the monkey house. A fat orange orangutan sitting in a tire swing looked at Bernadette impassively. In one of the cages, a wiry black monkey stopped swinging to look at Bernadette. A pink thing between his legs began to swell, and Bernadette became aware that he'd been pulling on it. She watched, fascinated, then realized that the monkey wasn't even looking at her but was staring glassily into space.

She stood in front of the lion house looking in, cold now, and terrified. She could see from the doorway that her class wasn't in there, and she could see the lion pacing, uttering a rhythmic unearthly roar. She began to panic and pictured her class entering the monkey house at the moment of her exit. Suddenly she saw them all on a grassy

mall, ran over and slid liquidly in line, but the corners of her mouth pulled uncontrollably downward, and she wept with relief.

"Bernadette," shrieked Miss Alba. "We've been looking all over for you! Where have you been!" She made Bernadette relinquish the line to stand in front of her.

"Do you realize how inconsiderate you are?"

Marc giggled. At first Bernadette was so relieved to be there she didn't mind the yelling, though tears ran again down her streaked filthy face.

"I lost my balloon," she said. She thought of her pale milky balloon floating out of reach, deserted on the cold bathroom ceiling.

"It's all alone," she wailed.

"I don't know what I'm going to do with you," said Miss Alba. Madeline, who had crept forward, took Bernadette's hand.

"I had to call your mother," said Miss Alba spuriously. Madeline felt Bernadette go rigid with fear, but she relaxed as they marched across the grassy mall.

"I'm hungry," said Bernadette.

"We've already eaten," said Miss Alba. "I'm afraid we've spent so much time looking for you, your punishment will have to be no lunch."

Bernadette dreamed of ice cream.

"Miss Skim Milk," said Sondra, "Bernadette wet her pants."

Bernadette remembered. Her overalls, wet, heavy and warm, were becoming cold, the cuffs going slosh-slosh on the ground.

"Miss Halac, do you believe this?" Miss Halac struggled along, carrying Charles.

"It's your turn now, Miss Alba, he's heavy."

"Bernadette, we went to the bathroom," said Miss Alba, beginning to weep. "There's no logic," she cried. "The best laid plans of mice and men— The world is falling apart. Tissue monitor—" The tissue monitor, draped over Miss Halac's shoulder, didn't respond.

"Use your sleeve," ventured Laura.

"As punishment, you'll be my partner, Bernadette," Miss Alba said when she stopped crying.

She held Bernadette's hand tightly, hurting her. Bernadette's fingers attempted to squirm in Miss Alba's dry, rough grasp, but she wouldn't let go. She could hear the class whispering and laughing, super-conscious of the slush-slush of her wet cuffs.

"Bernadette's a retard, Bernadette's a retard," they chanted. "Bernadette's a crybaby, pants-wetting retard, Bernadette's a crybaby pants-wetting retard—" She looked hopefully up at Miss Alba, who seemed to be enjoying the chant.

At the seals, Miss Alba forgot about Bernadette and let go of her. Tired but safe, Bernadette gazed at the deep calm water in a daze of peaceful exhaustion. Suddenly a seal broke through the calm water, nose first, fur glistening, then dove again. Bernadette strove unsuccessfully to see it. It popped up in an unlikely place. A larger seal popped up. They played tag for a while until the large one jumped on the concrete steps to sun, while the small one hopped about, attempting to coerce the other to play.

Small and plump, hair matted and tangled except for the invisible arterial integrity of two braids down her back, clothes filthy and wet, and face streaked in varying values of black and brown, Bernadette swayed in rhythm with the seal, seeing nothing else. She imagined she was a seal, swimming and playing and watched over by the fat mama, whose sleek black coat had become dry and brown like worn velvet movie seats.

"Bernadette," shouted Marc suddenly. "Let's play dodge ball."

Bernadette turned quickly, shocked out of her trance just in time to see Marc throw a tomato at her. She moved slightly, and it hit her on the leg, splashing all over her pants.

Bernadette silently decided to leave this class that treated her so badly. She no longer cared what happened to her. She'd become a seal, and they'd have to leave without her. She walked away just as Miss Halac was transferring Charles, knees still bent, to Miss Alba's shoulder. Half the class dumbly watched Bernadette walk into the park.

Bernadette kept walking. Her pants were dry, albeit stiff; she was filthy and starving, but she felt a sense of liberation and adventure, laced with the pleasure of spite. They'll be sorry, she thought, stupid Miss Skim Milk and those horrible kids. She recalled her mother and felt a deep pity for her. Even though she'd probably spank Bernadette if and when she ever got home, she knew her mother would be out of her mind with worry. She wandered up the dark street thinking about food, when she became aware of footsteps behind her.

Heart pounding she ran, but the footsteps also seemed to be running. Terrified, she kept her head down. It wasn't until she was upon it that she saw the small gaudy movie theater.

Bernadette entered quickly and looked around. There were a few people on line near a ticket taker, but she thought she'd eluded her pursuer. Suddenly she saw him enter, breathing hard. She wasn't positive it was he, but she thought so. She sneaked fearfully past the ticket taker, who seemed to see her but allowed her to enter anyway. What a nice man, thought Bernadette. She felt safer in the interior darkness. If her pursuer wished to catch her, he not only had to wait on line, but he'd have to locate her in the dark and drag her out silently. She carefully chose a seat next to a large man who, she felt, though engrossed in the film which flickered shadow-like across his face, would most likely be a fine protector. Soon she relaxed, enjoyed the Technicolor images and tried to figure out what the movie was about. She was almost asleep when she felt the man's hand on her thigh. It was large, warm and comforting. He was fiddling around with his other hand, but she was so sleepy she couldn't even turn her head. He took her hand and put it on his penis, which he'd removed from his pants. It felt smooth and hot.

"Please move your hand up and down," he whispered, placing his large hand over hers and moving it the way he liked.

"But I'm so tired," said Bernadette in a weepy whine.

"Then go to sleep while you do it," said the man. "It's not difficult, and it doesn't mean anything."

# Little Brown Jesus

## JOAN O'DONOVAN

"Pause," I said again. "You forgot the pause."

The Virgin Mary's eyes rolled in her brown-sugar face.

"Yes, miss," she said resignedly.

"Try once more. And watch me."

It was a pity, really, that Heliotrope Smith was the best. She would have to be the Virgin, but that made difficulties. For one thing, she was not only backward, she had the instincts of an artist . . . a tricky combination.

"*Pause!*" I said.

This time, Heliotrope bared her teeth in a wide, semi-circular grin.

"You do have to keep saying it!" she told me with enthusiasm.

I gave up. It was the fifteenth time that morning.

"All right, that'll do for now."

They were round me then, the children, twittering. This was the backward class, only at Gudge Street we called it "Opportunity." Gabriel had torn his halo and the fifth shepherd lost his lines.

"You must remember to watch the beat," I said to Heliotrope as I put a stitch in the halo. "I'm not standing up there to scare the birds."

Heliotrope jigged happily and her pencil-pigtails, each harvested from a square of black wool and tied with red tape, stood on end . . . all eight of them.

"In Jamaica we got things like a drain, miss, with holes; and the boys cover them with grass so the birds don't see, and when they stand there they catch their legs and the boys put them in cages."

She giggled and flattened her nose with a gesture of splayed fingers.

"Crool thing!" shouted Jim. Jim was a psychopath. He had driven two teachers to near suicide, but apparently had principles about little birds.

The class took it up.

"I'n't that Heliotrope crool, miss?"

''That Heliotrope'' was her usual designation.

It wasn't that the children didn't like her. You couldn't dislike her any more than you could dislike a puppy. But, with one exception, they preferred to keep their distance; for Heliotrope wasn't just naughty, she was dynamite. Even Jim, who had in his time thrown a bucket of worms at the needlework mistress and hit the caretaker with his own broom, tried to protect himself when she was around by sidling up to me and mumbling superstitiously, "I'n'it awful, miss, when there's *trouble?*"

I knew what he meant. Anything might happen. There had never been a colour problem at Gudge Street before Heliotrope came, but she had started one on her first day by calling us dirty whites. She was nearly lynched.

Oddly enough, it was Doreen Bax, the quietest girl in the class, who became Heliotrope's friend; and now, it seemed, the play was going to put paid to that, for . . . it was most unfortunate . . . Doreen had assumed she would be the Virgin. She was a pale, pretty girl with an oval face, soft curling hair and wide blue eyes. And she always had been the Virgin. When a doubt arose, her mother sent me a sharp note, with cuttings from the local paper and a tinted photograph. That settled it. I'm obstinate too. In my play she was an angel. She had been sulking for a fortnight.

The morning of the dress rehearsal came . . . we were to act the play for the school in the afternoon . . . and, to kick off, Gertie Pugh stole the blob of red glass from the teacosy worn by the first wise man under the impression that it was what she called a *jool*. We managed to coax it from her knicker leg, but it took time; and as, in snatching it, she had broken the pin, I had to stick it back on the teacosy with glue. Then Jim (seventh shepherd) had a fit of nerves and knocked Joseph down; and the innkeeper's wife turned up with a yellow paper crinoline, long black gloves and a Dolly Varden hat, which was her mother's interpretation of my request for an old sheet and a couple of safety pins; and she unnerved me further by going out to assembly in the hat and gloves. But worse than all that, far worse, was the crisis over the doll.

I had suggested that a bundle wrapped in a shawl was all that was needed for a stage baby, but the class wasn't having any. Even Jim, who sucked up to me in his calm spells, couldn't bring himself to let that pass.

"Anyone'd see it wasn't Jesus in them close," he explained. "Up our church they had a doll, miss. And strore."

Jim was an overgrown, loose-meshed boy with poor co-ordination and thick hobnails. Sometimes he fell flat on his face. It was news to me that he ever went to church.

"Yes, miss!" The class was censorious. "You gotter have a doll!"

So I chose Doreen to bring hers. It seemed to cheer her up.

"And strore," Jim reminded me. "It i'n't right without strore."

"All right, Jim, if you can get any straw, you bring it."

But I wasn't sorry when he turned up without it, for I had troubles enough. Certainly, Doreen brought her doll, a little cuddly doll, of the kind that in unenlightened times we would not have been ashamed to call a nigger doll. But Heliotrope brought a doll too, a white doll; and Heliotrope's doll was three feet tall and very much a lady doll.

"I got Jesus, miss!" she said.

The class gazed rapt at the sequinned ball dress and stiletto heels.

"It's bigger'n the one I seen up church," Jim gloated. "I'n'it like Diana Dors?"

He was right on both counts.

Doreen clutched her doll to her, and her face went slowly scarlet. Foolishly, I tried persuasion.

"That's a beautiful doll, Heliotrope, but I think it's a bit big."

"Big, miss?" Heliotrope went into a squeal of incredulous laughter. "*Big?* This is nothing! Why..."

"Besides," I interrupted, "Doreen has brought hers. I asked her to, you know. It was all arranged."

Heliotrope affected astonishment.

"Do you mean that little doll?" Her voice was objective. "That small one? I don't think that's good enough to be Jesus, miss, that *little* doll."

I had never before heard Doreen raise her voice. I should have said she was incapable of it. But it came now in a screech of rage.

"Jesus wasn't a *lady!*"

Heliotrope turned on her. The gloves were off.

"Jesus could've been anything he liked" she snapped. "He could've been a mouse, or a lion...anything! It says so in the Bible."

"Well he was a baby in the *play,* Heliotrope Smith, so there!"

I expected the class to concede that; but, hypnotised, the children continued to stare at Diana Dors, and Heliotrope made the most of it. She narrowed her cat-eyes to dull, spiteful slits.

"Your doll's black!" she said baldly. "The one thing Jesus never was was black. Jesus was real white." She jutted a shoulder contemptuously. "Little black thing!"

"Babies *are* little! We got one."

"Little! Only bad, low-class babies are little! Why, I seen babies in Jamaica, *huge* babies! Their mammies could hardly lift them...."

"Babies are little," Doreen repeated stubbornly. "And my doll says 'Ma-ma' like our baby does."

Furious, she shook the coloured doll and it bleated.

"So does mine! So does mine!"

Heliotrope tipped her doll at a dangerous angle. It had a powerful voice, like a tenor bull. And an American accent. Doreen began to cry.

"Mine walks too!" she sobbed.

Heliotrope cast a triumphant eye round the class.

"Mine walks..." she screamed "...*And* wets!"; and snatching up the ball dress, she revealed an incongruous pair of rubber pants.

It was high time to stop the demonstrations. We would rehearse, I said firmly, with a bundle. The dolls were put aside and the decision shelved till the afternoon. With luck, one of the children might come out in a rash and have to be sent home.

At lunchtime, I took four more aspirins and went to lie down. The rest of the staff were in the canteen, so I had the staffroom to myself. The playground noises came filtered by the distance, rare and a little unearthly. I began to relax. The Head, after all, was a reasonable man. He wouldn't expect the Opportunity class to do more than lumber on and lumber off; and, let's face it, I told myself, that's all they'll do. But did it matter? Whatever happened, the Opportunity class would be delighted. The Opportunity class had a great welcome for itself.

I was woken from a light doze by a pounding of boots on the stairs, and a terrible boy called Fisher burst in.

"You're wanted," he told me.

He was wearing Edwardian dress, a long velvet drape and a tie no thicker than a shoelace. I had an impulse to ask him why he did it, but thought better of it.

"Who wants me?" I said instead. "What is it?"

"A man wiv an 'orse and cart."

It came to me like a symbol in a dream. I went downstairs, past the children swinging on the main door and out into the stale cold of Gudge Street. A woman walked by with a cabbage under her arm and a thick, worn purse in her thick, worn hand. Opposite, a youth lounged in a doorway eating chips from a bag. But there was no man that I could see, and no cart, no horse.

Kennick, on playground duty, wandered across.

"You owe me five bob." He held out his hand. "Walton couldn't find you. I sent Fisher, but the bloke wouldn't wait so I paid."

"What for?"

"He said for obliging."

I gave him two half-crowns and he looked at me curiously.

"Aren't you having fun!"

I didn't answer. I was thinking of my predecessors. One was still in hospital. I decided that I must be less sincere about my job. I must look after myself. I must keep a grip on reality; and next time I mustn't take so much aspirin.

But back in the classroom the nightmare met me, and it had nothing to do with mental balance. Straw. A mountain of straw. My desk was submerged, and the top of the radiator showed like the fluted edging of a flower bed. Spikes stuck at bizarre angles from the inkwells, and the air was thick with dust.

I stared stupidly round. I tried to wade forward, but barked my shin against the nature table which I could no longer see. I was rescuing the terrapins when Jim skated up.

"I ain't letcher down!" he told me happily. "My dad says it's all right about the strore. The five bob was for the rag-and-bone man what lent him the 'orse. There was too much to go on his barrer." He tossed a handful joyously. "It's more than what we had up our church."

"It was very generous of your dad, Jim," I said in a controlled voice.

"Tha'sall right, miss!" He threw another fistful up and it came down on me. He began to scratch. "Fleas," he said cheerfully. "You don't half get a lotter fleas in strore."

When Heliotrope came in I saw she had a long scratch on her cheek, and Doreen had the beginnings of a black eye. The class was exhausted, It must have been quite an emotional dinner hour.

But there was still fight left in Heliotrope.

"Miss," she demanded in the voice of one who will be trifled with no longer, "which doll is Jesus?"

She didn't press her point, but I knew that look. If I wasn't careful, I could whistle for my Virgin.

Weakly, I glanced at Doreen. The swollen eye gave her an air of unwonted toughness, and for the first time I detected a resemblance to her mother. I felt I couldn't stand that either; so I asked myself the question that I had occasion to ask myself many times with the Opportunity class: What would Solomon have done now?

And then it came to me, the one solution possible.

"We're going to have *two* Jesuses," I said crisply.

Now that's where I hand it to an Opportunity class. There's no conventional prejudice.

"Smashing!" shouted Jim. "They only had one up our church!"

Heliotrope brightened. She began to giggle. Doreen's face lit into a slow, satisfied smile. They looked at each other. Heliotrope pranced up and flung an arm round her rival's neck.

"You know," she said judicially, "mebbe your little Jesus isn't so black as I thought. Mebbe he's just a little brown Jesus."

She took him up and began to nurse him.

So Diana Dors lay in the crib; or half of her did. The nylon legs and stiletto heels were embedded in the merciful *strore.*

And, really, it was astonishing, but no one forgot his words, not even Jim. True, the jool came unstuck and fell at Mary's feet, but I liked the symbolism; and, when it came to it, Doreen looked interesting in profile, and I alone could see the ripening eye. As for Heliotrope, she rooted the Christmas story in Gudge Street, and Gudge Street paid her the tribute of absorbed silence. After all these were the threatened children, the children of flits, evictions and eight to a room: they understood about having it the hard way.

I watched from the wings as the play swept through to its climax. There was just the solo now, and it would be over for another year. I raised a hand, the other on the pulley; and Heliotrope, alone on the stage, waited as I had told her to wait. The air was so still that I heard a man whistling a street away. But when we had both counted ten, she looked, not at me but at the bundle in her arms; and instead of beginning "Away in a Manger," she sang to a beat that I recognised as calypso:

"Little brown Jesus, go sleep um don't cry...."

I turned frightened eyes to the school. There was a sense of feet tapping, but not a foot moved:

and Heliotrope, easing herself as a mother nursing a baby might, sang with a sort of loving exasperation:

*"Little brown Jesus, go sleep um don't cry;*
*When you cry so bad you make Mammy boil.*
*Your Daddie Joseph he gone saw wood,*
*And Lord God he is busy with the weather,*
*So you go sleep, you brown-skin boy,*
*Your Mammie done smack you when you don't*
  *go sleep...."*

The voice got quieter. Heliotrope cast me a single authoritative glance, and the glance said *Curtain!*

"Um Lord. . . . U-u-um Lor-ord!"

I let the curtain slowly down.

Silence continued for perhaps five seconds; then thunder broke. I dashed on to the stage and caught Heliotrope up. She giggled wildly, and flung her arms and legs round me like a monkey.

"What you crying for, miss?"

"Write it out! You must write it down for me, that song! Do you hear?"

I felt the heart go out of her.

"Yes, miss," she said dully.

I remembered then. She was a backward child. Writing was a punishment and a pain.

"No, no, silly!" I said. "I like your song. I want to have it! You tell me the words; I'll write them down myself!"

She threw herself back and squealed with laughter, her limbs twitching with diabolical energy again.

"Hoo! I thought you was cross!" She looked at me now as if she feared I was daft instead. "I just sing to brown Jesus, see, miss? Any old words. They just come." She giggled again. "I forgot to watch for you scaring them birds, didn't I?"

Heliotrope's mother was waiting for me next morning. She was a serious little woman, and very angry. She asked me what the hell I meant teaching her daughter calypso. She said she wanted her eddicated proper, English style.

# CHAPTER 5

## A CHILD'S POINT OF VIEW

Edward P. Jones, "The First Day"
Richard Yates, "Fun with a Stranger"
Phillip Bonosky, "The First Robin in the World"
Paula Sharp, "Books"
Hugo Martínez-Serros, "Her"
Issac Asimov, "The Fun They Had"

These stories focus on some of the differences between the world as viewed by children and by adults. Each in its own way depicts the boundaries—and fault lines—that separate a child's perspective from that of an adult. The tension that occurs when these two views collide makes these stories especially interesting and at times ridiculously absurd.

"The First Day" by Edward P. Jones portrays a child's view of registering for kindergarten. For this young African-American girl, about to begin kindergarten, events do not go smoothly. By the time the day is over, she has learned much about her mother, school and the world beyond.

In "Fun with a Stranger" by Richard Yates, students compare two third-grade teachers, exposing views of classroom life usually hidden from adults. The children are active and accurate observers of adult behavior. Throughout the story the students are contrasting Miss Snell with the other third-grade teacher, Miss Cleary.

> All that summer the children who were due to start third grade under Miss Snell had been warned about her. "Boy, you're gonna get it," the older children would say, distorting their faces with a wicked pleasure. "You're really gonna get it. Mrs. Cleary's all right"...
> "—she's fine but boy, that Snell—you better watch out." So it happened that the morale of Miss Snell's class was low even before school opened in September, and she did little in the first few weeks to improve it.

In the story's two episodes, a field trip and a Christmas party, help to define the students' views about Miss Snell and Miss Cleary.

"The First Robin in the World" by Phillip Bonosky is an unflinching portrait of a child's cultural confusion and alienation. Tommy is a ten-year old boy unable to fully identify with any of the diverse cultural milieus that affect his life. His father is German; his mother is an Australian aborigine; he attends a Catholic school in a lower-class ethnic American neighborhood. This mix of cultures is revealed in a poem Tommy has written about the baby Jesus. Though it shows talent—and though Tommy genuinely "loves the baby Jesus"—his language, born of one culture, offends the sensibilities of another. Still, the story ends with a victory of sorts for Tommy, though he remains confused about the conflicting cultures that intersect in his life.

In "Books," Paula Sharp brings into focus a child's view of an elementary school in San Diego where three children from diverse cultures find common ground. Stanley and Joy befriend a new boy, Barry, in Mrs. Heffernan's third-grade classroom.

> *Mrs. Heffernan was a creative, at times exotic, disciplinarian. She was a large woman, with a large wooden chair parked behind her desk, and if she caught two boys fighting, she would place them together in her chair, and sit down on their legs five or six times....*

Stanley and Joy can barely read, but Barry can read fluently in both English and Spanish—a fact that irks Mrs. Heffernan. On the same day that Barry arrives in class, so does a new set of encyclopedias. Unfortunately, Mrs. Heffernan does not allow the three students to use them. Frustrated by this restriction, the trio make elaborate plans to abduct one of the volumes—with dramatic results.

In "Her" by Hugo Martínez-Serros, a Mexican American boy narrates a strident year-long account of a teacher's willful abuse and shrugging neglect of students whom she does not consider to be first-class citizens. In the following excerpt three students, who have arrived late for the start of class, push open the classroom door and enter.

> *A deep frown stops them, then a left arm reaches out and grabs one of them—the right arm goes on directing—shakes him and pinches him twice before he escapes her grasp.*
>
> *The singing ends and she turns on the late comers. "Disrupters of ceremony!" The three cringe. "I get here early for your benefit, not mine! Yours! Why can't you do the same! You're not in Mexico! You're in America! We do things on time here! Understand? On time!"*

In "The Fun they Had," Issac Asimov gives a glimpse of the future for books, teachers, and schools as seen through the eyes of two children. The date is May 17, 2157, and Tommy (thirteen years old) and Margie (eleven years old) discover a "real" book in Tommy's attic. They have heard about "real" books but have used only the "telebooks" available on their television screens. This starts a discussion between Tommy and Margie about "real" books, teachers, and schools, which do not exist in 2157. The story is particularly relevant at a time when technology is portrayed as a crucible for the future of education.

Each of the stories in this chapter brings into focus some of the differences between a world inhabited by children and by adults. They are also testimony to the notion that child and adult views of the same world are not contrasts in parallel perspectives, that is, childish versions of adult views, but instead are fundamentally different views.

# The First Day

## EDWARD P. JONES

In an otherwise unremarkable September morning, long before I learned to be ashamed of my mother, she takes my hand and we set off down New Jersey Avenue to begin my very first day of school. I am wearing a checkeredlike blue-and-green cotton dress, and scattered about these colors are bits of yellow and white and brown. My mother has uncharacteristically spent nearly an hour on my hair that morning, plaiting and replaiting so that now my scalp tingles. Whenever I turn my head quickly, my nose fills with the faint smell of Dixie Peach hair grease. The smell is somehow a soothing one now and I will reach for it time and time again before the morning ends. All the plaits, each with a blue barrette near the tip and each twisted into an uncommon sturdiness, will last until I go to bed that night, something that has never happened before. My stomach is full of milk and oatmeal sweetened with brown sugar. Like everything else I have on, my pale green slip and underwear are new, the underwear having come three to a plastic package with a little girl on the front who appears to be dancing. Behind my ears, my mother, to stop my whining, has dabbed the stingiest bit of her gardenia perfume, the last present my father gave her before he disappeared into memory. Because I cannot smell it, I have only her word that the perfume is there. I am also wearing yellow socks trimmed with thin lines of black and white around the tops. My shoes are my greatest joy, black patent-leather miracles, and when one is nicked at the toe later that morning in class, my heart will break.

I am carrying a pencil, a pencil sharpener, and a small ten-cent tablet with a black-and-white speckled cover. My mother does not believe that a girl in kindergarten needs such things, so I am taking them only because of my insistent whining and because they are presents from our neighbors, Mary Keith and Blondelle Harris. Miss Mary and Miss Blondelle are watching my two younger sisters until my mother returns. The women are as precious to me as my mother and sisters. Out playing one day, I have overheard an older child, speaking to another child, call Miss Mary and Miss Blondelle a word that is brand new to me. This is my mother: When I say the word in fun to one of my sisters, my mother slaps me across the mouth and the word is lost for years and years.

All the way down New Jersey Avenue, the sidewalks are teeming with children. In my neighborhood, I have many friends, but I see none of them as my mother and I walk. We cross New York Avenue, we cross Pierce Street, and we Cross I and K, and still I see no one who knows my name. At I Street, between New Jersey Avenue and Third Street, we enter Seaton Elementary School, a timeworn, sad-faced building across the street from my mother's church, Mt. Carmel Baptist.

Just inside the front door, women out of the advertisements in *Ebony* are greeting other parents and children. The woman who greets us has pearls thick as jumbo marbles that come down almost to her navel, and she acts as if she had known me all my life, touching my shoulder, cupping her hand under my chin. She is enveloped in a perfume that I only know is not gardenia. When, in answer to her question, my mother tells her that we live at 1227 New Jersey Avenue, the woman first seems to be picturing in her head where we live. Then she shakes her head and says that we are at the wrong school, that we should be at Walker-Jones.

My mother shakes her head vigorously. "I want her to go here," my mother says. "If I'da wanted her someplace else, I'da took her there." The woman continues to act as if she has known me all my life, but she tells my mother that we live beyond the area that Seaton serves. My mother is not convinced and for several more minutes she questions the woman about why I cannot at-

tend Seaton. For as many Sundays as I can remember, perhaps even Sundays when I was in her
womb, my mother has pointed across I Street to
Seaton as we come and go to Mt. Carmel. "You
gonna go there and learn about the whole world."
But one of the guardians of that place is saying no,
and no again. I am learning this about my mother:
The higher up in the scale of respectability a person is—and teachers are rather high up in her
eyes—the less she is liable to let them push her
around. But finally, I see in her eyes the closing
gate, and she takes my hand and we leave the
building. On the steps, she stops as people move
past us on either side.

"Mama, I can't go to school?"

She says nothing at first, then takes my hand
again and we are down the steps quickly and nearing New Jersey Avenue before I can blink. This is
my mother: She says, "One monkey don't stop no
show."

Walker-Jones is a larger, new school and I
immediately like it because of that. But it is not
across the street from my mother's church, her
rock, one of her connections to God, and I sense
her doubts as she absently rubs her thumb over the
back of her hand. We find our way to the crowded
auditorium where gray metal chairs are set up in
the middle of the room. Along the wall to the left
are tables and other chairs. Every chair seems occupied by a child or adult. Somewhere in the room
a child is crying, a cry that rises above the buzz-
talk of so many people. Strewn about the floor are
dozens and dozens of pieces of white paper, and
people are walking over them without any thought
of picking them up. And seeing this lack of concern, I am all of a sudden afraid.

"Is this where they register for school?" my
mother asks a woman at one of the tables.

The woman looks up slowly as if she has
heard this question once too often. She nods. She
is tiny, almost as small as the girl standing beside
her. The woman's hair is set in a mass of curlers
and all of those curlers are made of paper money,
here a dollar bill, there a five-dollar bill. The girl's
hair is arrayed in curls, but some of them are be-

ginning to droop and this makes me happy. On the
table beside the woman's pocketbook is a large
notebook, worthy of someone in high school, and
looking at me looking at the notebook, the girl
places her hand possessively on it. In her other
hand she holds several pencils with thick crowns
of additional erasers.

"These the forms you gotta use?" my mother
asks the woman, picking up a few pieces of the
paper from the table. "Is this what you have to fill
out?"

The woman tells her yes, but that she need fill
out only one.

"I see," my mother says, looking about the
room. Then: "Would you help me with this form?
That is, if you don't mind."

The woman asks my mother what she means.

"This form. Would you mind helpin me fill it
out?"

The woman still seems not to understand.

"I can't read it. I don't know how to read or
write, and I'm askin you to help me." My mother
looks at me, then looks away. I know almost all of
her looks, but this one is brand new to me. "Would
you help me, then?"

The woman says Why sure, and suddenly she
appears happier, so much more satisfied with everything. She finishes the form for her daughter
and my mother and I step aside to wait for her. We
find two chairs nearby and sit. My mother is now
diseased, according to the girl's eyes, and until the
moment her mother takes her and the form to the
front of the auditorium, the girl never stops looking at my mother. I stare back at her. "Don't
stare," my mother says to me. "You know better
than that."

Another woman out of the *Ebony* ads takes
the woman's child away. Now, the woman says
upon returning, let's see what we can do for you
two.

My mother answers the questions the woman
reads off the form. They start with my last name,
and then on to the first and middle names. This is
school, I think. This is going to school. My mother slowly enunciates each word of my name. This

is my mother: As the questions go on, she takes from her pocketbook document after document, as if they will support my right to attend school, as if she has been saving them up for just this moment. Indeed, she takes out more papers than I have ever seen her do in other places: my birth certificate, my baptismal record, a doctor's letter concerning my bout with chicken pox, rent receipts, records of immunization, a letter about our public assistance payments, even her marriage license—every single paper that has anything even remotely to do with my five-year-old life. Few of the papers are needed here, but it does not matter and my mother continues to pull out the documents with the purposefulness of a magician pulling out a long string of scarves. She has learned that money is the beginning and end of everything in this world, and when the woman finishes, my mother offers her fifty cents, and the woman accepts it without hesitation. My mother and I are just about the last parent and child in the room.

My mother presents the form to a woman sitting in front of the stage, and the woman looks at it and writes something on a white card, which she gives to my mother. Before long, the woman who has taken the girl with the drooping curls appears from behind us, speaks to the sitting woman, and introduces herself to my mother and me. She's to be my teacher, she tells my mother. My mother stares.

We go into the hall, where my mother kneels down to me. Her lips are quivering. "I'll be back to pick you up at twelve o'clock. I don't want you to go nowhere. You just wait right here. And listen to every word she say." I touch her lips and press them together. It is an old, old game between us. She puts my hand down at my side, which is not part of the game. She stands and looks a second at the teacher, then she turns and walks away. I see where she has darned one of her socks the night before. Her shoes make loud sounds in the hall. She passes through the doors and I can still hear the loud sounds of her shoes. And even when the teacher turns me toward the classrooms and I hear what must be the singing and talking of all the children in the world, I can still hear my mother's footsteps above it all.

# Fun with a Stranger

## RICHARD YATES

All that summer the children who were due to start third grade under Miss Snell had been warned about her. "Boy, you're gonna get it," the older children would say, distorting their faces with a wicked pleasure. "You're really gonna *get* it. Mrs. *Cleary's* all right" (Mrs. Cleary taught the other, luckier half of third grade) "—she's *fine,* but boy, that *Snell*—you better watch out." So it happened that the morale of Miss Snell's class was low even before school opened in September, and she did little in the first few weeks to improve it.

She was probably sixty, a big rawboned woman with a man's face, and her clothes, if not her very pores, seemed always to exude that dry essence of pencil shavings and chalk dust that is the smell of school. She was strict and humorless, preoccupied with rooting out the things she held intolerable: mumbling, slumping, daydreaming, frequent trips to the bathroom, and, the worst of all, "coming to school without proper supplies." Her small eyes were sharp, and when somebody sent out a stealthy alarm of whispers and nudges to try to borrow a pencil from somebody else, it almost never worked. "What's the trouble back there?" she would demand. "I mean you, John Gerhardt." And John Gerhardt—or Howard White or whoever it happened to be—-caught in the middle of a whisper, could only turn red and say, "Nothing."

"Don't mumble. Is it a pencil? Have you come to school without a pencil again? Stand up when you're spoken to."

And there would follow a long lecture on Proper Supplies that ended only after the offender had come forward to receive a pencil from the small hoard on her desk, had been made to say, "Thank you, Miss Snell," and to repeat, until he said it loud enough for everyone to hear, a promise that he wouldn't chew it or break its point.

With erasers it was even worse because they were more often in short supply, owing to a general tendency to chew them off the ends of pencils. Miss Snell kept a big, shapeless old eraser on her desk, and she seemed very proud of it. "This is *my* eraser," she would say, shaking it at the class. "I've had this eraser for five years. Five years." (And this was not heard to believe, for the eraser looked as old and gray and worn-down as the hand that brandished it.) "I've never played with it because it's not a toy. I've never chewed it because it's not good to eat. And I've never lost it because I'm not foolish and I'm not careless. I need this eraser for my work and I've taken good care of it. Now, why can't you do the same with *your* erasers? I don't know what's the matter with this class. I've never had a class that was so foolish and so careless and so *childish* about its supplies."

She never seemed to lose her temper, but it would almost have been better if she did, for it was the flat, dry, passionless redundance of her scolding that got everybody down. When Miss Snell singled someone out for a special upbraiding it was an ordeal by talk. She would come up to within a foot of her victim's face, her eyes would stare unblinking into his, and the wrinkled gray flesh of her mouth would labor to pronounce his guilt, grimly and deliberately, until all the color faded from the day. She seemed to have no favorites; once she even picked on Alice Johnson, who always had plenty of supplies and did nearly everything right. Alice was mumbling while reading aloud, and when she continued to mumble after several warnings Miss Snell went over and took her book away and lectured her for several minutes running. Alice looked stunned at first; then her eyes filled up, her mouth twitched into terrible shapes, and she gave in to the ultimate humiliation of crying in class.

It was not uncommon to cry in Miss Snell's class, even among the boys. And ironically, it always seemed to be during the lull after one of these scenes—when the only sound in the room was somebody's slow, half-stifled sobbing, and the rest of the class stared straight ahead in an agony of embarrassment—that the noise of group laughter would float in from Mrs. Cleary's class across the hall.

Still, they could not hate Miss Snell, for children's villains must be all black, and there was no denying that Miss Snell was sometimes nice in an awkward, groping way of her own. "When we learn a new word it's like making a friend," she said once. "And we all like to make friends, don't we? Now, for instance, when school began this year you were all strangers to me, but I wanted very much to learn your names and remember your faces, and so I made the effort. It was confusing at first, but before long I'd made friends with all of you. And later on we'll have some good times together—oh, perhaps a little party at Christmastime, or something like that—and then I know I'd be very sorry if I hadn't made that effort, because you can't very well have fun with a stranger, can you?" She gave them a homely, shy smile. "And that's just the way it is with words."

When she said something like that it was more embarrassing than anything else, but it did leave the children with a certain vague sense of responsibility toward her, and often prompted them into a loyal reticence when children from other classes demanded to know how bad she really was. "Well, not too bad," they would say uncomfortably, and try to change the subject.

John Gerhardt and Howard White usually walked home from school together, and often as not, though they tried to avoid it, they were joined by two of the children from Mrs. Cleary's class who lived on their street—Freddy Taylor and his twin sister Grace. John and Howard usually got about as far as the end of the playground before the twins came running after them out of the crowd. "Hey, wait up!" Freddy would call. "Wait up!" And in a moment the twins would fall into step beside them, chattering, swinging their identical plaid canvas schoolbags.

"Guess what we're gonna do next week," Freddy said in his chirping voice one afternoon. "Our whole class, I mean. Guess. Come on, guess."

John Gerhardt had already made it plain to the twins once, in so many words, that he didn't like walking home with a girl, and now he very nearly said something to the effect that one girl was bad enough, but two were more than he could take. Instead he aimed a knowing glance at Howard White and they both walked on in silence, determined not to answer Freddy's insistent "Guess."

But Freddy didn't wait long for an answer. "We're gonna take a field trip," he said, "for our class in Transportation. We're gonna go to Harmon. You know what Harmon is?"

"Sure," Howard White said. "A town."

"No, but I mean, you know what they *do* there? What they do is, that's where they change all the trains coming into New York from steam locomotives to electric power. Mrs. Cleary says we're gonna watch 'em changing the locomotives and everything."

"We're gonna spend practically the whole day," Grace said.

"So what's so great about that?" Howard White asked. "I can go there *any* day, if I feel like it, on my bike." This was an exaggeration—he wasn't allowed out of a two-block radius on his bike—but it sounded good, especially when he added, "I don't need any Mrs. Cleary to take me," with a mincing, sissy emphasis on the "Cleary."

"On a school day?" Grace inquired. "Can you go on a *school* day?"

Lamely Howard murmured, "Sure, if I feel like it," but it was a clear point for the twins.

"Mrs. Cleary says we're gonna take a lotta field trips," Freddy said. "Later on, we're gonna go to the Museum of Natural History, in New York, and a whole lotta other places. Too bad you're not in Mrs. Cleary's class."

"Doesn't bother me any," John Gerhardt said. Then he came up with a direct quotation from his father that seemed appropriate: "Anyway, I don't *go* to school to fool around. I go to school to work. Come on, Howard."

A day or two later it turned out that both classes were scheduled to take the field trip together; Miss Snell had just neglected to tell her pupils about it. When she did tell them it was in one of her nice moods. "I think the trip will be especially valuable," she said, "because it will be instructive and at the same time it will be a real treat for all of us." That afternoon John Gerhardt and Howard White conveyed the news to the twins with studied carelessness and secret delight.

But the victory was short-lived, for the field trip itself only emphasized the difference between the two teachers. Mrs. Cleary ran everything with charm and enthusiasm; she was young and lithe and just about the prettiest woman Miss Snell's class had ever seen. It was she who arranged for the children to climb up and inspect the cab of a huge locomotive that stood idle on a siding, and she who found out where the public toilets were. The most tedious facts about trains came alive when she explained them; the most forbidding engineers and switchmen became jovial hosts when she smiled up at them, with her long hair blowing and her hands plunged jauntily in the pockets of her polo coat.

Through it all Miss Snell hung in the background, gaunt and sour, her shoulders hunched against the wind and her squinted eyes roving, alert for stragglers. At one point she made Mrs. Cleary wait while she called her own class aside and announced that there would be no more field trips if they couldn't learn to stay together in a group. She spoiled everything, and by the time it was over the class was painfully embarrassed for her. She'd had every chance to give a good account of herself that day, and now her failure was as pitiful as it was disappointing. That was the worst part of it: she was pitiful—they didn't even want to look at her, in her sad, lumpy black coat and hat. All they wanted was to get her into the bus and back to school and out of sight as fast as possible.

The events of autumn each brought a special season to the school. First came Halloween, for which several art classes were devoted to crayoned jack-o'-lanterns and arching black cats. Thanksgiving was bigger; for a week or two the children painted turkeys and horns of plenty and brown-clad Pilgrim Fathers with high buckled hats and trumpet-barreled muskets, and in music class they sang "We Gather Together" and "America the Beautiful" again and again. And almost as soon as Thanksgiving was over the long preparations for Christmas began: red and green predominated, and carols were rehearsed for the annual Christmas Pageant. Every day the halls became more thickly festooned with Christmas trimmings, until finally it was the week before vacation.

"You gonna have a party in your class?" Freddy Taylor inquired one day.

"Sure, prob'ly," John Gerhardt said, though in fact he wasn't sure at all. Except for one vague reference, many weeks before, Miss Snell had said or hinted nothing whatever about a Christmas party.

"Miss Snell tell ya you're gonna have one, or what?" Grace asked.

"Well, she didn't exactly *tell* us," John Gerhardt said obscurely. Howard White walked along without a word, scuffing his shoes.

"Mrs. Cleary didn't tell us, either," Grace said, "because it's supposed to be a surprise, but we know we're gonna have one. Some of the kids who had her last year said so. They said she always has this big party on the last day, with a tree and everything, and favors and things to eat. You gonna have all that?"

"Oh, I don't know," John Gerhardt said. "Sure, prob'ly." But later, when the twins were gone, he got a little worried. "Hey, Howard," he said, "you think she *is* gonna have a party, or what?"

"Search *me*," Howard White said, with a careful shrug. "*I* didn't say anything." But he was uneasy about it too, and so was the rest of the class. As vacation drew nearer, and particularly during the few anticlimactic days of school left after the Christmas Pageant was over, it seemed less and less likely that Miss Snell was planning a party of any kind, and it preyed on all their minds.

It rained on the last day of school. The morning went by like any other morning, and after lunch, like any other rainy day, the corridors were packed with chattering children in raincoats and rubbers, milling around and waiting for the afternoon classes to begin. Around the third-grade classrooms there was a special tension, for Mrs. Cleary had locked the door of her room, and the word soon spread that she was alone inside making preparations for a party that would begin when the bell rang and last all afternoon. "I peeked," Grace Taylor was saying breathlessly to anyone who would listen. "She's got this little tree with all blue lights, and she's got the room all fixed up and all the desks moved away and everything."

Others from her class tagged after her with questions—"*What'd* you see?" "All blue lights?"—and still others jostled around the door, trying to get a look through the keyhole.

Miss Snell's class pressed self-consciously against the corridor wall, mostly silent, hands in their pockets. Their door was closed too, but nobody wanted to see if it was locked for fear it might swing open and reveal Miss Snell sitting sensibly at her desk, correcting papers. Instead they watched Mrs. Cleary's door, and when it opened at last they watched the other children flock in. All the girls yelled, "Ooh!" in chorus as they disappeared inside, and even from where Miss Snell's class stood they could see that the room was transformed. There *was* a tree with blue lights—the whole room glowed blue, in fact—and the floor was cleared. They could see the corner of a table in the middle, bearing platters of bright candy and cake. Mrs. Cleary stood in the doorway, beautiful and beaming, slightly flushed with welcome. She gave a kindly, distracted smile to the craning faces of Miss Snell's class, then closed the door again.

A second later Miss Snell's door opened, and the first thing they saw was that the room was unchanged. The desks were all in place, ready for work; their own workaday Christmas paintings still spotted the walls, and there was no other decoration except for the grubby red cardboard letters spelling "Merry Christmas" that had hung over the blackboard all week. But then with a rush of relief they saw that on Miss Snell's desk lay a neat little pile of red-and-white-wrapped packages. Miss Snell stood unsmiling at the head of the room, waiting for the class to get settled. Instinctively, nobody lingered to stare at the gifts or to comment on them. Miss Snell's attitude made it plain that the party hadn't begun yet.

It was time for spelling, and she instructed them to get their pencils and papers ready. In the silences between her enunciation of each word to be spelled, the noise of Mrs. Cleary's class could be heard—repeated laughter and whoops of surprise. But the little pile of gifts made everything all right; the children had only to look at them to know that there was nothing to be embarrassed about, after all. Miss Snell had come through.

The gifts were all wrapped alike, in white tissue paper with red ribbon, and the few whose individual shapes John Gerhardt could discern looked like they might be jackknives. Maybe it would be jackknives for the boys, he thought, and little pocket flashlights for the girls. Or more likely, since jackknives were probably too expensive, it would be something well-meant and useless from the dime store, like individual lead soldiers for the boys and miniature dolls for the girls. But even that would be good enough—something hard and bright to prove that she was human after all, to pull out of a pocket and casually display to the Taylor twins. ("Well, no, not a *party,* exactly, but she gave us all these little presents. Look.")

"John Gerhardt," Miss Snell said, "if you can't give your attention to anything but the… things on my desk, perhaps I'd better put them out of sight." The class giggled a little, and she smiled. It was only a small, shy smile, quickly corrected before she turned back to her spelling book, but it was enough the break the tension. While the spelling papers were being collected Howard White leaned close to John Gerhardt and whispered, "Tie clips. Bet it's tie clips for the boys and some kinda jewelry for the girls."

"Sh-sh!" John told him, but then he added, "Too thick for tie clips." There was a general shifting around; everyone expected the party to begin as soon as Miss Snell had all the spelling papers. Instead she called for silence and began the afternoon class in Transportation.

The afternoon wore on. Every time Miss Snell glanced at the clock they expected her to say, "Oh, my goodness—I'd almost forgotten." But she didn't. It was a little after two, with less than an hour of school left, when Miss Snell was interrupted by a knock on the door. "Yes?" she said irritably. "What is it?"

Little Grace Taylor came in, with half a cupcake in her hand and the other half in her mouth. She displayed elaborate surprise at finding the class at work—backing up a step and putting her free hand to her lips.

"Well?" Miss Snell demanded. "Do you want something?"

"Mrs. Cleary wants to know if—"

"Must you talk with your mouth full?"

Grace swallowed. She wasn't the least bit shy. "Mrs. Cleary wants to know if you have any extra paper plates."

"I have no paper plates," Miss Snell said. "And will you kindly inform Mrs. Cleary that this class is in session?"

"All right," Grace took another bite of her cake and turned to leave. Her eyes caught the pile of gifts and she paused to look at them, clearly unimpressed.

"You're holding up the class," Miss Snell said. Grace moved on. At the door she gave the class a sly glance and a quick, silent giggle full of cake crumbs, and then slipped out.

The minute hand crept down to two-thirty, passed it, and inched toward two-forty-five. Finally, at five minutes of three, Miss Snell laid down her book. "All right," she said, "I think we may all put our books away now. This is the last day of school before the holidays, and I've prepared a—little surprise for you." She smiled again. "Now, I think it would be best if you all stay in your places, and I'll just pass these around. Alice Johnson, will you please come and help me? The rest of you stay seated." Alice went forward, and Miss Snell divided the little packages into two heaps, using two pieces of drawing paper as trays. Alice took one paperful, cradling it carefully, and Miss Snell the other. Before they started around the room Miss Snell said, "Now, I think the most courteous thing would be for each of you to wait until everyone is served, and then we'll all open the packages together. All right, Alice."

They started down the aisle, reading the labels and passing out the gifts. The labels were the familiar Woolworth kind with a picture of Santa Claus and "Merry Christmas" printed on them, and Miss Snell had filled them out in her neat blackboard lettering. John Gerhardt's read: "To John G., From Miss Snell." He picked it up, but the moment he felt the package he knew, with a little shock, exactly what it was. There was no surprise left by the time Miss Snell returned to the head of the class and said, "All right."

He peeled off the paper and laid the gift on his desk. It was an eraser, the serviceable ten-cent kind, half white for pencil and half gray for ink. From the corner of his eye he saw that Howard White, beside him, was unwrapping an identical one, and a furtive glance around the room confirmed that all the gifts had been the same. Nobody knew what to do, and for what seemed a full minute the room was silent except for the dwindling rustle of tissue paper. Miss Snell stood at the head of the class, her clasped fingers writhing like dry worms at her waist, her face melted into the soft, tremulous smile of a giver. She looked completely helpless.

At last one of the girls said, "Thank you, Miss Snell," and then the rest of the class said it in ragged unison: "Thank you, Miss Snell."

"You're all very welcome," she said, composing herself, "and I hope you all have a pleasant holiday."

Mercifully, the bell rang then, and in the jostling clamor of retreat to the cloakroom it was no longer necessary to look at Miss Snell. Her voice rose above the noise: "Will you all please dispose of your paper and ribbons in the basket before you leave?"

John Gerhardt yanked on his rubbers, grabbed his raincoat, and elbowed his way out of the cloakroom, out of the classroom and down the noisy corridor. "Hey, Howard, wait up!" he yelled to Howard White, and finally both of them were free of school, running, splashing through puddles on the playground. Miss Snell was left behind now, farther behind with every step; if they ran fast enough they could even avoid the Taylor twins, and then there would be no need to think about any of it any more. Legs pounding, raincoats streaming, they ran with the exhilaration of escape.

# The First Robin in the World

## PHILLIP BONOSKY

It was because his mother was a pagan—a real pagan, a gypsy—or even something worse, something without a name, his father had told him with a cry, half of hope, half of hopelessness. They had had to call her back into the house to put on her shoes—she had been half-way to the grocery store, padding along in bare feet, oblivious of shoes, of people staring.

Nevertheless, Tommy looked at his father with something close to horror. He knew what a pagan was all right! It would be a long time before the pagans gutted by the holy sword of the Christian Knights—as *seen* in his Bible History—would leave his nightmares, or the faces of innocent babes, of angels, in fact, wreathed in ecstasy that they were bound for the arms of their heavenly Father waiting for them in the clouds, though they were transported on the points of swords, or rather, and he learned the word for the first time, *scimitars* wielded by *pagans*—yes, *pagans*—wild, raging and delirious with the sight of spilled Christian blood.

He wished, for instance, that his mother wouldn't sit at the window when she fed little Frances at her breast. Other kids would see her there—and laugh—and mock him later. For she sat open, bounteous, unclothed, overflowing, and smiled a big missing-toothed smile at the children staring at her from the alley.

But in the house itself it was different. Tommy liked nothing better than to watch as his mother dipped little prune-faced Frances into the tub water, which he had filled for his mother from steaming pots on the stove, was delighted to hear the first squall come out of that toothless mouth, then the gurgle of pleasure that followed as her mother soothed her and sang one of her mysterious songs.

He loved to follow the whole ritual: watch mother take the baby, dripping and steam-pink, out of its watery bed, lay her on the clean thin blanket, where she cooed kicking her legs and flailing her stubby arms, as she oiled her and dusted her with lilac-smelling baby powder.

He knew he would remember lilac forever as the baby's smell. And would bend over and sniff the baby's arms and legs and bottom until his head was blown up with the perfume. Then, if the baby had been crying before and not eating right, his mother would whittle down a piece of Ivory soap into a two-pointed sliver, like a tiny sword, and slide it into and out of the angry hole which was puckered up, pink and crinkled.

This done, his mother would pick her up into her big brown bosom with the star-shaped mole on its plumpish side, and stick the big nipple, almost purple with the passion to give its milk into the crying mouth with no teeth. The greedy, sucking noises that followed relaxed them both. "Ah," his mother would say, "the little mole." But Tommy was no longer surprised to hear a mole referred to so tenderly.

This is the way it was morning after morning, before school, during the summer, and Tommy loved what he was doing. He never missed not having a dog or even a cat as long as he had a little sister. The three of them would spend the morning together and talked to each other in her language. She didn't know English—nor his father's language either very well—but she had her own language, which, when he sat with her, Tommy thought he understood. Later, he realized it wasn't the words he understood at all.

She told both of them—baby Frances as much and maybe even more than him—stories that had to do with snow princesses, wolves with eyes glowing in the dark pine forest of winter, gods of thunder and lightning that stormed through the skies in great angers and domestic frenzies of their own, of girls who had married handsome strangers only to discover that the man they married in such transports of romance was actually the devil himself, and they died forthwith, denied Christian burial; of returning three days after from the grave to haunt the home of their parents who double-locked the door and slammed shut the shutters; all this, hours of it, and then little poems, songs and riddles. What was a white swan on a yellow river? Where do the moon and the sun go when they go out? What does it mean if the window rattles two nights after the death of a young virgin? And the poems were nonsense poems, which excited him most of all, and when his mother had finished one, it continued going on in his head, and one day he found himself writing his poems down. But much as he longed to read them back to her, and ask her what she thought of them—for he was sure somehow she was a taster of verse—she'd either laugh at the idea or—cry. Why she'd cry she never explained; and yet he wanted to read to her to see what she would do—laugh or cry. But she didn't know English.

It was useless: she'd look at him, holding the baby close, cooing to it, starting to croon God knows what about: all he knew was that there were storks in the songs, devils in the stories, drunkards in the verses, and that night was darker there in her land then he had ever heard of its being in any other land in the world. Through all of it he would catch glimpses of her running with her bare feet flashing, her skirts for some reason tucked up above her knees.

He liked hearing her sing best when he was lying across her lap, his head just washed in the same water the baby had been washed, resting against her bosom into which it partly sank, as she carefully combed with a fine-toothed comb through the wet tangle to catch the sly cooties which she'd nick dead, one thumbnail against the other, when she caught them. The little click he heard told him they were dead. Then it was he was most at peace. Then it was that angels danced in the coal fire, sad pagans sang songs in the hills.

Everything became different when his father came home from the mill. It was almost as if they had to change the furniture. They had to make a pathway for him clear from kitchen to living-bedroom where he went right off for a drink of

home-made *schnapps.* Then, to the sink, hard hands crushing the bar of yellow soap which foamed white as if squeezed out of it, the reach for the roller towel, the hard scrub of his face, and then the cleaner, bristled cheeks, eyes blinking from leftover soap there.

Nothing stood on the supper table but a bowl of soup. It was as though his mother had put the bowl there in passage and forgotten it, and he had to nudge her to get the rest of the meal ready. Then it was supper of boiled chuck meat, of boiled potatoes and bread, and afterwards his father would go to the other room again for another minute with his *schnapps.* His father called it by the German name—it was homemade brew, which he distilled in the kitchen and put away in the cellar in kegs and even small barrels, sold a little of it, drank most of it himself. The cellar reeked of mash and cane sugar, of the dark oozing in moist corners where if you threw a rotten potato, it would one day send out naked pale arms into the black, turn then into witches' hair, then finding no sunlight rot in its own bed.

Everything unpleasant his father said to him, he said in English. Everything pleasant, which usually was when he had had a few, he said in their own language. It was as if for his father two worlds existed: one in which he suffered, hated and screamed in pain; the other—though he drank in that one, too—in which he sang songs, cracked huge jokes, danced, kissed him on the belly until he died laughing, and all that came in words that were so snug, so insinuating in their sweetness and fitness, that he felt wrapped in a fur, like a fox, warm and terribly pleased with himself.

He didn't remember exactly, but one day he asked his mother where Australia was, and she had looked blankly at him, all six years old of him, and one-half year at St. Teresa's, and smiled at him in a kind of soft rebuke that he should ask such questions of her, when he knew she had better and more secret things to think about. She had answers but not to that kind of question.

Only then did he realize that his mother had never been able to read; what she knew she remembered. But many things that now existed didn't exist when she was growing up in the other country, when she was a girl before she left for America: and she had never learned that they had been invented. But, of course, Tommy knew even then—he knew so much about so many things that he'd learned not only in school but on the street, that he felt his mother was getting smaller and more like a child as he was getting bigger and older: and finally, at ten, what was left of him and her were moments like this when he watched the baby and she combed his hair for cooties.

Except that she was a pagan, she behaved in a way nobody else did, and seemed not to care at all, not even to know that she was. And he had learned to fear for her, and—but this was only lately—to begin to be ashamed of her, too.

He screamed at her, for instance, when she sat in front of the window nursing the baby, visible to the whole passing world. He never told other boys he'd seen his little sister naked—warned by some sixth sense about it, though many of them had little sisters too, but none with mothers like his. In fact, he had to school himself to keep aware that the way they lived wasn't the way other people lived. It made him more fiercely Catholic, the more his mother forgot about telling him to go to Mass, or remember when Easter came up, and what Easter meant. It was he who prodded her to church, where she would sit with a half-smile on her face looking with interest over the congregation, following the solemn activity at the altar, sniffing as the censer sent its whiff across the heads of the worshippers, or she would cry out with delight when the altar boys rang their silver bells, Later, walking home, she would hum to herself, and once she bent down to him and told him a little rhyme which she'd just made up in which she'd called him, by name, like a wiggling fish, dared to call him, "my own little Baby Jesus." And at that he screamed at her, for it showed him that she hadn't been paying any attention to the meaning of the Mass at all: her mind had been busy in her pagan way making up silly rhymes, which he loved so much at home as she combed his hair, but not now.

And that's what troubled him. He, too, long before he had even thought about it, had found himself making rhymes, helplessly, dreamily, finally wrote some down and read them to his best friend. Written with a big black pencil in his school tablet with a schooner in full sail on its cover, he hid it in the the corner of a closet.

The truth was he loved little Baby Jesus, too; saw him often kicking off his blankets and diaper in the manger, just like Frances, heard his mother Mary scold him, wash him, tickle him, kiss his dimpled knees, feed him—but Tommy didn't dare to "see" her bounteous bosom exposed, though somehow he established the idea of it nevertheless—while God sat in a corner puffing on an old wooden pipe, his long beard wet with short-aimed spits and sometimes grumbling because supper of ambrosia (which was like golden honey) was late, throwing corn cobs at the barn door to keep the lowing cattle quiet. Joseph, Jesus' father, was somewhere in the fields, doing Tommy never bothered to imagine what.

He'd written a poem about them, in fact. He loved the poem so much he felt guilty when Sister Roberta had asked them all to write a poem about spring—a religious poem, it had to be, with Jesus somewhere in it—and he'd already had one written: that one.

She promised to let him read it before the class, and his heart had started beating like a fist against his side, like the poem itself demanding to be free. Half-way through the day, Tommy had to sit down, catch his breath as though he'd been running, close his eyes, and place his hands squarely on his chest and *push* his heart back where it belonged. The poem would show them how good a Catholic he was and how much he loved Baby Jesus, with all his fervent heart. And, of course, since he'd seen his first robin only a few days ago, pulling up a worm out of the earth as if the worm was a piece of rubber—it would stretch all the way out and suddenly snap back— the poem had to have a robin in it. In fact, it would be about the *first* robin—the first robin in all the world, the one Jesus saw.

He had wanted desperately to read his poem to his mother, but there was no way he could do that. Even so, he wondered if she would understand—though he wanted to tell her that in some mysterious way she had helped him write it. For she had been sitting there, suckling the baby, crooning to it, and he had wet his pencil tip on his tongue—the tongue tip was almost always black as if he had a disease—and worked at it, grunting and sighing. And then he'd read it to her in English and she had smiled uncomprehendingly and that was it. Actually, he'd wanted to write in the language only she knew—if only she'd told him what it *was*! Did pagans still speak—did wind and storm still speak—through her?

Morning at St. Teresa's, with Sister Roberta, her narrow, scalded-looking face between the white cowl of her nun's habit, standing in front of the room under the gilded picture of Jesus holding back his robe to show his scarlet, pierced heart, crept slowly.

There was catechism to get through, Bible History, then ten minutes for exercises in the yard—and then, finally, English class, when Sister Roberta had promised. It seemed to Tommy she began the class carelessly, as though she didn't know what was burning in his tablet—the penciled poem, written so big it took two whole pages. In fact, as she stood up before the class and announced that they would start to parse the poetry of *Hiawatha* by Longfellow, he raised his hands furiously, and when she recognized him, said: "But Sister, you said we'd read our poems today."

"Oh," she said, "did I? And does anybody have any poem to read?"

His hand shot up. Only one more of the 25 boys and girls of the fifth grade held up their hands, and Sister Roberta did not look enthusiastic.

"Well," she said, and seemed as if she would pass off to *Hiawatha* after all.

"I'll read!" Tommy cried.

"In that case," Sister Roberta said, "females first." And she pointed to Mary Davis, whose yellow hair was braided in one pigtail that hung down her back with a pink ribbon tying off the end of it. She got up, smoothed down the front of her dress, unfolded her paper, and began:

> *Spring is here, it brings great cheer,*
> *Robins and sparrows are singing.*
> *I know that Jesus Christ is here*
> *Because my heart is tinkling.*

She sat down and folded her hands neatly on the top of the desk.

"What did you think of this nice poem?" Sister Roberta asked.

Tommy didn't care anything for it. He just wanted them all to get over talking about it and hear *him*. However, he did raise his hand and said: "Maybe Mary meant to write *tingling* instead of *tinkling*."

"Mary?"

Setting her jaw, Mary said firmly: "I meant to write *tinkling* and that's what I did write!"

Tommy sat down.

Sister Roberta looked reproachfully at him. "I think tinkling is a very good word," she said. "It's like a little bell—like a silver bell *tinkling*—" she emphasized, "at Mass that calls Jesus to us."

"Tingling," Tommy said, his head down.

"What?" she demanded sharply.

"Tingling," he said, lifting his head.

Mary Davis was crying now.

"Did you see what you did?" Sister Roberta demanded. "Tell her you're sorry!"

He told her nothing.

Everybody in the room was staring at him. He felt himself go hot to the tiniest bit of scalp on his head.

Tommy said: "Even tingling isn't the best word."

"Oh, really!" Sister Roberta cried. "You've become such an authority—" "What's that?" Tommy wanted to know. "Well, then," she went on, "let's see what kind of poet you are—whether you tinkle or tingle." The class laughed. "Read!" She leveled the pointer at him.

Now he didn't want to read. The poem that had burned in him all day long seemed dead now.

Mary Davis was crying. Sister Roberta was scowling. The other children were giggling. For a moment he couldn't get his feet untangled from under the desk, then he pulled himself free into the aisle, his pants stuck in the wrong place and he wiggled uncomfortably, and he wanted to wipe his nose too. A terrible itch had started up in it. But nothing could be done. He flipped open the tablet, in which he had written the huge penciled words. They swam in front of his eyes and he just stood still until his eyes cleared. Then he read the poem to them in a loud voice, like a train conductor, as though it was something he had to announce but didn't care more about it:

> God yelled at the first robin
> "Stop your bobbin'," said he.
> Mother Mary cried: "Sakes alive,
> Can't you just be?"
> Here's what Baby Jesus said:
> "Robby, Robby, juke your head!"

He went blind then. He sat down and dropped his head. Pain, fire, railroad trains crashing—all rushed through his body. It was so loud in his ears he hadn't heard the silence—only a gasp here and there—that followed the poem. He knew immediately he had made the greatest mistake, if not committed the greatest crime, of his life.

He raised his head to look at Sister Roberta. She seemed to have been turned to stone, for she hadn't moved a muscle. She was staring at him, her thin lips losing their pale pink and disappearing entirely into her mouth as though she had sucked them in. Only the faint mustache left behind on her upper lip quivered.

Somebody laughed nervously. This brought Sister Roberta to life and she went over to the boy who laughed and hit him on the head with her rosary from which dangled a heavy lead crucifix. Then she returned, drew in her breath and announced: "What we have just heard is—blasphemy!" The children were struck dumb. She looked piercingly at Tommy: "At your age to write—to think—such blasphemy is beyond belief! This is the work of a pagan!"

His face burned, and yet underneath he was saying: "Yes, yes, I'm a pagan. I'm a pagan. I'm a pagan." And said out loud: "I love Baby Jesus."

"Quiet!" Sister Roberta ordered, slapping her hand flat on the desk in front of her, so that the boy sitting there jumped. Mary Davis was looking at him with a kind of sly vindication in her eyes— it was plain she thought he was now exposed for what he really was, and that made her better. Because he had always liked her long yellow hair, he was sorry, and he wished he could say to her: "I like your poem, Mary Davis," but he knew he couldn't say that now—or ever.

All the boys and girls in the room were looking at him—they had never encountered blasphemy in their town before, nor seen a pagan—and although his skin prickled with reverence—still, he felt something like the quiet that precedes discovery. What was it? What was he about to know? What?

Sister Roberta had to tell him twice that he must go to Father Jerome's office and await his pleasure. She would send him to the office with Mary Davis—"Give me the tablet!"—and she would carry a note to Father Jerome from her, and he was to stand there and wait for Father Jerome to read it, read the poem, question Mary Davis and then—and then, obviously, he was to get ready to spend the rest of his life in hellfire.

*Poor Mama,* Tommy thought sadly: *You did this—you wrote this—this is your poem. They don't know that you're a pagan, and I'm a pagan, but that we like Baby Jesus so very much.*

Mary Davis was happy to carry out her assignment. She swung down the hall, her pigtail bouncing against the top of her just burgeoning bottom, and Tommy followed, trying not to look up at the disapproving Popes whose faces followed him, framed all the same size, along the wall. He had never known how really heavy his feet were. They had to be *pulled*—they wouldn't go by themselves. They had to be lifted, they had to be *ordered* to follow.

Father Jerome was tapping on a typewriter when they got into the office. He was tapping with one finger on the keys, his spectacles pushed up on his forehead, and didn't take his eyes off them, as though they'd get lost, even when Sister Martha his secretary led them into his room. She had knocked and he had made some noise but Tommy couldn't tell what it was.

When he finally did look up at them, it was with satisfaction for a job well done. His pleasure at himself extended to them. "Well, and what have we here?"

Mary Davis handed him the note; he pushed his spectacles down on his nose, and read it, and threw Tommy a glance, and then said: "Hmm." And: "You may go." Mary Davis trotted off, throwing Tommy a triumphant last look, and Tommy was alone with Father Jerome.

There was more silence as he read the poem, and immediately re-read it, turning the paper to the light as if to make sure of the words, and, finally, lifting his glasses again, he said: "Why did you write this?"

For a moment Tommy didn't know what to say; then he finally proposed: "I like Baby Jesus?"

"Yes," Father Jerome said, looking at the poem again. "But not God?"

"No."

"It doesn't sound like it. Nor Mother Mary?"

"No, not as much as Jesus."

"I see. Tell me," he said, "where did you learn those words? At home?" Tommy shook his head. He thought of his mother again, but shook his head. "Books," he said, nodding his head.

"But not *Catholic* books! And you're a Roman Catholic boy!" the priest said. "You made your first communion and first confession here—I know, I officiated—and you go to communion and confession each Saturday and Sunday. Don't you?"

Tommy nodded.

"That's so. And yet there's no reverence in this poem. You understand what is meant by 'reverence'?"

Tommy nodded.

"And yet you say God 'hollered'—*hollered!*—like a—like a—truck driver! And Mother Mary—so, so *peevish.* And Baby Jesus—well, now," he said, "it sounds like—well, as if they're living now, right here, like you and me. And they get angry, and scold, and so on, perhaps like your own family. They don't sound—" he hesitated—"godly."

Tommy almost said it but yanked it back out of his throat just in time: "But they're not. They're pagan. They're like I was, like I am."

"And if God isn't shown as godly," Father Jerome went on, "then you are committing blasphemy. God is God, and not your father—hollering! Nor your mother scolding you. Nor Jesus using slang—" He looked to confirm his fear. "Juke," he said. "Juke your head!" He looked at Tommy. "Do you understand?"

Tommy nodded, afraid to open his mouth, he didn't know what would come out.

"Therefore, one must say that the poem is impious and no good Catholic child would be happy to have written it and upset everybody's feelings. Your duty is not just to wipe the poem out—with an eraser; but to wipe it, with prayers of contrition, out of your mind. That's more important. Otherwise, there is Judgment Day, which, of course, waits for all of us, myself included." He paused, he had wanted to make sure that Tommy had got the point. "None of us," he said, "escapes. And each of us wishes to come before the throne of God with souls pure and our minds clean, and good Catholics in every little part of us, awake or asleep. No Catholic boy would want to give the impression, as you do in this poem, that either God or Mother Mary is going to—well—" he stopped and re-consulted the poem, "*hit* Baby Jesus on the head. Juke—" he repeated, shaking his head unbelievingly at the word. "This is vulgar street talk, not to be associated with our Lord. Do you understand that?"

He went on without waiting for Tommy to answer as though it was obvious he would agree although Tommy stood silent and immovable in every part of him.

Finally, Tommy said: "Sister Roberta said it was a pagan poem—a pagan wrote it."

"What?" Father Jerome was alerted, and jumped back to the tablet again, and re-read the poem with the same slowness with which he typed.

"Well-ll," he finally said, putting the tablet down again and pushing his glasses back up on his head. "It's impious—but, I would think, not really the work of a *pagan.* Pagans," he said, "are very rare. Here, anyhow—in our town. And in any case, how could a child born and raised, baptized, taken his first communion, and a regular visitor to the confessional—how could such a boy, who gets only A's in Bible History be anything but a good Catholic boy, perhaps set slightly astray by someone yet to be named? I feel the influence, true, of another force here," he said, staring at Tommy. Tommy burst into flame. "Am I right?" he asked, noting Tommy's face flaming, and pounced: "Who?"

"Nobody!" It broke out of him like a shot. "Nobody," he cried. "I thought it up all by myself. Nobody helped me. Nobody inspired—nobody inspired?—" Father Jerome nodded. "—me. Nobody."

"All right, all right," Father Jerome said, and tapped his finger on the desk. "In any case, will you pray with me? You'll excuse me if I don't get down on my knees—I have what doctors call arthritis, or rheumatism, as my mother would have called it—" he said to Tommy's head, which was already bowed, and who had fallen to his knees, right there on the floor, his hands clasped, his eyes tightly closed.

Father Jerome gave him a benediction, murmured some Latin phrases: *"Benedicant vos omnipotentas Deus, Pater et Filius, et Spiritus Sanctus. Amen."*

"Amen," Tommy echoed, only then letting go of his finger tips which he'd gripped between his teeth tightly.

"Well," Father Jerome said, refreshed. "That will help. Now return to your class, say an Act of Contrition, a Hail Mary, and when you get home tonight, ten Our Fathers. And don't do it again." This time he reached for the wooden paddle that lay on his desk and slapped it across the palm of his hand. It sounded like a pistol shot.

Tommy got up, and turned.

"One more thing." Father Jerome was handing him his tablet. "I must tell you that, despite what I've said, there's evidence of some talent here. Do you know what I mean?"

Tommy nodded.

"But don't be too happy," the priest said. "A gift of talent can be as much a curse as a blessing. Whether it comes from God or the devil is never quite certain. It's better for you if you can abandon it somewhere on a dark night in some deserted alleyway and think only of our beloved Lord, who knows all things—and," he added, "speaks softly, and does not—" and slowly he crossed himself, and Tommy stared at him, and he opened his eyes, and said: "and knows *all things,* and in his own wisdom brings peace and eternal glory to even the least worthy of us."

Something leaped in his soul with a cry! *He had won!* "You can keep my poem," he said, turning. "I've got lots of others, and I can write more." When he looked again, he saw his mother crooning a strange song to the baby, in a language nobody in the world knew but her, and other bygone pagans, and which he, Tommy, understood in a blinding glimpse for just one moment right here in this room. Yes, that was it: a door had unlocked.

He felt strong—sorry for Father Jerome—but strong; going down the hallway past the lines of mitred Popes, a mysterious thing had happened that morning—he knew now he possessed some kind of power. There was power in words. In his words. They had frightened Sister Roberta, stunned the children, and forced Father Jerome to beg him—that was what he'd felt—*beg* him to withhold his great power. It had made him even feel like laughing at Mary Davis and her bouncing pigtail and her poem!

He knew he had learned something so important it would take the rest of his life to understand it. His father was poor. His mother couldn't speak English.

But *he* could—he could speak—and it frightened everybody.

# Books

## PAULA SHARP

Whenever Stanley tried to read, the words crowded together and flipped over like fish swimming upstream, backward across the paper. Threats, coaxing, deprivation, and elaborate forms of humiliation would not move him to read aloud. Mrs. Heffernan, his third grade teacher in San Diego, had settled for making Stanley hold his book open while the other children in the slow reading group took their turns.

Mrs. Heffernan was a creative, at times exotic, disciplinarian. She was a large woman, with a large wooden chair parked behind her desk, and if she caught two boys fighting, she would place them together in her chair, and sit down on their legs five or six times. She was prone to fits of rage in which she would lift books high above her head and pound them once, deafeningly, on the edge of her desk, often cracking the bindings and breaking off a corner of the desk's wooden paneling.

Mrs. Heffernan excused herself to use the bathroom many times a day, always saying that she had to "step out to wash her hands," and leaving the class unattended. At these times she would pull her chair to the front of the room and place on it a green plastic figure of Jiminy Cricket.

"Jiminy is going to watch you while I'm gone," she would tell the class. "And he's going to decide who is bad and who has been good." Sometimes she only pretended to go to the bathroom, and stationed herself outside in the hall, spying on the third grade, testing their trustworthiness.

"Jiminy told me that Maritza Díaz has the filthiest habits of any girl who has ever been in the classroom," Mrs. Heffernan reported at the end of the first school day overseen by Jiminy Cricket. "But Stanley Wilkes is the real winner of the lazy boy contest." Mrs. Heffernan thereafter made similar pronouncements: she often noted that a particular boy or girl had "the dirtiest shirts," "the most unkempt hair," "the ugliest mouth," "the most backward math skills," or "the sloppiest artwork" she had seen in her fifteen years of teaching, as if her career consisted in part of keeping track of records continually being broken. She alternately called Stanley "the saddest reader" and "the least intelligible boy in the class," in reference to his twangy Arkansas accent, which also moved her on several occasions to call him Deputy Dog.

Stanley had not been placed in the slowest of the third grades, however. In 1967, Stanley's school divided children into gifted, average, and special classes. Average children included almost all of the students with Spanish surnames, any black children, and a half dozen white children who, like Stanley, were simply believed to be stupid. The special class was for children classified as "mentally retarded" from all over the city, and also the group in which children who spoke only Spanish were placed. The students in the gifted class ignored the others, and those in the average group generally beat up the gifted students and were thankful for the special class, which they saw as the only limit on their designated ineptitude. Years later, a group of parents would complain about the presence of children with Down's syndrome in the school, and the special class would disappear. After that, the students in the average class felt themselves to be walking the edge of a fathomless ravine.

There were thirty-six students in the average group, but Stanley had only two friends, Joy Revel and Barry Salazar. Joy painted her fingernails red and brushed Dippity-Do in her hair so that it curved around her head and pointed in the back like an inverted volcano. She claimed to be from New Jersey: she talked through her nose, a source of amusement for Mrs. Heffernan, who would pinch her nose between her thumb and forefinger and imitate Joy, sometimes sending the whole class, including Joy, into giggles. Joy also had foreign customs. When she saw a dandelion growing in a crack in the asphalt, she would pick it, flick off the yellow head with her thumbnail, and say as the flower went soaring: "Mrs. Heffernan had a baby and its head popped off!"

Joy's style of refusing to read differed from Stanley's. She pressed the book close to her eyes and picked her way through the sentences like someone walking barefoot on a hot road, skipping right over the new words and the long ones and generally landing on *the, where,* and *what,* shouting them with varying pronunciation. Sometimes as Joy began reading, Mrs. Heffernan would take a tortoiseshell compact from her purse and dab at her face. On one occasion she uprooted several eyebrow hairs with a pair of tweezers. The children around Joy would grow restless with happiness, lose their way in the story, and pinch each other under the reading table. Stanley would draw racing cars on a paper tucked into his reading book, and later show them to Joy. One of these drawings was of a hot rod running over a smirking Jiminy Cricket, and another depicted Joy riding on the hood of a box-shaped racing car, her hair standing straight up with alarm. Joy liked the pictures, and kept them in her desk.

Joy's mother came only once to the playground, on the third day of school. She exerted a kind of reverse magnetism, so that the other mothers backed away from her in startled radii. She was olive skinned, with dyed, whiskey-colored hair, and wore fishnet stockings, and a short polka-dot skirt. When she kissed Joy good-bye, Miss Revel handed her a red patent leather purse instead of a lunch box. At lunchtime, Joy revealed that the purse contained a sandwich with the crusts cut off and an olive speared through the center with a toothpick, four carrot sticks, a piece of wedding cake with a plastic bride and groom still standing on it, and four strands of black licorice.

The girls in the average group kept their distance from Joy, and she acted as if this was how she preferred things. Before she wandered into class on the afternoon of the second day of school, girls in the elementary grades had gathered

around a single jump rope to sing: "Not last night, but the night before, twenty-five robbers came aknocking at your door. One jumped in!" Joy watched them with her manicured hands on her hips. She selected two of the stupidest, least popular girls to turn her double clothesline and shouted over the playground as she jumped:

> *I look around the corner,*
> *and what do I see?*
> *A big fat policeman from Tennessee.*
> *Bet you five dollars*
> *I can kill that man*
> *with a gun from my own hand.*
> *Hands up! Billy billy bill.*
> *Hands down. Chilly chilly chill.*

When the mothers who supervised the playground at recess exchanged looks, Joy began a new song: "Oooooh, Mr. Willoughby, Willoughby, Willoughby—Oooooh, Mr. Willoughby, all night long."

For reasons Stanley did not understand, Joy spent her time with him. Stanley rarely spoke, and when he did, he revealed the incomprehensible Arkansas twang that moved Mrs. Heffernan to call him Deputy Dog. On hot days, Joy would walk around the blacktop with Stanley, talking while he listened. In early fall, the sun would warm the seams of the asphalt to a black putty, and together the two pried up whatever tar they could find, rolling it into an asphalt ball which rapidly grew to the size of a grapefruit, the largest anyone had ever seen. Stanley stored the tar ball in his desk between free periods.

Barry Salazar read fluently in both Spanish and English and arrived in the third month of third grade without explanation. Stanley and Joy were surveying the outer rim of the blacktop for melted tar when Barry appeared at the school entrance. Stanley picked him out because Mr. Salazar was the only father to appear that year on the playground. A few times, Stanley's mother's boyfriend, Buddy, had taken him to school, but recently Buddy had started working night shifts at the hotel, and did not come home for days. Stanley had not seen his real father in years, but knew that he called periodically, and that his calls upset Stanley's mother. One time, his mother had set down the phone and told him, "Don't ever go home with anyone but me or Buddy. If a stranger tells you to get in his car, you run, you hear?" Whenever Stanley saw a particularly large or fancy car pull up outside the school, he liked to imagine that a man would lean out and signal to him. Stanley would get close enough to the car to examine it, but stand back far enough to run if anyone did emerge and approach him.

Mr. Salazar carried a black oblong case. He stood near the fence in a bright red shirt, scowling at the school, and Barry stood beside him, also scowling and wearing a red shirt. They both had sun-scorched hair, the color of a dusty car tire. Mr. Salazar signaled in the direction of Joy and Stanley.

Joy turned around to see whom Mr. Salazar was calling, and then said, "Hey, that guy with the suitcase wants us to go over there." She and Stanley stayed where they were.

Mr. Salazar walked toward them, and addressed Stanley. "Son," he said. "Can you tell me where the third grade is?"

Stanley stood still with his mouth open.

"He don't always talk," Joy said, adjusting the asphalt ball to her shoulder.

"I do too tawk," Stanley told Mr. Salazar.

"Who's supposed to be his teacher?" Joy asked.

Mr. Salazar set down his case and opened it, saying, "I know I wrote that somewhere."

Joy looked at the open hand of black hair on Barry's head, passed her eyes down to his waist, and then back to his face, and met his gaze. "XYZ x-amining your zipper," she said.

Barry zipped his fly and flashed her a glittering smile. His front teeth were lined with gold.

Stanley peered over Mr. Salazar's shoulder and saw a trombone lying on moss green velvet

inside its case. Mr. Salazar pulled a square of blue paper from a square compartment. There were black dots and sticks, fractions, and a jumble of letters scrawled on the paper. Barry pulled a silver tube with a knob on the end from the case and blew through it. It made a rude noise.

Mr. Salazar took back the mouthpiece and, looking up at Stanley, winked and said, "That's J. J. Johnson speaking to you, son." Mr. Salazar turned the paper upside down and read from it, "Heffernan, Mrs. Heffernan's the teacher."

"That's us, the dumb class!" Joy said.

Mr. Salazar frowned at the air in front of Joy, as if studying her words. He closed his trombone case, studied Stanley for a moment, and said to Barry, "Well, I guess you'll be all right with this guy here." Mr. Salazar absent-mindedly passed his hand through Barry's bangs so that the fingers of hair at the top wiggled. Stanley imagined himself as Barry, his own red shirt slightly too big and with one hole in the shoulder, while Mr. Salazar passed a hand through his hair.

Joy led Barry across the blacktop to the classroom where the average class was lining up. On the way, she extracted from him the information that his mother was dead, that he had chipped his front teeth falling into a freezer at Safeway, and that the teeth had been capped with gold for three months. Stanley alone noticed that Mr. Salazar remained on the blacktop, turning to go only when Barry disappeared behind Joy into the classroom.

Barry carried an oversize cigar box stamped with a label which he later read to Joy and Stanley: MAN TO MAN, SMOKE A ROI-TAN, FOR A TASTE THAT IS BETTER BY FAR. Inside the box were dozens of gold-rimmed, green June beetles Barry had collected from a rotted tree. The box buzzed against his side like a radio.

Generally, new children were introduced to the class after lunch by preordained formula: first name, last name, reading group, school of origin. Barry's arrival, however, was obscured by the advent of a new set of encyclopedias. Mrs. Heffernan directed him into the back row, where

Barry chose a desk near Stanley's and Joy's, while two sixth graders unloaded a wooden crate. From the crate they pulled green and ivory volumes embossed with golden letters. Mrs. Heffernan opened some of the books and showed the class dissected frogs, transparent overlays of the human body, erupting volcanoes, planets, a photograph of an astronaut with a rocket ship in the background, and color plates of insects.

She directed the sixth graders to line up the encyclopedias on the highest shelf behind Barry's desk—students who finished their reading assignments early would be allowed to check out one volume at a time. At the moment, when the A volume settled into its inaccessible position, Joy and Stanley looked at each other and formed a silent agreement: they didn't want to *read* the encyclopedias; Stanley and Joy wanted to *have* them.

After three weeks, no student had earned the right to check out an encyclopedia. During this period, Barry was not assigned to a reading group, and in his ample free time he established a reputation for scholarly activities never detected by Mrs. Heffernan. He read Spanish-language comic books, translating them to Stanley in whispers, and filled out the pages Joy and Stanley were assigned in their reading workbooks. Barry molded the tar ball into a perfect sphere, and he rubbed down the free school erasers until they were flawless miniature racing cars. He invented the original picture of Mrs. Heffernan, which was passed around the room and embellished with extra breasts and penises, curse words, body hair, and curls of smoke to signify body odor. In a moment of brilliance inspired by boredom, Barry took off his shirt and put it on inside out and backward. He drew a picture of an astronaut circling Saturn in a rocket ship like that in the encyclopedia. Under the picture, he wrote: "The astronaut stood and wiped the sweat from his brow."

Mrs. Heffernan eventually started Barry in the slow group without testing him. He sat between Stanley and Joy, and read fast as a sports announcer in a clipped, Spanish accent, which Mrs. Heffernan mimicked after he had finished. He completed his workbook assignments before anyone else on the first day, but when he raised his hand and asked permission to see the encyclopedias, Mrs. Heffernan did not look up from her desk. However, when Barry walked to the back of the room in an attempt to take an encyclopedia, Mrs. Heffernan said, "Do me the favor of keeping your head on your desk until the end of the period, Barry Salazar, just do me that favor."

At recess, Joy proposed stealing the encyclopedias. She believed Mrs. Heffernan had forgotten about them, but suggested taking just one encyclopedia, and then waiting to see if Mrs. Heffernan noticed. After that, Stanley and Barry and Joy could steal the rest, one by one. Joy wanted the volume with the color plates of insects, but Barry said that a vowel like *I* would soon be missed. There were only five vowels. The three friends decided on the H volume, with its transparent overlays of the dissected man. Barry decided that he should be the one to take the encyclopedia, because he sat closest to the bookshelf. Joy and Stanley would distract Mrs. Heffernan by talking at the pencil sharpener.

Stanley surprised himself by speaking up. "We can hide the book in the cigar bawks," he suggested. He had noted that it would fit perfectly around an encyclopedia. He loved the Roi-Tan box, with its musky odor he associated with Mr. Salazar. Stanley wondered if the encyclopedia would take on the cigar smell.

Barry agreed to transfer the June beetles to a mason jar that night. Joy explained that her mother would become suspicious if she found a book at home—Joy could try hiding it under her bed, but her mother might find the encyclopedia when she vacuumed. When Joy questioned him, Stanley said that he had no space under his bed: his mother's boyfriend, Buddy, had left locked suitcases there. Barry volunteered that he could hide the encyclopedia in plain view in his house: he would camouflage it by placing it on the bookshelf, and his father would never notice.

The next day, Joy accompanied Stanley to the pencil sharpener, but Mrs. Heffernan, who was grading papers at her desk, and who had not appeared to be watching, called to Joy that only one person could use the pencil sharpener at a time. Joy sat down, shifted in her seat, raised her hand, shifted some more, and then walked over to Mrs. Heffernan's desk.

"Sit down and raise your hand if you want to ask something," Mrs. Heffernan said.

Joy stayed where she was, fidgeting first on one foot and then the other, until she leaned forward and lied: "Stanley swallowed tar."

Mrs. Heffernan looked up. Stanley returned to his desk.

"He found it on the playground and he swallowed it."

Mrs. Heffernan rose from her chair and walked to Stanley's desk. Joy followed her, and sat down across from Stanley. Mrs. Heffernan bent over with her back to the encyclopedias and, staring directly at him, said confusingly, "Do I see prying eyes? Is this your business? Don't we all have work to do?" Then, addressing Stanley, she said, "When did you swallow the tar?" As Stanley tried to think of an answer, he heard Barry push back his chair. "Answer me. When did you swallow the tar?" She examined Stanley's hands, black on the palms and under his fingernails from collecting asphalt that day for the tar ball. "Why did you swallow it?" she pressed. "Answer me!"

Stanley was puzzled by Mrs. Heffernan's tone of concern. What would happen if he swallowed a little tar? He put his head on his desk, and looked under his arm behind him: Barry slipped the encyclopedia into the cigar box and closed it.

When Stanley raised his head, he did not understand why Mrs. Heffernan looked so angry, or why she took him by the shoulder and pushed him toward her desk. She pulled out her chair and, setting Jiminy Cricket on it, said, "Jiminy wants all of you to open your desks, and then to sit with your hands folded in front of you. I wonder what he'll discover before I return!"

Mrs. Heffernan led Stanley to the nurse's office. He sat quietly outside while the nurse ran by him to the principal's office, and then ran back to her telephone, and tried unsuccessfully to reach Stanley's mother.

"Sweetheart," the nurse told him as she held her head to the phone, "don't you know that tar is poisonous?" She did not ask if he really had swallowed tar, and he wondered about this. He also pondered the fact that something as untempting and inedible as tar could be poisonous. How did the world know this? Did a man once swallow tar? Who was he and what made him think of doing it?

While Stanley waited, Mrs. Heffernan reappeared, leading Barry into the principal's office and holding Barry's cigar box in one hand. In Barry's free hand, wrapped in a piece of green construction paper, was the tar ball that Stanley and Joy had put together through so many weeks, and which Barry had molded into a perfect sphere. Mrs. Heffernan directed him to set the tar ball on the principal's desk.

Stanley heard Mrs. Heffernan say, "...a miniature thief. He is the most incorrigible, the least teachable boy I have dealt with. He stole it from the new set of encyclopedias—I found it concealed in this filthy box when I asked all the children to open their desks so that I could see if *they* had tar balls." Mrs. Heffernan leaned into view and dropped the Roi-Tan box into the principal's wastebasket. "He can't even read it! I've had to babysit him for a month, when he should be in the special class! A child like this demands more attention than all of the other children put together..." The door closed, leaving Barry outside.

Stanley waved, but just as Barry saw him, the nurse exited her office, carrying her purse, and ushered Stanley outside to her car.

"Don't you worry, sweetheart. We're taking you to the emergency ward and your mother's going to meet us there." She made him lie down in the backseat.

Stanley was aware that the school nurse drove too fast: the car rocked around turns and parked with a jerk at the hospital. She led him into a large hallway. When a man in a white uniform laid a hand on Stanley's shoulder, the school nurse said, "I have to stay here to call your mother's house again. Don't be afraid."

The man lifted Stanley up, set him on a wheeled bed, and pushed him into an area enclosed by a curtain, and left him there. Stanley peered through the curtain, but could not locate the school nurse.

A hospital nurse pushed another bed alongside the curtain. She did not notice Stanley. Stanley leaned forward and saw her show some papers to an old man lying in the bed.

The old man stared at the papers and cried, "I can't read the words! It doesn't make sense!" The nurse placed the papers on a table between the old man and Stanley, and departed.

"Help me," the old man said. One half of his lip twisted up and the other twisted down. One of his eyes was shut and the other was open. He turned and the open eye fixed on Stanley.

Stanley was afraid the eye would not turn away unless he answered. He leaned forward and said, "This is Stanley Salazar speaking to you, and I can read anythang."

"God help me!" the man answered.

Stanley peered at the papers on the table: he could not make out any of the words. Most of them were small and dark and long, separated by boxes. There were also blue and green words, and a large red word at the bottom.

"It says you are in a hospital."

"God *help* me, Nelly!" the man repeated, his voice louder, his open eye still directed at Stanley. "Nelly nelly!" he screamed.

Stanley drew back, dropping the papers to the floor. He slid down from his bed and ran through the curtain, into the hallway.

"Nelly nelly!" the man hollered after him.

Stanley passed a moaning man wearing a bloodied shirt, and a pale, motionless woman lying on a cot surrounded by doctors. He backed away and turned into another hall, and there was his mother in a yellow dress with her black hair flying.

"Stanley!" she called. He stopped where he was while she rushed to him and knelt down before him. "I was so worried when they called! I thought your father had shown up again and done something terrible, and—what did the doctor do? Have you seen the doctor?"

Stanley shook his head.

"No? Stanley, how long ago did you swallow the tar? Why did you do it, hun? Did you? Did you really eat tar? You didn't eat it at all, did you? Oh Jesus Christ in a bucket, this is funny. Why did they think you swallowed tar? Didn't you tell anyone that you hadn't? Did you eat tar?"

"No," Stanley answered.

Barry did not return to school. The next morning, Joy and Stanley had to stand against the fence before morning recess. They arrived early enough to see Mr. Salazar arguing with Mrs. Heffernan in the classroom before first period. His trombone case bobbed at his side like an angry black dog as he talked. Then he walked out of the room, straight across the playground, oblivious of the four-square and hopscotch grids.

At lunchtime a week later, Stanley loitered at the edge of a jump rope game Joy had started. Joy leapt into the rope, singing:

*Gypsy, Gypsy, Gypsy Rose Lee,*
*Where on earth can your old man be?*
*He's a lover undercover*
*getting down with your mother,*
*so spell your name on one foot,*
*You got J-O-Y R-E-V-E-L!*

All the mothers on the playground seemed to watch Joy and Stanley.

When she finished her turn at the rope, Joy pointed to the mothers and told Stanley, "They're on the lookout for tar balls." Sixth graders had been sent to all the classrooms to give talks on the new school rule against tar balls. Joy crouched and pretended to pry something from the asphalt. One of the mothers drew closer. Behind her, Stanley saw Mr. Salazar leading Barry along the sidewalk bordering the fence.

They were walking fast and the trombone case loped beside them. Barry was dressed in the stiff white shirt, clip-on tie, and gray flannel pants that marked the children who attended the Catholic school four blocks away. When he saw Stanley, Barry grabbed his tie, held it like a noose over his head, and rolled his eyes. Mr. Salazar turned and waved, and father and son continued up the street.

# Her

## HUGO MARTÍNEZ-SERROS

You open your eyes before the alarm clock in the kitchen goes off. You roll onto your back and lie there, looking up at the ceiling and thinking about her, wondering again if all they say about her is really true, hoping they've made a lot of it up. All summer long you've thought about her and now the summer is over and you must face her, be with her.

Your day starts and you are nervous. You draw back the cotton spread, swing out your thin legs and sit on the edge of your cot. You pull on your socks, close your eyes momentarily, then stand up and step into your knickers. You sit down now, slip on your shoes and lace them.

There is no one in the bathroom; the others are still asleep. You plug the basin with a wash cloth, fill it with cold water from both faucets and submerge your hands. Slowly you soap your hands, then your face, rinse carefully and dry yourself. When you pull the wash cloth the drain swallows the water noisily, leaving a scummy film. You wash the basin and your hands, pour toothpowder into your cupped palm, stick your wet index finger into it and then rub your teeth vigorously. You dip your finger repeatedly, rubbing until you feel smoothness between finger and teeth, until the powder is gone. Now you fill your mouth with water, swelling your cheeks as you work the water round and round. Then you spit it out and smile, pleased with the sweet taste.

In the kitchen the alarm sounds. You reach it before your mother. When you finish dressing you will have more than enough time to eat and get your things ready. Summer's end doesn't sadden you—like school. But you feel uneasy about her. What will happen to you today? You wonder.

Outside the school you mill with the others, renew friendships, exchange stories, anticipate the return to discipline and routine. The first bell rings. You enter the building and go directly to your classroom on the second floor. A girl posted just inside the room at the door to the cloakroom, which is closed, won't let you go in there to hang up your sweater. "Get away," she says, "you can't go in there. She's changin' her clothes an' doesn't want no one peekin' at her." Her voice threatens, crackles with new power and authority. They are the same words she aims at those who come later. At the back of the class a second girl guards the other cloakroom door.

Buttoning the smock she wears over her skirt and blouse, she comes out before the last bell rings and stands in front of her desk. She is tall, strong-looking, has her hands on her hips and scowls at the boys who dare look at her. She jerks up her right hand and begins firing her index finger at every body in the classroom, emphasizing the gesture with one word: "You!...You!... You!..." When she has singled all of you out she pauses, then she suddenly steps forward and shoots a warning, "Just let me catch one of you peeking at me when I'm changing!"

The bell rings loud and long.

"Up, up on your feet, get up!" she orders, her hands beating the air. She goes to the door and closes it, and from there, right hand on her heart, she leads all of you with her shrill voice: "I pledge allegiance TO"—the word explodes, a signal for you to hurl your hands, palms upturned, at the flag to one side of her desk—"the flag of the United States of America and to the republic for which it stands, one nation, indivisible, with liberty and justice for all." Then you sing, "My country 'tis of thee, sweet land of liberty..." She directs you with great energy, her arms thrashing, her whole person commanding you to sing louder and louder.

Three tardy pupils push open the door and enter. A deep frown stops them, then a left arm reaches out and grabs one of them—the right arm goes on directing—shakes him and pinches him twice before he escapes her grasp.

The singing ends and she turns on the late comers, "Disrupters of ceremony!" The three cringe. "I get here early for your benefit, not mine! Yours! Why can't you do the same! You're not in Mexico! You're in America! We do things on time here! Understand? On time!" She pauses to breathe then continues scolding, "You've abused the privilege of pledging allegiance to the greatest nation in the world. We do it only five times a week! Don't you have any pride? They should send you back where you came from!"

She starts the same way every morning, the heat of her fury unchanged as the school year wears on.

"*Papá,* she makes us pledge allegiance to the flag," you say to your father in Spanish. "She says it's an honor to die for the flag." You look deep into your father's face.

"¡*Mierda*! She's wrong! She shouldn't make children say what they don't understand," he answers you. "Tell me what you say," he demands. He knows the pledge, had to learn it when he became a citizen of the United States, but he wants to test you, wants to see how well you know it.

You learned the pledge in kindergarten and said it every school day the year before, in the first grade. But your teacher did not explain it to you. You and the others said it at the beginning of each school day. Nothing more. You clear your throat and recite: "I pledge allegiance to . . . with liberty and justice for all."

"¡*Pura mierda*! It's not true!" your father protests. "That liberty and justice for all doesn't include Mexicans. They crap on us! They've been doing it since they stole all that land from us— California, Texas, New Mexico . . ."

"I don't understand, *papá,*" you say, and you want to understand.

"They don't treat us right, haven't you noticed? We aren't like them, *real* people, as far as they're concerned."

"The flag, *papá,* is it wrong to pledge allegiance to it?"

"The trouble with you Americans," your *papá* answers as he winks at you, "is that you wave your flag and play your national anthem every time you take a shit!" He laughs; you remain silent. "We don't do that in Mexico. We wave the flag and play our national anthem only on special occasions. Not every day. How can those things have any meaning if you do them every day?"

Then he talks to you about the Mexican flag, lovingly, about Hidalgo, Pípila, Juárez, the *niños héroes,* talks to you as no one has ever talked to you about the American flag. He talks to you about Mexico, its beauty, its poverty. He explains to you that for Mexicans, Mexico is the best country in the world, even when they have to leave it.

Once, a stranger asked you, "Boy, what's your nationality?" And you answered, throwing out your chest, "American!" The stranger laughed and said, "Yeah, you're American all right, but with a black Mexican ass!" It made you mad, made you think of what your *güero* playmates say to you when they get angry with you—"Fuckin' Messkin, why don'tcha go back to Mexico where you came from!"

She does not, cannot, know the turmoil she causes in you. At seven you already know you are and are not an American. You were born in Chicago and that makes you an American citizen, but it is not the same as being an *American.* She, your teacher, hurts and confuses you more than anybody else, always saying ugly things about what and who and how you are. In the morning she wraps you and your classmates in the American flag; afterwards she tells Manny and others of you, "I don't know why they let people like you into *our* country. Ugh!" Like the other children of Mexican parents at your school, you learn to write "Mexican" on forms that ask for your nationality. Yet you know you are not Mexican like those born and educated in Mexico. *Real* Mexicans make a distinction between themselves and *pochos* like you; for them, not even your father is a real *Mexican* any more.

A week ago you were working on your penmanship, squeezing the ink pens so hard that your fingers hurt, your fists slowly guiding the wood shafts fitted with steel points across sheets of wide-lined paper. The inkwell lids were opened and the pens, dipped after every word, stained middle fingers at the first joint. She walked up and down the rows observing, scolding, correcting, and paused to watch Teresa Vidal, the best writer in the class. Teresa got nervous and dropped her pen, tried to retrieve it and spattered her with black ink. She looked at the ink spots, grabbed Teresa by the hair and pulled her to her feet. Still holding Teresa's hair, she shook her again and again, screaming, "You idiot! Why are *you people* such idiots? Look at my smock! If you were a boy, I'd show you something you'd never forget!"

Around school the older boys say she is built. She has big hips and breasts and when she crosses her legs you look furtively at her exposed thigh where it fleshes out into her rump and makes you think of the wonderful haunch of the horse that pulls the milk wagon past school in the morning. In the beginning you think her face is pretty—pronounced chin, large mouth with very white teeth, and a straight nose beneath an expanse of forehead that is cleanly curved. She has very large clear eyes and soft-looking brown hair. Younger and prettier than your kindergarten and first grade teachers, she wears nice clothes, smells of perfume and is always very clean. Whenever they get the least bit soiled, she washes her hands in a small corner sink and then rubs scented cream into them. She is the cleanest person you know.

You know as much about girls as anyone your age. You have learned from older boys and from pictures. You know about their secret. Their secret place—know where it is and what it's for. But you have never seen a real one, only those of babies and animals, especially dogs. Once you touched Margie's, but you couldn't see anything because the basement was dark and you were scared—it was soft and had a deep line in it. *Pussy* is like *puppy* or *bunny,* a soft word, like the young rabbits in the park, frightened and always trying to hide; like the pussy willows you love to touch with your fingertips. After a time you do not think

of her pussy or any other part of her. But in the beginning you wished you could go into the cloakroom when she was changing, smell her there in the dark, lift her skirt and breathe her sweetness and see what she guards from you so carefully, see the hair the older boys say she has there, beautiful like the hair on her head, soft and brown.

Nobody misbehaves in her class. She closes her door to laughter and happiness and nobody defies her. And nobody whispers in her class. She teaches you fear, makes you nervous, confuses you, and when she scolds you she makes you lose your self-control, which makes her furious. On her desk she keeps two wood pointers, yard-long spears that taper into bullet-shaped tips of black rubber. They are there for emergencies, to throw at anyone who forgets where he is, above all at sassers—she can't stand a single word of back talk. She keeps them there for Manuel Campos and Mario López and Frederick Douglass Snead and Ernest Krause and Yonko Babich, who howl at the top of their voice when she so much as touches them. With the pointers she keeps their voices down.

Mrs. Bolen's class is next door. She teaches vocational arts and her pupils are the biggest, toughest boys in school—delinquents or near-delinquents who refuse to study but are forced to attend school. The print shop is their classroom and Mrs. Bolen gets them to do beautiful work with the old equipment and machinery. Her boys call her Mom and everybody calls them Mom Bolen's boys. One afternoon Mom is called away and she distributes her boys among the other teachers. The worst boy is sent to your class. He throws open the door and explain as he walks in, "Mom hadda go somewheres. She told me to come here." He scowls and taps his feet impatiently.

"Mrs. Bolen had to go somewhere, not Mom!" she corrects.

"That's what I said, she hadda go somewheres," he growls.

"Sit back there, dummy!" she shouts, pointing to an empty desk at the back of the class. "And I don't want any trouble from you, just sit there and shut up! I'm not Mrs. Bolen and I won't fool with you! You should have brought a book."

He looks at her, pulls a comic book from his pocket, walks to the back of the class and sits down. His body is too big for the little desk and he squirms, his legs thrash, he mumbles to himself and talks to those around him. They try to ignore him but he keeps at them.

"I told you to shut up," she threatens, "now shut up!"

"Shuddup yourself!" he challenges.

She grabs one of her spears and throws it at the trouble maker. He ducks—and those around him do too—and the spear crashes against the wall. Silent and unbelieving, all of you watch. He leaps from his seat and picks up the spear as she reaches for the second one. He wings it at her; she dodges it. It bangs into the corner behind her and his words explode in the air, "Stick it up your ass!"

She springs from behind her desk, swinging the spear like a sword, chasing him. He darts into the cloakroom, through it and the doors before she can catch him. She turns to face all of you and finds your eyes fixed on her. She screams, "Get back to work, you busy bodies!" She shakes the weapon at you and threatens, "Or I'll give you some of this! Who said you could watch? Why didn't somebody trip him if you're so interested?" Then she brings the pointer crashing down on one desk after another, just missing arms, hands, heads.

Slowly, weeks and months pass by and it seems to you and your classmates that you spend more time watching her from the corner of your eye than you do on school work. You do only one thing that everybody—including her—enjoys. You don't know why she does it, don't know if it's a game. Suddenly she tells you to stop what you're doing, and then she gives you words and tells you to give her words that rhyme with the ones she gives you.

"Run," she starts.

You respond with, "Fun, bun, sun, gun, ton, done, none, one." And finding the rhythm, know-

ing, without having to be told, that she wants one-syllable words, the most daring of you invent them: "pun, shun, kun," and then others take courage and join in: "chun, blun, hun, scun, mun," until you exhaust the rhyme and she moves on to another word. She never interrupts you. Sometimes she smiles, sometimes laughs.

"Stumble," she continues.

You offer, "Bumble, crumble, tumble, grumble, mumble, jumble, fumble, humble," and then, "dumble, kumble, lumble, wumble, chumble, drumble, trumble."

Once she says, "Kiss."

The words come fast, "Miss, sis, this, hiss, Chris, bliss," and you say, "piss," realizing too late what you have said. You cringe and await the inevitable, but it does not come. She says nothing and moves on to the next word, but you never again take part in her word-rhyming exercise.

Her favorites are her cloakroom guards and two or three other girls. They are like puppets when she needs them. Some of you say she hates boys. But there are girls, Teresa Vidal for example, who say she is like those aunts and uncles who prefer some nieces and nephews to others. There are even parents like that. She is moody and you find safety in being as watchful and silent as you can. You do not tell your parents about her because they believe your teachers outdo themselves for you. She is there always, never sick, always there.

In time your learn things about her personal life. She brings pictures to school, holds them at arm's length to look at them, smiles, laughs, spreads them across her desk, does everything possible to attract your attention to what she is doing. When she tires of looking alone she calls her girls to join her: "Dorothy, Ann, Margaret, come up here. I want to show you something. The rest of you go on working. Don't let me catch you looking up here!" She shares nothing with you.

She has two children, girls six and eight. Her husband is good-looking. All wear nice clothes. Her house is beautiful; only they live in it. There are pictures of her back yard, of birthday parties, her church, the zoo, museums . . .

The second year is coming to an end and you have all these things to remember.

What you will remember more than anything else is what she does to Manuel Campos in the final week. Manny is the toughest boy in the class, and the dirtiest. His pants are dirty and torn and so is his shirt and you can see the safety pins that hold them together. He wears the same clothes day after day and every morning she orders him to wash his face and hands in the low sink in the hallway where the janitor washes his mops. He doesn't wear socks and his shoes are so full of holes and so scuffed that they're gray. On his feet you can see *costras,* crusts of dirt. He never combs his hair. That's how Manny is and all of you know it and all of you accept it. Manny is smart and, whatever she thinks, he doesn't make trouble in class. But outside he doesn't take anything from anybody and fights a lot because the older boys make fun of his clothes and the way he sometimes smells.

Something Manny does—you don't know what, never will—suddenly makes her roar, pounce on him, grab him by the hair and drag him to the front of the class. She slaps him and he doesn't even try to protect himself. She makes him stand there and tells all of you to punch him in the face and says that she'll punch anyone who refuses. You line up along the side wall and across the back of the room, all of you, boys and girls, and start punching him. He is your best friend because he protects you on the playground. When it's your turn she is washing her hands in her little sink and she doesn't see everything. You stand before Manny and tears rush to your eyes. Manny's mouth and nose are bleeding; his lips and face are swollen. He looks right into your eyes and without saying a word orders you to punch him, you will still be friends. You ball up your hand and punch him. Through the whole thing Manny doesn't cry out or flinch.

When it's all over she drags him down the hall to the janitor's low sink where she makes him wash his face with the strong brown bar of American Family soap.

# The Fun They Had

## ISAAC ASIMOV

Margie even wrote about it that night in her diary. On the page headed May 17, 2157, she wrote, "Today Tommy found a real book!"

It was a very old book. Margie's grandfather once said that when he was a little boy *his* grandfather told him that there was a time when all stories were printed on paper.

They turned the pages, which were yellow and crinkly, and it was awfully funny to read words that stood still instead of moving the way they were supposed to—on a screen, you know. And then, when they turned back to the page before, it had the same words on it that it had when they read it the first time.

"Gee," said Tommy, "what a waste. When you're through with the book, you just throw it away, I guess. Our television screen must have had a million books on it and it's good for plenty more. I wouldn't throw *it* away."

"Same with mine," said Margie. She was eleven and hadn't seen as many telebooks as Tommy had. He was thirteen.

She said, "Where did you find it?"

"In my house." He pointed without looking, because he was busy reading. "In the attic."

"What's it about?"

"School."

Margie was scornful. "School? What's there to write about school? I hate school."

Margie always hated school, but now she hated it more than ever. The mechanical teacher had been giving her test after test in geography and she had been doing worse and worse until her mother had shaken her head sorrowfully and sent for the County Inspector.

He was a round little man with a red face and a whole box of tools with dials and wires. He smiled at Margie and gave her an apple, then took the teacher apart. Margie had hoped he wouldn't know how to put it together again, but he knew how all right, and, after an hour or so, there it was

again, large and black and ugly, with a big screen on which all the lessons were shown and the questions were asked. That wasn't so bad. The part Margie hated most was the slot where she had to put homework and test papers. She always had to write them out in a punch code they made her learn when she was six years old, and the mechanical teacher calculated the mark in no time.

The Inspector had smiled after he was finished and patted Margie's head. He said to her mother, "It's not the little girl's fault, Mrs. Jones. I think the geography sector was geared a little too quick. Those things happen sometimes. I've slowed it up to an average ten-year level. Actually, the over-all pattern of her progress is quite satisfactory." And he patted Margie's head again.

Margie was disappointed. She had been hoping they would take the teacher away altogether. They had once taken Tommy's teacher away for nearly a month because the history sector had blanked out completely.

So she said to Tommy, "Why would anyone write about school?"

Tommy looked at her with very superior eyes. "Because it's not our kind of school, stupid. This is the old kind of school that they had hundreds and hundreds of years ago." He added loftily, pronouncing the word carefully, "*Centuries* ago."

Margie was hurt. "Well, I don't know what kind of school they had all that time ago." She read the book over his shoulder for a while, then said, "Anyway, they had a teacher."

"Sure they had a teacher, but it wasn't a *regular* teacher. It was a man."

"A man? How could a man be a teacher?"

"Well, he just told the boys and girls things and gave them homework and asked them questions."

"A man isn't smart enough."

"Sure he is. My father knows as much as my teacher."

"He can't. A man can't know as much as a teacher."

"He knows almost as much, I betcha."

Margie wasn't prepared to dispute that. She said, "I wouldn't want a strange man in my house to teach me."

Tommy screamed with laughter. "You don't know much, Margie. The teachers didn't live in the house. They had a special building and all the kids went there."

"And all the kids learned the same thing?"

"Sure, if they were the same age."

"But my mother says a teacher has to be adjusted to fit the mind of each boy and girl it teaches and that each kid has to be taught differently."

"Just the same they didn't do it that way then. If you don't like it, you don't have to read the book."

"I didn't say I didn't like it," Margie said quickly. She wanted to read about those funny schools.

They weren't even half-finished when Margie's mother called, "Margie! School!"

Margie looked up. "Not yet, Mamma."

"Now!" said Mrs. Jones. "And it's probably time for Tommy, too."

Margie said to Tommy, "Can I read the book some more with you after school?"

"Maybe," he said nonchalantly. He walked away whistling, the dusty old book tucked beneath his arm.

Margie went into the schoolroom. It was right next to her bedroom, and the mechanical teacher was on and waiting for her. It was always on at the same time every day except Saturday and Sunday, because her mother said little girls learned better if they learned at regular hours.

The screen was lit up, and it said: "Today's arithmetic lesson is on the addition of proper fractions. Please insert yesterday's homework in the proper slot."

Margie did so with a sigh. She was thinking about the old schools they had when her grandfather's grandfather was a little boy. All the kids from the whole neighborhood came, laughing and shouting in the schoolyard, sitting together in the schoolroom, going home together at the end of the day. They learned the same things, so they could help one another on the homework and talk about it.

And the teachers were people....

The mechanical teacher was flashing on the screen: "When we add the fractions ½ and ¼—"

Margie was thinking about how the kids must have loved it in the old days. She was thinking about the fun they had.

# CHAPTER 6

## PRIDE AND PREJUDICES

John H. Clarke, "The Boy Who Painted Christ Black"
Mary Elizabeth Vroman, "See How They Run"
Abioseh Nicol, "As the Night the Day"
Eddie Stack, "Limbo"
George Milburn, "Revenge"

These stories paint painful pictures illustrating how students may be damaged when prejudice is allowed to enter the classroom environment. In all of them students fall victim to prejudice yet often their healthy sense of pride prevents them from submitting in spirit to the hostile conditions that seem to dominate their lives.

John Clarke's story "The Boy Who Painted Christ Black" is set in a school for "colored" children in the segregated South. The artistic talent of a young boy is recognized and nurtured by the principal as well as the teachers, and his work, a beautiful picture of a black Christ, is proudly exhibited at the end of the year on the occasion of the supervisor's visit.

The white supervisor is offended by what he calls "... this sacrilegious nonsense ..." of a Black Jesus and demands that Aaron explain himself. Although the boy's confident and dignified justification of his work extracts a high price from the school that has encouraged him, it is a tribute both to what education and the human spirit can accomplish.

Mary Elizabeth Vroman's story "See How They Run" also takes place in a Southern school where prejudice has become institutionalized. Jane Richards is the first and only African American teacher in a school attended only by African American children. Her efforts at changing other teachers' expectations, and providing more challenging instruction in her classroom are ridiculed by her colleagues and resisted by her students. She focuses particularly on C.T., a boy other teachers dismiss as incorrigible and incapable of learning much. Her various approaches fail as C.T. does his best to resist her overtures. But Ms. Richards does not give up in seeking a way to connect with the rebellious C.T. By the last day of school she can take pride in many significant accomplishments.

"As the Night the Day" by Abioseh Nicol, set in Sierra Leone, is a grim depiction of the damage prejudice can inflict. Basu, the only Muslim boy in a classroom of Christians, is falsely accused of wrongdoing by those who were at fault. He is also savagely punished by his classmates. A teacher rescues Basu and consoles the boy by telling him that "men are punished not always for what they do, but often for what people think they will do, or for what they are." The next day one of Basu's guilt-ridden classmates experiences the truth of that statement.

Brother Mahon's low opinion of his students is amply documented in Eddie Stack's story "Limbo," a shameful story of abusive behavior by a teacher and, worse, one who claims a privileged relationship with God. The teacher's cruelty is juxtaposed with his intense religious fervor. In a monastery school in Ireland, Brother Mahon is described by his students as being on "tablets" that sometimes make him joyful and at other times violent. On the day described "things were looking grey." Brother Mahon's abuse of his students gradually escalates to unbelievable violence and of course, a closing prayer.

Rolland, the central character in "Revenge," is an older student in an elementary classroom; though conspicuous among the other students, his successful efforts towards earning his diploma have imbued him with a healthy pride. His spoiled, slightly handicapped classmate who, unlike Rolland, is the teacher's pet conspires to thwart Rolland's success by arranging a deeply humiliating incident to embarass Rolland. Despite the tragic result of this scheme, fate itself seems to intervene to avenge Rolland by turning the tables on the cruel classmate and an unfeeling teacher.

These stories reveal the potential danger in the power teachers have over students. In the first two selections this power is directed at benefitting students through a teacher's creativity. However, the other stories offer cautionary tales on the abuse of power and its effects on diligent students who deserve respect and encouragement.

# The Boy Who Painted Christ Black

## JOHN H. CLARKE

He was the smartest boy in the Muskogee County School—for colored children. Everybody even remotely connected with the school knew this. The teacher always pronounced his name with profound gusto as she pointed him out as the ideal student. Once I heard her say: "If he were white he might, some day, become President." Only Aaron Crawford wasn't white; quite the contrary. His skin was so solid black that it glowed, reflecting an inner virtue that was strange, and beyond my comprehension.

In many ways he looked like something that was awkwardly put together. Both his nose and his lips seemed a trifle too large for his face. To say he was ugly would be unjust and to say he was handsome would be gross exaggeration. Truthfully, I could never make up my mind about him. Sometimes he looked like something out of a book of ancient history...looked as if he was left over from that magnificent era before the machine age came and marred the earth's natural beauty.

His great variety of talent often startled the teachers. This caused his classmates to look upon him with a mixed feeling of awe and envy.

Before Thanksgiving, he always drew turkeys and pumpkins on the blackboard. On George Washington's birthday, he drew large American flags surrounded by little hatchets. It was these small masterpieces that made him the most talked-about colored boy in Columbus, Georgia. The Negro principal of the Muskogee County School said he would some day be a great painter, like Henry O. Tanner.

For the teacher's birthday, which fell on a day about a week before commencement, Aaron Crawford painted the picture that caused an uproar, and a turning point, at the Muskogee County School. The moment he entered the room that morning, all eyes fell on him. Besides his torn book holder he was carrying a large-framed concern wrapped in old newspapers. As he went to his seat, the teacher's eyes followed his every motion, a curious wonderment mirrored in them conflicting with the half-smile that wreathed her face.

Aaron put his books down, then smiling broadly, advanced toward the teacher's desk. His alert eyes were so bright with joy that they were almost frightening. The children were leaning forward in their seats, staring greedily at him; a restless anticipation was rampant within every breast.

Already the teacher sensed that Aaron had a present for her. Still smiling, he placed it on her desk and began to help her unwrap it. As the last piece of paper fell from the large frame, the teacher jerked her hand away from it suddenly, her eyes flickering unbelievingly. Amidst the rigid tension, her heavy breathing was distinct and frightening. Temporarily, there was no other sound in the room.

Aaron stared questioningly at her and she moved her hand back to the present cautiously, as if it were a living thing with vicious characteristics. I am sure it was the one thing she least expected.

With a quick, involuntary movement I rose up from my desk. A series of submerged murmurs spread through the room, rising to a distinct monotone. The teacher turned toward the children, staring reproachfully. They did not move their eyes from the present that Aaron had brought her.... It was a large picture of Christ—painted black!

Aaron Crawford went back to his seat, a feeling of triumph reflected in his every movement.

The teacher faced us. Her curious half-smile had blurred into a mild bewilderment. She searched the bright faces before her and started to smile again, occasionally stealing quick glances at the large picture propped on her desk, as though doing so were forbidden amusement.

"Aaron," she spoke at last, a slight tinge of uncertainty in her tone, "this is a most welcome present. Thanks. I will treasure it." She paused, then went on speaking, a trifle more coherent than before. "Looks like you are going to be quite an artist....Suppose you come forward and tell the class how you came to paint this remarkable picture."

When he rose to speak, to explain about the picture, a hush fell tightly over the room, and the children gave him all of their attention... something they rarely did for the teacher. He did not speak at first; he just stood there in front of the room, toying absently with his hands, observing his audience carefully, like a great concert artist.

"It was like this," he said, placing full emphasis on every word. "You see, my uncle who lives in New York teaches classes in Negro History at the Y.M.C.A. When he visited us last year he was telling me about the many great black folks who have made history. He said black folks were once the most powerful people on earth. When I asked him about Christ, he said no one ever proved whether he was black or white. Somehow a feeling came over me that he was a black man, 'cause he was so kind and forgiving, kinder than I have ever seen white people be. So, when I painted this picture I couldn't help but paint it as I thought it was."

After this, the little artist sat down, smiling broadly, as if he had gained entrance to a great storehouse of knowledge that ordinary people could neither acquire nor comprehend.

The teacher, knowing nothing else to do under prevailing circumstances, invited the children to rise from their seats and come forward so they could get a complete view of Aaron's unique piece of art.

When I came close to the picture, I noticed it was painted with the kind of paint you get in the five and ten cent stores. Its shape was blurred slightly, as if someone had jarred the frame before the paint had time to dry. The eyes of Christ were deep-set and sad, very much like those of Aaron's father, who was a deacon in the local Baptist

Church. This picture of Christ looked much different from the one I saw hanging on the wall when I was in Sunday School. It looked more like a helpless Negro, pleading silently for mercy.

For the next few days, there was much talk about Aaron's picture.

The school term ended the following week and Aaron's picture along with the best handwork done by the students that year, was on display in the assembly room. Naturally, Aaron's picture graced the place of honor.

There was no book work to be done on commencement day and joy was rampant among the children. The girls in their brightly colored dresses gave the school the delightful air of Spring awakening.

In the middle of the day all the children were gathered in the small assembly. On this day we were always favored with a visit from a man whom all the teachers spoke of with mixed esteem and fear. Professor Danual, they called him, and they always pronounced his name with reverence. He was supervisor of all the city schools, including those small and poorly equipped ones set aside for colored children.

The great man arrived almost at the end of our commencement exercises. On seeing him enter the hall, the children rose, bowed courteously, and sat down again, their eyes examining him as if he were a circus freak.

He was a tall white man with solid gray hair that made his lean face seem paler than it actually was. His eyes were the clearest blue I have ever seen. They were the only life-like things about him.

As he made his way to the front of the room the Negro principal, George Du Vaul, was walking ahead of him, cautiously preventing anything from getting in his way. As he passed me, I heard the teachers, frightened, sucking in their breath, felt the tension tightening.

A large chair was in the center of the rostrum. It had been daintily polished and the janitor had laboriously recushioned its bottom. The supervisor went straight to it without being guided, knowing that this pretty splendor was reserved for him.

Presently the Negro principal introduced the distinguished guest and he favored us with a short speech. It wasn't a very important speech. Almost at the end of it, I remember him saying something about he wouldn't be surprised if one of us boys grew up to be a great colored man, like Booker T. Washington.

After he sat down, the school chorus sang two spirituals and the girls in the fourth grade did an Indian folk dance. This brought the commencement program to an end.

After this the supervisor came down from the rostrum, his eyes tinged with curiosity, and began to view the array of handwork on display in front of the chapel.

Suddenly his face underwent a strange rejuvenation. His clear blue eyes flickered in astonishment. He was looking at Aaron Crawford's picture of Christ. Mechanically he moved his stooped form closer to the picture and stood gazing fixedly at it, curious and undecided, as though it were a dangerous animal that would rise any moment and spread destruction.

We waited tensely for his next movement. The silence was almost suffocating. At last he twisted himself around and began to search the grim faces before him. The fiery glitter of his eyes abated slightly as they rested on the Negro principal, protestingly.

"Who painted this sacrilegious nonsense?" he demanded sharply.

"I painted it, sir." These were Aaron's words, spoken hesitantly. He wetted his lips timidly and looked up at the supervisor, his eyes voicing a sad plea for understanding.

He spoke again, this time more coherently. "Th' principal said a colored person have jes as much right paintin' Jesus black as a white person have paintin' him white. And he says . . ." At this point he halted abruptly, as if to search for the next words. A strong tinge of bewilderment dimmed the glow of his solid black face. He stammered out a few more words, then stopped again.

The supervisor strode a few steps toward him. At last color had swelled some of the lifelessness out of his lean face.

"Well, go on!" he said, enragedly, ". . . I'm still listening."

Aaron moved his lips pathetically, but no words passed them. His eyes wandered around the room, resting finally, with an air of hope, on the face of the Negro principal. After a moment, he jerked his face in another direction, regretfully, as if something he had said had betrayed an understanding between him and the principal.

Presently the principal stepped forward to defend the school's prize student.

"I encouraged the boy in painting that picture," he said firmly. "And it was with my permission that he brought the picture into this school. I don't think the boy is so far wrong in painting Christ black. The artists of all other races have painted whatsoever God they worship to resemble themselves. I see no reason why we should be immune from that privilege. After all, Christ was born in that part of the world that had always been predominantly populated by colored people. There is a strong possibility that he could have been a Negro."

But for the monotonous lull of heavy breathing, I would have sworn that his words had frozen everyone in the hall. I had never heard the little principal speak so boldly to anyone, black or white.

The supervisor swallowed dumbfoundedly. His face was aglow in silent rage.

"Have you been teaching these children things like that?" he asked the Negro principal, sternly.

"I have been teaching them that their race has produced great kings and queens as well as slaves and serfs," the principal said. "The time is long overdue when we should let the world know that we erected and enjoyed the benefits of a splendid civilization long before the people of Europe had a written language."

The supervisor coughed. His eyes bulged menacingly as he spoke. "You are not being paid

to teach such things in this school, and I am demanding your resignation for overstepping your
limit as principal."

George Du Vaul did not speak. A strong quiver swept over his sullen face. He revolved himself
slowly and walked out of the room towards his
office.

The supervisor's eyes followed him until he
was out of focus. Then he murmured under his
breath: "There'll be a lot of fuss in this world if
you start people thinking that Christ was a nigger."

Some of the teachers followed the principal
out of the chapel, leaving the crestfallen children
restless and in a quandary about what to do next.
Finally we started back to our rooms. The supervisor was behind me. I heard him murmur to himself: "Damn, if niggers ain't getting smarter."

A few days later I heard that the principal had accepted a summer job as art instructor of a small
high school somewhere in south Georgia and had
gotten permission from Aaron's parents to take

him along so he could continue to encourage him
in his painting.

I was on my way home when I saw him leaving his office. He was carrying a large briefcase
and some books tucked under his arm. He had already said good-by to all the teachers, And
strangely, he did not look brokenhearted. As he
headed for the large front door, he readjusted his
horn-rimmed glasses, but did not look back. An
air of triumph gave more dignity to his soldierly
stride. He had the appearance of a man who has
done a great thing, something greater than any ordinary man would do.

Aaron Crawford was waiting outside for him.
They walked down the street together. He put his
arm around Aaron's shoulder affectionately. He
was talking sincerely to Aaron about something,
and Aaron was listening, deeply earnest.

I watched them until they were so far down
the street that their forms had begun to blur. Even
from this distance I could see they were still walking in brisk, dignified strides, like two people who
had won some sort of victory.

# See How They Run

## MARY ELIZABETH VROMAN

A bell rang. Jane Richards squared the sheaf of records decisively in the large Manila folder, placed it in the right-hand corner of her desk, and stood up. The chatter of young voices subsided, and forty-three small faces looked solemnly and curiously at the slight young figure before them. The bell stopped ringing.

*I wonder if they're as scared of me as I am of them.* She smiled brightly.

"Good morning, children, I am Miss Richards." As if they don't know—the door of the third-grade room had a neat new sign pasted above it with her name in bold black capitals; and anyway, a new teacher's name is the first thing that children find out about on the first day of school. Nevertheless, she wrote it for their benefit in large white letters on the blackboard.

"I hope we will all be happy working and playing together this year." *Now why does that sound so trite?* "As I call the roll will you please stand, so that I may get to know you as soon as possible, and if you like you may tell me something about yourselves, how old you are, where you live, what your parents do, and perhaps something about what you did during the summer."

Seated, she checked the names carefully. "Booker T. Adams."

Booker stood, gangling and stoop-shouldered; he began to recite tiredly, "My name is Booker T. Adams, I'se ten years old." *Shades of Uncle Tom!* "I live on Painter's Path." He paused, the look he gave her was tinged with something very akin to contempt. "I didn't do nothing in the summer," he said deliberately.

"Thank you, Booker." Her voice was even. "George Allen." *Must remember to correct that stoop....Where is Painter's Path?...How to go about correcting those speech defects?...Go easy, Jane, don't antagonize them....They're clean enough, but this is the first day....How can one*

*teacher do any kind of job with a load of forty-three?...Thank heaven the building is modern and well built even though it is overcrowded, not like some I've seen—no potbellied stove.*

"Sarahlene Clover Babcock." *Where do these names come from?...Up from slavery....How high is up?* Jane smothered a sudden desire to giggle. Outside she was calm and poised and smiling. Clearly she called the names, listening with interest, making a note here and there, making no corrections—not yet.

She experienced a moment of brief inward satisfaction: *I'm doing very well, this is what is expected of me...*Orientation to Teaching...Miss Murray's voice beat a distant tattoo in her memory. Miss Murray with the Junoesque figure and the moon face.... "The ideal teacher personality is one which, combining in itself all the most desirable qualities, expresses itself with quiet assurance in its endeavor to mold the personalities of the students in the most desirable patterns. ...Dear dull Miss Murray.

She made mental estimates of the class. *What a cross section of my people they represent,* she thought. *Here and there signs of evident poverty, here and there children of obviously well-to-do parents.*

"My name is Rachel Veronica Smith. I am nine years old. I live at Six-oh-seven Fairview Avenue. My father is a Methodist minister. My mother is a housewife. I have two sisters and one brother. Last summer mother and daddy took us all to New York to visit my Aunt Jen. We saw lots of wonderful things. There are millions and millions of people in New York. One day we went on a ferryboat all the way up the Hudson River—that's a great big river as wide as this town, and—"

The children listened wide-eyed. Jane listened carefully. *She speaks good English. Healthy, erect, and even perhaps a little smug. Immaculately well dressed from the smoothly braided hair, with two perky bows, to the shiny brown oxford....Bless you, Rachel, I'm so glad to have you.*

"—and the buildings are all very tall, some of them nearly reach the sky."

"Haw-haw"—this from Booker, cynically.

"Well, they are too." Rachel swung around, fire in her eyes and insistence in every line of her round, compact body.

"Ain't no buildings as tall as the sky, is dere, Miz Richards?"

Crisis No. 1. Jane chose her answer carefully. *As high as the sky...musn't turn this into a lesson in science...all in due time.* "The sky is a long way out, Booker, but the buildings in New York are very tall indeed. Rachel was only trying to show you how very tall they are. In fact, the tallest building in the whole world is in New York City."

"They call it the Empire State Building," interrupted Rachel, heady with her new knowledge and Jane's corroboration.

Booker wasn't through. "You been dere, Miz Richards?"

"Yes, Booker, many times. Someday I shall tell you more about it. Maybe Rachel will help me. Is there anything you'd like to add, Rachel?"

"I would like to say that we are glad you are our new teacher, Miss Richards." Carefully she sat down, spreading her skirt with her plump hands, her smile angelic.

*Now I'll bet you a quarter her reverend father told her to say that.* "Thank you, Rachel."

The roll call continued....Tanya, slight and pinched, with the toes showing through the very white sneakers, the darned and faded but clean blue dress, the gentle voice like a tinkling bell, and the beautiful sensitive face....Boyd and Lloyd, identical in their starched overalls, and the slightly vacant look....Marjorie Lee, all of twelve years old, the well-developed body moving restlessly in the childish dress, the eyes too wise, the voice too high....Joe Louis, the intelligence in the brilliant black eyes gleaming above the threadbare clothes. *Lives of great men all remind us—Well, I have them all...Frederick Douglass, Franklin Delano, Abraham Lincoln, Booker T., Joe Louis, George Washington....What a great burden you bear, little people, heirs to all your parents' stillborn dreams of greatness. I must not fail you.* The last name on the list...C. T. Young. Jane paused, small lines creasing her forehead. She checked the list again.

"C. T., what is your name? I have only your initials on my list."

"Dat's all my name, C. T. Young."

"No, dear, I mean what does C. T. stand for? Is it Charles or Clarence?"

"No'm, jest C. T."

"But I can't put that in my register, dear."

Abruptly Jane rose and went to the next room. Rather timidly she waited to speak to Miss Nelson, the second-grade teacher, who had the formidable record of having taught all of sixteen years. Miss Nelson was large and smiling.

"May I help you, dear?"

"Yes, please. It's about C. T. Young. I believe you had him last year."

"Yes, and the year before that. You'll have him two years too."

"Oh? Well, I was wondering what name you registered him under. All the information I have is C. T. Young."

"That's all there is, honey. Lots of these children only have initials."

"You mean...can't something be done about it?"

"What?" Miss Nelson was still smiling, but clearly impatient.

"I...well...thank you." Jane left quickly.

Back in Room 3 the children were growing restless. Deftly Jane passed out the rating tests and gave instructions. Then she called C. T. to her. He was as small as an eight-year-old, and hungry-looking, with enormous guileless eyes and a beautifully shaped head.

"How many years did you stay in the second grade, C. T.?"

"Two."

"And in the first?"

"Two."

"How old are you?"

"'Leven."

"When will you be twelve?"

"Nex' month."

*And they didn't care... nobody ever cared enough about one small boy to give him a name.*

"You are a very lucky little boy, C. T. Most people have to take the name somebody gave them whether they like it or not, but you can choose your very own."

"Yeah?" The dark eyes were belligerent. "My father named me C. T. after hisself, Miz Richards, an dat's my name."

Jane felt unreasonably irritated. "How many children are there in your family, C. T.?"

"'Leven."

"How many are there younger than you?" she asked.

"Seven."

Very gently. "Did you have your breakfast this morning, dear?"

The small figure in the too-large trousers and the too-small shirt drew itself up to full height. "Yes'm, I had fried chicken, and rice, and coffee, and rolls, and oranges too."

*Oh, you poor darling. You poor proud lying darling. Is that what you'd like for breakfast?*

She asked, "Do you like school, C. T.?"

"Yes'm," he told her suspiciously.

She leafed through the pile of records. "Your record says you haven't been coming to school very regularly. Why?"

"I dunno."

"Did you eat last year in the lunchroom?"

"No'm."

"Did you ever bring a lunch?"

"No'm, I eats such a big breakfast, I doan git hungry at lunchtime."

"Children need to eat lunch to help them grow tall and strong, C. T. So from now on you'll eat lunch in the lunchroom"—an afterthought: *perhaps it's important to make him think I believe him*—"and from now on maybe you'd better not eat such a big breakfast."

Decisively she wrote his name at the top of what she knew to be an already too-large list.

"Only those in absolute necessity," she had been told by Mr. Johnson, the kindly, harassed principal. "We'd like to feed them all, so many are underfed, but we just don't have the money." Well, this was absolute necessity if she ever saw it.

"What does your father do, C. T.?"

"He works at dat big factory cross-town, he make plenty money, Miz Richards." The record said "unemployed."

"Would you like to be named Charles Thomas?"

The expressive eyes darkened, but the voice was quiet. "No'm."

"Very well." Thoughtfully Jane opened the register; she wrote firmly: *C. T. Young.*

October is a witching month in the Southern United States. The richness of the golds and reds and browns of the trees forms an enchanted filigree through which the lilting voices of children at play seem to float, embodied like so many nymphs of Pan.

Jane had played a fast-and-furious game of tag with her class and now she sat quietly under the gnarled old oak, watching the tireless play, feeling the magic of the sun through the leaves warmly dappling her skin, the soft breeze on the nape of her neck like a lover's hands, and her own drowsy lethargy. *Paul, Paul my darling... how long for us now?* She had worshiped Paul Carlyle since they were freshmen together. On graduation day he had slipped the small circlet of diamonds on her finger.... "A teacher's salary is small, Jane. Maybe we'll be lucky enough to get work together, then in a year or so we can be married. Wait for me, darling, wait for me!"

But in a year or so Paul had gone to war, and Jane went out alone to teach.... Lansing Creek—one year... the leaky roof, the potbellied stove, the water from the well.... Maryweather Point—two years... the tight-lipped spinster principal with the small, vicious face and the small, vicious soul.... Three hard, lonely years and then she had been lucky.

The superintendent had praised her. "You have done good work, Miss—ah—Jane. This year you are to be placed at Centertown High—that is, of course, if you care to accept the position."

Jane had caught her breath. Centertown was the largest and best equipped of all the schools in the county, only ten miles from home and Paul—for Paul had come home, older, quieter, but still Paul. He was teaching now more than a hundred miles away, but they went home every other weekend to their families and each other.... "Next summer you'll be Mrs. Paul Carlyle, darling. It's hard for us to be apart so much. I guess we'll have to be for a long time till I can afford to support you. But, sweet, these little tykes need us so badly." He had held her close, rubbing the nape of her neck under the soft curls. "We have a big job, those of us who teach," he had told her, "a never-ending and often thankless job, Jane, to supply the needs of these kids who lack so much."

They wrote each other long letters, sharing plans and problems. She wrote him about C. T. "I've adopted him, darling. He's so pathetic and so determined to prove that he's not. He learns nothing at all, but I can't let myself believe that he's stupid, so I keep trying."

"Miz Richards, please, ma'am." Tanya's beautiful amber eyes sought hers timidly. Her brown curls were tangled from playing, her cheeks a bright red under the tightly stretched olive skin. The elbows jutted awkwardly out of the sleeves of the limp cotton dress, which could not conceal the finely chiseled bones in their pitiable fleshlessness. As always when she looked at her, Jane thought, *What a beautiful child!* So unlike the dark, gaunt, morose mother, and the dumpy, pasty-faced father who had visited her that first week. A fairy's changeling. *You'll make a lovely angel to grace the throne of God, Tanya! Now what made me think of that?*

"Please, ma'am, I'se sick."

Gently Jane drew her down beside her. She felt the parchment skin, noted the unnaturally bright eyes. *Oh, dear God, she's burning up!* "Do you hurt anywhere, Tanya?"

"My head, ma'am, and I'se so tired." Without warning she began to cry.

"How far do you live, Tanya?"

"Two miles."

"You walk to school?"

"Yes'm"

"Do any of your brothers have a bicycle?"

"No'm."

"Rachel!" *Bless you for always being there when I need you.* "Hurry, dear, to the office and ask Mr. Johnson please to send a big boy with a bicycle to take Tanya home. She's sick."

Rachel ran.

"Hush now, dear, we'll get some cool water, and then you'll be home in a little while. Did you feel sick this morning?"

"Yes'm, but Mot Dear sent me to school anyway. She said I just wanted to play hooky." *Keep smiling, Jane. Poor, ambitious, well-meaning parents, made bitter at the seeming futility of dreaming dreams for this lovely child...willing her to rise above the drabness of your own meager existence...too angry with life to see that what she needs most is your love and care and right now medical attention.*

Jane bathed the child's forehead with cool water at the fountain. *Do the white schools have a clinic? I must ask Paul. Do they have a lounge or a couch where they can lay one wee sick head? Is there anywhere in this town free medical service for one small child...born black?*

The boy with the bicycle came. "Take care of her now, ride slowly and carefully, and take her straight home.... Keep the newspaper over your head, Tanya, to keep out the sun, and tell your parents to call the doctor." But she knew they wouldn't—because they couldn't!

The next day Jane went to see Tanya.

"She's sho' nuff sick, Miz Richards," the mother said. "She's always been a puny child, but this time she's took real bad, throat's all raw, talk all out of her haid las' night. I been using a poultice and some herb brew but she ain't got no better."

"Have you called a doctor, Mrs. Fulton?"

"No'm, we cain't afford it, an' Jake, he doan believe in doctors nohow."

Jane waited till the tide of high bright anger welling in her heart and beating in her brain had subsided. When she spoke, her voice was deceptively gentle. "Mrs. Fulton, Tanya is a very sick little girl. She is your only little girl. If you love her, I advise you to have a doctor to her, for if you don't...Tanya may die."

The wail that issued from the thin figure seemed to have no part in reality.

Jane spoke hurriedly. "Look, I'm going into town, I'll send a doctor out. Don't worry about paying him. We can see about that later." Impulsively she put her arms around the taut, motionless shoulders. "Don't you worry, honey, it's going to be all right."

There was a kindliness in the doctor's weather-beaten face that warmed Jane's heart, but his voice was brusque. "You sick, girl? Well?"

"No, sir, I'm not sick." *What long sequence of events has caused even the best of you to look on even the best of us as menials?* "I'm a teacher at Centertown High. There's a little girl in my class who is very ill. Her parents are very poor. I came to see if you would please go to see her."

He looked at her, amused.

"Of course I'll pay the bill, doctor," she added hastily.

"In that case...well...where does she live?"

Jane told him. "I think it's diphtheria, doctor."

He raised his eyebrows. "Why?"

Jane sat erect. *Don't be afraid, Jane! You're as good a teacher as he is a doctor, and you made an A in that course in childhood diseases.* "High fever, restlessness, sore throat, headache, croupy cough, delirium. It could, of course, be tonsillitis or scarlet fever, but that cough—well, I'm only guessing, of course," she finished lamely.

"Hmph." The doctor's face was expressionless. "Well, we'll see. Have your other children been inoculated?"

"Yes, sir. Doctor, if the parents ask, please tell them that the school is paying for your services."

This time he was wide-eyed.

The lie haunted her. She spoke to the other teachers about it the next day at recess. "She's really very sick, maybe you'd like to help?"

Mary Winters, the sixth-grade teacher, was the first to speak. "Richards, I'd like to help, but I've got three kids of my own, and so you see how it is?"

Jane saw.

"Trouble with you, Richards, is you're too emotional." This from Nelson. "When you've taught as many years as I have, my dear, you'll learn not to bang your head against a stone wall. It may sound hardhearted to you, but one just can't worry about one child more or less when one has nearly fifty."

The pain in the back of her eyes grew more insistent. "I can," she said.

"I'll help, Jane," said Marilyn Andrews, breathless, bouncy newlywed Marilyn. "Here's two bucks. It's all I've got, but nothing's plenty for me." Her laughter pealed echoing down the hall.

"I've got a dollar, Richards"—this from mousy, severe little Miss Mitchell—"though I'm not sure I agree with you."

"Why don't you ask the high school faculty?" said Marilyn. "Better still, take it up in teachers' meeting."

"Mr. Johnson has enough to worry about now," snapped Nelson. *Why, she's mad,* thought Jane, *mad because I'm trying to give a helpless little tyke a chance to live, and because Marilyn and Mitchell helped.*

The bell rang. Wordlessly, Jane turned away. She watched the children troop in noisily, an ancient nursery rhyme running through her head:

> *Three blind mice, three blind mice,*
> *See how they run, see how they run,*
> *They all ran after the farmer's wife,*
> *She cut off their tails with a carving knife.*
> *Did you ever see such a sight in your life*
> *As three blind mice?*

Only this time, it was forty-three mice. Jane giggled. *Why, I'm hysterical,* she thought in sur-

prise. *The mice thought the sweet-smelling farmer's wife might have bread and a wee bit of cheese
to offer poor blind mice, but the farmer's wife
didn't like poor, hungry, dirty blind mice. So she
cut off their tails. Then they couldn't run anymore,
only wobble. What happened then? Maybe they
starved, those that didn't bleed to death. Running
round in circles, Running where, little mice?*

She talked to the high-school faculty, and Mr.
Johnson. Altogether she got eight dollars.

The following week she received a letter
from the doctor:

Dear Miss Richards:

*I am happy to inform you that Tanya is
greatly improved, and with careful nursing she
will be well enough in about eight weeks to return
to school. She is very frail, however, and will require special care. I have made three visits to her
home. In view of the peculiar circumstances, I am
donating my services. The cost of the medicines,
however, amounts to the sum of $15. I am refer-
ring this to you as you requested. What a beautiful
child!*

> *Yours sincerely,*
> JONATHAN H. SINCLAIR, M.D.

*P.S. She had diphtheria.*

*Bless you forever and ever, Jonathan H. Sin-
clair, M.D. For all your long Southern heritage,
"a man's a man for a' that . . . and a' that!"*

Her heart was light that night when she wrote
to Paul. Later she made plans in the darkness.
*You'll be well and fat by Christmas, Tanya, and
you'll be a lovely angel in my pageant. . . . I must
get the children to save pennies. . . . We'll send you
milk and oranges and eggs, and we'll make funny
little get-well cards to keep you happy.*

But by Christmas Tanya was dead!

The voice from the dark figure was quiet, even
monotonous.

"Jake an' me, we always work so hard, Miz
Richards. We didn't neither one have no school-

ing much when we was married—folks never had
much money, but we was happy. Jake, he tenant
farm. I tuk in washing—we plan to save and buy
a little house and farm of our own someday. Den
the children come. Six boys, Miz Richards—all
in a hurry. We both want the boys to finish
school, mebbe go to college. We try not to keep
them out to work the farm, but sometimes we
have to. Then come Tanya. Just like a little yellow rose she was, Miz Richards, all pink and
gold . . . and her voice like a silver bell. We think
when she grow up an' finish school she take
voice lessons—be like Marian Anderson. We
think mebbe by then the boys would be old
enough to help. I was kinda feared for her when
she get sick, but then she start to get better. She
was doing so well, Miz Richards. Den it get cold,
an' the fire so hard to keep all night long, an'
eben the newspapers in the cracks doan keep the
win' out, an' I give her all my kivver; but one
night she jest tuk to shivering an' talking all out
her haid—sat right up in bed, she did. She call
your name onc't or twice, Miz Richards, then she
say, 'Mot Dear, does Jesus love me like Miz Richards say in Sunday school?' I say, 'Yes, honey,
but you ain't gwine die.' But she did, Miz
Richards . . . jest smiled an' laid down—jest
smiled an' laid down."

It is terrible to see such hopeless resignation
in such tearless eyes. . . . One little mouse stopped
running. . . . *You'll make a lovely angel to grace
the throne of God, Tanya!*

Jane did not go to the funeral. Nelson and
Rogers sat in the first pew. Everyone on the faculty contributed to a beautiful wreath. Jane preferred not to think about that.

C. T. brought a lovely potted rose to her the next
day. "Miz Richards, ma'am, do you think this is
pretty enough to go on Tanya's grave?"

"Where did you get it, C. T.?"

"I stole it out Miz Adams' front yard, right
out of that li'l' glass house she got there. The door
was open, Miz Richards, she got plenty, she won't
miss this li'l' one."

*You queer little bundle of truth and lies. What do I do now?* Seeing the tears blinking back in the anxious eyes, she said gently, "Yes, C. T., the rose is nearly as beautiful as Tanya is now. She will like it."

"You mean she will know I put it there, Miz Richards? She ain't daid at all?"

"Maybe she'll know, C. T. You see, nothing that is beautiful ever dies as long as we remember it."

*So you loved Tanya, little mouse? The memory of her beauty is yours to keep now forever and always, my darling. Those things money can't buy. They've all been trying, but your tail isn't off yet, is it, brat? Not by a long shot.* Suddenly she laughed aloud.

He looked at her wonderingly. "What are you laughing at, Miz Richards?"

"I'm laughing because I'm happy, C. T.," and she hugged him.

Christmas with its pageantry and splendor came and went. Back from the holidays, Jane had an oral English lesson.

"We'll take this period to let you tell about your holidays, children."

On the weekends that Jane stayed in Centertown she visited different churches, and taught in the Sunday schools when she was asked. She had tried to impress on the children the reasons for giving at Christmastime. In class they had talked about things they could make for gifts, and ways they could save money to buy them. Now she stood by the window, listening attentively, reaping the fruits of her labors.

"I got a doll and a doll carriage for Christmas. Her name is Gladys, and the carriage has red wheels, and I got a tea set and—"

"I got a bicycle and a catcher's mitt."

"We all went to a party and had ice cream and cake."

"I got—"

"I got—"

"I got—"

Score one goose egg for Jane. She was suddenly very tired. "It's your turn, C. T." *Dear God,*

*please don't let him lie too much. He tears my heart. The children never laugh. It's funny how polite they are to C. T. even when they know he's lying. Even that day when Boyd and Lloyd told how they had seen him take food out of the garbage cans in front of the restaurant, and he said he was taking it to some poor hungry children, they didn't laugh. Sometimes children have a great deal more insight than grownups.*

C. T. was talking. "I didn't get nothin' for Christmas, because mamma was sick, but I worked all that week before for Mr. Bondel what owns the store on Main Street. I ran errands an' swep' up an' he give me three dollars, and so I bought mamma a real pretty handkerchief an' a comb, an' I bought my father a tie pin, paid a big ole fifty cents for it too... an' I bought my sisters an' brothers some candy an' gum an' I bought me this whistle. Course I got what you give us, Miz Richards" (she had given each a small gift) "an' mamma's white lady give us a whole crate of oranges, an' Miz Smith what live nex' door give me a pair of socks. Mamma she was so happy she made a cake with eggs an' butter an' everything; an' then we ate it an' had a good time."

Rachel spoke wonderingly. "Didn't Santa Claus bring you anything at all?"

C. T. was the epitome of scorn. "Ain't no Santa Claus," he said and sat down.

Jane quelled the age-old third-grade controversy absently, for her heart was singing. *C. T.... C. T., son of my own heart, you are the bright new hope of a doubtful world, and the gay new song of a race unconquered. Of them all—Sarahlene, sole heir to the charming stucco home on the hill, all fitted for gracious living; George, whose father is a contractor; Rachel, the minister's daughter; Angela, who has just inherited ten thousand dollars—all of them who got, you, my dirty little vagabond, who have never owned a coat in your life, because you say you don't get cold; you, out of your nothing, found something to give, and in the dignity of giving found that it was not so important to receive.... Christ Child, look down in blessing on one small child made in Your image and born black!*

Jane had problems. Sometimes it was difficult to maintain discipline with forty-two children. Busy as she kept them, there were always some not busy enough. There was the conference with Mr. Johnson.

"Miss Richards, you are doing fine work here, but sometimes your room is a little... well—ah—well, to say the least, noisy. You are new here, but we have always maintained a record of having fine discipline here at this school. People have said that it used to be hard to tell whether or not there were children in the building. We have always been proud of that. Now take Miss Nelson. She is an excellent disciplinarian." He smiled. "Maybe if you ask her she will give you her secret. Do not be too proud to accept help from anyone who can give it, Miss Richards."

"No, sir, thank you, sir, I'll do my best to improve, sir." *Ah, you dear, well-meaning, short-sighted, round, busy little man. Why are you not more concerned about how much the children have grown and learned in these past four months than you are about how much noise they make? I know Miss Nelson's secret. Spare not the rod and spoil not the child. Is that what you want me to do? Paralyze these kids with fear so that they will be afraid to move? afraid to question? afraid to grow? Why is it so fine for people not to know there are children in the building? Wasn't the building built for children?* In her room Jane locked the door against the sound of the playing children, put her head on the desk, and cried.

Jane acceded to tradition and administered one whipping. Booker had slapped Sarahlene's face because she had refused to give up a shiny little music box that played a gay little tune. He had taken the whipping docilely enough, as though used to it; but the sneer in his eyes that had almost gone returned to haunt them. Jane's heart misgave her. *From now on I positively refuse to impose my will on any of these poor children by reason of my greater strength.* So she had abandoned the rod in favor of any other means she could find. They did not always work.

There was a never-ending drive for funds. Jane had a passion for perfection. Plays, dances, concerts, bazaars, suppers, parties followed one on another in staggering succession.

"Look here, Richards," Nelson told her one day, "it's true that we need a new piano, and that science equipment, but, honey, these drives in a colored school are like the poor: with us always. It doesn't make too much difference if Suzy forgets her lines, or if the ice cream is a little lumpy. Co-operation is fine, but the way you tear into things you won't last long."

"For once in her life Nelson's right, Jane," Elise told her later. "I can understand how intense you are because I used to be like that; but, pet, Negro teachers have always had to work harder than any others and till recently have always got paid less, so for our own health's sake we have to let up wherever possible. Believe me, honey, if you don't learn to take it easy, you're going to get sick."

Jane did. Measles!

"Oh, no," she wailed, "not in my old age!" But she was glad of the rest. Lying in her own bed at home, she realized how very tired she was.

Paul came to see her that weekend, and sat by her bed and read aloud to her the old classic poems they both loved so well. They listened to their favorite radio programs. Paul's presence was warm and comforting. Jane was reluctant to go back to work.

What to do about C. T. was a question that daily loomed larger in Jane's consciousness. Watching Joe Louis's brilliant development was a thing of joy, and Jane was hard pressed to find enough outlets for his amazing abilities. Jeanette Allen was running a close second, and even Booker, so long a problem, was beginning to grasp fundamentals, but C. T. remained static.

"I always stay two years in a grade, Miz Richards," he told her blandly. "I does better the second year."

"Do you *want* to stay in the third grade two years, C. T.?"

"I don't keer." His voice had been cheerful.

*Maybe he really is slow,* Jane thought. But one day something happened to make her change her mind.

C. T. was possessed of an unusually strong tendency to protect those he considered to be poor or weak. He took little Johnny Armstrong, who sat beside him in class, under his wing. Johnny was nearsighted and nondescript, his one outstanding feature being his hero-worship of C. T. Johnny was a plodder. Hard as he tried, he made slow progress at best.

The struggle with multiplication tables was a difficult one, in spite of all the little games Jane devised to make them easier for the children. On this particular day there was the uneven hum of little voices trying to memorize. Johnny and C. T. were having a whispered conversation about snakes.

Clearly Jane heard C. T.'s elaboration. "Man, my father caught a moccasin long as that blackboard, I guess, an' I held him while he was live right back of his ugly head—so."

Swiftly Jane crossed the room. "C. T. and Johnny, you are supposed to be learning your tables. The period is nearly up and you haven't even begun to study. Furthermore, in more than five months you haven't even learned the two-times table. Now you will both stay in at the first recess to learn it, and every day after this until you do."

*Maybe I should make up some problems about snakes,* Jane mused, *but they'd be too ridiculous. . . . Two nests of four snakes—Oh, well, I'll see how they do at recess.* Her heart smote her at the sight of the two little figures at their desks, listening wistfully to the sound of the children at play, but she busied herself and pretended not to notice them. Then she heard C. T.'s voice:

"Lissen, man, these tables is easy if you really want to learn them. Now see here. Two times one is two. Two times two is four. Two times three is six. If you forgit, all you got to do is add two like she said."

"Sho' nuff, man?"

"Sho'. Say them with me . . . two times one—" Obediently Johnny began to recite. Five minutes later they came to her. "We's ready, Miz Richards."

"Very well, Johnny, you may begin."

"Two times one is two. Two times two is four. Two times three is. . . . Two times three is—"

"Six," prompted C. T.

In sweat and pain, Johnny managed to stumble through the two-times table with C. T.'s help.

"That's very poor, Johnny, but you may go for today. Tomorrow I shall expect you to have it letter perfect. Now it's your turn, C. T."

C. T.'s performance was a fair rival to Joe Louis's. Suspiciously she took him through in random order.

"Two times nine?"

"Eighteen."

"Two times four?"

"Eight."

"Two times seven?"

"Fourteen."

"C. T., you could have done this long ago. Why didn't you?"

"I dunno. . . . May I go to play now, Miz Richards?"

"Yes, C. T. Now learn your three-times table for me tomorrow."

But he didn't, not that day, or the day after that, or the day after that. . . . *Why doesn't he? Is it that he doesn't want to? Maybe if I were as ragged and deprived as he I wouldn't want to learn either.*

Jane took C. T. to town and bought him a shirt, a sweater, a pair of dungarees, some underwear, a pair of shoes, and a pair of socks. Then she sent him to the barber to get his hair cut. She gave him the money so he could pay for the articles himself and figure up the change. She instructed him to take a bath before putting on his new clothes, and told him not to tell anyone but his parents that she had bought them.

The next morning the class was in a dither.

"You seen C. T.?"

"Oh, boy, ain't he sharp!"

"C. T., where'd you get them new clothes?"

"Oh, man, I can wear new clothes any time I feel like it, but I can't be bothered with being a fancypants all the time like you guys."

C. T. strutted in new confidence, but his work didn't improve.

Spring came in its virginal green gladness and the children chafed for the out-of-doors. Jane took them out as much as possible on nature studies and excursions.

C. T. was growing more and more mischievous, and his influence began to spread throughout the class. Daily his dross wit became more and more edged with impudence. Jane was at her wit's end.

"You let that child get away with too much, Richards," Nelson told her. "What he needs is a good hiding."

One day Jane kept certain of the class in at the first recess to do neglected homework, C. T. among them. She left the room briefly. When she returned C. T. was gone.

"Where is C. T.?" she asked.

"He went out to play, Miz Richards. He said couldn't no ole teacher keep him in when he didn't want to stay."

Out on the playground C. T. was standing in a swing, gently swaying to and fro, surrounded by a group of admiring youngsters. He was holding forth.

"I gets tired of stayin' in all the time. She doan pick on nobody but me, an' today I put my foot down. 'From now on,' I say, 'I ain't never goin' to stay in, Miz Richards.' Then I walks out." He was enjoying himself immensely. Then he saw her.

"You will come with me, C. T." She was quite calm except for the telltale veins throbbing in her forehead.

"I ain't comin'." The sudden fright in his eyes was veiled quickly by a nonchalant belligerence. He rocked the swing gently.

She repeated, "Come with me, C. T."

The children watched breathlessly.

"I done told you I ain't comin', Miz Richards." His voice was patient, as though explaining to a child. "I ain't...comin'...a...damn...tall!"

Jane moved quickly, wrenching the small but surprisingly strong figure from the swing. Then she bore him bodily, kicking and screaming, to the building.

The children relaxed and began to giggle. "Oh, boy! Is he goin' to catch it!" they told one another.

Panting, she held him, still struggling, by the scruff of his collar before the group of teachers gathered in Marilyn's room. "All right, now *you* tell me what to do with him!" she demanded. "I've tried everything." The tears were close behind her eyes.

"What'd he do?" Nelson asked.

Briefly she told them.

"Have you talked to his parents?"

"Three times I've had conferences with them. They say to beat him."

"That, my friend, is what you ought to do. Now he never acted like that with me. If you'll let me handle him, I'll show you how to put a brat like that in his place."

"Go ahead," Jane said wearily.

Nelson left the room, and returned with a narrow but sturdy leather thong. "Now, C. T."—she was smiling, tapping the strap in her open left palm—"go to your room and do what Miss Richards told you to."

"I ain't gonna, an' you can't make me." He sat down with absurd dignity at a desk.

Still smiling, Miss Nelson stood over him. The strap descended without warning across the bony shoulders in the thin shirt. The whip became a dancing demon, a thing possessed, bearing no relation to the hand that held it. The shrieks grew louder. Jane closed her eyes against the blurred fury of a singing lash, a small boy's terror, and a smiling face.

Miss Nelson was not tired. "Well, C. T.?"

"I won't. Yer can kill me but I *won't!*"

The sounds began again. Red welts began to show across the small arms and through the clinging sweat-drenched shirt.

"Now will you go to your room?"

Sobbing and conquered, C. T. went. The seated children stared curiously at the little procession. Jane dismissed them.

In his seat C. T. found pencil and paper.

"What's he supposed to do, Richards?"

Jane told her.

"All right, now write!"

C. T. stared at Nelson through swollen lids, a curious smile curving his lips. Jane knew suddenly that come hell or high water, C. T. would not write. *I musn't interfere. Please, God, don't let her hurt him too badly. Where have I failed so miserably?... Forgive us our trespasses.* The singing whip and the shrieks became a symphony from hell. Suddenly Jane hated the smiling face with an almost unbearable hatred. She spoke, her voice like cold steel.

"That's enough, Nelson."

The noise stopped.

"He's in no condition to write now anyway."

C. T. stood up. "I hate you. I hate you all. You're mean and I hate you." Then he ran. No one followed him. *Run, little mouse!* They avoided each other's eyes.

"Well, there you are," Nelson said as she walked away. Jane never found out what she meant by that.

The next day C. T. did not come to school. The day after that he brought Jane the fatal homework, neatly and painstakingly done, and a bunch of wild flowers. Before the bell rang, the children surrounded him. He was beaming.

"Did you tell yer folks you got a whipping, C. T.?"

"Naw! I'd a' only got another."

"Where were you yesterday?"

"Went fishin'. Caught me six cats long as your haid, Sambo."

Jane buried her face in the sweet-smelling flowers. *Oh, my brat, my wonderful resilient brat. They'll never get your tail, will they?*

It was seven weeks till the end of term when C. T. brought Jane a model wooden boat.

Jane stared at it. "Did you make this? It's beautiful, C. T."

"Oh, I make them all the time...an' airplanes an' houses too. I do 'em in my spare time," he finished airily.

"Where do you get the models, C. T.?" she asked.

"I copies them from pictures in the magazines."

*Right under my nose...right there all the time,* she thought wonderingly. "C. T., would you like to build things when you grow up? Real houses and ships and planes?"

"Reckon I could, Miz Richards," he said confidently.

The excitement was growing in her. "Look, C. T. You aren't going to do any lessons at all for the rest of the year. You're going to build ships and houses and airplanes and anything else you want to."

"I am, huh?" He grinned. "Well, I guess I wasn't goin' to get promoted nohow."

"Of course, if you want to build them the way they really are, you might have to do a little measuring, and maybe learn to spell the names of the parts you want to order. All the best contractors have to know things like that, you know."

"Say, I'm gonna have real fun, huh? I always said lessons wussent no good nohow. Pop say too much study eats out yer brains anyway."

The days went by. Jane ran a race with time. The instructions from the model companies arrived. Jane burned the midnight oil planning each day's work:

*Learn to spell the following words: ship, sail, steamer—boat, anchor, airplane wing, fly.*

*Write a letter to the lumber company, ordering some lumber.*

*The floor of our model house is ten inches wide and fourteen inches long. Multiply the length by the width and you'll find the area of the floor in square inches.*

*Read the story of Columbus and his voyages.*

*Our plane arrives in Paris in twenty-eight hours. Paris is the capital city of a country named France across the Atlantic Ocean.*

*Long ago sailors told time by the sun and the stars. Now, the earth goes around the sun—*

Work and pray, work and pray!

C. T. learned. Some things vicariously, some things directly. When he found that he needed multiplication to plan his models to scale, he learned to multiply. In three weeks he had mastered simple division.

Jane bought beautifully illustrated stories about ships and planes. He learned to read.

He wrote for and received his own materials. Jane exulted.

The last day! Forty-two faces waiting anxiously for report cards. Jane spoke to them briefly, praising them collectively, and admonishing them to obey the safety rules during the holidays. Then she passed out the report cards.

As she smiled at each childish face, she thought, *I've been wrong. The long arm of circumstance, environment, and heredity is the farmer's wife that seeks to mow you down, and all of us who touch your lives are in some way responsible for how successful she is. But you aren't mice, my darlings. Mice are hated, hunted pests. You are normal, lovable children. The knife of the farmer's wife is double-edged for you because you are Negro children, born mostly in poverty. But you are wonderful children, nevertheless, for you wear the bright protective cloak of laughter, the strong shield of courage, and the intelligence of children everywhere. Some few of you may indeed become as the mice—but most of you shall find your way to stand fine and tall in the annals of men. There's a bright new tomorrow ahead. For every one of us whose job it is to help you grow that is insensitive and unworthy there are hundreds who daily work that you may grow straight and whole. If it were not so, our world could not long endure.*

She handed C. T. his card.

"Thank you, ma'am."

"Aren't you going to open it?"

He opened it dutifully. When he looked up, his eyes were wide with disbelief. "You didn't make no mistake?"

"No mistake, C. T. You're promoted. You've caught up enough to go to the fourth grade next year."

She dismissed the children. They were a swarm of bees released from a hive. "'By, Miss Richards.". . ."Happy holidays, Miss Richards."

C. T. was the last to go.

"Well, C. T.?"

"Miz Richards, you remember what you said about a name being important?"

"Yes, C. T."

"Well, I talked to mamma, and she said if I wanted a name it would be all right, and she'd go to the courthouse about it."

"What name have you chosen, C. T.?" she asked.

"Christopher Turner Young."

"That's a nice name, Christopher," she said gravely.

"Sho' nuff, Miz Richards?"

"Sure enough, C. T."

"Miz Richards, you know what?"

"What, dear?"

"I love you."

She kissed him swiftly before he ran to catch his classmates.

She stood at the window and watched the running, skipping figures, followed by the bold mimic shadows. *I'm coming home, Paul. I'm leaving my forty-two children, and Tanya there on the hill. My work with them is finished now.* The laughter bubbled up in her throat. *But Paul, oh Paul. See how straight they run!*

# As the Night the Day

## ABIOSEH NICOL

Kojo and Bandele walked slowly across the hot green lawn, holding their science manuals with moist fingers. In the distance they could hear the junior school collecting in the hall of the main school building, for singing practice. Nearer, but still far enough, their classmates were strolling toward them. The two reached the science block and entered it. It was a low building set apart from the rest of the high school which sprawled on the hillside of the African savanna. The laboratory was a longish room and at one end they saw Basu, another boy, looking out of the window, his back turned to them. Mr. Abu, the ferocious laboratory attendant, was not about. The rows of multicoloured bottles looked inviting. A bunsen burner soughed loudly in the heavy weary heat. Where the tip of the light-blue triangle of flame ended, a shimmering plastic transparency started. One could see the restless hot air moving in the minute tornado. The two African boys watched it, interestedly, holding hands.

"They say it is hotter inside the flame than on its surface," Kojo said doubtfully. "I wonder how they know."

"I think you mean the opposite; let's try it ourselves," Bandele answered.

"How?"

"Let's take the temperature inside."

"All right, here is a thermometer. You do it."

"It says ninety degrees now. I shall take the temperature of the outer flame first, then you can take the inner yellow one."

Bandele held the thermometer gently forward to the flame and Kojo craned to see. The thin thread of quicksilver shot upward within the stem of the instrument with swift malevolence and there was a slight crack. The stem had broken. On the bench the small bulbous drops of mercury which had spilled from it shivered with glinting, playful malice and shuddered down to the cement floor, dashing themselves into a thousand shiny pieces, some of which coalesced again and shook gaily as if with silent laughter.

"Oh my God!" whispered Kojo hoarsely.

"Shut up!" Bandele said, imperiously, in a low voice.

Bandele swept up the few drops on the bench into his cupped hand and threw the blob of mercury down the sink. He swept those on the floor under an adjoining cupboard with his bare feet. Then, picking up the broken halves of the thermometer, he tiptoed to the waste bin and dropped them in. He tiptoed back to Kojo, who was standing petrified by the blackboard.

"See no evil, hear no evil, speak no evil," he whispered to Kojo.

It all took place in a few seconds. Then the rest of the class started pouring in, chattering and pushing each other. Basu, who had been at the end of the room with his back turned to them all the time, now turned round and limped laboriously across to join the class, his eyes screwed up as they always were.

The class ranged itself loosely in a semicircle around the demonstration platform. They were dressed in the school uniform of white shirt and khaki shorts. Their official age was around sixteen although, in fact, it ranged from Kojo's fifteen years to one or two boys of twenty-one.

Mr. Abu, the laboratory attendant, came in from the adjoining store and briskly cleaned the blackboard. He was a retired African sergeant from the Army Medical Corps and was feared by the boys. If he caught any of them in any petty thieving, he offered them the choice of a hard smack on the bottom or being reported to the science masters. Most boys chose the former as they knew the matter would end there with no protracted interviews, moral recrimination, and an entry in the conduct book.

The science master stepped in and stood on his small platform. A tall, thin, dignified Negro, with greying hair and silver-rimmed spectacles badly fitting on his broad nose and always slipping down, making him look avuncular. "Vernier" was his nickname as he insisted on exact measurement and exact speech "as fine as a vernier scale," he would say, which measured, or course, things in thousandths of a millimetre. Vernier set the experiments for the day and demonstrated them, then retired behind the *Church Times* which he read seriously in between walking quickly down the aisles of lab benches, advising boys. It was a simple heat experiment to show that a dark surface gave out more heat by radiation than a bright surface.

During the class, Vernier was called away to the telephone and Abu was not about, having retired to the lavatory for a smoke. As soon as a posted sentinel announced that he was out of sight, minor pandemonium broke out. Some of the boys raided the store. The wealthier ones swiped rubber tubing to make catapults and to repair bicycles, and helped themselves to chemicals for developing photographic films. The poorer boys were in deadlier earnest and took only things of strict commercial interest which could be sold easily in the market. They emptied stuff into bottles in their pockets. Soda for making soap, magnesium sulphate for opening medicine, salt for cooking, liquid paraffin for women's hairdressing, and fine yellow iodoform powder much in demand for sprinkling on sores. Kojo protested mildly against all this. "Oh, shut up!" a few boys said. Sorie, a huge boy who always wore a fez indoors and who, rumour said, had already fathered a child, commanded respect and some leadership in the class. He was sipping his favourite mixture of diluted alcohol and bicarbonate—which he called "gin and fizz"—from a beaker. "Look here, Kojo, you are getting out of hand. What do you think our parents pay taxes and school fees for? For us to enjoy—or to buy a new car every year for Simpson?" The other boys laughed. Simpson was the European headmaster, feared by the small boys, adored by the boys in the middle school, and liked, in a critical fashion, with reservations, by some of the senior boys and African masters.

He had a passion for new motor-cars, buying one yearly.

"Come to think of it," Sorie continued to Kojo, "you must take something yourself, then we'll know we are safe." "Yes, you must," the other boys insisted. Kojo gave in and, unwillingly, took a little nitrate for some gunpowder experiments which he was carrying out at home.

"Someone," the look-out called.

The boys dispersed in a moment. Sorie swilled out his mouth at the sink with some water. Mr. Abu, the lab attendant, entered and observed the innocent collective expression of the class. He glared round suspiciously and sniffed the air. It was a physics experiment, but the place smelled chemical. However, Vernier came in then. After asking if anyone was in difficulties, and finding that no one could momentarily think up anything, he retired to his chair and settled down to an article on Christian reunion, adjusting his spectacles and thoughtfully sucking an empty tooth-socket.

Towards the end of the period, the class collected around Vernier and gave in their results, which were then discussed. One of the more political boys asked Vernier: if dark surfaces gave out more heat, was that why they all had black faces in West Africa? A few boys giggled. Basu looked down and tapped his clubfoot embarrassedly on the floor. Vernier was used to questions of this sort from the senior boys. He never committed himself as he was getting near retirement and his pension, and became more guarded each year. He sometimes even feared that Simpson had spies among the boys.

"That may be so, although the opposite might be more convenient."

Everything in science had a loophole, the boys thought, and said so to Vernier.

"Ah! that is what is called research," he replied, enigmatically.

Sorie asked a question. Last time, they had been shown that an electric spark with hydrogen and oxygen atoms formed water. Why was not that method used to provide water in town at the height of the dry season when there was an acute water shortage?

"It would be too expensive," Vernier replied, shortly. He disliked Sorie, not because of his different religion, but because he thought that Sorie was a bad influence and also asked ridiculous questions.

Sorie persisted. There was plenty of water during the rainy season. It could be split by lightning to hydrogen and oxygen in October and the gases compressed and stored, then changed back to water in March during the shortage. There was a faint ripple of applause from Sorie's admirers.

"It is an impracticable idea," Vernier snapped.

The class dispersed and started walking back across the hot grass. Kojo and Bandele heaved sighs of relief and joined Sorie's crowd which was always the largest.

"Science is a bit of a swindle," Sorie was saying. "I do not for a moment think that Vernier believes any of it himself," he continued. "Because, if he does, why is he always reading religious books?"

"Come back, all of you, come back!" Mr Abu's stentorian voice rang out, across to them.

They wavered and stopped. Kojo kept walking on in a blind panic.

"Stop," Bandele hissed across. "You fool." He stopped, turned and joined the returning crowd, loosely followed by Bandele. Abu joined Vernier on the platform. The loose semicircle of boys faced them.

"Mr. Abu just found this in the waste bin," Vernier announced, grey with anger. He held up the two broken halves of the thermometer. "It must be due to someone from this class as the number of thermometers was checked before being put out."

A little wind gusted in through the window and blew the silence heavily this way and that.

"Who?"

No one answered. Vernier looked round and waited.

"Since no one has owned up, I am afraid I shall have to detain you for an hour after school as punishment," said Vernier.

There was a murmur of dismay and anger. An important soccer house-match was scheduled for that afternoon. Some boys put their hands up and said that they had to play in the match.

"I don't care," Vernier shouted. He felt, in any case, that too much time was devoted to games and not enough to work.

He left Mr. Abu in charge and went off to fetch his things from the main building.

"We shall play 'Bible and Key,'" Abu announced as soon as Vernier had left. Kojo had been afraid of this and new beads of perspiration sprang from his troubled brow. All the boys knew the details. It was a method of finding out a culprit by divination. A large doorkey was placed between the leaves of a Bible at the New Testament passage where Ananias and Sapphira were struck dead before the Apostles for lying, and the Bible suspended by two bits of string tied to both ends of the key. The combination was held up by someone and the names of all present were called out in turn. When that of the sinner was called, the Bible was expected to turn round and round violently and fall.

Now Abu asked for a Bible. Someone produced a copy. He opened the first page and then shook his head and handed it back. "This won't do," he said, "it's a Revised Version; only the genuine Word of God will give us the answer."

An Authorized King James Version was then produced and he was satisfied. Soon he had the contraption fixed up. He looked round the semicircle from Sorie at one end, through the others, to Bandele, Basu, and Kojo at the other, near the door.

"You seem to have an honest face," he said to Kojo. "Come and hold it." Kojo took the ends of the string gingerly with both hands, trembling slightly.

Abu moved over to the low window and stood at attention, his sharp profile outlined against the red hibiscus flowers, the green trees, and the molten sky. The boys watched anxiously. A black-bodied lizard scurried up a wall and started nodding its pink head with grave impartiality.

Abu fixed his ageing bloodshot eyes on the suspended Bible. He spoke hoarsely and slowly:

*"Oh, Bible, Bible on a key,*
*Kindly tell it unto me,*
*By swinging slowly round and true,*
*To whom this sinful act is due...."*

He turned to the boys and barked out their names in a parade-ground voice, beginning with Sorie and working his way round, looking at the Bible after each name.

To Kojo, trembling and shivering as if ice-cold water had been thrown over him, it seemed as if he had lost all power and that some gigantic being stood behind him holding up his tired aching elbows. It seemed to him as if the key and Bible had taken on a life of their own, and he watched with fascination the whole combination moving slowly, jerkily, and rhythmically in short arcs as if it had acquired a heart-beat.

"Ayo Sogbenri, Sonnir Kargbo, Oji Ndebu." Abu was coming to the end now. "Tommy Longe, Ajayi Cole, Bandele Fagb..."

Kojo dropped the Bible. "I am tired," he said, in a small scream. "I am tired."

"Yes, he is," Abu agreed, "but we are almost finished; only Bandele and Basu are left."

"Pick up that book, Kojo, and hold it up again." Bandele's voice whipped through the air with cold fury. It sobered Kojo and he picked it up.

"Will you continue please with my name, Mr. Abu?" Bandele asked, turning to the window.

"Go back to your place quickly, Kojo," Abu said. "Vernier is coming. He might be vexed. He is a strongly religious man and so does not believe in the Bible-and-Key ceremony.

Kojo slipped back with sick relief, just before Vernier entered.

In the distance the rest of the school were assembling for closing prayers. The class sat and stood around the blackboard and demonstration bench in attitudes of exasperation, resignation, and self-righteous indignation. Kojo's heart was beating so loudly that he was surprised no one else heard it.

*"Once to every man and nation*
*Comes the moment to decide..."*

The closing hymn floated across to them, interrupting the still afternoon.

Kojo got up. He felt now that he must speak the truth, or life would be intolerable ever afterwards. Bandele got up swiftly before him. In fact, several things seemed to happen all at the same time. The rest of the class stirred. Vernier looked up from a book review which he had started reading. A butterfly, with black and gold wings, flew in and sat on the edge of the blackboard, flapping its wings quietly and waiting too.

"Basu was here first before any of the class," Bandele said firmly.

Everyone turned to Basu, who cleared his throat.

"I was just going to say so myself, sir," Basu replied to Vernier's inquiring glance.

"Pity you had no thought of it before," Vernier said, dryly. "What were you doing here?"

"I missed the previous class, so I came straight to the lab and waited. I was over there by the window, trying to look at the blue sky. I did not break the thermometer, sir."

A few boys tittered. Some looked away. The others muttered. Basu's breath always smelt of onions, but although he could play no games, some boys liked him and were kind to him in a tolerant way.

"Well if you did not, someone did. We shall continue with the detention."

Vernier noticed Abu standing by. "You need not stay, Mr. Abu," he said to him. "I shall close up. In fact, come with me now and I shall let you out through the back gate."

He went out with Abu.

When he had left, Sorie turned to Basu and asked mildly:

"You are sure you did not break it?"

"No, I didn't."

"He did it," someone shouted.

"But what about the Bible-and-key?" Basu protested. "It did not finish. Look at him." He pointed to Bandele.

"I was quite willing for it to go on," said Bandele. "You were the only one left."

Someone threw a book at Basu and said, "Confess!"

Basu backed on to a wall. "To God, I shall call the police if anyone strikes me," he cried fiercely.

"He thinks he can buy the police," a voice called.

"That proves it," someone shouted from the back.

"Yes, he must have done it," the others said, and they started throwing books at Basu. Sorie waved his arm for them to stop, but they did not. Books, corks, boxes of matches rained on Basu. He bent his head and shielded his face with his bent arm.

"I did not do it. I swear I did not do it. Stop it, you fellows," he moaned over and over again. A small cut had appeared on his temple and he was bleeding. Kojo sat quietly for a while. Then a curious hum started to pass through him, and his hands began to tremble, his armpits to feel curiously wetter. He turned round and picked up a book and flung it with desperate force at Basu, and then another. He felt somehow that there was an awful swelling of guilt which he could only shed by punishing himself through hurting someone. Anger and rage against everything different seized him, because if everything and everyone had been the same, somehow he felt nothing would have been wrong and they would all have been happy. He was carried away now by a torrent which swirled and pounded. He felt that somehow Basu was in the wrong, must be in the wrong, and if he hurt him hard enough he would convince the others and therefore himself that he had not broken the thermometer and that he had never done anything wrong. He groped for something bulky enough to throw, and picked up the Bible.

"Stop it," Vernier shouted through the open doorway. "Stop it, you hooligans, you beasts."

They all became quiet and shamefacedly put down what they were going to throw. Basu was crying quietly and hopelessly, his thin body shaking.

"Go home, all of you, go home. I am ashamed of you." His black face shone with anger. "You are an utter disgrace to your nation and to your race."

They crept away, quietly, uneasily, avoiding each other's eyes, like people caught in a secret passion.

Vernier went to the first-aid cupboard and started dressing Basu's wounds.

Kojo and Bandele came back and hid behind the door, listening. Bandele insisted that they should.

Vernier put Basu's bandaged head against his waistcoat and dried the boy's tears with his handkerchief, gently patting his shaking shoulders.

"It wouldn't have been so bad if I had done it, sir," he mumbled, snuggling his head against Vernier, "but I did not do it. I swear to God I did not."

"Hush, hush," said Vernier comfortingly.

"Now they will hate me even more," he moaned.

"Hush, hush."

"I don't mind the wounds so much, they will heal."

"Hush, hush."

"They've missed the football match and now they will never talk to me again, oh-ee, oh-ee, why have I been so punished?"

"As you grow older," Vernier advised, "you must learn that men are punished not always for what they do, but often for what people think they will do, or for what they are. Remember that and you will find it easier to forgive them. 'To thine own self be true!' " Vernier ended with a flourish, holding up his clenched fist in a mock dramatic gesture, quoting from the Shakespeare examination set-book for the year and declaiming to the dripping taps and empty benches and still afternoon, to make Basu laugh.

Basu dried his eyes and smiled wanly and replied: " 'And it shall follow as the night the day.' Hamlet, Act One, Scene Three, Polonius to Laertes."

"There's a good chap. First Class Grade One. I shall give you a lift home."

Kojo and Bandele walked down the red laterite road together, Kojo dispiritedly kicking stones into the gutter.

"The fuss they made over a silly old thermometer," Bandele began.

"I don't know, old man, I don't know," Kojo said impatiently.

They had both been shaken by the scene in the empty lab. A thin invisible wall of hostility and mistrust was slowly rising between them.

"Basu did not do it, of course," Bandele said.

Kojo stopped dead in his tracks. "Of course he did not do it," he shouted; "we did it."

"No need to shout, old man. After all, it was your idea."

"It wasn't," Kojo said furiously. "You suggested we try it."

"Well, you started the argument. Don't be childish." They tramped on silently, raising small clouds of dust with their bare feet.

"I should not take it too much to heart," Bandele continued. "That chap Basu's father hoards foodstuff like rice and palm oil until there is a shortage and then sells them at high prices. The police are watching him."

"What has that got to do with it?" Kojo asked.

"Don't you see, Basu might quite easily have broken that thermometer. I bet he has done things before that we have all been punished for." Bandele was emphatic.

They walked on steadily down the main road of the town, past the Syrian and Lebanese shops crammed with knick-knacks and rolls of cloth, past a large Indian shop with dull red carpets and brass trays displayed on its windows, carefully stepping aside in the narrow road as the British officials sped by in cars to their hill-station bungalows for lunch and siesta.

Kojo reached home at last. He washed his feet and ate his main meal for the day. He sat about heavily and restlessly for some hours. Night soon fell with its usual swiftness, at six, and he finished his homework early and went to bed.

Lying in bed he rehearsed again what he was determined to do the next day. He would go up to Vernier:

"Sir," he would begin, "I wish to speak with you privately."

"Can it wait?" Vernier would ask.

"No, sir," he would say firmly, "as a matter of fact it is rather urgent."

Vernier would take him to an empty classroom and say, "What is troubling you, Kojo Ananse?"

"I wish to make a confession, sir. I broke the thermometer yesterday." He had decided he would not name Bandele; it was up to the latter to decide whether he would lead a pure life.

Vernier would adjust his slipping glasses up his nose and think. Then he would say:

"This is a serious matter, Kojo. You realize you should have confessed yesterday?"

"Yes, sir, I am very sorry."

"You have done great harm, but better late than never. You will, of course, apologize in front of the class and particularly to Basu who has shown himself a finer chap than all of you."

"I shall do so, sir."

"Why have you come to me now to apologize? Were you hoping that I would simply forgive you?"

"I was hoping you would, sir. I was hoping you would show your forgiveness by beating me."

Vernier would pull his glasses up his nose again. He would move his tongue inside his mouth reflectively. "I think you are right. Do you feel you deserve six strokes or nine?"

"Nine, sir."

"Bend over!"

Kojo had decided he would not cry because he was almost a man.

Whack! Whack!!

Lying in bed in the dark thinking about it all as it would happen tomorrow, he clenched his teeth and tensed his buttocks in imaginary pain.

Whack! Whack!! Whack!!!

Suddenly, in his little room, under this thin cotton sheet, he began to cry. Because he felt the sharp lancing pain already cutting into him. Because of Basu and Simpson and the thermometer. For all the things he wanted to do and be which would never happen. For all the good men they had told them about, Jesus Christ, Mohammed, and George Washington who never told a lie. For Florence Nightingale and David Livingstone. For Kagawa, the Japanese man, for Gandhi, and for Kwegyir Aggrey, the African. Oh-ee, oh-ee. Because he knew he would never be as straight and strong and true as the school song said they should be. He saw, for the first time, what this thing would be like, becoming a man. He touched the edge of an inconsolable eternal grief. Oh-ee, oh-ee; always, he felt, always I shall be a disgrace to the nation and the race.

His mother passed by his bedroom door, slowly dragging her slippered feet as she always did. He pushed his face into his wet pillow to stifle his sobs, but she had heard him. She came in and switched on the light.

"What is the matter with you, my son?"

He pushed his face farther into his pillow.

"Nothing," he said, muffled and choking.

"You have been looking like a sick fowl all afternoon," she continued.

She advanced and put the back of her moist cool fingers against the side of his neck.

"You have got fever," she exclaimed. "I'll get something from the kitchen."

When she had gone out, Kojo dried his tears and turned the dry side of the pillow up. His mother reappeared with a thermometer in one hand and some quinine mixture in the other.

"Oh, take it away, take it away," he shouted, pointing to her right hand and shutting his eyes tightly.

"All right, all right," she said, slipping the thermometer into her bosom.

He is a queer boy, she thought, with pride and a little fear as she watched him drink the clear bitter fluid.

She then stood by him and held his head against her broad thigh as he sat up on the low bed, and she stroked his face. She knew he had been crying but did not ask him why, because she was sure he would not tell her. She knew he was learning, first slowly and now quickly, and she would soon cease to be his mother and be only one of the womenfolk in the family. Such a short time, she thought, when they are really yours and tell you everything. She sighed and slowly eased his sleeping head down gently.

The next day Kojo got to school early, and set to things briskly. He told Bandele that he was going to confess but would not name him. He half hoped he would join him. But Bandele had said, threateningly, that he had better not mention his name, let him go and be a Boy Scout on his own. The sneer strengthened him and he went off to the lab. He met Mr. Abu and asked for Vernier. Abu said Vernier was busy and what was the matter, anyhow.

"I broke the thermometer yesterday," Kojo said in a businesslike manner.

Abu put down the glassware he was carrying.

"Well, I never!" he said. "What do you think you will gain by this?"

"I broke it," Kojo repeated.

"Basu broke it," Abu said impatiently. "Sorie got him to confess and Basu himself came here this morning and told the science master and myself that he knew now that he had knocked the thermometer by mistake when he came in early yesterday afternoon. He had not turned round to look, but he had definitely heard a tinkle as he walked by. Someone must have picked it up and put it in the waste bin. The whole matter is settled, the palaver finished."

He tapped a barometer on the wall and, squinting, read the pressure. He turned again to Kojo.

"I should normally have expected him to say so yesterday and save you boys missing the game. But there you are," he added, shrugging and trying to look reasonable, "you cannot hope for too much from a Syrian boy."

# Limbo

## EDDIE STACK

Sounds from the town seeped through the tall Monastery windows and mingled with the Hail Mary. The whine of the sawmill, milk churns rattling home from the creamery. Horse carts creaking. Motor cars honking, people hailing each other. An assurance that there was another world out there after school. Some day, the Monastery would only be a memory. But now we were having a prayer break with Brother Mahon.

Back at class he resumes the tirade, prancing around the room like Groucho Marx. Mahoney hears the little rattle as he passes and writes TABLETS on the cover of his grammar book. I make a check mark with my finger: Brother was back on the tablets alright, it was written all over the Monastery.

"The trouble with ye is that ye don't want to learn," he fumed. "Now it isn't the lack of brains that's effectin' ye . . . and I'm sayin' that in plain English so that ye'll understand me . . . no . . . ye have brains alright . . . but ye're as lazy as Sin."

He halted behind the table and waved a bundle of homework copies like a tomahawk. He glared at us and asked,

"Have ye any shame?"

Then he closed his eyes and leaned forward on his tip-toes. A smile ran around the class.

"Alright," he whispered, dropping the bundle of blue copy books on the table with a dull thud. "Alright. Now a simple three-page composition called 'What I Can See from My Front Door' is not a lot to ask twenty hardy young fifteen-year-old fellows to do . . . I was making it easy for ye." He paused and his eyes shot open.

"But such . . . such utter trash," he wailed. "Such utter filth . . . I have never read in my entire life. Stop grinning Horan! I'll wipe that leer from your puss when your turn comes and you can be sure of that my boy!"

Brother Mahon could go any way with the tablets. Sometimes he jumped over desks three at a time, kicked our school bags and glared at us like he said God would on the Last Day. Other times he could be great fun and tell us stories about the world and how happy he was to be a monk. One day he played the whistle in class and we sang rebel songs, but that only happened once. It was hard to tell how the dice might roll with the tablets. But things were looking grey today.

Today he had no hope for us. He said we had nothing to look forward to but *an Bád Bán*—the emigration boat. We were born to emigrate, he said it was in our blood. We were not worth educating—sons of small farmers and publicans, we were the flotsam left behind by the tide. His eyes closed slowly and he beckoned us to stand. Another Hail Mary for Our Lady smiling in the corner.

Brother Mahon rapped the copy books against the table.

"I have a few right gems here. First, O'Loughlin's. Where is O'Loughlin?"

"Here brother."

"O'Loughlin . . . what in Hell's Blue Blazes are you doing sitting in Friel's desk?"

"Brother O'Brien put me here."

"Am I Brother O'Brien? Am I? Is this Brother O'Brien's class? Come up here near me! And stay in your own sty in future!"

O'Loughlin moved like a defendant crossing the courtroom.

"Now," began Brother Mahon, "we all know that Master O'Loughlin is descended from a great line of bards. His family were once Chief Bards to the Earl of Killty." The eyes closed slowly. "But that was a long time ago. Now O'Loughlin . . . tell us where you live."

"Castletown brother."

"Louder."

"CASTLETOWN."

"Now O'Loughlin, if you live in Castletown, how in the name of God and his Blessed Mother can you see the Aran Islands from your front door? And before you answer, spell Island?"

"O-i-l-a-n-d."

"Dooney. Spell Island for your cousin."

"I-s-l-a-n-d."

"Now O'Loughlin. Remember that...you glugger head. But now, tell us how you can see Aran from your front door."

"I was just using my imagination," he muttered.

"Well don't bother to use your imagination...use your brains instead. Sit down and give me peace."

He made exceptions for O'Loughlin who had an uncle in the order. O'Loughlin was timid. But not so his cousin Fanta Dooney.

"Dooney did you write this?"

"I did brother."

"Are you sure you didn't get a bit of help from someone."

"No brother—I mean yes brother."

"Which is it?"

"I did it myself brother."

"Hand me up a copy without paw marks the next time."

Coyne was nibbling paper when his turn came.

"Coyne you fathead!" bellowed the monk. "Stop chewing the cud like a good bullock."

Coyne was a nervous wreck and fidgeted with the piece of paper he had been nibbling. A white envelope with a note from his mother which he handed to the monk.

"What is it this time?" he mocked. "Ye ran out of candles? Or have you given me that excuse already?"

Brother Mahon knew that Dada Coyne drank the creamery check every month and was more often in court than most lawyers. Willie could only muster up a half page about a view that was part of a nightmare. Brother Mahon read the note, closed his eyes and whispered—

"Take this copy back and have a full page for me by Friday."

He beckoned us to rise for another prayer.

A few copies skimmed through the air, nothing of great substance, fair attempts conceded the monk. Then there was Murphy's. Waving Murphy's copy, he glanced around the room. Murphy had switched seats and was now sitting at Clancy's desk.

"Murphy! Yes you! Get back to your own stable. What in the name of God are you doing in Clancy's seat?"

He didn't answer, just flashed a grin and zipped back to his own perch. Murphy was worldwise, smoked Woodbines, drank beer, backed horses and played poker. For him school was a place to pass adolescence, punch in time between summers and getting wiser in the ways of the outside world. He had run away from three boarding schools before joining our team, a high-risk pupil, even though he was the sergeant's son. He had the finest of vistas from his front door—his house looked down on the town and the strand. But he ignored it all and wrote about the Monastery instead. Brother Mahon cleared his throat and read in a mocking voice:

*"The Monastery was built in 1829 by a band of monks from Dublin. It has very big gardens and one time the monks used to make cider which they sold. The monastery is across the road from the dancehall..."*

He shook his head.

"I was waiting for him to tell me that the *band* of monks played in the dancehall. Trash! Murphy, what in the name of God has any of this tripe to do with anything?"

Murphy shrugged and smiled as if saying—life's like that. A nervous titter escaped from the back bench and Kerrigan was ordered to stand at the head of the room and face the statue of Our Lady.

"It's the likes of you Kerrigan who encourage Murphy to dish up this tripe. And I wouldn't mind...but nowhere does he mention the name of the monastery—Murphy...stand up. What is the name of this school?"

"Saint...ahmm the Monastery."

The monk looked at us, his jury, and shook his head.

"Saint Patrick's!" he howled, arching his back like a cat. "But what does it matter to you? Your father'll find your way into some job. Sit down you clown."

Malone's copy fell apart as it sailed over our heads, cover departing from body. Mine was next, then Friel's, then Horan's.

"Horan come up here to me. Do you hear me? Come up!"

Horan edged to the head of the room and the monk withdrew the black leather cosh from his robe.

"Out with it."

Horan's hand trembled and the monk lashed it six times, becoming more demonic with every stroke. His eyes were blazing and his head and neck glowed when he turned around.

"Horan," he panted, "handed me up a yarn about a football match. It had nothing to do with his front door, he titled it 'A day I will always remember.'"

The taste of blood put Brother Mahon into another world. The animal in him was roused and he became a schoolboy's nightmare. His nostrils flared and he looked possessed, satanic. The voice got shriller and he strutted around the room pelting abuse at us. We were failures, and if we were the best our parents could produce, then God help Ireland. But while we were in class we would pay attention to him and do the correct homework, not like Horan.

He rummaged through the copies. He was frantic and scattered them all over the table until he pulled Kerrigan's from the chaos.

"Where are you Kerrigan?"

"Behind you brother."

"Well stand over here where we can see you ... and don't always be looking like a moon calf. Kerrigan—what is the meaning of this drivel? Where do you live?"

"Boland's Lane."

"Boland's Lane what?"

"Boland's Lane, brother."

"Alright. And have you anything else to write about but a ... a tinkers' brawl? Hah? How dare you hand me up this ... this drivel about two families of tinkers murdering each other!"

"That's all I could think of ... we had Yanks home from Boston ..."

"Shut up you lout and come here to me!"

Brother Mahon gaffed him by the ear and lifted him like a piece of meat. Kerrigan pleaded—

"Brother, brother ..."

"Now listen to this all of ye! Kerrigan is the type of fool who is a cute fool. When he leaves here in a couple of years what will he do? Like his father before him, his first port of call will be the dole office. Then he'll put his feet up, warm his toes to the fire and wait for Wednesday—dole day. Alright ... he'll get married, get a council house, free milk and shoes. His wife will give him a child every year and when they're crying for attention, our hero will be down the town—strapping pints of porter or holding up Coleman's Corner with his broad back, passing smart remarks to other cute fools like himself. Alright?"

Kerrigan wept and wriggled with rage. He staggered loose with a scream and Brother Mahon jumped away from him.

"Go back to your hovel Kerrigan."

The class was battered, beaten and humiliated. The monk closed his eyes slowly and whispered that we could always pray. Prayer could move mountains and even get us to heaven—if we were lucky. But we were too lazy to pray, he said softly. And everything began with prayer. If we didn't pray right, then nothing could be right.

From there he wandered off to the foreign missions and explained the great work monks were doing harvesting souls in darkest Africa. He wondered aloud if any of us would like [to] take up the work. But our heros were not in the black cloth. Anyway, seams of outside world had already permeated the class. Cigarette smoking was rife, swearing was commonplace and girls came up in conversation—there were few vocations here.

A cloud came over his brow when he picked the last blue copy book from the table. The main feature.

"Stand up Gregory McNamara and face the class. Now McNamara, I know all your brothers and those who went before them, but you are the worst of the brood, you great big jackass. What in the name of God do you mean by handing me up a shovel of dung like this for my breakfast? What?" His eyes darted from pupil to copy.

"A simple essay that a nine-year-old child in the heart of London could write...and a fifteen-year-old *sutach* from Ballyglan can only come up with this...this manure."

McNamara was doomed for the back streets of Soho like his brothers before him, Brother Mahon told us. Bound for sleaze and slaughter. Not even a flicker of hope for him.

"Stand to attention McNamara and face me...and before we start...the next time you hand me up a copy, give me one without the butter and jam...spare the butter and jam for your lunch. Alright? Alright, to begin at the beginning:

"*'It was only early yesterday morning that I was wondering what kind of view we would have if we had a front door to our house. We have only a back door to the kitchen...'* Alright? So far, so good...but listen to this... *'Our house faces north...'* spelled n-o-r-d... *'in the direction of Russia where Napoleon was born.'*" His voice trailed off in horror.

"I'll read that again, just in case ye didn't hear it... *'in the direction of Russia where Napoleon was born...'* and listen to what comes next... *'The great monk Rasputin was Napoleon's son and a neighbor of my grandmothers knew Rasputin.'*"

A red flag to a bull. Brother Mahon was aghast. He closed the eyes and seemed to be praying for patience, or the school bell or maybe a tablet.

"That's true," bungled McNamara. "Oh God...my grandmother told me that."

"You bloody bogman!" bellowed Brother Mahon, tears in his eyes. "You Heretic! How dare you insist that Napoleon was born in Russia...or that he sired Rasputin."

McNamara blushed and looked towards the Blessed Virgin. The monk was breathing heavily, his knobbly fists clenched white.

"And on top of all that heresy, McNamara drops this bombshell on me... *'they make great vodka in Russia.'* They make great vodka in Russia! What in the name of God and his Blessed Mother has all or any of this to do with the great view you have from the front door ye don't have? Answer me McNamara you ass!"

McNamara awkwardly shifted his weight from foot to foot and stared at his desk. Brother Mahon was tortured. Mention of drink, Rasputin and red Russia in the same page was the height of treason. He dabbed the beads of sweat from his brow.

"ANSWER ME!" he screamed, stamping his foot.

"I was stuck for something to say," McNamara said suddenly—hoping to stonewall the charging monk.

Gregory ducked Brother Mahon's fist and slid under the desk like an eel. The monk ordered him to stand by the wall, firing in threats of expulsion and terms in hell. He moved in on his prey and lashed out his boot as McNamara darted beneath the desks. We scattered out of their way and grouped at the head of the class room.

"Jaysuz lads," whispered Murrihy, "but this is serious."

"Come out of it McNamara! Out!" roared Brother Mahon, kicking over school bags and thumping desks.

"Come out of it and get up to the Superior you pagan!" He flushed McNamara from cover and lunged at him with a primeval groan. Suddenly, alarm flashed across Brother Mahon's face. We saw him stagger, then tumble heavily on the floor, brought down by Murphy's schoolbag. The door banged and McNamara was home. The monk was robbed of the kill.

Brother Mahon struggled to his feet and dusted himself. He stared at us, and looked bewildered, as if he had just fallen through the roof.

"What are ye doing standing there like a flock of sheep?" he demanded, "Go back to your seats! Quickly!"

We were only sitting down when he ordered us to stand and face the statue of the Blessed Virgin.

"We are now going to offer up a decade of the rosary for those in need," he said quietly, eyes closing slowly.

"In the name of the Father, the Son and the Holy Ghost." began Brother Mahon, tears rolling down his face.

# Revenge

## GEORGE MILBURN

We were all very proud when school opened again that Fall, because we were going into the sixth grade. The grades before the sixth were on the ground floor of the school building, but the sixth was upstairs with the higher grades. We had been wondering for a long time how it would feel, marching in from recess, to go on up the stairs instead of turning in at a room on the first floor. The year we were in the fifth we envied the sixth-graders almost as much as the eighth-graders envied the high-school freshmen.

There were other things that had made the sixth grade one that we were eager to be in. One thing was that we could have ink in the inkwells. Some of the desks in the fifth grade had nothing but round holes where the inkwells should have been, and we had kept the few inkwells there were stuffed with chewed-up paper. We had used only pencils. But in the sixth, we knew, we would use ink. That would be something new.

We had a new teacher from the State Normal School that year, too. We were curious about her, and the ones who had been lucky enough to get first sight of her were questioned anxiously. Already the rumor had gone around the school-yard that first day, telling that the new teacher was a funny looker, and that she wasn't in favor of whipping. That was good news for several of us. Miss Spandrel, the fifth-grade teacher, had been strong on whipping. Boys who knew said that she whipped harder than Professor Butler, the superintendent, who kept a length of rubber tubing in his desk drawer and used it to wear out anyone who was sent up to him.

The new sixth-grade teacher wasn't out to watch the lines pass that first morning. She was sitting at her desk when we marched in. We all took seats, some of which we had spotted the year before. We sat up very straight with our hands folded in front of us, fresh and clean for the first day of school, and very happy to be starting the sixth grade. The new teacher sat plucking her lower lip and looking us over distantly. We gazed back at her. She was a neat, starched woman, with a square-tipped pink nose and an upper lip too short to cover her teeth.

After she had looked at us a while, she said, "You two boys sitting in the back seats bring your books up here to the front seats. I know about boys who always take the back seats the first day of school. I like to have them up here by me."

We all laughed heartily at that, and Loppy Crashaw and Gus Belcher took their second-hand books and brand-new pencil tablets out of the back desks and came slowly up to the front of the room with them.

The new teacher went to the front blackboard and wrote, "*My* name is *Miss* Manchester," on it in round letters.

While she had her back turned, Loppy Crashaw, who was the meanest kid in our grade, tripped Gus Belcher. That made a big clatter, because Gus, the big cow, dropped all his books, and everyone began laughing again.

Miss Manchester turned around quickly and rapped on her desk with a ruler. We stopped laughing. She stood glaring at us so hard that her eyes, as round and hard blue as china taws, seemed ready to pop out of her head. Later we learned that glaring was one of Miss Manchester's punishment methods. We never did feel hurt by it. It only made her look funnier, her eyes starting out of their sockets like that. But as soon as we found that she meant it for punishment, to keep her from doing anything worse, we always tried to look shamed and uncomfortable when she glared at us.

She shifted her glare to Gus Belcher and she kept it on him until he had finished picking up his books and had taken a front seat. When everything was in order again, Miss Manchester said, "I may as well tell you at the beginning that I do not believe in whipping pupils. But that does not mean that I do not believe in punishment.

"I have my own system of punishments. Of course you all know that there are certain things we can't have. Among them are: whispering, chewing gum in the classroom, note writing, bringing candy, or marbles, or tops, or any kind of plaything into the classroom, throwing paper wads, speaking out without permission, using ugly words or names, such as liar and fool, and several other things which I shall mention later. I shall give demerits for each of these, one demerit for some offenses, as many as five demerits for others.

"When any pupil gets five demerits within one month, he will have shown that he can't behave as a big boy or girl should, and I shall punish him just as Mrs. Wellborn punishes her little primary pupils downstairs. When any pupil gets five demerits he will be made to sit on the floor under my desk for two hours.

"When any pupil gets ten demerits in one month he will have to stay in after school and commit to memory twenty-five lines of poetry. They won't be these little short lines of poetry, either. Let me tell you that!

"When any pupil gets fifteen demerits he will have to stand at the front blackboard for one hour with the tip of his forefinger in a small chalk circle which I shall place up as high as he can reach, standing tiptoe." Miss Manchester went over and took a piece of chalk and high up on the blackboard she drew a circle about the size of a quarter. "And if any pupil lets his finger slip and smudges the circle," she went on, "that will add fifteen minutes more to the time he must stand there.

"Perhaps I should add here that I have some special punishments for special offenses. For example, when one of you is guilty of continual whispering, I shall seal your lips with a piece of adhesive plaster. I believe that that punishment is more effective than demerits for boys and girls who whisper."

Miss Manchester paused for a moment, and then, glaring hard at us all, she said in a slow,

tense voice, "*And* when any pupil gets *twenty* demerits before the end of the month, I shall send him in to have a little talk with Professor Butler, the superintendent."

What difference did it make if Miss Manchester didn't believe in whipping? We all knew what would happen to anyone who got sent in to have a little talk with Professor Butler.

### II

The school year hadn't got very far along before most of us were sick and tired of Miss Manchester and her new system of punishments. Sometimes, when our backs and legs were aching from the strain of standing tiptoe with our fingers in the chalk circle, or when the lines of *Hiawatha* wouldn't stick in our memories, we thought that whipping would have been much easier.

She was near-sighted, and she was always getting the wrong person. She wouldn't listen to any explanation.

"Why, I wasn't doing anything!" one of us would complain.

"Oh, so you weren't doing anything?" she would say. "Well, why weren't you, then? You're not coming to school to sit idle, are you?" And she would double the punishment.

The only boy in the room who escaped her, those first months, was Loppy Crashaw, and he was the meanest kid in our grade. He had had some kind of sickness when he was a baby, and one of his legs had never grown to full size. We called him Loppy because he was lopsided. But sometimes we wouldn't have minded being like him. He could do almost anything without fear of punishment. Teachers never had done anything to him, because he was crippled.

Back in the fifth grade Miss Spandrel thrashed all the other boys, but she never did lay a switch on Loppy. One day, in the fifth, Loppy kept shooting Gus Belcher with tinfoil wads. He shot them with a rubber band and they stung hard. Gus stood it as long as he could. Then he jumped up and knocked Loppy clear out of his seat. Miss Spandrel came over and grabbed Gus by the collar. She didn't ask any questions. She got out the bamboo stick and she whipped Gus until his stocking legs showed blood. "You great big brute!" she said. "I'll teach you not to strike a poor little crippled child!"

It didn't do any good for us to catch Loppy out and beat him up after school hours, because he always tattled, and that meant our getting whipped harder than ever when we came back to school the next day.

He was good in his books, and that gave him time to think up tricks to play while school was going on. Many of us suffered long hours with our fingers stretched up to the chalk circle for things that Loppy pulled. If he put a pin in the toe of his shoe and stuck somebody with it, the one who cried out in pain was the one who was punished. If he made a funny face that caused some girl to giggle, the girl was the one who stayed in after school. If he threw an apple core across the room, the one who got hit and yelled had to take the blame. Miss Manchester had put Loppy up in a front seat the first day of school, but he was too slick to let her see him do anything.

That was why the rest of us were tickled, even though it was too late then for us to get any great satisfaction out of it, when we heard how Loppy and Miss Manchester had been made victims of a strange revenge—strange, because neither the ones whom it caught, nor the one who caused it, knew that the score had been evened.

We never did forget the dirty trick Loppy Crashaw played on Rolland Gentry.

Rolland was a big country boy. He was five or six years older than any of the rest of us. His people had kept him out of school to pick cotton so much when he was little that he had got a late start. But he had his mind made up that he was going to get an education, and he came to town to school after he was almost ten years behind his grade. He was getting along fine, though, making two grades each year. He was passed on from the fifth to the sixth at Christmas, and Miss Manchester had told him that if he worked hard enough in the sixth he might be able to skip the seventh

grade altogether. Then he could go into high-school from the eighth at Christmas the next year and he would be almost up with pupils of his own age.

Rolland soon took his place as the brightest boy in our grade. He always had all the problems in arithmetic, he made 100 in spelling every month, and he answered questions in geography and physiology that stumped the rest of the class.

But Rolland looked funny sitting up there in the back seat, way too small for him, and the desk too low. Even if he was taller than we were, we thought that he was a big sissy. He had kidney trouble, and we thought that that was a sissy thing to have. He was pale and blue-veined, with blond, curly hair and long, nervous fingers. He had won a gold medal for penmanship in the county contest the Spring before, and he wore the medal on his coat lapel. He was so nervous he couldn't sit still when the teacher asked a question. He would wave his hand wildly. The teacher wouldn't call on him often, because she knew that he always had the right answer. He never swore, or fought, or played marbles for keeps on the playground. Rolland was too nice.

Loppy Crashaw had been the brightest boy in the sixth grade until Rolland came up from the fifth that Christmas. Loppy had even made the highest grades in penmanship. His sentences were almost exactly like those in the copybook. Then when Rolland Gentry came up from the fifth it wasn't long before Loppy had to take second place in everything. That made him dislike Rolland. He was always picking on the big country boy. He knew that Rolland was too goodie-goodie to do anything back, even if he was big enough to clean up on any two of us.

One of Miss Manchester's new methods was the way she had for letting us go out. She had a little wooden paddle hung up by the door. On one side it had "In" printed, and on the other side "Out." When one of us wanted to be excused we had to turn up the side that had "Out" on it, and then no one else could go out until that one had come back and turned up the "In" side again.

Miss Manchester said, when she was explaining this new system to us, "Now in the lower grades, I know, you have been accustomed to holding up two fingers when you wished to be excused. But in the sixth, of course, we are getting a little more grown up, and we can adopt a new method. More than one person's being out of the room at a time leads to disorder and confusion. So when the 'Out' side is showing, you all will know that some person is out of the room, and you must wait until he or she returns. So please do not hold up your hands to be excused any more, because only one person will be permitted to leave the room at a time."

One day, just as the study hour before noon was beginning, the "In" side of the paddle was showing, and Rolland Gentry left his seat and started toward the door. But Loppy Crashaw looked back and saw him coming down the aisle. He jumped up from his front seat and turned the paddle and went limping out.

Rolland went quietly back to his seat. Miss Manchester was sitting at her desk, reading, and she did not see what had happened.

Loppy stayed and stayed. Rolland began twisting around in his seat and sliding back and forth. Finally he raised his hand with two fingers up. Miss Manchester glanced up from her book and frowned and shook her head. Rolland put his hand down.

After a few minutes he put it up again, and began snapping his fingers. Miss Manchester looked up from her book again, glared hard, and said, "No!" loudly. Then she looked down at her book again and went on reading.

Rolland shuddered violently. All at once he put his head down on his arms and began sobbing. Miss Manchester snapped her book to. Then she went back and stood by Rolland's desk. She could see that she was too late. There was a big puddle on the floor. But she said softly, "You may leave the room now, if you wish to, Rolland."

But Rolland wouldn't raise his head. He kept his face buried in his arms, sobbing, a big boy like that.

Loppy Crashaw came back just before the bell rang for noon. Miss Manchester turned her glare on him. "How long have you been out, young man?" she said.

"Just a few minutes," Loppy said.

"Well, you stayed out too long, and I'm going to give you two demerits."

When the bell rang for noon, Miss Manchester said, "Attention!" but Rolland did not raise his head.

"Turn!" said Miss Manchester. We pivoted our legs out into the aisles, but Rolland didn't move.

"Stand! March!" said Miss Manchester, clapping her hands for the march-step.

When we glanced back, leaving the room, we saw Rolland still hunched up with his face hidden on his desk. That was the last time we ever saw him at school.

### III

Some of the older girls used to get up in the sixth-grade room and practice dancing in the latter part of the noon hour, before the teacher came in. They played the phonograph and kept a sharp look-out for Miss Manchester, who was a strict Baptist.

There were some good-sized girls in the sixth grade, and girls get interested in dancing before boys do. They would waltz around with an imaginary partner, sashaying up and down the aisles and around the front of the room, humming the tunes. We would make fun of them, but they would only make slapping motions at us, and go on. They didn't know how silly they looked.

One day in April, a few minutes before time for the last bell at noon, Loppy Crashaw went up to a big girl named Anna Lance, who was feisting around, trying to dance. He grabbed her around the waist, pretending that he was going to dance with her. Anna gave Loppy a big shove, but as he went stumbling backward, he yelled, "Oh, Anna's got on a corset! I felt it on her just then! Anna's got on a corset! Anna's got on a corset!"

About that time Miss Manchester came into the room. She grabbed Loppy by the shoulders and began shaking him. Loppy was so surprised he didn't know what to do. That was the first time any teacher had ever punished him. It was the first time he had ever been caught outright. He whimpered.

"You dirty-minded little *thing,* you!" said Miss Manchester. "I'll teach you that you can't talk that way to girls. Now you get under my desk there, and don't you come out until I give you permission."

She kept Loppy under her desk until recess time.

That same afternoon Miss Manchester was keeping some of us in after school for punishment. She had caught me chewing gum, and I had to write "I must not chew gum in the classroom" two hundred times.

Reverend Reynolds, the young man who had the Baptist pulpit for a while, used to come around to keep Miss Manchester company while she was keeping us in after school. He was there that afternoon, and they had been talking together in low voices. She was tidying up around her desk, straightening up the theme papers, emptying the pencil sharpener, and cleaning out the desk drawer, while she talked to the preacher.

I finished my two hundred sentences and came up to hand them in. When Miss Manchester took them, I said, "Gee, my arm is about give out from all that writing."

Reverend Reynolds frowned at me and said, "Any boy who takes the Name of the Lord in vain like that ought to be made to write the Third Commandment two hundred times."

I hadn't known that there was anything wrong with "Gee," (I didn't discover until later that it was short for "Jesus") and I was standing there trying to figure it out when Miss Manchester picked up her desk drawer, the wide, flat one that went under the top, and turned it upside down to shake the dust out of it.

We all three saw it at the same time: a sentence about Miss Manchester chalked across the bottom of the drawer. It had one word in it that caused the preacher and the teacher both to turn red. It was written in good handwriting, almost as

good as that in the copybook. Loppy Crashaw had been under the desk that afternoon, and, since Rolland Gentry had left school, Loppy was the only boy in the room who could make such a graceful capital F.

Miss Manchester put the drawer back in her desk quickly, and, with her face as red as a beet, said to me, "You may go."

The next morning when school took up, Miss Manchester glared at Loppy for several minutes. Then she said, "Young man, your dirty-mindedness is going to get you into very serious trouble one of these days."

"What about?" Loppy asked boldly.

"You know what about," the teacher said, blushing.

The last week of school, a month later, we had an oral spelling examination. We were divided up into sides, standing along opposite walls of the room. Anna Lance was the last one left standing on her side, and she was standing near Loppy Crashaw's desk.

Anna Lance had spelled down all but two or three on the other side, but she was faltering because she felt her underpants slipping down. Finally they fell down around her ankles. Miss Manchester had her back turned, giving out a word to the other side. Anna quickly kicked the panties under Loppy Crashaw's desk. Loppy had already missed a word, and he was in his seat.

Nearly all of us saw what Anna had done, and we began to giggle. Miss Manchester stopped giving out words and came over to that side of the room. She looked down and saw the white drawers under Loppy's desk.

"What is this?" she said, dragging them out into the aisle with her toe.

"They're hers," Loppy said calmly, pointing to Anna.

"They are not!" Anna said loudly. She started crying. "He's been tormenting me with them. He just brought them to school to torment me. He's been tormenting me like that all year." Anna sobbed wildly.

"Why she's a big liar!" Loppy said.

"What was that word you used?" said Miss Manchester.

"I said, she's a liar," Loppy said firmly.

"Young man, do you remember what I told you about your dirty-mindedness getting you into very serious trouble some day? I've had some experience with your nasty tricks, myself. I haven't forgotten that vulgar sentence you wrote on the bottom of my desk drawer that day I put you under there."

"What sentence?"

"You know very well what sentence."

"I never wrote nothing on the bottom of your desk drawer."

Miss Manchester was aghast. "Oh, I suppose you're going to try to tell me that I'm storying, too," she said, sarcastically.

Loppy looked down at the floor. "You're lying if you say I wrote anything on the bottom of your desk drawer," he mumbled, but loud enough for everyone to hear.

That made Miss Manchester so mad she couldn't keep her feet still. "I heard what you said!" she cried. "I heard what you said, young man! There's a limit to what a teacher can put up with. Now you hustle right out and cut me some switches. There's only one punishment for a boy of your type."

That Spring the Ladies' Civic Club had planted shade tree slips all along the sides of the cement walk leading up to the school building. They were Lombardy poplars. Shade trees were scarce around there, and the *Weekly Recorder* had given the tree-planting a big write-up. When Loppy came back he had an armload of Lombardy poplar switches. They still had the nursery tags on them.

Miss Manchester shrieked, "Oh, what have you done! You nasty little brat, you! Don't you know that those shade tree slips cost three dollars apiece?"

Loppy let the bundle of switches fall clattering to the floor. "I cain't he'p what they cost," he said sullenly. "You told me to get switches, and them's switches, ain't they?"

Miss Manchester grabbed up one of the sticks and took hold of Loppy. She began striking him across the back. She had given him about three licks when he twisted out of her grasp. They stood there glaring at each other, both breathing hard and trembling.

"I never done nothing, and I ain't going to take any whupping off of you, you danged old fool!" Loppy yelled, "You and your new-fangled ideas. Pooh! I thought you wasn't in favor of whupping!"

"I'm not, but a good, sound thrashing is the only way to appeal to a boy like you," Miss Manchester said in a strained, high voice. "Come here to me!" She made a grab for Loppy, but he jumped nimbly out of reach. "Come here to me!" she shrilled.

"Yah, what do I want to come there to you for, you blamed old near-sighted fool, you! You won't lay hand on me!" Loppy turned and went limping toward the door.

"If you leave this room, I'll fail you!" Miss Manchester called after him. "If you go out of that door, you needn't come back!"

Loppy went on out and slammed the door behind him.

While this had been going on the rest of us had been sitting with our mouths open. Miss Manchester sat down at her desk. She was trembling so hard she couldn't hold a book. She turned her glare on us.

"I don't think any of you have any time to be idling," she said, "because we're having the final examination in arithmetic the first thing after recess."

None of us was prepared for the final examination in arithmetic, because it had been promised for the next day, the last day of school. We were frightened.

When we came in from afternoon recess Miss Manchester was writing the problems on the board. We were all feeling sick and weak, waiting to see how hard the examination was going to be. The first example looked pretty hard.

She had finished putting on two problems when the door flew open and in marched Mrs. Crashaw, a big, black-haired woman. Loppy followed along behind her.

"Did you strike this pore little cripple' child of mine?" said Mrs. Crashaw in a loud, trembling voice.

Miss Manchester was startled. "Why, I—" she said.

"Do you know what ought to be done with any grown woman that would whip a cripple' child?" Mrs. Crashaw stooped over and picked up one of the sticks from the bundle in the corner. She began switching Miss Manchester about the legs. Miss Manchester started screaming and grabbed Mrs. Crashaw by the hair.

Professor Butler, the superintendent, heard the screams and he came dashing into the room, his dyed, purplish-black pompadour waving and his glasses askew.

"Here, here! Ladies! Ladies! What's the meaning of this?" He thrust himself between Miss Manchester and Loppy's mother.

Mrs. Crashaw, with her hair all down, looked like a wild woman. She still held her switch. "I'll show *you* the meaning," she yelled and she turned around and started hitting Professor Butler. As soon as she got loose, Miss Manchester went running out of the room. Professor Butler turned and ran out too. Mrs. Crashaw ran after him, cutting at him with the switch.

We heard the door of Professor Butler's office bang to down at the end of the hall. Then we heard Mrs. Crashaw pounding on it, calling to them to let her in. No one laughed. Everyone sat very still for a while. Loppy was sitting at his desk, looking very solemn. Pretty soon Mrs. Crashaw came back down the hall and put her head in at the door. She said, "Come on, son." Loppy got up and picked up his books and went out.

We had started throwing chalk and whispering loudly by the time Professor Butler came back into the room.

"Miss Manchester is not feeling well," he said, "and she will not be able to give the final examination in arithmetic. But she asks me to tell you that you are all passed to the seventh grade next year." He smiled thinly. "So it will not be necessary for you to come back to school any more this term. Your report cards will be mailed out to your parents. Pass out quietly so as not to disturb the other rooms. Dismissed!"

## IV

Outside it was late May and the afternoon was warm. It was about three o'clock. When we came out of the school building into the bright air, we felt dizzy. We didn't even whoop because it was the end of school. Too much had happened that day. We were dazed by all that.

Gus Belcher said, "Let's go out to Edwards' tanks and go swimming."

None of us had been swimming that year, and two or three thought that the water was still too cold. But the rest of us scoffed at that. Everything was perfect that day. Everything had come out right. So we went on, five or six of us, walking out to Edwards' cattle pond.

We were still wearing our shoes and stockings. When we were about a mile out of town we sat down and pulled them off. We wriggled our tender toes in the warm dust as we walked.

We were cutting across a pasture when we saw a tall boy over in the next field, chopping cotton. He looked toward us and leaned on his hoe and called out, "Hi, there, you fellers!"

We walked over to the barb-wire fence, and when we got up close we saw that it was Rolland Gentry. It had been two months since we had last seen him, and he didn't look so sissified any more. When he pulled off his straw hat we saw that he had had his curly hair cropped close to his scalp. He was chewing a big quid of tobacco. But he was wearing his gold penmanship medal on his overall bib.

He came over to the fence where we were standing. "Hello, Rolland," we said. "Where have you been keeping yourself?"

"Oh, me, I been doing a little share-cropping. This here is my stand of cotton. And making some corn whiskey on the side. There's where the real jack is." He talked louder than he ever had before. He spurted tobacco juice a long way. He had got pretty tough and we were awed.

"Are you coming back to school next year, Rolland?" Gus Belcher asked him.

"Me! Naw, I'm not never coming back to school," he said. "I don't like them educated fools they got teaching over there. What does a man like me want with schooling?" He began cursing, calling Miss Manchester all kinds of names. We never had heard Rolland talk like that before.

We wanted to tell him about what had happened at school that afternoon, but he swore so hard it made us timid. We sought an opening. I asked him, meekly, "Say, Rolland, what did the teacher say to you that day you—aw, uh—that noon after all the rest of us had marched out?"

Rolland scowled. "She didn't say nothing to me, the damned old rip. She knew better than to,

because I was all set to get her told. She hung around awhile, like she wanted to make it up to me, but finally she went on off to dinner and left me there."

He chewed tobacco for a while and looked at us with squinted eyes. None of us dared say anything more about his shame.

"Well," he said musingly, "all I hope is one thing. All I hope is that the blamed old heifer found that about her what I chalked on the bottom of her desk drawer. I told her what she could do, all right. If she ever sees that, that'll fix her."

# CHAPTER 7

## REWARDS AND PRIVILEGES

Andrea Freud Loewenstein, "Awards"
Frances Silverberg, "Rebecca by Any Other Name"
Joanne S. Primoff, "Discipline"
Ann Patchett, "All Little Colored Children Should Play the Harmonica"
Nicholasa Mohr, "The Wrong Lunch Line"

The stories in this chapter concern the adjudication of rewards and privileges in school. In one way or another, the children in these stories find themselves excluded from the recognition available to others. Andrea Freud Loewenstein, Frances Silverberg, and Joanne S. Primoff describe children who strive to gain acceptance. The children in Ann Patchett's and Nicholasa Mohr's stories willingly step outside the established routes to reward and recognition in order to achieve their own goals and make their own judgments about what is worth striving for.

The chapter begins with Loewenstein's "Awards." Rachel, the narrating third-grader tells us in no uncertain words what she thinks about school prizes and the well-meaning adults who invent them:

> The most improvement. *Those words stuck in my throat like stone. I knew what they meant. . . . It was a fake award. . . .*
>
> *Grownups must have thought we were stupid, really, because they were always trying things like that, praising kids who hadn't done anything special and inventing fake awards for kids who didn't deserve them.*

The story reveals students' awareness of the ruses and manipulation sometimes used by teachers to motivate and encourage them.

Whereas "Awards" discusses awards in general, the next two stories, Silverberg's "Rebecca by Any Other Name" and Primoff's "Discipline," illustrate how prejudice can influence teachers' decisions. In the first one, Rebecca, a poor and studious Jewish girl who gets little support from her family or teacher, nonetheless invests a great amount of time in completing a class assignment. The teacher has promised the prize of a book to the student who draws the best map of the United States. She has also devised a plan to ensure a fairly judged contest. Yet ideals of fairness are stretched to the breaking point in this story of dedicated effort meeting the indifference caused by prejudice.

The teacher in Primoff's story is inclined to favor one of her students, Kenneth, a bright boy with "slicked-down hair, so clean and blond" in a school full of Italian immigrants. She is sure that he will be the school winner of the citywide contest for the best score on an examination on local government. Kenneth's main competitor is another one of her students, Angeline, the daughter of an Italian grocer who "spoke no English at all."

Kenneth, in fact, assumes he will win but events leading up to the examination and beyond cause the teacher to explore her biases, both her resistance to viewing the Italians as equals and her blindness to Kenneth's flaws.

Patchett's story deals with another type of reward: special opportunities for students with exceptional talent. Grover, a "colored" boy, surprises the school's white music teacher, Miss Neville, with his expressive and masterly playing of the harmonica. In the black community Grover is deemed as an entertainer, and he enjoys this role. As soon as she becomes aware of his enormous talent, Miss Neville begins to make plans for Grover. She offers "special opportunities" that would comandeer the development of his talent, a task he himself has managed magnificently up to this point without teachers. Grover's response to this opportunity ends the story.

"The Wrong Lunch Line" relates a less momentous but nonetheless painful incident: a Puerto Rican girl is invited by Mildred, her Jewish friend, to partake of the special Passover menu offered by the school. They are both excited to share this special occasion but the actions of classmates and teachers shame and ostracize them. Still, the two girls turn out to be more sensible than the adults who seek to teach them. Their sense of humor and resilient spirits put the incident in perspective and they maintain their interest in each other's heritage.

A teacher's power is too often used selectively to benefit some children and exclude others. These stories illustrate mistreated students' reactions: some rise above the callousness of their teachers, whereas others are crushed by it—but all suffer confusion and pain in the experience.

# Awards

## ANDREA FREUD LOEWENSTEIN

By the third grade we all knew, despite the evidence of our own sense, that boys were smarter than girls. Science had proven it. The only reason all the smartest kids in our class were girls was that girls matured earlier. By the seventh and eighth grades, the grownups assured us, Elizabeth Carlson and Susan Doralski would already have passed their prime and would have to yield up their places to some hitherto undistinguished boy, like Chester Laughton or Charlie Nails, who might even go straight on to be President, while Elizabeth and Susan could only hope to wait at home for them, ironing their shirts and packing their kids' lunchboxes with nutritional snacks.

Our head start on maturity, although nothing to write home about in the long run, was at least supposed to provide us girls with good penmanship, a skill which boys were supposed to lack. The monthly Penmanship Award was generally acknowledged to be a contest for the girls. It was the only contest, except for sports, that involved collective rather than individual achievement. It was also the only one in which the high and low classes competed against each other. The way it worked was that on a certain day of the month, every child in every class was asked to copy out the same passage—something about a lazy but fast-jumping brown fox—in our very best cursive, using special ball-point pens and white paper. All these passages were collected and sent away to the Penmanship Inspector, an important man who lived somewhere else. I pictured him as sitting in the top room of a castle like the Wizard's in the Emerald City, served by pages who, bending down on one knee, offered him silver trays of penmanship.

After a few weeks the Penmanship Inspector sent down his verdict, which the teachers announced solemnly in a special grade-wide ceremony involving the exchange of the scrolls which held the penmanship seals. These embossed, heraldic seals were awarded to the room as a whole, and were kept on the class bulletin board all month long. Like the ribbons the horse girls won for riding and scotchtaped to the insides of their lockers, the seals came in five shiny colors: gold, silver, blue, red, and shameful green. Each large scroll contained one of the seals and an inscription, in the very finest cursive, proclaiming it an award for *excellent, very good, average,* or *poor* work in Penmanship.

As in all group efforts, extremes counted too much. Susan Doralski, an earnest, strangely wooden girl who lived on my street, who often consulted me as we waited for the morning bus about how to act in various situations, or about what a certain kid had really meant by what she said, had an uncanny ability to produce writing just like the writing on the scroll. Susan was our greatest asset, with Mandy Sacrin, the Brownie leader's goody-goody daughter who, Sidney and I were convinced, spent hours practicing her perfectly round, perfectly even handwriting, not far behind. But our top third-grade class never got the gold seal all year, and I was sure it was all because of me. No matter how much I tried, my writing came out wobbly, different shapes and sizes, refusing to stay inside the lines. Such aberrant handwriting would have been O.K. for a boy—it might even be a sign of budding genius. But for a girl it was something of a disgrace. As the only girl with bad handwriting, I was convinced that even my very best effort always kept our class at red, or blue at best.

Our third-grade teacher, Mrs. Blanchard, tried to use the penmanship competition to bring our class down a peg or two, as the grownups used to say.

"Shame on you! You let 3B beat you again," she reproached us every month, but no one but Susan Doralski took her very seriously. The kids in my class knew that no competition that 3B could win really counted. Also, while decent handwriting was important for girls, excessively good handwriting was a somewhat dubious quality for anyone. For a boy, it meant being a sissy. For a girl, it meant maturity, a state we weren't sure we wanted that much. Not only did girls get it faster than boys and end up dumber in the end, but everyone knew that the girls in the low groups matured faster than we did and would probably all be wearing bras by fifth grade. Although I could tell Mrs. Blanchard was upset by my classmates' monthly accusations and the fingers which pointed at me when we failed once again to win the gold seal, I bore the ritual stoically, as an annoyance rather than a major humiliation. All this changed at the end-of-the-year awards ceremony.

The real awards for our grade had already been given out, and it was Penmanship's turn. Mrs. Blanchard presented Susan Doralski with the first prize, a book on handwriting around the world, and Mandy Sacrin with an honorable mention, a rather superior ball-point pen. We all clapped, pleased with the justice of it. Then she paused impressively and announced a special, new award for "The most improvement in Penmanship—and for all around improvement—to Rachel!" Dazed, I advanced to the front of the room, where, with a special flourish and a warm smile, Mrs. Blanchard presented me with the scroll containing the same gold seal which my bad handwriting had kept our room from ever winning. I remember the half-hearted, embarrassed clapping, the slimy feel of that glossy piece of paper, and how, returning to my seat, I looked away from Sidney's pitying face.

*The most improvement.* Those words stuck in my throat like a stone. I knew what they meant. It was a consolation prize for the crazy person—the one who had something wrong with her and had been sent to Serena. It was a fake award invented especially for the one with the very worst penmanship of all, the one who could never win a real award, to fool her and make her feel better. Looking back on it I imagine Mrs. Blanchard must have felt pleased with her idea for the new award—a way to make up, at one stroke, for my monthly teasing and raise my status with my peers.

Grownups must have thought we were stupid, really, because they were always trying things like that, praising kids who hadn't done anything special and inventing fake awards for kids who didn't deserve them. Mrs. Blanchard was a nice teacher, with red hair and soft pink-and-white freckled arms, who had never spoken to me with anything sticky in her voice, or anything different than the way she spoke to all of us, until she gave me that award. I dreaded bringing the gold seal home to show my mother, who, I knew, would understand what it really was.

Quite different was the award I got for my book report from the town library earlier that same year. My mother tells me that soon after we moved to the town, when I was in the second grade, she became fed up with the school's ineffectual efforts and taught me to read herself. It must have been a fairly painless process because I remember nothing about it. In my own memory, being able to read was a gift that descended on me suddenly like manna from heaven, at the same time as I learned to ride my bike.

After that I could ride to school on my own in the morning, with Dusty running panting behind me. She lay patiently waiting for me in the shade next to my bike all day, and then when school was over, followed after Sidney and me as we biked to the solid red brick town library. Much later I encountered the lines *luxe, calme, et volupté,* and recognized the feeling I got every time I opened the library door and contemplated the rows and rows of books I hadn't yet read, then curled up with four or five of them in the big green leather window seat. Sidney and I were both reading all the biographies of famous people, a set of grown-up looking thick orange books which took up a whole shelf in the library. Amelia Earhart and Abe Lincoln were the best, we agreed. The people in books, who before I learned to read were a gift my mother conferred on me every night when she read to me, were suddenly there, waiting for me whenever I wanted them—after I got home from school, on weekends, or at night when I was supposed to be asleep, under the covers with a flashlight. I didn't need my mother any more to spend time with Jo March or *Anne of Green Gables* or Sarah Crewe or Mary Lennox of *The Secret Garden*—I had a life of my own.

The librarians were Mrs. Felix, an old, strict-looking lady with a bony face, a limp, and a permanently hoarse voice, and Mrs. Bride, who was younger, plump, and more friendly. They both talked like the horse girls' mothers, but I could tell they liked me and took me seriously. When Mrs. Bride put her finger to her chin, gazed at me, and thought as hard as she could about which book to recommend to me next, I could tell she was seeing an especially smart, ordinary girl, not one with something wrong with her. Sometimes even Mrs. Felix, who everyone was scared of, and who rarely spoke to children except to rasp at them to be quiet or leave, would emerge from her special office at the top of the stairs and beckon me with a crooked arthritic finger to come up to her so she could recommend a book. The librarians, especially Mrs. Bride, were my friends, but when I wanted to take out books from the grown-up part of the library, they exchanged glances, hesitated, and said they would have to ask my mother. It was because grownup books had sex in them, my mother explained. Lots of grownups thought children should be ignorant about sex, but that was a superstition, like believing in God. Sigmund Freud had discovered that children knew all about sex anyway, and so she had a talk with the librarians and I was allowed to take out any book in the whole library.

When I learned to read, I worried that my mother might be mad at me for deserting her and that she would stop reading with me, but she didn't. We still read together every night, only now we took turns reading, and sometimes we read poems and books in French. She told me about grown-up books that had children in them, mostly orphans like Jane Eyre, who had to make their own way in the world with a friend. I loved books like that because after I stopped reading them I could go on with them in my head, with myself as the orphan's friend and rescuer. Other books she told me about were ones she had read as a child—*Buddenbrooks* and *The Three Musketeers*—and the books she had read to learn English—*The Great Gatsby, The Grapes of Wrath,* and *The Wasteland.* The last and best of these was by a writer called Jo Sinclair, who was really a woman, only she'd had to pretend to be a man when she wrote the book because it was hard for women to be writers in those days. It was about a man who went to see a psychiatrist because he had a bad childhood and hated himself, and he told the psychiatrist about all the different Passovers he had ever had, and in the end he got cured and wasn't embarrassed to be Jewish any more and changed his name from Jack back to Jake and helped his parents and took his nephews to a baseball game so they wouldn't turn out bad the way he had. After that his sister Debby, who was my favorite character, didn't have to be the man of the family any more. Debby had light blonde very short hair, only wore pants, and never went out with men, just with her best friend who was a Negro girl. She took care of the whole family, and it was Jake's fault she had turned out like that. I especially liked to think about Debby at night. When the library announced its book report contest, however, I decided to pick not *The Wasteland* or any of the other fat books from the grown-up section, but my favorite book of all, *Baby Island.*

*Baby Island* was the story of two girls, nine and eleven, who were shipwrecked on a desert island with no grownups, but a whole shipload of babies whom they took care of by themselves. I remember copying the report several times, bad penmanship and all, full of that slightly tremulous but satisfying feeling I still get after having written something that comes from my deepest self. I won the Grand Prize, a silver cup, for that report, and knew that I deserved it.

It was easy to tell the fake awards from the real. Another fake one, established when I was in junior high school, was the Good Citizenship

Award, something the grownups invented for the kids who would never win the academic awards: those in the middle and low groups, though never the very lowest; the many nice girls and fewer nice boys who always tried hard and never got in trouble; the boys who, in high school, coached the teams but never played on them; and the girls who joined Future Homemakers of America and decorated the gym for the dances they never attended. Sidney and I used to dread these citizenship awards. We sat during the assemblies devoted to them avoiding each other's eyes and blushing. We never questioned the fact that the world and everyone in it was ordered from best to worst, but it seemed like needless cruelty on the part of the grownups to invent fake awards which fooled nobody and only rubbed it in.

The last fake award, given in eighth grade, when we had all heard about the Civil Rights Movement, was the D.A.R. Award. Sidney had told me all about the D.A.R. Her mother was always getting calls from ladies who wanted her to join it, since she had come over on the Mayflower, but she refused because she said it was vulgar. Polly's and Sal's and the horse girls' mothers were invited to be in it too, but they all said no.

The D.A.R. meant Daughters of the American Revolution, and it stood for everything bad: the policy the next town over from ours had of not letting Jews buy a house there; the South—and lynchings and segregated water fountains and how Negroes couldn't vote there or buy a cup of coffee at a lunch counter; the John Birch Society; and burning books. Only vulgar people like Mandy Sacrin's mother, who was Catholic and hadn't really come over on the Mayflower with Sidney's mother anyway, but only liked to pretend she had, were in it.

Our town had no Black families during all the years I lived in it, and before we came, no Jews either. New people who wanted to move in had to be able to afford an acre and a half of land along with their house. I was never invited to the country club dances Sidney and Sal and the horse girls were asked to, and almost all the Catholic kids were stuck forever in the lowest groups and would not be able to go on to college. Sidney and I didn't think about any of these things, but we did make a mental list of all the eighth-grade girls who had gotten the D.A.R. Award in previous years. There had been Melanie King, who was legally blind; Ann Robinson, who'd had polio and walked with a brace; and Trixie Ushida, who was almost a horse girl, and very popular, but who was Chinese or Japanese—we weren't sure which. We figured that there hadn't been any foreign kids in the town at first, so they'd had to give it to kids with something wrong with them, but obviously the award was meant to trick us into believing the D.A.R. wasn't prejudiced after all.

Sidney was clearly not at risk for this year's prize, we reasoned, but I as the only Jewish girl, was a prime candidate. We spent hours composing a speech of rejection, just in case, and Sidney coached me on it as I sat on the horse-tying posts in front of her house where we used to play Electric Chair.

As it worked out, I didn't get to make our speech. They gave the D.A.R. Award to Beryl Wong, the only Chinese girl in our grade, who went up to the stage to accept it with her head down, as though she might burst into tears. We turned away and never spoke of it again.

# Rebecca by Any Other Name

## FRANCES SILVERBERG

Rebecca hurried home for lunch, climbed the twelve steps of the brownstone house on East Sixty-Ninth Street, between First and Second Avenues, rang the bell three times, and shading her eyes from the brilliant May sun, craned her neck to watch for her mother's face from the parlor window on the top floor.

"A loaf of rye bread, a quarter-pound Swiss cheese, a box of candles, and a bar of Octagon soap," Mrs. Abramowitz called down, and threw the paper-wrapped money to her daughter. The packet fell into the areaway. She ran down and retrieved it near the grilled-iron doorway to the Felkin kitchen. Mrs. Felkin spied her and said, "Rebecca, would you please get me a dozen Sunkist oranges?" The child took the dollar. The fruit store was on First Avenue, the grocery on Second Avenue; two trips on this special day, and she was in such a hurry.

Today, Friday, was the day to hand in the map of the United States. She had decided against doing it in color: all the maps in the 7-B geography book were delicately tinted in light pinks, soft greens, pale blues, but Rebecca had wanted her map to be different, like an etching. With the money Mrs. Felkin gave her for running errands she had bought special pencils for this assignment, No. 1, No. 2, No. 3. She was proudest of the mountains, tiny semi-circles alternately spaced with the hard No. 3 lead. *I love you, Rocky Mountains,* she whispered to herself. *I love you, curving rivers. I love you, Great Lakes. I love you, divided states. I love you, capital cities, especially Baltimore, Maryland, my Maryland, how green thy boughs, my Maryland,* she hummed. Such a beautiful state to be born in!

"You forgot the soap," her mother said when she returned from the store.

"I'm sorry, Mama. Can't I get it at three o'clock?"

"You'd forget your head if it wasn't tied to your body. I'll make you a nice cheese sandwich for lunch."

"No, Mama, I have no time. I'm in a hurry to get back to school."

Her mother felt her forehead. "You haven't any temperature," she said, surprised her daughter wasn't hungry.

It would be nice if she could tell Mama what was going to happen today, why it was so special, but it seemed whenever she tried to tell her about things, either Mama didn't understand the importance of it, or she wasn't interested. It was better not to speak, nor let your face or eyes show what you were feeling, because if people didn't know how you felt about them, or things, or maybe thought you had no feelings at all, they couldn't hurt you as much, only a little. Nothing definite had ever happened that she could remember, but it was necessary never to let anybody see how important certain things are.

## II

This afternoon Miss Prior, the seventh grade geography teacher, was going to mark the maps. She had said she was going to grade them differently than last time when Rebecca had only gotten sixty-five per cent because the crayon was smeary. The girls were to write their names on the backs of the maps, and Miss Prior would put them on a cardboard and judge each one without knowing who had drawn it, then show it to the class and grade it. The best map was to win a copy of Daniel Defoe's *Robinson Crusoe*. Last time Alice Robinson had gotten ninety per cent for the map of North America, and won *Tom Sawyer.* Some of the girls had whispered "teacher's pet," and Miss Prior had then announced the new system for marking. Alice was smart, and beautiful, so blonde. Rebecca was sorry her hair had turned brown. It had once been blonde, too.

She went into the bedroom she used to share with her sister Sylvia, which was now hers alone. Sylvia was married and lived in Brooklyn. In the bottom drawer of Rebecca's mahogany dresser, under her pajamas and vest and panties, was hidden her diary. She felt the embossing on the brown leather cover, touched the fake lock that didn't lock, and buried it deeper under the clothing. The diary was safe. Mama didn't read English, only Yiddish and German. Papa could, but wouldn't. Only Sylvia might. Sometimes she visited on Friday night for supper.

She removed the *Saturday Evening Post* and from its pages took the map of the United States, and allowed herself to admire it.

Mama hadn't understood that this was homework. She thought that Rebecca was spending every evening wasting her time playing, while she had done her work on the magazine spread on the kitchen table. She hadn't made a single erasure, not one. The hardest part had been the free hand drawing of the outline of the United States. It was almost perfect, as correct as the printed maps in her book. Tracing wasn't allowed, of course, and she had used up nearly the whole pad of specially-matted paper she had bought for twenty-five cents. After the outline it was easy, not a chore like homework usually was, but Mama was right, it was a game, like a wonderful game, knowing you were best and were going to win. Papa worked late every night. She was asleep when he got home. She wished she had remembered to show it to him. He was home on Sundays.

Passing the bureau mirror, she took a deep breath, sucked in her round cheeks, and flattened her stomach with the palms of her hands. She examined her reflection, admiring the slimming effect, then exhaled. Maybe next year. Her friend, Sarah Cohen, had overheard some 8-B girls talking about how the body changed when you got to be thirteen. So maybe next year.

As she hurried back to school, magazine with precious map tucked under her arm, she passed Julia Richman High School on Second Avenue, which the Prince of Wales had visited last year. It was the newest school in the city, all girls, and even had a swimming pool. She would go there and learn how to swim. She thought perhaps she had once known how to swim when she was younger, but had forgotten, as if she were afraid of the blue water, not so much of drowning in it, more like having to live in it, like a cold-blooded fish. It was a strange feeling.

Rebecca took different routes each day on the four trips to and from school, sometimes up one street and down another, passing the brownstone houses and picturing who lived inside them, even imagining their face and what kind of people they were. She wished she had more friends. None of the girls on her block went to her school. They attended St. Catherine of Siena, the Catholic school east of First Avenue; Sarah, her only other friend, lived on Sixty-Second and went to a different school.

Public School 176 was at Lexington Avenue and Sixty-Eighth Street; across the street, catty-cornered, was Hunter College. She looked up at the castlelike structure. This fairy tale would come true. She'd go to the all-girl Hunter, she didn't much care for boys, and become a teacher. Not a teacher like Miss Prior, who was always saying how it was destined she was teaching in this particular school, 176, talking about being a Daughter of the American Revolution, in capital letters she said it, as if that made her better than anyone else. The Prince of Wales had nothing to do with being born to the king and queen of England, instead of to the Abramowitzes of McGillicuddys. It had nothing to do with you as a person, it was more something you did yourself, like picking the school you wanted to work in, or like falling off a horse, or like drawing an extra special map. No, not a teacher like Miss Prior, but a teacher like Mrs. Hempel, who wasn't even pretty, yet beautiful, like her eyes understood you.

### III

Mrs. Hempel had been her fifth-grade teacher. Once, in the English class, Rebecca had written a composition about a Friday night supper. The assignment was really your birthday party, but she had never had a birthday party. The family didn't believe in it. So she had imagined that a Friday night was her birthday and described it. It was her turn to write on the blackboard, and proud of her Palmer script, careful to keep the lines straight, because they always slanted upward, she had chalked it on the board one afternoon before the rest of the class returned from lunch. Mrs. Hempel read it aloud. Most of the girls only tittered, but some of them laughed out loud, hard.

It told about a Friday night when her mother put a shawl on her head and lighted the candles, whispering a prayer into her hands as she cupped them over her face, swaying her body to and fro. It told about the gelid gefilte fish and the strong red horseradish that tickled the nose and made the eyes water. It described the clear chicken soup with the soft, curling noodles that Mama cut on the wooden board that Papa had made himself, sanding it down to smoothness; and the succulent boiled chicken, tender and tasty, served with a delicious crispy potato pudding that Rebecca had helped to make, grating the potatoes quickly so they wouldn't turn brown. Instead of the usual dessert of applesauce, she wrote of a chocolate cake her mother had baked with a colored candle on it, and her father had blown it out, making a wish for her, then she sang *"Happy Birthday."*

It was meant to be beautiful, it could have been like that, everything but the cake was true, just like a Friday night, only special. But they had all laughed, except Mrs. Hempel.

"That was well done, Rebecca," said Mrs. Hempel, and from her desk drawer she took a book. "This is a prize for a very good composition," and patted her head.

The book was Rudyard Kipling's *Jungle Book.* If she could write like Mr. Kipling she would write about people, not animals.

Yes, it would be good to be a teacher like Mrs. Hempel, even when you knew she was being nice, maybe because she was sorry for you.

### IV

The maps were on Miss Prior's desk, Rebecca slipped hers somewhere in the middle. Then, putting on her pince-nez, Miss Prior took a large cardboard, placed it under all the thirty-two maps, and said, "Now, we shall see what we shall see," and proceeded to mark the maps. Seventy-five, Mary, seventy, Josephine, eighty, Amelia, sixty-five, Matilda, calling the mark, turning the paper over and naming the first name of each girl. Amelia's was good, Rebecca thought, but not as good as mine. Then she saw hers. Miss Prior gasped, "Perfect!" she said, and adjusting her glasses which were slipping from her small nose, "Magnificent!" She held it high for all to see, carefully keeping the cardboard on the back so she could not seem the name. Oh, Rebecca thought, it is beautiful, and tears came to her eyes. I made it, she said to herself, all by myself, I made it.

"This map deserves more than one hundred per cent, but what can be better than the perfect number?" Miss Prior waved her right hand, tightly holding the rest of the maps with her left, "I mark you one-hundred-five per cent," like a fairy queen transforming a toad into a princess. "One-hundred-five per cent." Her voice rose, "You can see it's drawn freehand, not traced. How wise the girl was not to cover it with crayon! We can clearly see each river, each mountain, each state, each capital city. Now, we shall see who drew this fine map." She seemed to be looking at Alice. The map looked like Alice, so clean, so neat, so perfect. Rebecca sat straighter in her seat, glad today had been an assembly day, happy that she looked nice in the white middy-blouse and pleated navy-blue serge skirt. With sweating hands she smoothed the pleats over her stomach.

Miss Prior turned the map over. "Rebecca Abramowitz?" Her voice dropped, and she looked at her. "You?" She examined the back of the paper. "Are you sure you didn't trace this?" she asked.

"No, Miss Prior," Rebecca said.

"Perhaps someone helped you with this? Like an older brother doing your homework for you?" Miss Prior smiled. It was an ugly thing.

Rebecca didn't answer. It didn't make much sense to defend yourself, or do your homework, or write things about yourself, or your family, or try to get people to understand you, and the things you daydreamed about. Not the night dreams—they were never any good, confused and frightening, only the dreams in the daytime were happy and hopeful; now that was being spoiled too. So she didn't answer, even if she wanted to, she couldn't, her mouth was all twisted and wouldn't work.

"As the Scots say, I ha' ma doots," Miss Prior continued. "I ha' ma doots." She fixed her with a stony stare, back to a toad, princess for such a short moment. "Know what that means, Rebecca Abramowitz?" She took off her glasses. "It means I have my doubts. But I marked it, and the mark stands. Some people never learn." She shook her head, then firmly replaced her spectacles, and finished marking the rest of the papers. But Rebecca didn't hear her voice after that. She didn't get *Robinson Crusoe.*

## v

At three o'clock Rebecca walked home alone, as usual. She glanced across at the towered Hunter College. No, she wouldn't be a teacher. Maybe a reporter. Yes, she would go to Columbia University after she got out of high school, even if it was coeducational, and become a reporter, write for a newspaper, then she'd be able to tell the truth about things. Newspapers always printed the truth, didn't they? Like her diary, where she could write about what she felt, and dreamed, and wanted; nothing important ever happened to her,

but it was nice to be able to tell someone what you were thinking about, and you could trust them, they wouldn't laugh or twist it around. Like her diary. That was good. If anything ever happened to her right hand and she couldn't write, she would die, surely die.

The map in her hand reminded her of Miss Prior's face. She crumpled it into a ball and threw it into a trash can in front of a house. Her hand hurt from the force of destroying the stiff paper.

At home she went immediately to her dresser and removed her diary.

"Rebecca," her mother called, "you forgot the soap again."

"Can I get it later, Mama?"

"No, now. Sylvia and Herman are coming for supper, and I need some things right away."

She thrust the diary under her pillows. It was only fair, she knew, that she do the shopping. The stairs were bad for Mama's heart which had been injured because Rebecca was so big when she was born, fourteen pounds. That's why she was the youngest. I guess I didn't come out right, she thought, few things do.

"Rebecca!" her mother called again, "take a pencil! Write it down. A pound of coffee, a dozen best white eggs, a pound of lima beans, not the small ones you bought last time, I don't know why I let you do the shopping, you never buy the right thing. Where's the pencil? Write it down."

The girl squeezed her eyes shut, tight, very tight, but the tears wouldn't come. She opened them, picked up the pencil, and wrote.

One pound of limas, *not small, but very large*

One dozen eggs, *I wish I'd never been born*

One pound of coffee, *ground into dust*

One bar of Octagon soap, *many sided, to wash everything clean*

When she got back from the store, Sylvia, who had come too early, was sitting in the kitchen reading the diary aloud to her mother and brother-in-law Herman. The three of them were laughing, hard. She put the bag of groceries on the kitchen table, and face turned sideways, she slitted her eyes and squinted at them, a bad habit recently acquired. She put on a Miss Prior smile and went downstairs. Who cares about a silly dumb stupid stinking lousy freehand hundred-and-five per cent map? Or a diary? Or a composition? Or anybody? Or anything?

On the corner she went into Mrs. Wolf's candy store. With the quarter Mrs. Felkin had given her for the errand this noon, she bought a chocolate malted and a new *Frank Merriwell*. The malted was thick and delicious, felt good inside. Mrs. Wolf was a nice woman. She wished she hadn't bought the book, then she could have another malted. She felt in her pocket, she'd forgotten to give Mama the change. She bought another malted, two pretzels, and it was good, almost as good as the first one. She started to walk to Sarah Cohen's house.

One the way she changed her mind. She went to the public library on Sixty-Seventh Street, got a copy of *Robinson Crusoe* from the shelf, and began to read. When she got hungry, she went home.

# Discipline

## JOANNE S. PRIMOFF

Miss Tremaine stood for a moment outside Taler-ico's Market, her arms full of books and the scrawly homework papers she had corrected the night before. The spring sunlight felt delicious on her back, and she noticed too how it surprised into life the pale, wintry oranges and apples displayed outside the little store. Behind the dirty window she could dimly see Mr. Talerico in his shirt sleeves, stacking the canned goods. His daughter, Angeline, was one of Miss Tremaine's best pupils in the sixth grade at Joseph Patterson school. It was hard to believe when you saw Mr. Talerico; he spoke no English at all.

She shifted the books and looked at her watch. It was eight o'clock, and already she could hear shouts and wild activity in the schoolyard. She sighed and stood a little stiffer, then stepped around the corner.

Yes, the children were already there. No matter how early she tried to come, they were always there before her. They would fall back when they saw her, stopping their games and watching her soundlessly, shiny eyes in smeared faces revolving as she moved. Always she had to walk through them, her feet crunching sharply on the cinder yard. Sometimes Kenneth was among them, his hair bright against all the greasy Italian heads. If he were there, Kenneth would say: "Good morning, Miss Tremaine." Otherwise there would only be silence and sullen eyes watching carefully until she reached the door and it clanged safely behind her.

To herself, Miss Tremaine called that first walk across the yard "running the gantlet." Sometimes, standing in the hall and listening to the voices rising again in forgetfulness after she had passed, she would feel her legs tremble slightly, and then she would be angry. It was the worst part of the day.

This morning it was the same as always. Only Kenneth was there to hold open the door for her

and smile, and Miss Tremaine was glad. She thought perhaps it would be a good day. And it was the day of the contest.

Briskly she walked down the hall to room 45. But outside the door she paused for a moment, wondering if the words would be chalked on the board again as they had so often been this past month. They were horrible, obscene words, and Miss Tremaine did not like to find them there. They made her a little sick, like the heavy, garlicky odor of the children themselves. She could see no reason for them, none at all, except the maliciousness and filth of the mind that put them there. And although she could not discover who was doing it, she imagined it was the work of some ill-adjusted boy like Charlie Pelozza, or perhaps the Talerico child with her quick mind and sly ways. They were of the type who would pick up things like that at home.

She opened the door. A splash of color upon her desk caught her eye. Even before she glanced at the blackboard she walked over and looked at it. It was an orange, a round, full, ripe one. When she picked it up, it felt heavy and firm in her hand. She straightened and looked at the front of the room. The black slate of the board was empty and clean.

She took off her white gloves and put them in a drawer of the desk, next to the compartment where she kept confiscated yo-yos and marbles and tops. She laid the orange beside the gloves and thought with pleasure that she would eat it for lunch. I guess this is one of the things that keeps me teaching, she said to herself. Thank goodness I have Kenneth in my class.

After she had hung her coat on its hanger in the little boxed-off section of the cloakroom reserved for her and placed her hat on the tiny shelf, she pushed up all the windows in the classroom. It was wonderful to have it so warm, to have the smell of sweaty bodies and wet wool that had nauseated her all winter blown away in fresh gusts over the roofs of the small, sooty buildings. She felt relaxed now and almost happy. Kenneth would win the contest; she was sure he would.

The hands on the big wall clock jumped a little, and Miss Tremaine looked at it, calculating mentally as she always did. Forty minutes yet. It was only twenty after eight, and the children did not come in until nine o'clock. She still had a long time to herself.

She took the library book out of the bottom drawer. She relished this time, saving her book for these last few precious minutes before the noisy voices of ten- and eleven-year-olds brought her back and caught her up in the reality of school. The clock jumped again but she did not look up.

*"The young man clad in a blue uniform stumbled into the dark porch of the tall Southern home and spoke softly to the white shadow that was waiting for him there. 'If I'm found here I'll be shot,' he whispered hoarsely to the dark-haired girl. 'But I love you so. I had to see you.' 'Oh, Jeff,' she said, 'you shouldn't have come. But . . . but I'm glad you did.' 'A Yankee uniform cannot make you hate me, then?' The strong arms held her and she felt herself drowning in a sea of feeling too strong for her to resist. 'No, Jeff. No!' His arms tightened—"*

"Miss Tremaine?"

Her hands jerked convulsively on the book, hastily covering its bright wrapper with the brown-backed sixth-grade geography that lay near. Her voice was sharp; it needled her own ears with its sound. "What do you want?"

She looked up and saw that Kenneth stood hesitating in the doorway. "Oh, Kenneth." She smiled at him and he grinned back, coming all the way into the room and shutting the door behind him.

"Gee, Miss Tremaine, I hope I'm not bothering you." His eyes went to the book she had covered up.

"No, Kenneth, of course not. What did you want?"

He was so clean, she thought, looking at his white shirt and the slicked-down hair, so clean and blond. There was warm color in his face and a sprinkling of freckles across his nose. The nicest boy she had taught in the seven years she had been at Joseph Patterson was Kenneth Marble. She was sure of that. And how glad she was that the Marbles had not moved away from their lovely home on Front Street just because the neighborhood was becoming more and more Italian. The big brick house made an island for itself, standing securely behind the wrought-iron railing that marked it off from all the cheap little foreign shanties that had sprung up around it. She often went out of her way walking home just to go past it. Kenneth had told her once why they stayed there.

"My mom wants to go away," he had said, "but Father won't. He says nobody but a Marble has ever lived in that house and nobody but a Marble ever will as long as he's alive. He doesn't care if every wop in Italy moves in next door, he says. But maybe I'll have to go to boarding school pretty soon because of the wops. Mom thinks I'll have to, but I don't want to. I hope I won't have to go."

Miss Tremaine hoped so too. She dreaded the day she would lose Kenneth. He responded so well, he was so much more intelligent than anyone else in the class, even than Angeline Talerico. None of the thirty other children could take his place.

"Yes, Kenneth," she said now. "What did you want?"

"Say, Miss Tremaine, it's about that contest."

The contest. She had thought about it for days; preparing her pupils carefully for Kenneth's sake. Since February they had been studying local government. Now the city was sponsoring this examination. From each grade school in the city the finest, most perfect paper was to be chosen. These were to be read by the judges, and the writer of the best one was going on a two-day trip to the State capital. Miss Tremaine thought that Kenneth would certainly turn in the top paper at Joseph Patterson. The only real competition he could possibly have was Angeline. And he also might easily be the one to go to the capital. She did not know exactly why but she felt it was very important that he win. He had to win.

"What about the contest, Kenneth?"

"Well, golly, do you think there's a chance I can win, Miss Tremaine?" The last words came in a rush of eagerness. His eyes were shining.

"Why, yes, I think perhaps you can, if you really try."

"Gosh, do you?"

"Well, you know the desire to win is half the battle."

"Uh-huh."

"Why do you want to win so badly?"

"Well . . ." he hesitated a moment. "Well, it's because my father says if I win he'll give me five dollars, and I can do whatever I want with it. I can spend it if I want. And golly, Miss Tremaine, I just gotta get that five dollars!"

"I wouldn't be too surprised if you did. But tell me, Kenneth, why do you want it so much? Have you something special to do with it?"

His eyes dropped. He rubbed the toe of his sneaker back and forth along a crack in the floor. "Uh . . . well. Nothin' special, I guess. I just want it, that's all."

The bell rang shrilly. They were both startled. "I better sit down." He raced to his seat, the second one in the middle row, right in front of Miss Tremaine's desk. The other children, warm and dirty from their playing, crowded through the doors. The day began.

When the ten-thirty bell rang and they all streamed out to recess, Miss Tremaine sat at her desk, forgetting the book in the bottom drawer. She was thinking about Kenneth.

Mrs. Marble had talked with her after the last P.T.A. meeting. She was a thin, worried woman, blond like Kenneth but faded and dry. Still, she had seemed very nice and sympathetic. And among all the fat, laughing mothers in faded wash dresses with broken English she had seemed wonderful to Miss Tremaine. She had been worried about Kenneth, though. "He's been dreadfully

moody and sullen around the house lately. My husband is simply at his wit's end about it. And yet he does so well in school. I simply cannot understand it."

"Kenneth is very cooperative with me," Miss Tremaine had answered, a little stiffly.

"I'm so glad of that," said Mrs. Marble. "Although it almost makes me feel as if I had failed somewhere. That he should be happier at school—"

"Oh, no," Miss Tremaine said quickly. Mrs. Marble's words made her somehow uncomfortable. "It's Kenneth's lovely bringing up that makes him so different from all these . . . from all my other children."

After that Mrs. Marble only smiled, and in a moment she had moved away.

But now, remembering the worried look on Kenneth's face when he had told her how much he wanted the five dollars, Miss Tremaine wondered if Mrs. Marble understood Kenneth very well. Perhaps they did not give him money of his own to spend; perhaps he had to depend on their whims for money and now that there was something he really wanted he could not tell them. Miss Tremaine wished she had known a little sooner that something like that was bothering Kenneth; she would have told Mrs. Marble, explained that every child should have an allowance. If that was what was wrong, no wonder Kenneth was happier at school. And he had given her the orange, probably saved his pennies for it. Her throat was rough with the thought.

She was still sitting there when they came back in from recess, and she continued to sit, staring icily ahead of her, until the whispering and scuffling stopped and an uneasy quiet held them all. Then she rose.

"Get out paper and pens," she said. She waited again, the question sheet in her hand, until the desk lids stopped banging. "We are going to take our test on city government now, for the contest. Everyone is going to try his or her best, I am sure. I think we are going to have a school winner from this room. And it may be that we will even have the final winner. That would make us all very proud, I know. I will write the questions on the board, and we shall begin." She looked at Kenneth. He was staring out of the window, but beside him Angeline fastened her brown gaze on Miss Tremaine as if trying to draw the answers from her teacher's mind. Miss Tremaine hated the way the girl's eyes followed her around the room. She could never escape them. She turned and started putting the questions on the blackboard in her neat, Palmer-method hand. As she finished the first question she could hear, above the scraping of her own chalk, the dipping of thirty pens and the first hesitant rustle of reply. The Pelozza boy started the rhythmic snuffling of his nose that somehow pushed him through his examinations, and a window rattled in the light breeze. The quietness was full of painful thinking.

It took her some time to write all the questions. As she finished, put the chalk on the rail and turned, Miss Tremaine saw something out of the corner of her eye. Kenneth was sitting in a strange position. He was leaning so far out of his seat that he was in danger of toppling to the floor, and his eyes were fastened upon Angeline Talerico's paper. Even as she saw this the boy straightened, and by the time she was actually facing him his eyes were again looking out of the window in calm reverie and his back was stiff in his own chair. She hesitated a moment and as she stood there she looked at Angeline. The brown eyes stared into her own. Miss Tremaine sat down.

She picked up her pen and began to correct some arithmetic exercises. As she made her first angry check mark beside a column of straggling figures she realized her pen was dry. The mark she had made was not legible.

When she opened the drawer to get the bottle of ink, the orange rolled to the front. Its sharp, sweet odor had filled the drawer and she smelled it deliciously as she straightened up once more.

She filled the pen and started over on the papers, really working now, looking up at the class only once in a while. She did not see Kenneth lean over again.

Kenneth finished his paper quickly. So did Angeline. But the rest of the children spent a long time over theirs. When Miss Tremaine finally collected them, it was lunch time and the bell was ringing.

She sat still after they had gone, not moving, although she was usually the first one to enter the teachers' room with her neatly wrapped sandwich in its wax-paper bag. The pile of test papers lay in front of her. She shuffled through them, coming upon Kenneth's nearly at the bottom, with Angeline's just beneath. She read them. The two papers were the same, word for word, even to the misspelling of "legislature." Apart from that they were both perfect. She put Kenneth's on top, stacked them all neatly and went to lunch.

Miss Lee, the other sixth-grade teacher, sat beside her on the wicker couch as they ate. "Well, I'm certainly glad that contest is over, aren't you, Miss Tremaine?"

"Yes, it is a bother."

"Especially when I know none of my children have a chance to win. Not when you have Kenneth Marble. And your Talerico child is quick too, isn't she?"

"Yes, they both have good minds. Though Kenneth..." She paused. Her hands were busy with the peeling of the orange.

"Oh, he's the brightest. It shows on his face. I suppose he turned in a beautiful paper."

"Yes." The orange was sweet and juicy. She offered a piece to Miss Lee. They finished it.

Miss Lee went on. "There isn't much doubt that Kenneth will be the school winner?"

"I don't think so."

"Do you suppose he'll get the big prize too?"

"Why, I rather hope so."

"Do you know, Miss Tremaine, I'd love to see his paper. Just to compare, you know, with what mine have done. Do you suppose I could?"

"Well...I guess so." Then she was afraid she had sounded reluctant. "I'll get it now."

As she opened the door to the classroom she stopped, jerked into the sudden stiffness of surprise. Kenneth had turned when he heard her, and now they both stared for a long breath until he smiled shyly. He stepped back a little from the desk, turning away from the pile of papers that lay on it. "Miss Tremaine?"

"What are you doing here, Kenneth?" He had started so when she came in. "Why aren't you down in the lunchroom?"

He almost whispered. "I had to find out."

"Find out what?" Her voice was flat and cold.

"About the contest." The toe of the sneaker rubbed the crack again, and one hand twisted some small object around and around in his palm. "That's why I came up to see you now. I couldn't wait."

He came up close to her and touched her arm. His eyes were looking into hers; they shone clear and gray. "Miss Tremaine," he said breathlessly, "did I win?"

"Why are you so sure I have already corrected the papers?"

"Oh." He drooped.

"Well, you're right. I have read yours." He said nothing, but his eyes questioned once more. "But before I tell you about your test, I would like to know something, Kenneth. I would like to know why you want to win so badly?"

"Well . . . gosh."

"Is it that you want to win the contest itself so much? Or is it the five dollars your father has promised you?"

"Gosh, I wanted to win the contest, but . . ."

"But the money is more important. Is that right?"

"Golly, Miss Tremaine, you don't understand!"

"I had hoped you were anxious to win just for the honor of it, Kenneth."

"I am. Honest I am. But . . . well, but I need the money too."

"What for?"

His head was bent. The sneaker rubbed the crack again. He dropped the thing in his hand, and it rolled for a foot or two, then stopped, lodged against the leg of her desk. He picked it up quickly, but Miss Tremaine had seen that it was a small piece of chalk. The silence seemed to go on for a long time after that. Finally she started toward the door. "Well, if you don't want to tell me . . ."

"Miss Tremaine, please don't go."

She paused, raising her eyebrows slightly, and looked at him.

"Aw, gosh, Miss Tremaine, I'll tell. I'll tell you why. Don't go yet."

She waited.

"Only please don't tell Mom. Don't tell her or Dad, because they'll be awful mad."

"Have you been doing something you shouldn't?"

"Aw, no, it was just an accident. But . . ."

"Tell me what has happened, Kenneth."

"Well, it's a bike. I gotta have the money to get a bike fixed."

"You mean something has happened to your bicycle and you're afraid to tell your parents? Is that it?"

"No, not exactly. It isn't my own bike, see. It's Charlie Pelozza's. I borrowed it, though. I didn't think Charlie'd mind. But I crashed into the light pole on the corner of Orchard Street. It wasn't my fault; that old bike doesn't work so good. It was terrible."

"Were you hurt?"

"Naw. But Charlie got awful mad. His father got mad too, and he yelled at me in Italian, and he told me I gotta pay for the damage. It'll cost five dollars, and the only way I can get that much money is if I win the contest and Dad gives it to me. So you see how I gotta have the money. You see, don't you, Miss Tremaine?"

"But your mother or—"

"Oh, I can't tell them," he said quickly. "I can't tell them because . . . well, because I'm not supposed to play with the wops. They'd be awful mad if they found out I was foolin' around with Charlie Pelozza, or his bike either. They might even send me to boarding school. I don't want to go away to school. I just can't go, Miss Tremaine."

"I see." Her voice was softer now. She walked over to the desk and looked down, looked at the paper with "Kenneth Marble" written across the top. "You had a perfect paper, Kenneth," she said slowly.

A grin stretched itself across his face.

"Of course, yours may not be the best in the city," she said dryly. "Angeline's was perfect, too." Something had made her add that, but she knew Angeline's handwriting was not as neat as Kenneth's. Sometimes it was hardly readable, and on the front of her paper there was an enormous blot.

Kenneth was still smiling, though. "I bet mine will win," he said. "I bet it will...because I think you're the best teacher in the city, Miss Tremaine!"

She was astonished to feel herself blushing a little. Kenneth started toward the door, walking jauntily now, flipping the little piece of chalk into the air and catching it as he went. Before he left he turned again. "Gee, thanks for telling me about it," he said. "I just had to find out. I was pretty sure I did win, but I sort of had to look, to make certain. I didn't think you'd mind if I looked through the papers. But I'm glad you told me too."

Suddenly Miss Tremaine found that her legs were trembling. She wished Kenneth were one of the other children; one of the greasy, black-haired ones. Then she would not stand here like this; then she could grab him by the shoulder, shake him, slap him if she pleased. He must have seen the look on her face. He backed up a little and felt with his hand for the doorknob. She stepped toward him. "Before you go, Kenneth, there's something else. I think you know..."

Even as she spoke she noticed that his white shirt was still very clean. His hair had escaped from its stiff morning subservience and curled a little on his forehead. He was poised anxiously, ready to run but waiting for her to continue with what she was saying. She stopped. Almost unconsciously she sighed. And then she touched his shoulder.

"It's about the orange," she said. "It was very thoughtful of you to bring it."

He was still stiff under her hand, expecting something different, something more, and his face was blank and puzzled. "The orange?" he said.

"The one you left this morning."

"Oh." Then suddenly he understood. "Oh, yes."

"I enjoyed it very much."

"That's...that's okay. I mean, that's good." He edged away. "I gotta go finish my lunch now." He smiled again, a trifle uneasily this time. "Thanks." Then he was gone.

When he had left, she walked back to the desk and picked up his paper. She had almost forgotten; she was going to show it to Miss Lee. But before she reached the door she went back and laid it down again, sliding it under so that it was on the very bottom of the pile now. And when she got back to the teachers' room she told Miss Lee that she had misplaced it for the moment.

The clock jumped and clicked the afternoon away. Kenneth grinned secretly to himself, but Angeline watched Miss Tremaine. It began to rain.

They went at three-thirty, tumbling their eagerness through the doors into the wet streets. Miss Tremaine stood watching them, and only Kenneth turned to say good-by.

When they had gone she sat still in the silent room, not thinking, just listening to the soft April sound of the rain on the windows, wishing dimly she had brought an umbrella to save her hat.

After a while she rose and went into the cloakroom. She put on her coat. Straightening her hat, she did not use the crooked little mirror that hung over the shelf. She went back and opened her desk drawer, taking out her gloves and the library book.

Then, nearly ready to leave, she realized that the blackboard was not clean. The janitor had not come in, as he usually did, to wash it. She had not used it in the afternoon, and the slates were still covered with the questions from the contest. Miss Tremaine picked up an eraser and began rubbing them out, moving the felt pad steadily up and down until the words were gone. She walked over to one of the windows, opened it, and stood clapping the dusty eraser against another, clean one. And as she did this, she saw that the rain was lessening.

Yes, it had almost stopped, but the sky was darker than before. She leaned her head against the pushed-up pane of glass for a moment; she was aware of a dull throbbing behind her eyes. It was cooler now, and a little shiver clutched her. I hope I get home before the next downpour, she thought.

Below, on the sidewalk, she could see a group of children. Kenneth was squatting in the midst of them, writing something on the sidewalk. When he had finished he stood up, and she could see one of the bigger boys laughing. But two little girls turned quickly and walked away. Down on the corner Mr. Talerico was unfurling his striped awning over the already dampened fruit, and Angeline was there helping him. Miss Tremaine knew that before she got down there the words Kenneth had scrawled on the cement would be washed away. Already the rain was coming down harder; the children were running on up the street.

She closed the window and put the erasers back on the rail. At her desk, she paused before she picked up the gloves and the book. Reaching under the pile of papers, she took out Kenneth's. Slowly, not looking at it, she tore it into long strips and threw them in the wastepaper basket.

The heavy outer door crashed behind her, and she stood for a second under the shelter of the eaves, watching the quick, slanting drops. As she looked down the walk she could see that the words had dissolved: there was nothing left now but a white blur. And she was going to get wet after all.

# All Little Colored Children Should Play the Harmonica

## ANN PATCHETT

Sampson, Skipworth, Slonecker, Small, Smiley. Smiley, Grover T. There are still four people ahead of me on the list. I've got a while to wait. The *s*'s, we're way the hell down there so we gotta hear everybody before our turn comes around. At first I thought I was miserable, but after the thirty-fourth audition (Claire Beth Fibral, who said God told her she could play the flute), I decided it was poor old Miss Neville who was having a rough go of it. She calls out a name on the list and hands over a piece of sheet music, asking if they can make any sense of it, most everybody says no. Then she asks them if there is anything in particular they think they could play. This is where she makes her big mistake, if you ask me; just cram something in their hands and talk about it later. Every kid says they's just sure they can play the so and so. The girls all say they can play the flute, the boys say the bass. They is all lying.

Some group of old white men decided all little colored children should play musical instruments, that it would keep their minds off breaking out store windows or sitting in front of the Five and Dime looking uppity. That's why we're all here now, Miss Neville says that's legislating. I think they must have legislated this one up in spring, when it was cool outside and music sounded real pretty. But this here's August and even the flies are looking for a house with the fan on. It's Miss Neville who's got to decide who's gonna play what. She's gotta listen to every kid in Central Valley Junior High blow or bang or strum on something before she can assign them a place in the school orchestra. Ain't no telling how long she's been the music teacher here, most everybody's got a story or a guess. Harvey Rachlin says his older sister was in Miss Neville's orchestra when she went here, and his sister is a grown-up woman now, with a baby and everything. Some people say that Miss Neville stays at school all the time, that they let her sleep under the piano or

something. I can't figure her out; I crawled up on the bleachers to watch her for a while and she looked like she was listening to all of them. You can tell by her face that she thinks every kid that comes up might really be able to play. Then when she really hears them her face gets kinda sick, like they were all hitting her in the stomach. I would think that going through an audition once would be more than any regular person could suffer, I don't know what it would be like year after year.

They've got the whole school mashed into this one basketball gym. The ninth graders get folding chairs, which they make a very big deal of. The rest of us get bleachers or the floor. I got this nice little spot between the door and the risers where nobody can step on me. From where I'm sitting the whole world is knees and ankles, not one person in there who cares a rip about keeping his socks pulled up or his shoelaces tied. You never think about feet until you're down there with them. Miss Neville calls out a name and then I see a pair shuffle onto the stage and wait a minute, then shuffle back to their place, which has almost always been snatched up.

I don't want nothing to do with their spitty old instruments. No way am I gonna spend four years sucking on some piccolo that somebody sucked on before me. It had been my intention to keep Roy Luther out of school, sorta separating my class time from my free time, but this is an emergency.

Me and Roy Luther hooked up when I was six years old, so we've been together a little more than half of my natural lifetime. My daddy, Mr. Nigel T. Smiley, runs the numbers where he works in the bakery making fancy doughnuts. He used to let a couple of us kids sit in the back room with his business friends, we made the place look honest. One day I was hanging out on a cherry crate playing with this special aggie that had been my birthday present. This man comes over and says that it was a real fine marble, that he'd never seen a shooter quite like it. I say, Yessir. He says he'd like to have that marble for his little boy. I didn't look up, I was scared he was gonna take it. He says, wouldn't I like to bet him something for that aggie? He pulls out this silver bar, the size of three Havana cigars. Then I look up, it was the most beautiful thing I'd ever seen.

"We'll shoot us out some craps, boy." The man says to me, "I win, I take your marble home to my boy; you win, you get to keep this here harmonica."

Man, I'll tell you I wanted that thing. I didn't know what it was or how to use it, only that I'd die right then and there if I didn't get it. I nodded my head. The man dips one of his fingers into a tiny pocket on his vest. He must have just been eating Cracker Jacks or something cause when he pulled it out there were two dice hanging on it. The other guys, mostly soldiers that hung out during the day started coming around, checking out the action and laughing at me 'cause I'm the sucker. Just then, a big metal door smashes open and Papa walks in from the front room. Kids used to tease me about my father being white, 'cause he was always plastered with flour. Nobody ever said anything to him about it.

"What you doing with my boy?"

"Just a friendly game of craps, Nigel. Your little shark here's hot after my harmonica." He shook up the dice to show he meant business.

Papa looked down at me. "You gambling with this man?"

I was pretty little then, I just nodded my head yes. One giant, floury hand come swinging down through the air and clipped me right above the ear. I went sailing off my cherry crate and slammed back against some drums of cooking oil. What everybody says about seeing stars ain't true. I saw big, furry spiders.

"How many times I got to tell you kids? You never, ever gamble with a man without letting me check out the dice. Jesus you is a fool." Papa plucked the pair of spotted cubes out of the other fella's hand and rattled them around. "Loaded."

He shook them in my face, "Loaded!" I thought he was gonna hit me again, but he walked into the other room and got a fresh pair. Everybody knew Papa used clean dice. He gave the new set to the man. "Now you talk about gambling with my son."

The man shook his head like a little black bunny rabbit. "Just joking with you, Nigel, just trying to teach the boy here a lesson, hee hee. He can keep his dirty old marble."

"You gamble with my boy, mister." Papa picked me up with one hand and shook me like a sneaker with a rock inside. "You let the man roll first, Grover."

His roll came up two specks, Papa says Snake Eyes. I gathered up the dice and threw them out again. A howl went up. A two and a five, sweet, sweet seven. Roy Luther must have been the man's name, because it was engraved on the side of my "Hohner Marine Band." I thought it had a good, solid sound to it. I knew right away this was going to be my special thing. All the other kids in my family got something special. There's the oldest and the youngest, and the twins that get all their clothes to look alike and get their picture taken a lot, and my brother Wilson who has his very own fish, and Delilah who twirls in the marching band, and Albert who skipped two whole grades just for being smart. Up till now I never had a thing that made me me. I'd walk into a room and Mama would call me two dozen names before she could place who I was. That first night I was sitting there staring at Roy Luther when the twins come up and try to take him away. Mama tells them to scat, "That's Grover's thing," she told them. "Leave it be." I slept with Roy Luther between my head and shoulder, so I'd be sure to wake up if someone tried to make off with him. Me and Albert share a bed, he thinks it's him I don't trust, but I couldn't let it go. Albert slept facing the wall after that.

There was a good three years I didn't have too many friends. My brothers and sisters told other kids they didn't know me, even Mama made me stay a good piece behind her when we went out. My thing wasn't so much being a harmonica player as it was being a bad harmonica player. I played all the time, grinding up and down that same old scale any place I could catch my breath, in the bathtub, under the dinner table. I was as bad as Original Sin. It was like learning to talk all over again, except this time there was no one to listen to. My hands didn't know anything about playing harmonicas, they knew about marbles and baseballs, and my mouth was a gum-chewing mouth. There wasn't no music in that mouth when things started out.

Back then, I took Roy Luther to school. Every five minutes or so a new sound would come into my head and I would raise my hand, asking if I could visit the washroom or get a drink of water. If the teacher said yes I would dart outside and try blocking up a different set of holes, blowing harder or softer than the day before to see how it sounded. Somebody'd always rat on me and Roy Luther would spend the rest of the day sitting in the principal's desk drawer.

I got used to the way it was always cold, tasting part like a tin can and part like the old Lifesavers and ticket stubs I kept in my pocket. As much as I loved the sound, I loved just putting it in my mouth, letting it hit against a filling in my tooth and running a shock clear through my eyes. It got to where I couldn't walk through a door without someone saying, "Grover, go way!" I'd shinny up into the sugar maple and stay there. First the birds all flew away, then after a while they got used to me, I even learned a few of their songs. One morning I was playing outside the kitchen window before breakfast, I heard Mama say, "Listen to the nightingale, will you? Glory but that ain't God's finest bird."

And that's when things started turning around.

I sat under the front porch and played a fire engine and my little brother ran outside, hooping and hollering for everybody to come watch the fire. Then he spent the whole day looking for one. I sat in the alley behind the white grocery store and played "What'll I Do?" so soft you could barely hear it, and just about everybody that walked out of the store was humming that song without knowing why.

It was like one day I was the stinkbug somebody stepped and the next day I was a fistful of wisteria. Mama stopped sending me outside all the time. I could play the things she heard in church on Sunday. When the radio went out I was the chief source of entertainment in the family. I got to sit in the red leather chair and blow my brains out till I got dizzy or my tongue went thick; once I got going I could feel the vibrations go past my jaw and head for my stomach. The whole family spread out at my feet, except for Papa, who would listen from the other room. On those days it could rain ice or be a hundred and five in the shade and everybody was happy. I could play the popular stuff and make them dance till they fell down. I could play the blues and break them in half.

Suddenly nobody remembered that I'd ever been bad. Now folks say, "Grover! Hey, Grover T., that sounds real fine, come play in my store," or, "Hey son, come sit in my diner where it's cool." Like we was all best friends or something. Mr. Thompson used to say I wasn't even to think about walking down the street where his soda fountain was; now he calls me over all the time, tells me I'm good for business. I go, he gives me free lemon Cokes.

After school I went to the community library and tried to teach myself how to read music. The place had two or three books called *How To*. I'd sit there for hours looking at the henscratches, trying to make sense of it all. Finally I figured out that each line was two spaces on the harmonica, and that the black spots were where my fingers should go and how long I should leave them there. I'd run down to the bathroom with the book inside my sweater and give it all a try. The guy who stacked the books caught me a few times, said I was a real stupid kid, then he'd show me how to do it. He said he had a girl once who played the harmonica, said that's why he dumped her. You play a long time and your lips go funny on you he told me.

On Fridays, Papa had me come down to the business to play while the men waited to find out who won the races. It seemed to calm them down a whole lot. They all wanted to hear the new Benny Goodman stuff, everybody liked swing. A bunch of their sweeties waltzed in and said I was awfully good. One of them said I was cute as hell, and I was only ten back then. Everybody made a circle around me and started laughing and clapping their hands. Papa told me to get him a cigarette from the front room. One of the women held my arm, told me to stay put, that she had plenty of smokes. Papa looked down at me, way down, like I wasn't any bigger than a lizard. He said go get him a cigarette. I did. He told me to light it so I did that too. He said he was glad to see I could do something useful for a change. The one with the peach-colored dress that swung way down in the back, the one who said I was cute, asked couldn't they have another song, maybe "Coming in on a Wing and a Prayer"? I looked up at Papa, he liked that song a lot. But he said it was a fool's song, that it was a good one for me 'cause any fool could play the harmonica. Then he ripped Roy Luther out of my hands. I felt all dizzy, like I couldn't breathe. He might as well have ripped off my face. All of the sudden I remembered I wasn't nobody, just another little nobody colored kid at the bottom of the barrel. Then I heard him blow, Lord, you'da thought they was killing a cow, *slowly.* His hands were so big and dry they couldn't move to change the scale. Nobody laughed, he wasn't the kind of person you'd laugh at. He didn't say a word, just gave Roy Luther back to me and left. After that, we didn't talk too much about music.

Miss Neville calls out my name. I am number sixty-nine and she looks like somebody's hit her in the stomach hard. She's this little bitty old white woman with her hair knotted to the back of her head in a vise.

"Grover T. Smiley?"

"Yessum."

She hands over a piece of sheet music, "Can you make any sense of this?"

I glance over it; it's something I already learned, a real easy piece. "Yessum."

She looks up a little bit, I'm only the third person to even say I knew what it was. "What would you like to play Grover? Do you know the bass?"

"No, ma'am, I brought my own."

The kids in the assembly hall aren't listening, most of them are asleep or whispering. Miss Neville sits down at the edge of the table and folds her arms across her chest. "Alright then."

"You want me to play this, ma'am?" I hold up the music. I was hoping she'd say no 'cause I know stuff that's a lot prettier than this.

"That will be fine."

I pull out Roy Luther from my pocket and put him in my mouth real quick. If you go too slow, somebody always says, "Oh no, not the harmonica. I thought you could play a real instrument." I jump right in, without even getting a good breath. Miss Neville looks up, first to stop me and then to listen. After the first few bars the kids that were asleep wake up and the kids that were talking get quiet and everybody sits up real straight, like it was gonna make them hear better. Roy Luther has that sort of effect on people. I finish, it was an okay job I guess. Everybody claps real politely, like they were at a picture show. Miss Neville takes my arm.

"Do your parents know about this?"

She let everybody else go on. Carl Smith through Herman Zweckler got to miss their audition altogether. Roy Luther and I were taken to the principal's office and asked to wait there.

Miss Neville comes in looking all pink and flustered. That's one thing you can say about white people, they're always changing color on you. She smacks this stack of sheet music in front of me and says, "Can you play this?" When I know she thinks I can't. I don't know what to do, if I should tell her no, that I can't read a note of the stuff and the other thing was just a freak of God, or that I can, which I could. Mama says to always tell the truth, Papa say to go with the flow. The piece on top is one of my favorites, Schumann's "Scenes from Childhood." I say yes.

Miss Neville tapped her foot real fast and looked at me like she thought I was crazy. Finally she threw her hands in my face and said, "Well then *play* for God's sake!"

I never heard a teacher take the name of God in vain before, it made me like her. I folded my lips into my mouth to get them ready and then pulled up Roy Luther. He tasted like my house keys. Harmonicas remind you that everything in your head is all hooked together, playing is a lot more than the mouth, it rolls into the back of your neck and through every tooth individually. My eyes don't read music anymore, it goes straight to my tongue and fingers, each pressing on the two different sides like they was trying to break through for company. My head likes this piece a lot. The notes sound real good in the little office and I start to forget all about Miss Neville and the school orchestra. I just keep my eyes on the paper and play. It's a real pretty song.

When I get through, Miss Neville is looking up at the ceiling real hard, like there's something important up there. I look up too. She turns around, all watery and pale again. She thinks I'm making fun of her by looking up, but she lets it go. "That was lovely, Grover."

I knock the spit out of Roy Luther and thank her kindly.

She swats at her eyes with the back of her hand. "Have you been playing the harmonica a long time?"

"Six, seven years."

"That's just fine."

"You want to hear something else? Some swing maybe?"

She looks like she's come back down now. "I'll have to contact your parents at once, your father has a phone where he works, doesn't he?"

Papa didn't like being bothered at work. "You gotta call my folks?"

"Certainly, yes."

She rang up Central and got connected. Papa didn't like being bothered at work.

"Mr. Smiley? Yes, hello, this is Miss Neville down at Central Valley. I'm calling about your son. No, Grover. No, there isn't anything wrong, quite to the contrary."

This was news to me.

"It seems we have stumbled upon a rather remarkable musical gift... yes, I do think this is important. Did you know about the situation? About his music?"

I motion for her to hold the line, she puts her little hand over the receiver. "Tell him it's about Roy Luther."

She looked confused so I nodded at her, the way Mama does us kids when we're not sure if we're doing something right. "Mr. Smiley? Grover says to tell you it's about Roy Luther... you know about that? Well, he demonstrates an amazing aptitude for the instrument. I would like to have a conference with you and your wife at once, to make arrangements to put Grover in a special program, perhaps even a special school. I've never seen a talent like this, Mr. Smiley. It is a force to be reckoned with."

I was sent home early with a "Gifted Child Form," and told that it should be completed and returned the next day so that plans could be made. The form was pretty easy stuff, name, age, place I was born. One space needed my middle name. I thought about it, I'd always just written Grover T., nothing more than that. I asked my folks about it, they said there were lots of kids, they couldn't remember no fool *middle* name. I wrote the *T* in the blank. It looked kinda stupid sitting there by itself. I wrote in Truman, because he's the vice president and seems like a real friendly white guy. On my form for gifted children my name was Grover Truman Smiley. It looked pretty good. Papa signed the form without reading it, said he didn't want no more *music* teachers calling him at work. I said I was sorry.

I found Miss Neville in the principal's office typing away. I gave her the form, which she clipped onto the thing she'd been working on.

"I've been doing a lot of planning for us, Grover." She didn't look at me, she just worked at her desk, shuffling and making notes in a little pad. Somehow it all looked real important, the way she was putting it together so carefully.

"I didn't mean to be a bother, ma'am."

This stopped her dead. She laid all the papers back down and took hold of my hand, you could tell she wanted to be real nice. "You won't ever be a bother, Grover. You are the most important person in this whole school to me."

I looked at the floor, there was a little red ant making his way toward the bookshelves.

"Do you know how long I've been a music teacher?"

"No, ma'am."

"A very long time, and I've had a few good students. Not very many, but enough to make it worth my while."

She let go of my hand, I was glad and stuffed it in my pocket. She went beneath her desk and brought a wallet out of her purse. "I've kept photographs of all of them. I felt like they were my children." She unfolded this strip of plastic and out stumbled about five little colored children, one of them's got a violin and the next is standing beside a piano. They all look like regular kids, they's *all* smiling. "Every one of these children had a chance to be very fine musicians, to do something important with their lives. And do you know what happened?"

"No."

"Well, Charles Hunt," she pointed to the kid with the piano, "he got a job in his uncle's filling station, and my prize pupil, Cynthia Rachlin, she married a checkout boy at the A&P and had a baby."

It was old Cindy Dobbs, Harvey Rachlin's big sister.

"And all the rest of them did about the same. They all had a chance and gave it away. I didn't become a music teacher to force children with no musical ability to join an orchestra, I simply wanted to find the ones who could make something of themselves. This," she held up the papers, "is my letter to the governor, it's all about you . . . and . . ."

"Roy Luther."

"Yes, I've told them how talented you are and what I think we should do about it. They'll listen to me."

"You wrote the governor?" I rocked back on my heels a little. I remember seeing his picture in the post office. He was the only person besides famous criminals who got his picture there. "You think he's going to want to hear me play? You think he's got a favorite song or something?"

Miss Neville licked the envelope and pressed on a stamp with the heel of her hand. "I'm positive you'll play for the governor someday, you might even play for the president of the United States." She smiled at me for a second and then her face got all busy again. "Of course, you won't be playing the harmonica then, you'll have learned a real instrument."

I thought I must have heard her wrong. "Ma'am?"

"Grover, you certainly don't expect to become great while playing a bucolic instrument."

I wasn't even sure what she said, but I knew what it meant. I could feel myself getting lightheaded, the same way I did the night Papa tried to play. I never talked back to a teacher, come to think about it, I'd never talked back to anybody. I wasn't looking to cause trouble. All I ever wanted to do was play, maybe someday get that job in the bakery that every kid in the world wanted. Miss Neville was going to mail the letter.

"If it's alright, I think I don't really want to play for the governor after all." It sounded pretty polite to me.

"I wouldn't worry about it too much."

"Do you think I shouldn't be playing the harmonica?"

She let out this big breath and turned around, she didn't want to miss the postman. "I think you've done a wonderful job with what you have. I think all little colored children should play the harmonica if it would help bring them to the point you're at now. But people get older and they move on to different things. That's where you are now, that's why I'm trying to help you."

I drew in my breath, which is a lot. "No. No thank you, ma'am."

She was just as surprised as I was. "I beg your pardon?"

"They're talking about giving me a job at the theater, playing before the Sunday matinee. I'd like that, playing my harmonica for people." I tried to look at her, but decided best that I go before I lose my nerve. I darted past her out the doors and down the front steps. I could feel her watching me run down the street with Roy Luther flat inside my hand, her holding onto the letter.

By the time I got to Mr. Thompson's soda fountain I was all out of breath. I stood there for a long time, just fogging up the glass. Every now and then I'd take my thumb and make a mark showing I was here. I wondered if she'd mail the letter, but I was pretty sure not. She'd find somebody else for her wallet quick enough.

Mr. Thompson caught sight of me standing on the sidewalk. Any other kid he would have run off, but he calls me inside and asks if I'd please play him a song. Old Cindy Dobbs was sitting at the counter with her baby and gives me a nice smile, asks how I'm doing. Mr. Thompson says, "What do you feel like humming up today, Grover?" Suddenly I knew that everything was good, so I tell him, anything he's wanting to hear. They decide on "Don't Sit Under the Apple Tree With Anyone Else But Me." Then he draws me up an extra large lemon Coke, but I ask him, wouldn't he please give it to Mrs. Dobbs, cause I'm not so thirsty. I slip in Roy Luther, he tastes like butterscotch Lifesavers and warm nickels. I play so loud that people come in off the street to listen. It's the best feeling in the world, when you're playing one the people really like, especially when it's a happy song. If you ask me, nobody gives the happy songs half enough credit.

# The Wrong Lunch Line

## NICHOLASA MOHR

The morning dragged on for Yvette and Mildred. They were anxiously waiting for the bell to ring. Last Thursday the school had announced that free Passover lunches would be provided for the Jewish children during this week. Yvette ate the free lunch provided by the school and Mildred brought her lunch from home in a brown paper bag. Because of school rules, free-lunch children and bag-lunch children could not sit in the same section, and the two girls always ate separately. This week, however, they had planned to eat together.

Finally the bell sounded and all the children left the classroom for lunch. As they had already planned, Yvette and Mildred went right up to the line where the Jewish children were filing up for lunch trays. I hope no one asks me nothing, Yvette said to herself. They stood close to each other and held hands. Every once in a while one would squeeze the other's hand in a gesture of reassurance, and they would giggle softly.

The two girls lived just a few houses away from one another. Yvette lived on the top floor of a tenement, in a four room apartment which she shared with her parents, grandmother, three older sisters, two younger brothers, and baby sister. Mildred was an only child. She lived with her parents in the three small rooms in back of the candy store they owned.

During this school year, the two girls had become good friends. Every day after public school, Mildred went to a Hebrew school. Yvette went to catechism twice a week, preparing for her First Communion and Confirmation. Most evenings after supper, they played together in front of the candy store. Yvette was a frequent visitor in Mildred's apartment. They listened to their favorite radio programs together. Yvette looked forward to the Hershey's chocolate bar that Mr. Fox, Mildred's father, would give her.

The two girls waited patiently on the lunch line as they slowly moved along toward the food counter. Yvette was delighted when she saw what was placed on the trays: a hard-boiled egg, a bowl of soup that looked like vegetable, a large piece of cracker, milk, and an apple. She stretched over to see what the regular free lunch was, and it was the usual: a bowl of watery stew, two slices of dark bread, milk, and cooked prunes in a thick syrup. She was really glad to be standing with Mildred.

"Hey Yvette!" She heard someone call her name. It was Elba Cruz, one of her classmates. "What's happening? Why are you standing there?"

"I'm having lunch with Mildred today," she answered, and looked at Mildred, who nodded.

"Oh yeah?" Elba said. "Why are they getting a different lunch from us?"

"It's their special holiday and they gotta eat that special food, that's all," Yvette answered.

"But why?" persisted Elba.

"Else it's a sin, that's why. Just like we can't have no meat on Friday," Yvette said.

"A sin... Why—why is it a sin?" This time, she looked at Mildred.

"It's a special lunch for Passover," Mildred said.

"Passover? What is that?" asked Elba.

"It's a Jewish holiday. Like you got Easter, so we have Passover. We can't eat no bread."

"Oh...."

"You better get in your line before the teacher comes," Yvette said quickly.

"You're here!" said Elba.

"I'm only here because Mildred invited me," Yvette answered. Elba shrugged her shoulders and walked away.

"They gonna kick you outta there... I bet you are not supposed to be on that line," she called back to Yvette.

"Dumbbell!" Yvette answered. She turned to Mildred and asked, "Why can't you eat bread, Mildred?"

"We just can't. We are only supposed to eat matzo. What you see there." Mildred pointed to the large cracker on the tray.

"Oh," said Yvette. "Do you have to eat an egg too?"

"No... but you can't have no meat, because you can't have meat and milk together... like at the same time."

"Why?"

"Because it's against our religion. Besides, it's very bad. It's not supposed to be good for you."

"It's not?" asked Yvette.

"No," Mildred said. "You might get sick. You see, you are better off waiting like a few hours until you digest your foods and then you can have meat or the milk. But not together."

"Wow," said Yvette. "You know, I have meat and milk together all the time. I wonder if my mother knows it's not good for you."

By this time the girls were at the counter. Mildred took one tray and Yvette quickly took another.

"I hope no one notices me," Yvette whispered to Mildred. As the two girls walked toward a long lunch table, they heard giggling and Yvette saw Elba and some of the kids she usually ate lunch with pointing and laughing at her. Stupids, thought Yvette, ignoring them and following Mildred. The two girls sat down with the special lunch group.

Yvette whispered to Mildred, "This looks good!" and started to crack the eggshell.

Yvette felt Mildred's elbow digging in her side. "Watch out!" Mildred said.

"What is going on here?" It was the voice of one of the teachers who monitored them during lunch. Yvette looked up and saw the teacher coming toward her.

"You! You there!" the teacher said, pointing to Yvette. "What are you doing over there?" Yvette looked at the woman and was unable to speak.

"What are you doing over there?" she repeated.

"I went to get some lunch," Yvette said softly.

"What? Speak up! I can't hear you."

"I said... I went to get some lunch," she said a little louder.

"Are you entitled to a free lunch?"

"Yes."

"Well... and are you Jewish?"

Yvette stared at her and she could feel her face getting hot and flushed.

"I asked you a question. Are you Jewish?" Another teacher Yvette knew came over and the lunchroom became quiet. Everyone was looking at Yvette, waiting to hear what was said. She turned to look at Mildred, who looked just as frightened as she felt. Please don't let me cry, thought Yvette.

"What's the trouble?" asked the other teacher.

"This child," the woman pointed to Yvette, "is eating lunch here with the Jewish children, and I don't think she's Jewish. She doesn't—I've seen her before; she gets free lunch, all right. But she looks like one of the—" Hesitating, the woman went on, "She looks Spanish."

"I'm sure she's not Jewish," said the other teacher.

"All right now," said the first teacher, "what are you doing here? Are you Spanish?"

"Yes."

"Why did you come over here and get in that line? You went on the wrong lunch line!"

Yvette looked down at the tray in front of her.

"Get up and come with me. Right now!" Getting up, she dared not look around her. She felt her face was going to burn up. Some of the children were laughing; she could hear the suppressed giggles and an occasional "Ooooh." As she started to walk behind the teacher, she heard her say, "Go back and bring that tray." Yvette felt slightly weak at the knees but managed to turn around, and going back to the table, she returned the tray to the counter. A kitchen worker smiled nonchalantly and removed the tray full of food.

"Come on over to Mrs. Ralston's office," the teacher said, and gestured to Yvette that she walk in front of her this time.

Inside the vice-principal's office, Yvette stood, not daring to look at Mrs. Rachel Ralston while she spoke.

"You have no right to take someone else's place." Mrs. Ralston continued to speak in an even-tempered, almost pleasant voice. "This time we'll let it go, but next time we will notify your parents and you won't get off so easily. You have to learn, Yvette, right from wrong. Don't go where you don't belong . . ."

Yvette left the office and heard the bell. Lunchtime was over.

Yvette and Mildred met after school in the street. It was late in the afternoon. Yvette was returning from the corner grocery with a food package, and Mildred was coming home from Hebrew school.

"How was Hebrew school?" asked Yvette.

"O.K." Mildred smiled and nodded. "Are you coming over tonight to listen to the radio? 'Mr. Keene, Tracer of Lost Persons' is on."

"O.K.," said Yvette. "I gotta bring this up and eat. Then I'll come by."

Yvette finished supper and was given permission to visit her friend.

"Boy, that was a good program, wasn't it, Mildred?" Yvette ate her candy with delight.

Mildred nodded and looked at Yvette, not speaking. There was a long moment of silence. They wanted to talk about it, but it was as if this afternoon's incident could not be mentioned. Somehow each girl was afraid of disturbing that feeling of closeness they felt for one another. And yet when their eyes met they looked away with an embarrassed smile.

"I wonder what's on the radio next," Yvette said, breaking the silence.

"Nothing good for another half hour," Mildred answered. Impulsively, she asked quickly, "Yvette, you wanna have some matzo? We got some for the holidays."

"Is that the cracker they gave you this afternoon?"

"Yeah. We can have some."

"All right." Yvette smiled.

Mildred left the room and returned holding a large square cracker. Breaking off a piece, she handed it to Yvette.

"It don't taste like much, does it?" said Yvette.

"Only if you put something good on it," Mildred agreed, smiling.

"Boy, that Mrs. Ralston sure is dumb," Yvette said, giggling. They looked at each other and began to laugh loudly.

"Old dumb Mrs. Ralston," said Mildred, laughing convulsively. "She's scre . . . screwy."

"Yeah," Yvette said, laughing so hard tears began to roll down her cheeks. "Dop . . . dopey . . . M . . . Mi . . . Mrs. Ra . . . Ral . . . ston . . ."

# CHAPTER 8

# THE WORLD BEYOND

Hugo Martínez-Serros, "Ricardo's War"
William Saroyan, "Citizens of the Third Grade"
Clark Blaise, "How I Became a Jew"
Davida Adedjouma, "The Day We Discovered We Were Black"

The classrooms represented in these stories are invaded by events beyond their doors; students' awareness of international events, ethnic and racial differences, and social class affects their behavior in the classroom. National, ethnic, and family loyalties and prejudices influence the actions of students and teachers.

A Mexican American boy is the title character in Hugo Martínez Serros's "Ricardo's War." He is terrified by the news of Japan's bombing of Pearl Harbor. The school's new emphasis on the progress of the war involving frequent patriotic assemblies and air raid drills only serves to heighten his fears. It is only when a scarcity of paper gives direction to the school's war effort that Ricardo finds an outlet for his feelings. For him and his friends collecting paper becomes their patriotic service, and the area in which they live their battleground.

When the rest of the class's interest in the collection project slackens, Ricardo and his friends continue to bring in more and more paper. Mrs. Gleason, their teacher, is surprised: "She had expected the *most American* of her pupils to collect the largest amounts of paper." Still, she finds ways of deprecating these children despite their achievements, but their lack of sophistication in the ways of subtle irony prevent them from understanding the full import of their teacher's condescending words.

William Saroyan's "Citizens of the Third Grade" depicts a classroom in which students replicate international battles by taking sides according to their parents' racial and ethnic identities. The story takes place in "the foreign section" of a city in California; the 1935 war between Italy and Abyssinia inflames relationships between Italian American and African American students in the classroom. The teacher, fearing the increasing tension, does not know what to do. When the situation explodes in a fight, she intervenes but discovers that classroom discipline is not enough to stop the small-scale war.

Clark Blaise's "How I Became a Jew" speaks to a different way in which the outside world affects the classroom. Gerald, a Southern boy, enters an urban junior high school in the North, where he encounters Jewish and African American students as peers for the first time. Suddenly the protected world in which he had lived and succeeded changes into a threatening environment in which he is the outsider mocked even by his teachers. In an alienated frame of mind Gerald also finds himself at the end of the day in a classroom full of Jewish students; a Jewish teacher has set the curriculum aside in favor of discussions about Israel. After the ordeals of his first day, this idealized picture of Israel has an unusually potent effect on Gerald, offering him hope in the midst of the limiting, smug confines of his new junior high school and his parents' prejudiced world view.

In Davida Adedjouma's tale, "The Day We Discovered We Were Black," certain harsh realities of the outside world are brought home to a classroom of African American children by a new white teacher. Until then the closest the narrator and her classmates "... had ever come in touching range of living, breathing white people was the sales clerks downtown and they didn't count because we didn't know them personally." The new teacher, Miss Fleischhacker, however, changes that.

Miss Fleischhacker soon demonstrates intolerance for humor; when the children begin to giggle uncontrollably over a humorous incident, Miss Fleischhacker is determined to exercise her authority. As she bangs her yardstick on her desk, "something was cracking her friendly-teacher's-mask into little tiny pieces." Though most of the children are scared into stillness, one of the students can't stop laughing. The way Miss Fleischhacker brings his laughing to a halt leaves a lasting impression on the young students: from that day on "we [the students] divided the world up into black people and white people."

Thus in several different ways the permeability of the school and classroom to outside events and influences is made evident in this set of stories. Although all of them are based on events that may be considered in the past, analogous situations continue to affect life in the classrooms of today.

# Ricardo's War

## HUGO MARTÍNEZ-SERROS

Ricardo pulled on his coat in the lobby. Something was going on outside and he hurried through the big door of the movie theatre to see what it was. Then he heard the news boys: "Extra! Extra! Japs bomb Pearl Harbor! War! War!" Newspapers under their arms, they barked their message over and over. Everywhere people swarmed around them and traffic slowed in the streets. The air was charged with commotion.

Alarm gripped Ricardo and he felt a deep instantaneous chill. He buttoned his coat, turned up his collar and looked fearfully into the night sky. He fought back his tears as a single thought slashed at him: *War! War! That's what they're sayin'; it's war! I'll never get home! I'm too far away, never!* He was eleven and had never left the city, had ridden in an automobile twice, and had never seen a plane up close. But he knew about war—it changed everything right away, destroyed everything in a flash. At the corner, close to panic, he boarded a streetcar.

That afternoon, in the bright sun the streetcars had carried him along, swaying from side to side when they sped, making him smile because he swayed with them. He had always felt safe in streetcars, liked the feeling of independence they gave him. Now it was dark and he pressed his face to the window, searched the sky for bombers. *I'd rather see them in the daytime,* he thought, *know where they are so I can get ready.* He felt trapped in that red and yellow cage—so much glass and steel that ran along on tracks—and felt his fear grow. They flew at him from his memory, planes he had seen dropping bombs—newsreel planes that for years had been bringing the wars in Europe and Asia to everyone who went to the movies, and picture-card war planes.

When he was younger he had collected bubblegum picture cards of those far-off wars. He was thinking now of the two most terrifying cards: one, its background a burning mountain of human bodies, showed a horde of naked yellow men firing rifles at onrushing tanks and infantrymen; in the other, planes were bombing a city, buildings everywhere exploding, crumbling, frightened people fleeing in confusion. His eyes continued to search the sky. Each time they found what they were looking for, he stiffened, drew in his breath, listened and waited. But the blinking lights moved across the black sky and nothing happened. He exhaled slowly and looked around at the other riders. Their composure mocked him, appalled him, and he dried his hands on his coat.

From the streetcar everything looked unchanged. Familiar buildings stood where they always had and there were no signs of rubble. But time had slowed. This ride home had always been fast and now it was taking forever. In his mind he sped on in search of his house, and, where it should have been, he found a hole. Two transfers and a long time afterward he finally spied his house. Before the streetcar came to a full stop, its doors swung open and he jumped from it, ran across the street, pushed through the front door and hurried up the stairs, not knowing what he would find. He entered the flat. Nothing had changed. He undressed silently and went to bed.

Bombers and tanks hunted him. He was naked but did not feel cold. In the dark he ran looking for a street that would lead him out of the city. A street unknown to him. If he did not find it before dawn they would see him. They were in hot pursuit when he opened his eyes.

Monday morning. *I must be crazy,* he thought, his heart racing. It seemed no different from other mornings. He got out of bed, heard the others' voices, then he heard it on the radio. It was true! Buttoning his shirt, he tried not to listen to the radio. It terrified him with details. He plugged his ears with his hands, pressing hard, and went to the kitchen. From the table the newspaper fired its headline at him: JAPS BOMB PEARL HAR-

BOR! His hands fell from his head, his arms dropped to his sides. The radio blared.

At school he found things exactly as he had left them on Friday. There were no barricades. No gun emplacements. No troops stationed close by to protect the children, to guard the steel mills, two short blocks away, from surprise attacks. What would they do, Ricardo wondered, against guns and bombs and tanks? What if he never saw his family again? It had happened to his mother and father—in Mexico, the Revolution. They had told him. Without warning, the machine-guns started. Children running in the streets, dropping books, caught in crossfire. Shells. Falling buildings, people inside. They came with guns, looking for food and money. Killed. At night too, when nobody expected them. And the stink of dead bodies.

Before the week was out Germany had declared war on the United States. Ricardo was struck dumb with fear.

It baffled Ricardo that they were not afraid, wounded him that they were so unfeeling, so different from him. More than anything, it shamed him, shamed him to speechlessness, separated him from them, casting him deeper into fear and shame. How could he tell them? How could he explain to them what they could see?—that everything was unprotected! They would laugh at him, single him out, call him names. *Coward!* He buried his head in his hands. *¡Cobarde!* It was the worst thing his father could say of anyone. *¡Cobarde!* What his mother called him when he struck his younger sister. *¡Cobarde!*

There it was, his terror. He wanted to push the war away. If he didn't think about it, didn't hear or read about it, it would go away. News of defeat terrified him, and reports of victory only meant that the war went on. He would avoid it, it was the only way.

In the early months of the war, a current events class was held once a week, more often than that if the fighting was fierce. Using large maps, the teachers tracked the war for the children. They answered questions and explained why America would win: "We've never lost a war because we're the most powerful nation in the world. We've never had to fight a foreign war on our own soil. And we're the world's first democracy, the land of the free and the home of the brave." They explained how America was winning the war even when it seemed that she was not: "We've just begun to fight. Wait until we reach full production. They sneaked up on us, but things will be different now that we know what's what." Ricardo tried not to hear, thought of the park, movies he had seen, the swimming pool at the YMCA.

As if to mock Ricardo, the whole school was suddenly caught up in "the war effort." "Patriotism" became a common word and the principal, Mr. Fitts, spoke of it repeatedly in assemblies that were held often now. In the auditorium, principal, teachers and students gathered to sing songs ("God bless America," "Anchors aweigh," "Over hill, over dale, as we hit the dusty trail," "From the halls of Montezuma," "O, semper paratus," "Off we go into the wild blue yonder"), to hear stories of American bravery and heroism, to cheer the teams of students that, armed with rifles and sabres and American flags, performed crisp drills. There was no let up.

All those assemblies made Frederick Douglass Sneed important. He was as big and strong as a man and never misbehaved in class, and Mrs. Gleason, the English teacher, put him in charge of a crew of boys to set up the stage on assembly days and to put things away afterward. She said it was a job for the boys who had learned all they ever would in class, those who didn't mind straining their backs or getting dirty and would do more good in the auditorium. Freddie, who had complete control of the boys, made Ricardo his "lieutenant," and Lalo, Mario and Manny rounded out the "squad."

Calls for national cooperation, vigilance and sacrifice reached Ricardo's classrooms from the White House. His teachers, their voices like bugles, sounded the alarms that came from Washington: "Now, children, we must be careful, we must all work together. Chicago is the most important city in the entire war effort because of our steel mills and railroads. It's something the enemy knows. We must be on our guard against spies and sabotage. Look out for strangers who ask about the steel mills. Tell the police. Tell your fathers not to talk about their work to strangers. Don't repeat anything your brothers in the service say about troop movements. Remember, 'A slip of the lip might sink a ship.'"

These warnings fueled Ricardo's fears, which flamed like the fires in the steel mills, burning day and night now and filling the sky with smoke. They were things he had to know for his protection, but he didn't want to know them.

One day the windows, eyes that looked out from the numbing drudgery of the classroom, began to be blinded one by one. Ricardo watched every detail of the operation. Measurements were taken, the blades of the big shears cut cleanly, cement was applied carefully. It took time, but in the end every window was blinded with a heavy gauze-like cloth. Now everybody was protected. In an air raid nobody would be slashed by flying knives of glass. The wounded-looking windows, bandaged like casualties of the war, oppressed Ricardo. He could no longer look out; he would not see *them* when they came. He would have felt much safer with a battery of anti-aircraft guns on the playground.

The air raid drills were orderly, full of urgency and fearful excitement. At the sound of the alarm the teachers, like platoon sergeants, quickly moved the children to prearranged areas. Taking shelter in the building, they shunned its most vulnerable spots—open spaces, windows—and found cover under tables and desks, along inner walls, in the basement. For several minutes—while imaginary planes flew overhead and until the all-clear signal sounded—they all curled up on the floor. Ricardo could hear some of the others whispering:

"If they come for the mills, we'll never escape, we're too close. My father says so. They'd hit us too."

"If they come! But they won't. They can't fly that far. Across the ocean."

"They take off from carriers. It'd be easy to get here."

"We'd shoot 'em down before they got this far!"

"Yeah! Like we did at Pearl Harbor!"

Easily stirred, Ricardo's imagination filled the skies with planes that dropped bombs on the steel mills. He curled up more tightly, pressing his hands to his ears, and waited for his bomb, knowing it would blow him to pieces when it found him. He remembered Fourth-of-July firecrackers he had set off under glass jars.

The war filled Ricardo's world. Day after day it made its way into everything, touched everybody's life. Young men over eighteen disappeared into the services, their lives represented by blue stars displayed in windows, their deaths by gold stars, and there was a lot of talk about blue-star and gold-star mothers. The dark green pack of Lucky Strike cigarettes abruptly turned white because "Lucky Strike green has gone to war." Suddenly there were more jobs than workers, and *braceros,* laborers from Mexico, appeared everywhere. In mills and factories women took over the work of men, carried lunch pails, began to drive taxicabs and trucks. Ricardo's father sometimes worked seven days a week and his older brothers found jobs. Debts of many years standing were finally paid off and, for the first time, worrylines disappeared from his mother's face. His father now kept a couple of bottles of beer in the icebox. Certain things that his mother needed became scarce or were rationed—sugar, coffee, meat, soap, paper goods. Some people bought them at high prices on the Black Market. For Ricardo's teachers it became harder to buy nylons, cigarettes, and gasoline; they did not hesitate to ask their students for ration coupons that their parents did not use. More than anywhere else, Ricardo heard the war in popular songs that filled the air: "Dear Mom, the weather today...all the boys in the camp"; "They're either too young or too old"; "There's a star-spangled banner waving somewhere"; "Praise the Lord and pass the ammunition"; "Comin' in on a wing an' a prayer"; "Rosie, the riveter"; "There'll be bluebirds over the White Cliffs of Dover." Ricardo, who loved the movies, seldom went now because movies about the war filled screens everywhere. Unendingly, the war dragged on.

Ricardo knew that the Japanese and the Germans were "the enemies of freedom." Everybody knew it. The Japanese even more than the Germans, because they were so sneaky. He did not know a Japanese; there were none in his school. But he knew what they looked like from newsreels and pictures in the paper. Mrs. Gleason explained that they were "just like Chinks, only smaller." Now, whenever he could, he would look through the window of the Chinese laundry a half block from the YMCA and feel that he was looking at "the enemies of freedom." Along with everybody else, Ricardo learned that the Japs were doubly yellow—they had yellow skins and they were cowards. *¡Cobardes!* Sneaks especially, that's what they were. Mrs. Gleason never tired of telling her students that "The lesson of Pearl Harbor is that those little animals can't be trusted. That's what we mean when we say, 'Remember Pearl Harbor!' We can't trust little animals anywhere in the world! It's like 'Remember the Alamo!'" And this made Ricardo very uneasy.

Japp's Potato Chips had been a part of Ricardo's life as long as he could remember. Their blue and gray waxed-paper bags hung temptingly on little stands in every store. Now suddenly they became Jay's Potato Chips. And now his older brother Ramiro called him Tojo when he got angry at him. It wasn't just that he, Ricardo, wore glasses. There was something more. "You look Japanese," Ramiro would say. "Look at your eyes, it's there. Hasn't anybody ever told you?" When he was alone, Ricardo searched his face in the mirror. And he studied Japanese faces whenever he saw them. In the end he saw that Ramiro was right; it was in his eyes—they were tipped and slightly puffy. And he was dark like some of them, had their dark eyes and black hair.

"What we gonna play?" somebody asked. It was recess and they were on the playground.

"Remember Pearl Harbor! Let's play war!"

"We need some Japs. Who's gonna be the Japs?"

Ricardo moved away slowly, hoping they wouldn't call him back. He took off his glasses and cleaned them.

"Hey Freddie, you be a Jap!"

"You crazy? I can't be no Jap, I'm colored an' big!"

"Well I can't be no damn Jap neither! My eyes ain't slanted or swolled up."

"Who's ever the Japs can win the battle!" somebody offered.

"Then you be a Jap, you're so interested!"

The bell rang, ending their quarrel.

The Germans were different. Not like the Japanese. Nobody said the Germans were sneaky. They were big, blond, blue-eyed, like many Americans; but they looked tougher. Everybody said they were smart, said their scientists were the best in the world. Only the Americans were smart enough and tough enough to beat Germany. Ricardo knew some Germans, German-Americans, had always known some because they went to his school. Ernie Krause and Olga Schmidt were in his class. Nobody said anything to Olga, she was quiet; but everybody jeered Ernie, called him Kraut, Heinie, Nazi, traitor, whenever he said, "The Germans got the best fighting force in the world. You'll see, they'll win the war." Nobody hit Ernie when he talked that way; his classmates argued with him, got angry with him the way they would have if he had cheered not his own but another school's team.

Ricardo wondered why nobody changed the names of German rye and sauerkraut. Wouldn't sabotage be easy for the Germans if they looked like Americans? And weren't they more dangerous than the Japanese if they were smarter? Someone was always willing to be a German in war games. And why didn't anyone say anything when children goose-stepped back and forth in front of Jake Bernstein's dry goods store, arms raised obliquely in front of them, palms open and down, shouting, "Heil Hitler, Heil Hitler!" until the old man, quivering with rage, came out with a broom and chased them away?

Germany made Ricardo think. He didn't want to, but he couldn't help it. The only way to understand the Germans was by accepting what others said—that even though they were wrong in what they were doing, you had to admire the Germans for opposing all Europe and beating the hell out of it. Ricardo understood the importance of force. It was what he and his schoolmates understood best. The trouble with this explanation was that it led you to conclude that Japan, which was smaller than Germany, deserved greater admiration because it had not only taken on some big countries, but had attacked the United States directly. It made no sense, what people said of the Germans and Japanese. Just as it made no sense, no sense at all, for people not to be afraid of war.

Everybody participated or wanted to participate in the war effort. People talked of how hard it was to do with less, and yet many seemed to have more. When he was finally forced to accept the reality of the war, Ricardo timidly began to think of how he might help. Some children felt themselves directly involved in the fighting every time they bought defense stamps and bonds. The teachers said everyone had to buy them. Anyone who didn't wasn't patriotic and wouldn't pass at the end of the semester. But few had money to help in this way and, in any case, they were not Ricardo and his friends. Mostly they were the *gueros,* those who looked like their teachers and had always boasted that they were the *real* Americans. Now they flaunted their patriotism in the faces of those who did not buy. Ricardo and his friends kept silent.

One day Ernie Krause made those who did not buy defense stamps and bonds feel good. In class one morning Ernie suddenly raised his hand. "What'll happen to the defense stamp an' bond money if we lose the war?" he asked. His tone was genuinely curious, his eyes inquisitively unblinking.

"That's a stupid thing to ask! How can we lose the war? They would take everything from us if we lost the war. Everyone would lose everything! Our defense stamps and bonds would be worth nothing!" Mrs. Gleason answered in a voice that had tightened, her eyes flashing with indignation.

"Suppose, just suppose. I mean, will the people who buy defense stamps an' bonds be treated worse'n the people who don't, I mean if the Germans find out who did an' who didn't?" Ernie insisted, unruffled by Mrs. Gleason's anger.

"How would I know that?" she snapped. "It's a horrible thing to ask! Shut up, shut up! Not one more word out of you! Why, that's impossible and you know it, you know it!"

Ricardo wondered if the war would ever end. Although his fear had receded, he had not learned to relax, and an adverse turn in the war would bring on old feelings. Air raid drills no longer aroused fear and uncertainty in the others. The teachers, annoyed by it all, no longer curled up on the floor with the students. One day Ricardo noticed that the cloth that covered the panes of glass in windows and doors had been pulled up in some corners. Occasionally, a clouded eye spied into an unsuspecting classroom from the corner of one of the door panes.

Toward the end of the second year of the war a scarcity of paper brought the war effort to the very door of Ricardo's school. A national call for an all-out effort to salvage cardboard and paper was aimed at school children. Ricardo's principal, Mr. Fitts, visited every classroom to explain what had to be done: "We need paper to win the war, mountains of paper! Paper for messages, paper to keep records, paper for maps, for war books and military manuals, paper to pack and ship things— food, equipment, clothing. Can we win it? Can we?"

"Yes! Yes! We can!" the children assured him, their voices ringing.

"Good! I knew I could count on you," he confided. "It'll be hard work," he added, "but we must do it, we must, for as long as it's necessary," and he clenched his fist and waved it at their enemies.

Mr. Fitts gave the children one afternoon off every two weeks to collect cardboard, newspapers, magazines, and to bring them to school, where they would be stored until a truck arrived to haul them away. For months Mr. Fitts and his teachers had worked to cultivate love of country in the children. The success of the paper drives rested on the strength of that love and the principal wondered how deep it went.

In Ricardo's class the first drive was a very great success. Spurred by patriotic zeal and a keen sense of purpose, the children hunted their prey like new warriors eager to prove their valor. They searched basements, attics, coalsheds, garages, and by three o'clock they returned to school with great piles of paper. They came with their arms full, stopping along the way to rest; they came pulling wagons, pushing wheelbarrows and buggies, all shouting, "We'll win the war with paper! We'll win the war with paper!" They collected so much that most of them had to make several trips to get it to school. Freddie, Ricardo, Mario, Lalo and Manny worked as a team and brought more paper than anybody else. But in all the commotion, in all the coming and going, the stacking, the shouting and laughing, the working and horsing around, nobody noticed it. And nobody noticed that Ernie Krause refused to have anything to do with "all that silly shit."

It was Ricardo who realized that the area where they lived, and beyond, had become their battleground. It was he who told his four friends that what they did in the drives would be their part in the war: "It'll be like fightin', really fightin', an' not any of that stamp an' bond stuff." They had been a working crew; now they would be a fighting squad. It was the turning point in the war for Ricardo.

Freddie, narrowing his eyes and talking through his teeth, said what they all felt: "Them bastards, Walker an' Ryan an' Pelky an' their friends! Think they're so goddamn American. Think, they're the only Americans aroun' here."

"We look for paper whenever we can, seven days a week. Then we store it until we pick it up drive-day," Ricardo explained to his friends after the first drive. They were in a corner of the school playground.

"Yeah, 'cause all that easy paper's gone now. Everybody got it. Everybody's gonna wanna get it an' there ain't gonna be that much," Manny added, gently moving his head in agreement. His eyes were shining with seriousness.

"We don't want nobody else comin' with us, right?" Freddie asked, the tone of exclusiveness hard in his throat.

"Right! We're a team! Only good team I ever been on. We don't need no damn *güeros* on it," spat Mario.

"While they're playin' an' screwin' aroun', we'll be fightin'. We'll be whippin' Jap ass an' Kraut ass with all that paper." Lalo's voice was steady, the words clear. He was jabbing the ground with a stick. Suddenly he laughed and said, "An' we'll be whippin' *güero* ass too!"

His voice bright with emotion, Ricardo told them, "I know where we can get a big goddamn wagon with iron wheels!"

Ricardo became their leader. He thought about where they might find paper and how they would collect and store it. "We go first to the houses with blue an' gold stars. They wanna help more'n anybody else, 'specially them blue-star an' gold-star mothers." He thought more about the whole thing than they did and he gave orders and they obeyed. Time began to slip away from him, to move forward too quickly.

It was harder to find paper for the second drive, and this discouraged many students. By the third, the fun was gone from their enterprise and grumbling became commonplace.

"Who ever heard of paper bombs?"

"Maybe they're shootin' spitballs at the Japs an' Krauts."

"We shouldda won the war long ago! Who are the Japs an' Krauts? Nobody!"

"Must be a lotta shittin' goin' on, all that paper our side's been usin'!"

"I'd show them Japs an' Krauts! Jus' gimme a machine-gun!"

Ricardo memorized a speech like the one Mr. Fitts had given, and he and his team went everywhere—to stores, taverns, restaurants, factories, packing houses, barbershops, beauty parlors, filling stations. Like guerillas, they learned more with each drive, broadened the range of their operations and became more single-minded in carrying out their mission.

In Mrs. Gleason's class only Ricardo and his men brought back larger and larger piles of paper with each drive. This puzzled her. She had expected the *most American* of her pupils to collect the largest quantities of paper, the pupils who got the best grades and bought most of the defense stamps and bonds. Something was wrong in all this, she knew it.

After the third drive she had devised a system for grading the paper-collecting effort of each student. Using colored stars, she inverted the color-order assigned to grades in class work. Those who brought no paper were dishonored with a gold star ("It means you're dead"); a silver star designated those who brought a modest amount ("At least you're moving"); a blue star went to those who really did their share ("You're fighting like our boys"); a red star honored Ricardo, Freddie, Lalo, Mario and Manny ("You're our commandos, school commandos").

When Ricardo and his squad returned to school with mountains of newspapers, cardboard and magazines in their wagons, they did it proudly, confidently, stirred by the approval and disbelief of fellow students:

"Wow! Lookit that paper!"

"Damn! Where'd you guys get all that paper?"

"You been savin' it for months!"

"Boy! You guys could start your own junkyard!"

Freddie's unassuming "Shhiiit! Ain't nothin' like the paper we bringin' nex' time!" expressed the feelings of his fellow commandos.

Now the days rushed by for Ricardo. He had put his fear behind him and followed news of the war with the keenest interest. When America or the Allies suffered a setback, he would rouse his commandos to an intense search for paper and cardboard, hoping to offset the defeat.

One afternoon Mrs. Gleason announced to her class that they no longer would take part in the drive since they were bringing in so little paper and staying out of class all afternoon. She made one exception—Ricardo and his squad. "After all," she told the others, "they're bigger and stronger than most of you and they know where to find it."

Mr. Fitts learned about the mountains of paper the five boys unfailingly delivered and he called them to his office to commend them. It forced Mrs. Gleason to get them larger red stars, and a bit later she named them the "Commando Reserves Enlisted To Increase National Strength." She entered their names on a special list with this title and displayed it prominently on the bulletin board. All this gave the boys a real sense of their worth, finally bringing them the official recognition they craved.

Then it occurred to Mrs. Gleason that the undue attention heaped on the five boys was working to the detriment of her best students. After all, they had feelings too; in fact, they were probably more sensitive. To put an end to bruised sensitivities, she bluntly addressed the class: "Now, all of you know that there's backwork and there's headwork. Let's put things in their proper perspective. Those of you who do backwork well should go on doing it, and those of us who do headwork well should get on with *it*. War turns everything upside-down. Do I make myself clear?"

Soon after this she began matter-of-factly to call Ricardo and his crew "the CRETINS," an acronym that filled them with pride. Without a single exception, their schoolmates called them "the COMMANDOS."

# Citizens of the Third Grade

## WILLIAM SAROYAN

Tom Lucca was incredible. Only eight years old, he was perhaps the brightest pupil in the third grade, certainly the most alert, the most intellectually savage, and yet the most humane. Still, his attitude seemed sometimes vicious, as when Aduwa was taken and he came to class leering with pride, the morning newspaper in his pants pocket, as evidence, no doubt, and during recess made the Fascist salute and asked the colored Jefferson twins, Cain and Abel, what they thought of old King Haile Selassie now.

Same as before, Miss Gavit heard Abel say, You got no right to go into Africa.

And Tom, who wouldn't think of getting himself into a fist-fight since he was too intelligent, too neat and good-looking, laughed in that incredible Italian way that meant he knew everything, and said, We'll take Addis Ababa day after tomorrow.

Of course this was only a gag, one of Tom Lucca's frequent and generally innocent outbursts, but both Abel and Cain didn't like it, and Miss Gavit was sure there would be trouble pretty soon no matter what happened.

If General Bono *did* take Addis Ababa and Tom Lucca forgot himself and irritated Cain and Abel, there would surely be trouble between the colored boys in the Third Grade and the Italian boys, less brilliant perhaps than Tom Lucca, but more apt to accept trouble, and fight about it: Pat Ravenna, Willy Trentino, Carlo Gaeta, and the others. Enough of them certainly. And then there were the other grades. The older boys.

On the other hand, if Ras Desta Demtu, the son-in-law of Emperor Haile Selassie, turned back the Italian forces at Harar, Cain and Abel, somewhat sullenly, would be triumphant without saying a word, as when Joe Louis, the Brown Bomber of Detroit, knocked out and humiliated poor Maxie Baer, and Cain and Abel had come to class whistling softly to themselves. Everybody, who normally didn't dislike the boys, quiet and easy-going as they were, deeply resented them that morning. No matter what happened, Miss Gavit believed, there would be trouble at Cosmos Public School, and it seemed very strange that this should be so, since these events were taking place thousands of miles away from the school and did not concern her class of school-children, each of whom was having a sad time with the new studies, fractions and English grammar.

Tom Lucca was impossible. He had no idea how dangerous his nervous and joyous behavior was getting to be. It was beginning to irritate Miss Gavit herself who, if anything, was in favor of having the ten million Ethiopians of Abyssinia under Italian care, which would do them much less harm than good and probably furnish some of the high government officials with shoes and perhaps European garments.

It was really amazing that many of the leaders of Abyssinia performed their duties barefooted. How could anybody be serious without shoes on his feet, and five toes of each foot visible? And when they walked no important sound of moving about, as when Americans with shoes on their feet moved about.

Of course she hated the idea of going into an innocent and peaceful country and bombing little cities and killing all kinds of helpless people. She didn't like all the talk about poison gases and machine guns and liquid fire. She thought it was very cruel of the Italians to think of killing people in order to gain a little extra land in which to expand, as Mussolini said.

Miss Gavit just bet ten cents the Italians could do all the expanding they needed to do right at home, in the 119,000 square miles of Italy. She just bet ten cents with anybody that Mussolini didn't really need more land, all he wanted to do was show off and be a hero. It was dreadful the way some people wanted to be great, no matter how many people they killed. It wasn't as if the people of Abyssinia were pagans; they were Christians, just like the Italians: their church was the Christian church, and they worshipped Jesus, the same as Pope Pius.

(The Pope, though, was a man Miss Gavit didn't like. She saw him in a Paramount News Reel, and she didn't like his face. He looked sly for a holy man. She didn't think he was really holy. She thought he looked more like a scheming politician than like a man who was humble and good and would rather accept pain for himself than have it inflicted upon others. He was small and old and cautious. First he prayed for peace, and then Italy went right ahead and invaded Abyssinia. Then Pope Pius prayed for peace again, but it was war just the same. Who did he think he was fooling?)

She guessed every important man in the world was afraid, the same as the Pope. Poor loud-mouthed Huey got his, and for what? What did poor Huey want for the people except a million dollars for every family? What was wrong with that? Why did they have to kill a man like that, who really had the heart of a child, even if he did shout over the radio and irritate President Roosevelt by hinting that he, Huey Long of Louisiana, would be the next President of the United States? What did they want to invent guns for in the first place? What good did guns do the people of the world, except teach them to kill one another? First they worried about wild animals, and then Indians, and then they began worrying about one another, France worrying about Germany, Germany worrying about France and England and Russia, and Russia worrying about Japan, and Japan worrying about China.

Miss Gavit didn't know. She couldn't quite understand the continuous mess of the world. When it was the World War she was a little girl in grammar school who thought she would be a nun in a convent, and then a little later, a singer in opera: that was after the San Carlo opera troupe came to town and gave a performance of *La Bohème* at the Hippodrome Theatre and Miss Gavit

went home crying about poor consumptive Mimi. Then the war ended and the parades ended and she began to forget her wilder dreams, like the dream of some day meeting a fine man like William Farnum and being his wife, or the still more fantastic dream of suddenly learning from authoritative sources that she was the true descendant of some royal European family, a princess, and all the other wild dreams of sudden wealth and ease and fame and importance, sudden surpassing loveliness, the most beloved young lady in the world. And sobering with the years, with the small knowledge of each succeeding grade at school, she chose teaching as her profession, and finally, after much lonely studying, full of sudden clear-weather dreaming of love, she graduated from the normal school, twenty-two years old, and was a teacher, if she could get a job.

She was very lucky, and for the past five years had been at Cosmos Public School, in the foreign section of the city, west of the Southern Pacific tracks, where she herself was born and lived. Her father was very happy about this good luck. The money she earned helped buy new furniture, a radio, and later on a Ford, and sent her little sister Ethel to the University of California. But she didn't know. So many things were happening all over the world she was afraid something dangerous would happen, and very often, walking home from school, late in the afternoon, she would suddenly feel the nearness of this danger with such force that she would unconsciously begin to walk faster and look about to see if anything were changed, and at the same time remember poignantly all the little boys and girls who had passed through her class and gone on to the higher grades, as if these young people were in terrible danger, as if their lives might suddenly end, with terrific physical pain.

And now, with this trouble between Italy and Abyssinia, Benito Mussolini, Dictator of Italy, and Haile Selassie, the Lion of Judah, Miss Gavit began, as Tom Lucca's joyousness increased, to feel great inward alarm about the little boy because she knew truthfully that he was very kind-hearted, and only intellectually mischievous. How many times had she seen him hugging Mrs. Amadio's little twenty-month-old daughter, chattering to the baby in the most energetic Italian, kissing it, shouting at Mrs. Amadio, and Mrs. Amadio guffawing in the loudest and most delightful manner imaginable, since Tom was such a wit, so full of innocent outspokenness, sometimes to the extent even of being almost vulgar. The Italians. That's the way they were, and it was not evil, it was a virtue. They were just innocent. They chattered about love and passion and childbirth and family quarrels as if it were nothing, just part of the day's experience. And how many times had she seen Tom Lucca giving sandwiches from his lunch to Johnny Budge whose father had no job and no money? And not doing it in a way that was self-righteous. She remembered the way Tom would say, Honest, Johnny, I can't eat another bite. Go ahead, I don't want this sandwich. I already ate three. I'll throw it away if you don't take it. And Johnny Budge would say, All right, Tom, if you're sure you don't want it. That was the strange part of it, the same little Italian boy being fine like that, giving away his lunch, and at the same time so crazy-proud about the taking of Aduwa, as if that little mud-city in Africa had anything to do with him, coming to class with the morning paper and leering at everybody, stirring the savage instincts of the Negro twins, Cain and Abel Jefferson.

Miss Gavit believed she would do something to stop all the nonsense. She wouldn't sit back and see something foolish and ugly happen right under her nose. She knew what she would do. She would keep Tom Lucca after school.

When the last pupil had left the room and the door was closing automatically and slowly, Miss Gavit began to feel how uneasy Tom was, sitting still but seeming to be moving about, looking up at her, and then at the clock, and then rolling his pencil on the desk. When the door clicked shut, she remembered all the little boys she had kept in after school during the five years at Cosmos and how it was the same with each of them, resent-ment at accusation, actual or implied, and dreadful impatience, agonized longing to be free, even if, as she knew, many of them really liked her, did not hate her as many pupils often hated many teachers, only wanting to be out of the atmosphere of petty crime and offense, wanting to be restored to innocence, the dozens and dozens of them. She wondered how she would be able to tell Tom why she had kept him after school and explain how she wanted his behavior, which was always subtle, to change, not in energy, but in impulse. How would she be able to tell him not to be so proud about what Mussolini was doing? Just be calm about the whole business until Italy annexed Abyssinia and everything became normal in the world again, at least more or less normal, and Cain and Abel Jefferson didn't go about the school grounds apart from everybody, letting their resentment grow in them.

What's the matter now? Tom said. He spoke very politely, though, the inflexion being humble, implying that it was *he* who was at fault: he was ready to admit this, and if his offense could be named he would try to be better. He didn't want any trouble.

Nothing's the matter, Miss Gavit said. I want to talk to you about the war, that's all.

Yes, ma'am, he said.

Well, said Miss Gavit, you've got to be careful about hurting the feelings of Cain and Abel Jefferson.

Hurting their feelings? he thought. Who the hell's hurting whose feelings? What kind of feelings get hurt so easily? What the hell did I ever say? The whole world is against the Italians and *our* feelings ain't hurt. They want to see them wild Africans kick hell out of our poor soft soldiers, two pairs of shoes each. How about our feelings? Everybody hates Mussolini. What for? Why don't they hate somebody else for a change?

He was really embarrassed, really troubled. He didn't understand, and Miss Gavit noticed how he began to tap the pencil on the desk.

I don't know, he began to say, and then began tapping the pencil swifter than before.

He gestured in a way that was very saddening to Miss Gavit and then looked up at her.

You are an American, said Miss Gavit, and so are Cain and Abel Jefferson. We are all Americans. This sort of quarreling will lead nowhere.

What quarreling? he thought. Everybody in the world hates us. Everybody calls us names. I guess Italians don't like that either.

He could think of nothing to say to Miss Gavit. He knew she was all right, a nice teacher, but he didn't know how to explain about everybody hating the Italians, because this feeling was in Italian and he couldn't translate it. At home it was different. Pa came home from the winery and sat at the table for supper and asked Mike, Tom's big brother in high school, what the afternoon paper said, and Ma listened carefully, and Mike told them exactly what was going on, about England and the ships in the Red Sea, and France, and the League of Nations, and Pa swallowed a lot of spaghetti and got up and spit in the sink, clearing his throat, and said in Italian, All right, all right, all right, let them try to murder Italy, them bastards, and Ma poured more wine in his cup and Pa said in American, God damn it, and Tom knew how the whole world was against Italy and he was glad about the good luck of the army in Africa, taking Aduwa, and all the rest of it, but now, at school, talking with Miss Gavit, he didn't know what to say.

Yes, ma'am, he said.

Miss Gavit thought it was wonderful the way he understood everything, and she laughed cheerfully, feeling that now nothing would happen.

All right, Tom, she said. Just be careful about what you say.

You may go now.

Jesus Christ, he thought. To hell with everybody.

He got up and walked to the door. Then he began walking home, talking to himself in Italian and cussing in American because everybody was against them.

Tom was very quiet at the supper table, but when Pa asked Mike how it was going in Abyssinia and Mike told him the Italians were moving forward very nicely and it looked like everything would turn out all right before the League would be able to clamp down on Italy, Tom said in Italian, We'll show them bastards. His father wondered what was eating the boy.

What's the matter, Tom? he said in American.

Aw, Tom said, they kept me in after school just because I talked about taking Aduwa. They don't like it.

His father laughed and spit in the sink and then became very serious.

They don't like it, hey? he said in Italian. They are sorry the Italian army isn't slaughtered? They hate us, don't they? Well, you talk all you like about the army. You tell them every day what the army is doing. Don't be afraid.

The next day Cain Jefferson swung at Tom Lucca and almost hit him in the eye. Willy Trentino then challenged Cain Jefferson to a fight after school, and on her way home Miss Gavit saw the gang of Italian and colored and Russian boys in the empty lot behind Gregg's Bakery. She knew for sure it was a fight about the war. She stood in the street staring at the boys, listening to their shouting, and all she could think was, This is terrible; they've got no right to make these little boys fight this way. What did they want to invent guns for in the first place?

She ran to the crowd of boys, trembling with anger. Everybody stopped shouting when Miss Gavit pushed to the center of the crowd where Willy Trentino and Cain Jefferson were fighting. Willy's face was bloody and Cain was so tired he could barely breathe or lift his arms. Miss Gavit clapped her hands as she did in class when she was angry and the two boys stopped fighting. They turned and stared at her, relieved and ashamed.

Stop this nonsense, she said, panting for breath from excitement and anger. I am ashamed of you, Willy. And you, Cain. What do you think you are fighting about?

Miss Gavit, said Cain Jefferson, they been laughing at us about the Ethiopians. All of them, teasing us every day.

How about you? said Willy. How about when Joe Louis knocked out Max Baer? How about when it looked like Abyssinia was going to win the war?

Then three or four Italian boys began to talk at once, and Miss Gavit didn't know what to think or do. She remembered a college movie in which two football players who loved the same girl and were fighting about her were asked to shake hands and make up by the girl herself, and Miss Gavit said, I want you boys to shake hands and be friends and go home and never fight again.

Miss Gavit was amazed when neither Willy Trentino nor Cain Jefferson offered to shake hands and make up, and she began to feel that this vicious war in Abyssinia, thousands of miles away, was going to bring about something very foolish and dangerous in the foreign section. In the crowd she saw Abel Jefferson, brooding sullenly and not speaking, a profound hate growing in him, and she saw Tom Lucca, his eyes blazing with excitement and delight, and she knew it was all very horrible because, after all, these were only little boys.

And then, instead of shaking hands and making up as she had asked them to do, Willy Trentino and Cain Jefferson, and all the other boys, began to move away, at first walking, and then, overcome with a sense of guilt, running, leaving the poor teacher standing in the empty lot, bewildered and amazed, tearing her handkerchief and crying. They hadn't shaken hands and made up. They hadn't obeyed her. They had run away. She cried bitterly, but not even one small tear fell from her eyes. When old Paul Gregg stepped from the bakery into the lot and said, What's the trouble, Miss Gavit? the little teacher said, Nothing, Mr. Gregg. I want a loaf of bread. I thought I would come in through the back way.

When she got home she took the loaf of white bread out of the brown paper bag and placed it on the red and blue checkered table-cloth of the kitchen table and stared at it for a long time, thinking of a thousand things at one time and not knowing what it was she was thinking about, feeling very sorrowful, deeply hurt, angry with everybody in the world, the Italians, the Pope, Mussolini, the Ethiopians, the Lion of Judah, and England.

She remembered the faces of the boys who were fighting, and the boys who were watching. She breathed in the smell of the bread, and wondered what it was all about everywhere in the world, little Tom Lucca kissing Mrs. Amadio's baby and giving Johnny Budge his sandwich and leering at everybody because of the taking of Aduwa, the Negro twins joyous about Joe Louis and sullen about Abyssinia. The bread smelled delicious but sad and sickening, and Abel Jefferson watching his brother fighting Willy Trentino, and the *Morning Chronicle* with news of crime everywhere, and the *Evening Bee* with the same news, and the holy Pope coming out on the high balcony and making a holy sign and looking sly, and somebody shooting poor Huey Long, and none of her pupils being able to understand about English grammar and fractions, and her wild dreams of supreme loveliness, and her little sister at the University of California, and the day ending. She folded her arms on the table and hid her head. With her eyes closed she said to herself, They killed those boys, they killed them, and she knew they were killing everybody everywhere, and with her eyes shut the smell of the fresh loaf of bread was sickening and tragic, and she couldn't understand anything.

# How I Became a Jew

## CLARK BLAISE

*Cincinnati, September 1950*

"I don't suppose you've attended classes with the coloured before, have you, Gerald?" the principal inquired. He was a jockey-sized man whose dark face collapsed around a greying mustache. His name was DiCiccio.

"No, sir."

"You'll find quite a number in your classes here—" he gestured to the kids on the playground, and the Negroes among them seemed to multiply before my eyes. "My advice is not to expect any trouble and they won't give you any."

"We don't expect none from them," my mother said with great reserve, the emphasis falling slightly on the last word.

DiCicico's eyes wandered over us, calculating but discreet. He was taking in my porkiness, my brushed blond hair, white shirt and new gabardines. And my Georgia accent.

"My boy is no troublemaker."

"I can see that, Mrs. Gordon."

"But I'm here to tell you—just let me hear of any trouble and I'm going straight off to the police."

And now DiCiccio's smile assessed her, as though to say *are you finished?* "That wouldn't be in Gerald's best interest, Mrs. Gordon. We have no serious discipline problems in the elementary school but even if we did, Mrs. Gordon, outside authorities are never the answer. Your boy has to live with them. Police are never a solution." He pronounced the word "pleece" and I wanted to laugh. "Even in the Junior High," he said, jerking his thumb in the direction of the black, prisonlike structure beyond the playground. "There are problems there." His voice was still far-off and I was smiling.

DiCiccio's elementary school was new: bright, low and long, with greenboards and yellow chalk, aluminum frames and blond, unblemished desks. My old school in Georgia, near Moultrie,

had had a room for each grade up through the sixth. Here in Cincinnati the sixth grade itself had ten sections.

"And Gerald, *please* don't call me 'sir.' Don't call anyone that," the principal said with sudden urgency. "That's just asking for it. The kids might think you're trying to flatter the teacher or something."

"Well, I swan—" my mother began. "He learned respect for his elders and nobody is taking that respect away. Never."

"Look—" and now the principal leaned forward, growing smaller as he approached the desk, "I know how Southern schools work. I know 'sir' and 'ma'am.' I know they must have beaten it into you. But I'm trying to be honest, Mrs. Gordon. Your son has a lot of things going against him and I'm trying to help. This intelligence of his can only hurt him unless he learns how to use it. He's white—enough said. And I assume Gordon isn't a Jewish name, is it? Which brings up another thing, Mrs. Gordon. Take a look at those kids out there, the white ones. They look like little old men, don't they? Those are *Jews,* Gerald, and they're as different from the others as you are from the coloured. They were born in Europe and they're living here with their grandparents—don't ask me why, it's a long story. Let's just say they're a little hard to play with. A little hard to like, O.K.?" then he settled back and caught his breath.

"They're the Israelites!" I whispered, as though the Bible had come to life. Then I was led to class.

But the sixth grade was not a home for long; not for the spelling champ and fastest reader in Colquitt County, Georgia. They gave me tests, sent me to a university psychologist who tested my memory and gave me some codes to crack. Then I was advanced.

Seventh grade was in the old building: Leonard Sachs Junior High. A greenish statue of Abraham Lincoln stood behind black iron bars, pointing a finger to the drugstore across the street. The outside steps were pitted and sagging. The hallways were tawny above the khaki lockers, and clusters of dull yellow globes were bracketed to the walls, like torches in the catacombs. By instinct I preferred the used to the new, sticky wood to cold steel, and I would have felt comfortable on that first walk down the hall to my new class, but for the stench of furtive, unventilated cigarette smoke. The secretary led me past rooms with open doors; all the teachers were men. Many were shouting while the classes turned to whistle at the ringing *tap-tap* of the secretary's heels. Then she stopped in front of a closed door and rapped. The noise inside partially abated and finally a tall bald man with furry ears opened the door.

"This is Gerald Gordon, Mr. Terleski. He's a transfer from Georgia and they've skipped him up from sixth."

"They have, eh?" A few students near the door laughed. They were already pointing at me. "George, you said?"

"Gerald Gordon *from* Georgia," said the secretary.

"Georgia Gordon!" a Negro boy shouted. "Georgia Gordon. Sweet Georgia Gordon."

Terleski didn't turn. He took the folder from the girl and told me to find a seat. But the front boys in each row linked arms and wouldn't let me through. I walked to the window row and laid my books on the ledge. The door closed. Terleski sat at his desk and opened my file but didn't look up.

"Sweet Georgia," crooned the smallish, fair-skinned Negro nearest me. He brushed my notebook to the floor. I bent over and got a judo chop on the inside of my knees.

"Sweet Georgia, you get off the floor, hear?" A very fat, coal-black girl in a pink sweater was helping herself to paper from my three-ring binder. "Mr. Tee, Sweet Georgia taking a nap," she called.

He grumbled. I stood up. My white shirt and baggy gabardines were brown with dust.

"This boy is *not* named Sweet Georgia. He *is* named Gerald Gordon," said Terleski with welcome authority. "And I guess he's some kind of genius. They figured out he was too smart for the sixth grade. They gave him tests at the university and—listen to this—Gerald Gordon is a borderline genius."

A few whistled. Terleski looked up. "Isn't that *nice* for Gerald Gordon? What can we do to make you happy, Mr. Gordon?"

"Nothing, sir," I answered.

"Not a thing? Not an itsy-bitsy thing, sir?"

I shook my head, lowered it.

"Might we expect you to at least look at the rest of us? We wouldn't want to presume, but—"

"Sweet Georgia crying, Mr. Tee," giggled Pink Sweater.

"And he all dirty," added the frontseater. "How come you all dirty, Sweet Georgia-man?" Pink Sweater was awarding my paper to all her friends.

"Come to the desk, Mr. Gordon."

I shuffled forward, holding my books over the dust smears.

"Face your classmates, sir. Look at them. Do you see any borderline types out there? Any friends?"

I sniffled loudly. My throat ached. There were some whites, half a dozen or so grinning in the middle of the room. I looked for girls and saw two white ones. Deep in the rear sat some enormous Negroes, their boots looming in the aisle. They looked at the ceiling and didn't even bother to whisper as they talked. They wore pastel T-shirts with cigarette packs twisted in the shoulder. And—God!—I thought, they had mustaches. Terleski repeated his question, and for the first time in my life I knew that whatever answer I gave would be wrong.

*"Mr. Gordon's reading comprehension is equal to the average college freshman.* Oh, Mr. Gordon, just *average?* Surely there must be some mistake."

I started crying, tried to hold it back, couldn't, and bawled. I remembered the rows of gold stars beside my name back in Colquitt County, Georgia, and the times I had helped the teacher by grading my fellow students.

A few others picked up my crying: high-pitched blubbering from all corners. Terleski stood, scratched his ear, then screamed: "Shut up!" A rumbling monotone persisted from the Negro rear. Terleski handed me his handkerchief and said, "Wipe your face." Then he said to the class: "I'm going to let our borderline genius himself continue. Read this, sir, just like an average college freshman." He passed me my file.

I put it down and knuckled my eyes violently. They watched me hungrily, laughing at everything. Terleski poked my ribs with the corner of the file. "Read!"

I caught my breath with a long, loud shudder.

*"Gerald Gordon certainly possesses the necessary intellectual equipment to handle work on a seventh grade level, and long consultations with the boy indicate a commensurate emotional maturity. No problem anticipated in adjusting to a new environment."*

"Beautiful," Terleski announced. "Beautiful. He's in the room five minutes and he's crying like a baby. Spends his first three minutes on the floor getting dirty, needs a hanky from the teacher to wipe his nose, and he has the whole class laughing at him and calling him names. Beautiful. That's what I call real maturity. Is that all the report says, sir?"

"Yes, sir."

"You're lying, Mr. Gordon. That's not very mature. Tell the class what else it says."

"I don't want to, sir."

"You don't want to. *I* want you to. *Read!*"

"It says: *'I doubt only the ability of the Cincinnati Public Schools to supply a worthy teacher.'*"

"*Well*—that's what we wanted to hear, Mr. Gordon. Do you doubt it?"

"No, sir."

"Am I worthy enough to teach you?"

"Yes, sir."

"What do I teach?"

"I don't know, sir."

"What have you learned already?"

"Nothing yet, sir."

"What's the capital of the Virgin Islands?"

"Charlotte Amalie," I said.

That surprised him, but he didn't show it for long. "Then I can't teach you a thing, can I, Mr. Gordon? You must know everything there is to know. You must have all your merit badges. So it looks like we're going to waste each other's time, doesn't it? Tell the class where Van Diemen's Land is."

"That's the old name for Tasmania, sir. Australia, capital is Hobart."

"If it's Australia that would make the capital Canberra, wouldn't it, Mr. Gordon?"

"For the whole country, yes, sir."

"So there's still something for you to learn, isn't there, Mr. Gordon?"

The kids in the front started to boo. "Make room for him back there," the teacher said, pointing to the middle. "And *now,* maybe the rest of you can tell me the states that border on Ohio. Does *anything* border on Ohio?"

No one answered while I waved my hand. I cared desperately that my classmates learn where Ohio was. And finally, ignoring me, Mr. Terleski told them.

*Recess:* on the sticky pavement in sight of Lincoln's statue. The windows of the first two floors were screened and softball was the sport. The white kids in the gym class wore institutional shorts; the other half—the Negroes—kept their jeans and T-shirts since they weren't allowed in the dressing room. I was still in my dusty new clothes. We all clustered around the gym teacher, who wore a Cincinnati Redlegs cap. He appointed two captains, both white. "Keep track of the score, fellas. And tell me after how you do at the plate individually." He blew his whistle and scampered off to supervise a basketball game around the corner.

The captains were Arno Kolko and Wilfrid Skurow, both fat and pale, with heavy eyebrows and thick hair climbing down their necks and up from their shirts. Hair like that—I couldn't believe it. I was twelve, and had been too ashamed to undress in the locker room. These must be Jews, I told myself. The other whites were shorter than the captains. They wore glasses and had bristly hair. Many of them shaved. Their arms were pale and veined. I moved towards them.

"Where *you* going, boy?" came a high-pitched but adult voice behind me. I turned and faced a six-foot Negro who was biting an unlit cigarette. He had a mustache and, up high on his yellow biceps, a flag tattoo. "Ain't nobody picked you?"

"No," I hesitated, not knowing if they were agreeing or answering.

"Then stay where you're at. Hey—y'all want him?"

Skurow snickered. I had been accustomed to being a low-priority pick back in ball-playing Colquitt County, Georgia. I started to walk away.

"Come back here, boy. Squirrel picking you."

"But you're not a captain."

"Somebody *say* I ain't a captain?" The other Negroes had fanned out under small clouds of blue smoke and started basketball games on the painted courts. "That leaves me and you," said Squirrel. "We standing them."

"I want to be with them," I protested.

"We don't want you," said one of the Jews.

The kid who said it was holding the bat cross-handed as he took some practice swings. I had at least played a bit of softball back in Colquitt County, Georgia. The kids in my old neighbourhood had built a diamond near a housing development after a bulldozer operator had cleared the lot for us during his lunch hour. Some of the carpenters had given us timber scrap for a fence and *twice*—I remember the feeling precisely to this day—I had lofted fly balls tightly down the line and over the fence. No question, my superiority to the Arno Kolkos of this world.

"We get first ups," said Squirrel. "All *you* gotta do, boy, is get yourself on base and then move your ass fast enough to get home on any-

thing I hit. And if I don't hit a home run, you gotta bring me home next."

"Easy," said I.

First three times up, it worked. I got on and Squirrel blasted on one hop to the farthest corner of the playground. But he ran the bases in a flash, five or six strides between the bases, and I was getting numb in the knees from staying ahead even with a two-base lead. Finally, I popped up for an out. Then Squirrel laid down a bunt and made it to third on some loose play. I popped out again and had to take his place on third, anticipating a stroll home on his next home run. But he bunted again, directly at Skurow the pitcher, who beat me home for a force-out to end the inning.

"Oh, you're a great one, Sweet Georgia," Squirrel snarled from a position at deep short. He was still biting his unlit cigarette. "You're a plenty heavy hitter, man. Where you learn to hit like that?"

"Georgia," I said, slightly embarrassed for my state.

"Georgia? *Joe-ja?*" He lit his cigarette and tossed me the ball. "Then I guess you're the worst baseball player in the whole state, Sweet Georgia. I *thought* you was different."

"From what?"

"From them." He pointed to our opponents. They were talking to themselves in a different language. I felt the power of a home-run swing lighten my arms, but it was too late.

"I play here," said Squirrel. "Pitch them slow then run to first. Ain't none of them can beat my peg or get it by me."

A kid named Izzie, first up, bounced to me and I tagged him. Then a scrawny kid lifted a goodly fly to left—the kind I had hit for doubles—but Squirrel was waiting for it. Then Wilfrid Skurow lumbered up: the most menacing kid I'd ever seen. Hair in swirls on his neck and throat, sprouting wildly from his chest and shoulders. Sideburns, but getting bald. Glasses so thick his eyeballs looked screwed in. But no form. He lunged a chopper to Squirrel, who scooped it and waited for me to cover first. Skurow was halfway down the line, then quit. Squirrel stood straight, tossed his cigarette away, reared back, and fired the ball with everything he had. I heard it leave his hand, then didn't move till it struck my hand and deflected to my skull, over the left eye. I was knocked backwards and couldn't get up. Skurow circled the bases; Squirrel sat at third and laughed. Then the Jews walked off together and I could feel my forehead tightening into a lump. I tried to stand, but instead grew dizzy and suddenly remembered Colquitt County. I sat alone until the bells rang and the grounds were empty.

*Every Saturday near Moultrie, I had gone to the movies. In the balcony they let the coloured kids in just for Saturday. Old ones came Wednesday night for Jim Crow melodramas with coloured actors. But we came especially equipped for those Saturday mornings when the coloured kids sat in the dark up in the balcony, making noise whenever we did. We waited for too much noise, or a popcorn box that might be dropped on us. Then we reached into our pockets and pulled out our broken yo-yos. We always kept our broken ones around. Half a yo-yo is great for sailing since it curves and doesn't lose speed. And it's very hard. So we stood, aimed for the projection beam, and fired the yo-yos upstairs. They loomed on the screen like bats, filled the air like bombs. Some hit metal, others the floor, but some struck home judging from the yelps of the coloured kids and their howling. Minutes later the lights went on upstairs and we heard the ushers ordering them out.*

A second bell rang.

"That burr-head nigger son-of-a-bitch," I cried. "That goddamn nigger." I picked myself up and ran inside.

I was late for geometry but my transfer card excused me. When I opened the door two Negro girls dashed out pursued by two boys about twice my size. One of the girls was Pink Sweater, who ducked inside a girls' room. The boys waited outside. The windows in the geometry room were open, and a few boys were sailing paper planes over the street and sidewalk. The teacher was addressing himself to a small group of students who sat in a semicircle around his desk. He was thin and red-cheeked with a stiff pelt of curly hair.

"I say, do come in, won't you? That's a nasty lump you've got there. Has it been seen to?"

"Sir?"

"Over your eye. Surely you're aware of it. It's really quite unsightly."

"I'm supposed to give you this—" I presented the slip for his signing.

"Gerald Gordon, is it? Spiro here."

"Where?"

"Here—I'm Spiro. Geoffrey Spiro, on exchange. And you?"

"Me what?"

"Where are you from?"

"Colquitt County, Georgia."

He smiled as though he knew the place well and liked it. "That's South, aye? Ex-cellent. Let us say for tomorrow you'll prepare a talk on Georgia—brief topical remarks, race, standard of living, labour unrest and what not. Hit the high points, won't you, old man? Now then, class"—he raised his voice only slightly, not enough to disturb the coloured boys making *ack-ack* sounds at pedestrians below—"I should like to introduce to you Mr. Gerald Gordon. You have your choice, sir, of joining these students in the front and earning an 'A' grade, or going back there and getting a 'B,' provided of course you don't leave the room."

"I guess I'll stay up here, sir," I said.

"Ex-cellent. Your fellow students, then, from left to right are: Mr. Lefkowitz, Miss Annaliese Graff, Miss Marlene Leopold, Mr. Willie Goldberg, Mr. Irwin Roth, and Mr. Harry Frazier. In the back, Mr. Morris Gordon (no relative, I trust), Miss Etta Bluestone, Mr. Orville Goldberg (he's Willie's twin), and Mr. Henry Moore. Please be seated."

Henry Moore was coloured, as were the Goldberg twins, Orville and Wilbur. The girls, Annaliese, Marlene, and Etta, were pretty and astonishingly mature, as ripe in their way as Wilfrid Skurow is his. Harry Frazier was a straw-haired athletic sort, eating a sandwich. The lone chair was next to Henry Moore, who was fat and smiled and had no mustache or tattoo. I took the geometry book from my scuffed, zippered notebook.

"The truth is," Mr. Spiro began, "that both Neville Chamberlain and Mr. Roosevelt were fascist, and quite in sympathy with Hitler's anticommunist ends, if they quibbled on his means. His evil was mere overzealousness. Public opinion in the so-called democracies could never have mustered against *any* anticommunist, whatever his program—short of invasion, of course. *Klar?*" He stopped in order to fish out a book of matches for Annaliese, who was tapping a cigarette on her desk.

*"Stimmt?"* he asked, and the class nodded. Harry Frazier wadded his waxed paper and threw it back to one of his classmates by the window, shouting, "Russian MIG!" I paged through the text, looking for diagrams. No one else had a book out and my activity seemed to annoy them.

"So in conclusion, Hitler was merely the tool of a larger fascist conspiracy, encouraged by England and the United States. What *is* it, Gerald?"

"Sir—what are we talking about?" I was getting a headache, and the egg on my brow seemed ready to burst. The inner semicircle stared back at me, except for Harry Frazier.

"Sh!" whispered Morris Gordon.

"At *shul* they don't teach it like that," said Irwin Roth, who had a bald spot from where I sat. "In *shul* they say it happened because God was punishing us for falling away. He was testing us. They don't say nothing from the English and the Americans. They don't even say nothing from the Germans."

"Because we didn't learn our letters good," said Morris Gordon. The matches were passed from the girls to all the boys who needed them.

*"What* happened?" I whispered to Henry Moore, who was smiling and nodding as though he knew.

"Them *Jews,* man. Ain't it great?"

"Then the rabbi is handing you the same bloody bullshit they've been handing out since I went to *shul*—ever since the bloody Diaspora," Spiro said. "God, how I detest it."

"What's *shul,* Henry? What's the Diaspora?"

"Look," Spiro continued, now a little more calmly, "there's only one place in the world where they're building socialism, really honestly *building* it"—his hands formed a rigid rectangle over the desk—"and that's Israel. I've seen children your age who've never handled money. I've played football on turf that was desert a year before. The desert blooms, and the children sing and dance and shoot—yes, shoot—superbly. They're all brothers and sisters, and they belong equally to every parent in the *kibbutz.* They'd die for one another. No fighting, no name-calling, no sickness. They're big, straight and strong and tall, and handsome, like the Israelites. I've seen it for myself. Why any Jew would come to America is beyond me, unless he wants to be spat on and corrupted."

*"Gott,* if the rabbi knew what goes on here," said Roth, slapping his forehead.

"What's a rabbi, Henry? *Tell me what a rabbi is!"*

*"Whatever* is your problem, Gerald?" Spiro cut in.

"Sir—I've lost the place. I just skipped the sixth grade and maybe that's where we learned it all. I don't understand what you-all are saying."

"I must say I speak a rather good English," said Spiro. The class laughed. "Perhaps you'd be happier with the others by the window. All that *rat-tat-tat* seems like jolly good fun, quite a lift, I imagine. It's all perfectly straightforward here. It's *your* country we're talking about, after all. Not mine. Not theirs."

"It's not the same thing up North," I said.

"No, I daresay...look, why don't you toddle down to the nurse's office and get something for your head? That's a good lad, and you show up tomorrow if you're feeling better and tell us about Georgia. Then I'll explain the things you don't know. You just think over what I've said, O.K.?"

I was feeling dizzy—the bump, the smoke— my head throbbed, and my new school clothes were filthy. I brushed myself hard and went into the boys' room to comb my hair, but two large Negroes sitting on the window ledge, stripped to their shorts and smoking cigars, chased me out.

Downstairs, the nurse bawled me out for coming in dirty, then put an ice pack over my eye.

"Can I go home?" I asked.

The nurse was old and fat, and wore hexagonal Ben Franklin glasses. After half an hour she put an adhesive patch on and since only twenty minutes were left, she let me go.

I stopped for a coke at the drugstore across from Lincoln's statue. Surprising, I thought, the number of school kids already out, smoking and having cokes. I waited in the drugstore until the sidewalk was jammed with the legitimately dismissed, afraid that some truant officer might question my early release. I panicked as I passed the cigar counter on my way out, for Mr. Terleski was buying cigarettes and a paper. I was embarrassed for him, catching him smoking, but he saw me, smiled, and walked over.

"Hello, son" he said, "what happened to the head?"

"Nothing," I said, "sir."

"About this morning—I want you to know there was nothing personal in anything I said. Do you believe me?"

"Yes, sir."

"If I didn't do it in *my* way first, they'd do it in their way and it wouldn't be pretty. And Gerald—don't raise your hand again, O.K.?"

"All right," I said. "Good-by."

"*Very* good," said Mr. Terleski. "Nothing else? No *sir*?"

"I don't think so," I said.

The street to our apartment was lined with shops: tailors with dirty windows, cigar stores piled with magazines, some reading rooms where bearded old men were talking, and a tiny branch of a supermarket chain. Everywhere there were school kids: Jews, I could tell from their heads. Two blocks away, just a few feet before our apartment

block, about a dozen kids turned into the dingy yard of the synagogue. An old man shut the gates in a hurry just as I stopped to look in, and another old man opened the main door to let them inside. The tall spiked fence was painted a glossy black. I could see the kids grabbing black silk caps from a cardboard box, then going downstairs. The old gatekeeper, a man with bad breath and puffy skin, ordered me to go.

At home, my mother was preparing dinner for a guest and she was in no mood to question how I got the bump on the head. The guest was Grady, also from Moultrie, a whip-thin red-faced man in his forties who had been the first of my father's friends to go North. He had convinced my father. His wife and kids were back in Georgia selling their house, so he was eating Georgia food with us till she came back. Grady was the man we had to thank, my father always said.

"Me and the missus is moving again soon's she gets back," he announced at dinner. "Had enough of it here."

"Back to Georgia?" my father asked.

"Naw, Billy, out of Cincinnati. Gonna find me a place somewheres in Kentucky. Come in to work every day and go back at night and live like a white man. A man can forget he's white in Cincinnati."

"Ain't that the truth," said my mother.

"How many niggers you got in your room at school, Jerry?" Grady asked me.

"That depends on the class," I said. "In geometry there aren't any hardly."

"See?" said Grady. "You know five years ago there wasn't hardly no more than ten per cent in that school? Now it's sixty and still going up. By the time you'n gets through he's gonna be the onliest white boy in the school."

"He'll be gone before *that*," my father promised. "I been thinking of moving to Kentucky myself."

"Really?" said my mother.

"I ain't even been to a baseball game since they got that nigger," Grady boasted, "and I ain't ever going. I used to love it."

"You're telling me," said my father.

"If they just paid me half in Georgia what they paid me here, I'd be on the first train back," said Grady. "Sometimes I reckon it's the devil himself just tempting me."

"I heard of kids today that live real good and don't even see any money," I said. "Learned it in school."

"That where you learned to stand in front of a softball bat?" my mother retorted, and my parents laughed. Grady coughed.

"And let me tell you," he began, "them kids that goes to them mixed schools gets plenty loony ideas. That thing he just said sounded comminist to me. Yes, sir, that was a Comminist Party member told him that. I don't think no kid of mine could get away with a lie like that in my house. No, sir, they got to learn the truth sometime, and after they do, the rest is lies."

Then Father slapped the fork from my hands. "Get back to your room," he shouted. "You don't get no more dinner till I see your homework done!" He stood behind me, with his hand digging into my shoulder. "Now say good night to Grady."

"Good night," I mumbled.

"Good night *what?*" my mother demanded. "Good night, *what?*"

"Sir," I cried, "sir, sir, sir! Good night, sir!" the last word almost screamed from the hall in front of my bedroom. I slammed the door and fell on the bed in the darkened room. Outside, I could hear the threats and my mother's apologies. "Don't hit him too hard, Billy, he done got that knot on the head already." But no one came.

They started talking of Georgia, and they forgot the hours. I thought of my first school day up North—then planned the second, the third—and I thought of Leonard Sachs Junior High, Squirrel, and the Jews. The Moultrie my parents and Grady were talking about seemed less real, then finally, terrifying. I pictured myself in the darkened balcony under a rain of yo-yos, thrown by a crowd of Squirrels.

I concentrated on the place I wanted to live. There was an enormous baseball stadium where I could hit home runs down the line; Annaliese Graff was in the stands and Mr. Terleski was a coach. We wore little black caps, even Squirrel, and there were black bars outside the park where old men were turning people away. Grady was refused, and Spiro and millions of others, even my parents—though I begged their admission. *No, stimmt?* We were building socialism and we had no parents and we did a lot of singing and dancing (even Henry Moore, even the chocolatey Goldberg twins, Orville and Wilbur) and Annaliese Graff without her cigarettes asked me the capitals of obscure countries. "Israel," I said aloud, letting it buzz; "Israel," and it replaced Mozambique as my favourite word; *Israel, Israel, Israel,* and the dread of the days to come lifted, the days I would learn once and for all if Israel could be really real.

# The Day We Discovered We Were Black

## DAVIDA ADEDJOUMA

It wasn't really Jo-Jo's fault. Honest it wasn't; if I'm lying, I'm flying. That Francis Scott Key man started the whole thing.

We got gypped in fourth grade, on the very first day of school. Mrs. Loving was sus-sposed to be our teacher and we'd been waiting for years to be in her class because she was the prettiest and the nicest teacher in the whole school. Everybody knows when you're pretty you just have to be nice, so you know what ugly means. All the boys wanted to marry Mrs. Loving and all us girls wanted to look just like her, but by 8:05 that Monday morning, we learned that she had gone and spoiled everything by using up our summer having an old-bald-headed baby.

Our principal Mrs. Strickland, who we already didn't like in the first place, waddled into our classroom with this...this woman and announced that she was going to be our new teacher. Mrs. Strickland could have warned us in advance, mailed one of those yellow school bulletins she was so good at making up and safety-pinning to our coats at 3:30 so we wouldn't lose them on our way home from school. At least then we would've had the chance to change schools or something. We would've come back by fifth grade, honestly.

But we got sicked; what did I tell you about ugly? Those two women stood in Mrs. Loving's place behind the teacher's desk at the front of the room, the American flag hanging down almost to the tops of their heads, and they frowned at us because we were rolling our eyes at them.

We hadn't learned to be prejudiced or anything like that yet. Shoot, the closest some of us had ever come in touching range of living, breathing white people was the sales clerks downtown and they didn't count because we didn't know them personally. It wasn't that this Miss Fleischhacker was white and had a funny name that didn't sound like nothing we'd ever heard before. And shoot, it wasn't that she dressed so tacky,

wearing all those old long dresses and shoes that curled up at the toes like a troll's or something's. It was just that she wasn't Mrs. Loving and we really, truly believed that Mrs. Strickland had done this to us on purpose because she hadn't ever liked our class. Well...sometimes we didn't mind our Ps and Qs, but even we didn't deserve this. So after Mrs. Strickland warned us to behave ourselves, and have a good year, she left us alone with this new teacher. Uumph, good year my foot.

We all had to stand up, one at a time, and tell her our names. We wouldn't've had to do that if Mrs. Loving had been our teacher, she knew who we were. And you could tell this teacher had been hipped to some of us—me and Jo-Jo and a couple of other kids, I won't say their names—by the way she looked at us when we said who we were, like she was taking Polaroids of us in her mind. I didn't like the way she looked at me when I stood up, put my hands on my hips and said "My name is Denise Robinson."

This roll-call stuff took forever because she kept looking at us all cross-eyed, repeating our names after we told her who we were like she had a bad remembery or something. We couldn't forget her name. She wrote it on the blackboard in big chalky-white letters like we were blind or something, "My name is MISS FLEISCHHACKER," and told us about 50 zillion times how to pronounce it. I kept thinking to myself it was a shame for a kid to get hooked with a name like that, and boy was I glad I hadn't had anything like that happen to me.

The boys didn't want to marry her, and we girls surely didn't want to look like her.

MISS FLEISCHHACKER had yellowed hair, and yellowed teeth...with halitosis; her eyes were watery blue and she had a long pointy nose her glasses used for a sliding board; she didn't have no shape at all, just a bean pole. And after what she did to Jo-Jo we wondered how long we'd be in jail if we killed her. Here's 'zactly what happened—not on the first day of school, this was later in the year—and then you tell me who was wrong.

Our school has this thing called Morning Exercises. When the bell screeches at 8:00 a.m., the twenty of us slide out of our seats, place our right hands over our hearts, say the Pledge of Allegiance and then sing *The Star-Spangled Banner.* And we're usually good little poll-parrots, too, chirping the words in unison—that means all together. Everything kids do in school is in unison: singing, saying multiplication tables, not liking substitute teachers, getting in trouble, everything. And that morning we decided, in unison, to have some fun with old MISS FLEISCHHACKER.

So when the bell rang and she told us to take our places, we saluted the flag and chanted: "I pledge allegiance, to the flag, of the United States of America. And to the Republic, for which it stands. One nation, under God, invisible . . ."

"Stop!" said MISS FLEISCHHACKER, rat-ta-tat-ting on Mrs. Loving's desk with the yardstick. "The correct word is indivisible."

Shoot we knew that, even though we weren't real sure of what indivisible meant. We were just having a little bit of fun. The fifth grade kids told us they'd always had fun with Mrs. Loving last year, but old lady Fleischhacker wouldn't know fun if it was standing up on tip-toe right in front of her face.

"You will now start at the beginning, and recite the pledge properly this time or you will keep reciting it until you do say it correctly."

So we did it differently this time: "I pledge allegiance, to the flag, of the United States of America. And to the Republic, for which it stands, one nation, under God, IN-DI-VIS-A-BLE, with liberty and justice for all."

MISS FLEISCHHACKER didn't like it any better that way and since being a teacher means she could do whatever she wanted to do to us from 8:00 till 3:30, we backed down the third time around and said it the way she wanted us to. Not because we were ascared of her or anything like

that; you may not like teachers, but you weren't ascared of them, even if your school did allow Corporal Punishment. We just said it the right way the third time because we figured if we didn't, this crazy old woman was just dumb enough to keep us standing up and pledging allegiance all day long. Some adults are like that you know, they'll hurt themselves just to get back at you.

As soon as we got through with liberty and justice for all, we made those cleaning-of-your-throat noises so we could launch into *The Star-Spangled Banner.* Oops, hold it, I forgot to tell you something. There were always two kids in charge of Morning Exercises: one kid held the flag and the other one directed the singing. The director had to give us our key, set the pitch if you wanta get technical about it. I don't know who that Francis Scott Key was thinking about when he wrote our national anthem, but he sure wasn't thinking about us.

I don't think old Francis was thinking about too many people at all because if you don't start singing that song in a low enough key, by the time you reach the "Rockets' red glare," you're into some notes it would take Grace Bumbry to reach. I know because she gave a concert at our school last year and I didn't know anybody could sing that high and still stay on key.

We didn't have any problems singing *Lift Every Voice and Sing.* Mr. James Weldon Johnson musta meant for anybody to sing his song, even little kids, because his notes were low enough so you could reach down in your guts and pull that song up through your throat and out your mouth like it was made for you. Wasn't no notes you could grab hold of. But I guess Francis Scott Key didn't want just anybody singing his song because he dangled his notes so high that little kids, and some adults, too, couldn't get a hold on them.

Anyway, up until fourth grade, whoever directed had always had enough sense to start us out on a real low note so we weren't squealing too bad by the time the rockets took off. But dumb old MISS FLEISCHHACKER, who was really pretty young to be honest about it, I guess—she just had some old ways about her—had the director use a pitch-pipe and we didn't know how to blow it too well. And that's what happened that day.

We started out too high and our voices cracked as we "Proudly held." We didn't have nowhere left to go when the rockets took off. It was really funny, you should've been there. Some kids kept trying to sing, some of us played charades with the words—Mrs. Loving's kids always played charades on Friday afternoons—but Jo-Jo started laughing. Real loud! At least he was being honest about it and not trying to fake the words. But fourth grade teachers like MISS FLEISCHHACKER don't want honesty, they just want you to sing when they tell you to. And Jo-Jo was cracking up.

Jo-Jo has one of those silly laughs, like a spastic pig snorting. And it was contagious, too, just like a sneeze or a yawn. We started giggling in unison. MISS FLEISCHHACKER ratta-tatted on Mrs. Loving's desk again which meant we were supposed to shut up. And normally we do. But that morning, Jo-Jo just wouldn't let us stop. I laughed so hard I caught the hiccups and thought to myself, "Shoot, the most she can make us do is re-sing it like she made us re-say the pledge." So I kept laughing and hiccuping. We all kept laughing and MISS FLEISCHHACKER kept beating on the desk.

She kept on beating on the desk, harder and harder, and I really looked at her for a change. I usually spent most of my time doing my work, trying to ignore her. But when her face started changing colors, I stopped hiccuping right in the middle of a hic. Something was cracking her friendly-teacher's-mask into little tiny pieces, and whatever it was, MISS FLEISCHHACKER aimed it directly at Jo-Jo.

I got ascared then, just a little bit though because the most she could do was smack Jo-Jo on his open palm five times with the yardstick and he was used to getting corporally punished. But all of a sudden the classroom was loud with quietness; everybody else had stopped laughing and looked ascared, too. All nineteen of us just stood

there and watched MISS FLEISCHHACKER and Jo-Jo.

Poor old Jo-Jo has one of those laughs that just has to die out on its own, so I'm not real sure if he ever saw her coming. But we did and somebody tugged at his sleeve, trying to get him to shut up. He still couldn't stop laughing. Jo-Jo snorted and honked right up until MISS FLEISCHHACKER slapped him across the face and called him a nigger.

I rubbed my cheek, that's how much I knew it hurt Jo-Jo. MISS FLEISCHHACKER walked back to Mrs. Loving's desk and said, "You will now start from the beginning and show respect for our national anthem. Ready…begin."

It was just pitiful. Some kids started crying; some kids tried to sing. But Jo-Jo called her the "b" word! I know that was wrong but we'd eavesdropped in on the big kids one day and bitch rhymed with witch and titty rhymed with kitty and a cherry didn't always go on top of a chocolate sundae, except we couldn't figure that one out until Jo-Jo snuck a Playboy to school one day—and I'm still not sure I get it. We knew Jo-Jo had called her something bad but she had no business slapping him like that and calling him that word our parents said you never call anybody, even if you're just playing.

I didn't understand what was going on. We'd always laughed whenever we missed that note and all we ever had to do before this woman came to our school was re-sing it, starting in a lower key. So she didn't have to slap his face like that—the Corporal Punishment Rulebook didn't say you could. I couldn't wait to get home and tell my parents about it. And just when I thought everything was all over, MISS FLEISCHHACKER walked back to Jo-Jo's desk and back-handed him for calling her something I bet you anything she was being.

Some kids fell into their chairs. Some of us kept standing up and stared at her, crying. A few kids found somebody's pitch and started singing. Netta, the girl who had been holding the flag, ran outta the classroom, tripped down to the principal's office and sent the assistant principal, Mrs. Warden, running down the hallway to see what was happening. Netta was too petrified-stiff to come back so she laid down on a cot in the office until her mother could take off work and pick her up.

Mrs. Warden took MISS FLEISCHHACKER by the arm and pulled her into the hallway. Didn't nobody say a word except Jo-Jo. He wasn't crying or anything, just standing there with two rocket-red-glaring cheeks and saying the "B" word, over and over and over.

And that's when we divided the world up into black people and white people. All our teachers had been black until fourth grade, and whenever they'd corporally punished us we knew we were being paddled for our own good. They'd always said it hurt them more than it hurt us—I wondered about that sometimes when I was waiting for my hand to stop stinging. They told us we were good kids who sometimes did bad things, but that they loved us. And they never called us names, even if Netta was a cry-baby and you-know-who was a rubber-butt.

But MISS FLEISCHHACKER was white, and she had called Jo-Jo a nigger and slapped him in the face, twice, just because she was mad at him for laughing about something funny. He wasn't laughing at her or anything she had said or done. Jo-Jo had laughed because we sounded silly trying to sing a song I don't think old Francis Scott Key meant for us to sing in the first place or he would have put the notes closer for us to reach. Jo-Jo had laughed during a Morning Exercise full of big words we didn't understand, like indivisible.

But we understood pain and embarrassment and scarediness. And after our new-new fourth grade teacher explained why we had Morning Exercises and what the Pledge of Allegiance really meant, we finally understood that indivisible was like singing in unison. So we decided, indivisibly, not to be too happy or laugh at anything for the rest of the year, even though MISS FLEISCHHACKER never came back.

We had long talks with our parents. We talked to the school psycho-logicalist. And we still wondered what people like MISS FLEISCHHACKER would do, and could do to us, if we ever did something they really didn't like.

# CHAPTER 9

# THE WORLD OF IMAGINATION

Bryan MacMahon, "The Windows of Wonder"
Zenna Henderson, "The Believing Child"
Zenna Henderson, "The Anything Box"
James Gunn, "Kindergarten"

All the stories within this section are about the world of imagination and fantasy, ranging from imaginative encounters in real classrooms to the realm of science fiction.

The "Windows of Wonder" by Bryan MacMahon takes place in Ireland, where a young substitute teacher finds herself facing a class of disinterested students. She tries to reach them in many different ways, but they remain detached until one day she discovers that they are totally ignorant of the myths and legends that are part of their Irish heritage.

> "Listen children," she said. "... Someone has robbed you of a very precious thing. I will not have you cheated. This thing I speak of is neither gold nor silver, neither a red nor a green jewel. It is something a great deal more valuable. The other things I teach you—the figures, the words, the lines and the letters—are not so important—as yet. Please try to understand! How shall I begin to tell you of the treasure you have lost? Your minds are like rooms that are dark or brown. But somewhere in the rooms, if only you can pull aside the heavy curtains, you will find windows—these are the windows of wonder."

The teacher sets out to open those windows of wonder and begins to see something precious being born in the children. But the magic ends when the "old mistress" returns to the school. On the way out of the village the teacher meets a kindred soul, an old man who understands what she has given her students, and he in turn gives her a wondrous gift to remember them by.

Whereas in MacMahon's story an adult brings fantasy into the classroom, in Zenna Henderson's stories, children entangle their teachers in fantasy. "The Believing Child" begins with a parent's concern for her trusting child.

> All this time the mother had been clutching Dismey's shoulders with both hands, and Dismey had just stood there, her back pressed against her mother, her face quiet, her pale eyes watching...the mother shoved Dismey at me abruptly and told me, "Mind the teacher." And said to me, "Teach her true. She's a believin' child."

Dismey's teacher soon learns about her young student's gullibility. Her willingness to believe the stories she is told soon leaves her vulnerable to two mischievous students who delight in scaring her. But Dismey's trust in stories also serves her frighteningly well. Through a story her teacher reads aloud she learns a way to take her revenge on the boys and baffles her teacher with the supernatural power that she summons up through her ability to believe.

In "The Anything Box" Zenna Henderson describes a teacher who is initially impatient and later concerned with the importance a student attaches to her fantasy world. Sue-lynn spends an inordinate amount of time staring into her clasped hands, which hold her Anything Box. But when the teacher tries to bring little Sue-lynn back to reality she succeeds only in leaving her bereft. When she realizes her mistake she swears to "...never, never again...take any belief from anyone without replacing it with something better."

James Gunn's brief story, "Kindergarten," sits unabashedly within the science-fiction genre. A less than successful kindergarten student decides to engage in the creation of planets and life forms. The teacher, who is initially amused with the seven-day project, begins to see its dangers and urges that the exercise be stopped.

These stories challenge our own willingness to believe in powers greater than ourselves and to cultivate our own creative spirit while they also remind us of the importance of imagination in students' lives. As Henderson says, "We may need 'hallucinations' to keep us going...."

# The Windows of Wonder

## BRYAN MacMAHON

The young woman wheeling the bicycle came up the roadway out of the bogland valley. Behind her, bulk on bulk outthrown across all exits, the mountains squatted. Beyond the valley a headland had thrust itself out into the sea. Over the scene hung the clarity that was a promise of rain.

On the crest of the gap the woman turned her bicycle. Placing her forearms on the handlebars, she eased her body, and looked steadfastly down into the valley she had just left. She saw the dark floor of low-lying land. She saw the ranked ricks of turf and beside them the glitter of white shirts. She saw the bright cabins and the scrawl of a hidden stream. Last of all she saw the tiny school in its cluster of windwhipped trees.

The woman's eyes became filled with a remote smouldering. Her breath came forcefully through her nostrils.

Six months before she had seen this valley for the first time. Her friends had tried to dissuade her from acting as substitute teacher in the valley school. "A queer clannish crowd—a place of appalling feuds and astonishing whims." "When the place gets you, you'll start clawing the walls.... The children will eat you with their big brown eyes."

The woman shifted her gaze from the valley to the distant sea. Out there the white-caps were lighting and quenching in the angry water.

Perversity had made her take the post. She remembered her first day—her first week in the valley. The ominous faces at the cottage windows as she rode past....The solemn principal who was flesh and blood of the valley....She taught the junior division—the senior boys and girls. The school-children sitting in grave rows consumed her with their large brown eyes and afforded her the traditional minimum of co-operation. Sometimes she felt afraid. Sometimes she was tempted to scream aloud, to abandon herself to welcome hysteria, to use her nails as God had intended they

should be used. But day after day had found her counseling herself to the patience necessary for the finding of the keys to the children's natures.

She had tried laughter: they had turned their heads sideways as if they were looking at an insane person. She had tried music: the music she was acquainted with was so wholly apart from their own grace-noted plaints that, on realizing her mistake, she had stopped suddenly. She had tried the unorthodox—leaping, grimacing and mimicry: one day she discovered in mid-antic that the principal was glaring at her through the glass partition. After this she yielded herself up to despair. Then, when she wasn't endeavouring, she stumbled on the secret.

It was a reading lesson. She had begun to explain the word "legend" which appeared in the text. "A legend is a tale of some event that happened so long ago that we have no means of telling whether it is true or not. You remember, children, the story of the *Children of Lir?*"

There was no sudden light in the children's eyes. Could it be that...? Mastering her emotion, she asked: "Hands up, the children who know the story of the Children of Lir?"

No hand moved. It wasn't possible! Was this the sole valley in Ireland that had let the legend die? Still, the children were obedient and dutiful. If they had heard the tale they would have....

"Of *Déirdre of the Sorrows?* Of the *Fairy Palace of the Quicken Trees?* Of the *Fate of the Sons of Usna?* Of *Diarmuid and Gráinne?* Surely, some child...?"

The children's eyes grew browner and rounder and wider. The girls stolidly planted their stout-soled boots beneath them while the bare toes of the boys squirmed on the boarded floor.

The woman was afraid to trust herself to words lest she should break into uncovered tears. She looked left, then right. She felt trapped and crushed. She looked at the wee ones and the ones that were not so wee. "Oh, children..." she began.

Briskly she gathered them in a ring around her.

"Listen, children," she said, "I don't know if you can understand me or not. But you must try: It's the only way. Someone has robbed you of a very precious thing. I will not have you cheated. This thing I speak of is neither gold nor silver, neither a red nor a green jewel. It is something a great deal more valuable. The other things I teach you—the figures, the words, the lines and the letters—are not so important–as yet. Please try to understand! How shall I begin to tell you of the treasure you have lost? Your minds are like rooms that are dark or brown. But somewhere in the rooms, if only you can pull aside the heavy curtains, you will find windows—these are the windows of wonder. Through these you can see the yellow sunlight or the silver stars or the many-colored wheel of the rainbow. You've all seen a rainbow?" The heads nodded. "Isn't it beautiful?" The heads nodded vigorously.

"The windows I speak of are the legends of our people. Each little legend is a window of wonder. Each time you hear a story or ponder upon a story or dream yourself into a story or break or re-make a story, you are opening a window of wonder. Children, please, please try to understand."

"Perhaps I had better begin with the story I myself like best: *Oisin in the Land of the Ever-Young.* Are you ready, children?" The solemn heads nodded in affirmation. "Long, long ago there lived..."

The woman on the hill-top sighed and looked across the northern rim of the valley. A Martello tower stood black against the livid northern sky. In the air between, the clean gulls were moving inland. The whimper of the nearing rain was in the chill wind that blew from the left hand.

She remembered the complaints of the parents, the semideputations, the cabin growlings and the slow contemptuous stares of elders from over the half-doors. Most keenly of all she recalled the stern rebuke of the principal—at the apparent waste of teaching time. Then she began to dissemble, for she had felt the children's imaginations coming alive under her care: she knew that something precious was being born in them. Already they were fusing warmly into her nature: the stir of their new life was implicit in the bright cries they uttered as they played along the valley. Now she and the children were conspirators—while she pretended to be reading from a textbook she was telling yet another tale, opening up another window of wonder. By now the children had begun to demand the stories. Their eyes that had been dull were ready to leap and frolic on small provocation. Now there was comradeship between the teacher and the taught.

And then the old mistress had returned. The young teacher's stay in the school was abruptly ended.

The evening smoke had begun to drift low from the chimneys of the valley. The watcher sighed and turned away.

It was then that she noticed the old russet-faced man. He was standing inside a rough timber gate on the roadside, resting his elbows on the top spar. His fists were securely clenched. A russet man with a russet face and merry blue eyes under a black caubeen. The young woman changed colour. Turning the bicycle, she faced it for the distant town. She had her right foot on the off pedal and was hopping with her left foot when he addressed her:

"Wait! Wait!"

One leg on the ground, one leg on the pedal, she waited.

"Come hether, woman!"

After a moment of puzzled delay she obeyed. The old man and the young woman looked at one another. His eyes were the bluest she had ever seen.

"You're the school-missus?"

"I am...I was!"

"I heard the children talkin' about yeh. So you're leavin' us?"

"I am!"

"Ah!" Slyly: "With no one to say good-bye to yeh only me. An' they have me down for bein' half-cracked. There's a lone bird like me in every parish in Ireland."

He laughed. It was a half-regretful but lovely laugh.

A warmth flowed between them. She looked first at his face, then at his clenched fists. She was dreaming his face young when he apprised her red-handed and, narrowing his eyes, said half-fooling, all in earnest:

"If I was fifty years younger, I'd chance me luck with yeh, me lovely woman. An' I'm not so sure that I'd fail! An' why do I say that? Because I know your mind the same as I know me own mind. You're a woman to whom I could talk about the grandeur of a lark, the swingin' of a caravan or the Resurrection of Our Lord. Together, me an' you, we'd open up many an' many a window of wonder. Then we'd be . . ."

He made to place his palms together and interlace his fingers. When he found his fists clenched he laughed at his small folly. Smiling he held out the two fists: "A present I have for yeh an' yeh goin'. A token to remember us by. Look!"

She watched the gnarled fists unlock. Clinging to the coarse palms were two butterflies—two Red Admirals—one on each palm. The blades of the butterflies' wings swung slowly from side to side to reveal their full beauty.

Her laughter and his laughter cancelled the disparity of years between them. She was bright-eyed; he was sure and old. Her breath came faster. The old man wore a smile of confidence and satisfaction.

Carefully and with a movement that reminded her of a conjurer he removed the butterflies from each palm with the thumb and forefinger of the other hand. The butterflies began to beat and thrum for freedom.

The old man tossed them into the air. At first, the butterflies flew wide apart; then the craziness of their flight begot a pattern. At last they found one another and began to lock and frolic and entwine their flights as they climbed higher and higher into the dark heavens.

The old man turned away, then strode slowly up the field. The young woman mounted her bicycle and began to pedal down into the town valley.

# The Believing Child

## ZENNA HENDERSON

No one seeing me sitting here, my hands stubbornly relaxed, my face carefully placid, could possibly know that a terrible problem is gnawing at me. In fact, I can't believe it myself. It couldn't possibly be. And yet I've got to solve it. Oh, I have lots of time to find a solution! I have until 2:15. And the hands on my watch are scissoring out the minutes relentlessly. 1:45. What will I do! What will I do if 2:15 comes and I haven't got through to Dismey? She's sitting over there by Donna now, her scraggly hair close to Donna's shining, well-nourished curls.

That hair of Dismey's. I saw it before I saw her face that October morning and knew, with a sigh for the entry of my forty-fifth child, that she was from the campground—a deprived child. Somehow it always shows in their hair. I breathed a brief prayer that she would be clean at least. She was—almost painfully so. Her hands and ankles were rusty with chapping, not with dirt. Her sagging dress, a soft faded blue down the front, with a hint of past pattern along the side seams and at the collar, was clean, but not ironed. Her lank, bleached-burlap hair lifelessly bracketed her thin face and descended in irregular tags roughly to her shoulders. But its combed-with-water patterns were bisected by a pink-clean parting.

Well, I welcomed her to my first grade classroom, pleased that she was a girl. I was so weary of the continual oversupply of little boys. I was surprised that her mother had come with her. Usually from that area, parents just point the kids toward the bus stop and give them a shove. But there the mother was, long in the wrist and neck and face. She was wearing levi's and a faded plaid shirt that had safety pins for buttons. She was older than I'd expect Dismey's mother to be. Her narrow shoulders were twisted to one side and a deep convex curve bent her spine out against the shirt. I couldn't tell if it was the result of a lifetime of sagging, or was an actual deformity. Her left cheek sucked in against no-teeth, and the sharp lines that crisscrossed her face reminded me of the cracklings of thin mud drying in the sun.

"Dismey?" I asked. "How do you spell it?"

"You're the teacher," said her mother, her voice a little hoarse as though not used as much. "Spell it the way you want. Her name's Dismey Coven. She's six She ain't been to school none yet. We been with the cabbages in Utah."

"We're supposed to have a birth certificate—" I ventured.

"Never had none," said Mrs. Coven shortly. "She was born anyway. In Utah. When we were there with the cabbage."

So I had her repeat the name and stabbed at the spelling. I put down October for a birthdate, counting backwards far enough to give her a birth-year to match her age—usual procedure, only sometimes they don't even know the month for sure—the crops harvesting at the time, yes, but not the month.

All this time the mother had been clutching Dismey's shoulders with both hands, and Dismey had just stood there, her back pressed against her mother, her face quiet, her pale eyes watching. When I'd got all the necessary information, including the fact that unless we had free lunch for Dismey, she wouldn't eat, the mother shoved Dismey at me abruptly and told her. "Mind the teacher." And said to me, "Teach her true. She's a believin' child."

And she left without another word or a backward glance.

So then, where to seat my forty-fifth child in my forty-four seat room. I took a quick census. Every child there. Not a vacant chair available. The only unoccupied seat in the room was the old backless chair I used for a stepstool and for a sin-

seat in the Isolation Corner. Well, Bannie could do with a little more distance between him and Michael, and knew the chair well, so I moved him over to the library table with it and seated Dismey by Donna, putting her in Donna's care for the day.

I gave Dismey a pencil and crayolas and other necessary supplies and suggested that she get acquainted with the room, but she sat there, rigid and unmoving for so long that it worried me. I went over to her and printed her name for her on a piece of our yellow practice paper.

"Here's your name, Dismey. Maybe you'd like to see if you can write it. I'll help you."

Dismey took the pencil from me, holding it as though it were a dagger. I had to guide every finger to its correct place before she could hold it for writing. We were both sweating when we got through the name. It had been like steering a steel rod through the formation of the letters. Dismey showed no signs of pleasure—shy or overt—that most beginners exhibit when confronted with their first attempt at their names. She looked down at the staggering letters and then up at me.

"It's your name, Dismey," I smiled at her and spelled it to her. She looked down again at the paper, and the pencil wavered and swung until she had it dagger-wise once more. She jabbed the point of the pencil down on the next line. It stabbed through the paper. With a quick, guilty hand, she covered the tear, her shoulders hunching to hide her face.

I opened the box of crayons and shook them out where she could see the colors, luring her averted face back toward me.

"Maybe you'd rather color. Or go around and see what the other children are doing." And I left her, somewhat cheered. At least she had known that a line is for writing on! *That* is a mark of maturity!

All the rest of the morning she roosted tentatively on the front four inches of her chair, stiff as a poker. At recess, she was hauled bodily by Donna to the bathroom and then to the playground.

Donna dutifully stayed by her side, wistfully watching the other children playing, until time to drag Dismey to the line and to point out that there was a girl line and a boy line.

After recess, Dismey unbent—once. Just enough to make two very delicate lines on a paper with her red crayon when she thought I wasn't looking. Then she just sat staring, apparently entranced at the effect. It was most probable that she had never held a crayon before.

Lunchtime came and in the cafeteria she stared at her plate a minute and then ate so fast with spoon and scooping fingers that she nearly choked.

"Would you like some more?" I asked her. She looked at me as though I were crazy for asking. She slowed down midway through her third helping. There was a quiver along her thin cheek when she looked at me. It could have been the beginning of a smile. Donna showed her where to put her dirty dishes and took her out to the playground.

During that first afternoon, she finally drew a picture—an amazingly mature one—of three wobbly plates full of food and a lopsided milk carton with a huge straw in it. Under Donna's urging she took up her red crayon and, down at the bottom, she carefully copied from her name paper a *Di,* but when the *s* turned backward on her, she covered it with a quick, guilty hand and sat rigid until dismissal time.

I worried about Dismey that afternoon after the children were gone. I was used to frightened, withdrawn children, terrified by coming into a new school, but nothing quite so drastic as Dismey. No talking, no laughing, no smiles, or even tears. And such wariness—and yet her mother had called her a believing child. But then, there's believing and believing. Belief can be a very negative thing, too. Maybe what Dismey believed the most was that you could believe in nothing good—except maybe three platefuls of food and a red crayon. Well, that was a pretty good start!

Next morning I felt a little more cheerful. After all, yesterday had been Dismey's first day at a new school. In fact, it had been her first day at any school. And children adjust wonderfully well—usually.

I looked around for Dismey. I didn't have to look far. She was backed into the angle of the wall by the door of our room, cornered by Bannie and Michael. I might have known. Bannie and Michael are my thorns-in-the-flesh this year. Separately they are alert, capable children, well above average in practically everything. But together! Together they are like vinegar and soda—erupting each other into the wildest assortment of deviltry that two six-year-olds could ever think up. They are flint and steel to the biggest blaze of mischief I've ever encountered. Recently, following a Contradict Everything Phase, they had lapsed into a Baby Phase, complete with thumb-sucking, baby talk and completely tearless infantile wailing—the noise serving them in the same capacity as other children's jet-zooming or six-gun banging or machine-gun rattling.

The two didn't see me coming and I stood behind them a minute, curious to see just what they had dreamed up so soon to plague Dismey with.

"And it's a 'lectric paddle and it's specially for girls," said Bannie solemnly.

"You stood up in the swing and the 'lectric paddle is specially for girls that stand up in swings," amplified Michael soberly. "And it hurts real bad."

"It might even kill you," said Bannie with relish.

"Dead," said Michael, round of eye that shifted a little to send a glint of enjoyment at Bannie.

Dismey hunched one shoulder and drew a shaking hand across her stricken cheek. "I didn't know—" she began.

"Of course she didn't know," I said sternly. "Bannie and Michael, indoors!" I unlocked the door and shooed them in. Then I stooped and put my arms around a rigid, unbending Dismey. I could feel her bones under her scant flesh and flimsy dress.

"It isn't so, Dismey," I said. "There isn't any electric paddle. There's no such thing. They were just teasing you. But we do have a rule about standing up in the swings. You might fall and get hurt. Here comes Donna now. You go play with her and she'll tell you about our rules. And don't believe Bannie and Michael when they tell you bad things. They're just trying to fool you."

In the room I confronted the two completely unrepentant sinners.

"You weren't kind to Dismey," I said. "And she's our new student. Do you want her to think that we're all unkind here at our school?"

They had no answer except Bannie's high-pitched giggle that he uses when he is embarrassed.

"Besides that, what you told her wasn't true."

"We were just playing," said Michael, trading side-glances with Bannie.

"Telling things that aren't true isn't a very good way to have fun," I reminded them.

"We were just playing," said Michael, while Bannie had recourse to his thumb.

"But Dismey didn't know you were only playing," I said. "She thought you were telling the truth."

"We were just playing," said Bannie around his thumb.

After we had gone around and around a couple more times, I sternly sent them outside. The two ran shrieking, holding the seats of their levi's yelling, "We got a licking! With the 'lectric paddle! A-wah! A-wah!"

And my heart sank. I had a premonition that the Baby Phase was about to give way to a Tease Dismey Phase.

Dismey came slowly to life in the classroom. She began to function with the rest of the class, catching up with ease with the children who had been in school a month before she arrived. She swooped through long and short vowels and caught us in initial consonants. She showed a flare for drawing and painting. Her number work and reading flowed steadily into her—and stayed there instead of ebbing and flowing as it does for so many children. But all the rest of the classroom activities paled to insignificance as far as Dismey was concerned before the wonder of story time. It was after the first few sessions of story time immediately following the afternoon recess that I realized what Dismey's mother meant by calling her a believin' child.

Dismey believed without reservation in the absolute truth of every story she heard. She was completely credulous.

It's hard to explain the difference between the fairy tales for her and for the rest of the class. The others believed wholeheartedly while the story was in progress and then set it aside without a pang. But there was a feeling of eager acceptance and—and recognition—that fairly exuded from Dismey during story time that sometimes almost made my flesh creep. And this believing carried over to our dramatization of the stories too, to such an extent that when Dismey was the troll under the bridge for the Billy Goats Gruff, even Bannie paled and rushed over the bridge, pell-mell, forgetting the swaggering challenge that he as the Big Billy Goat was supposed to deliver. And he flatly refused to go back and slay the troll.

But this credulity of hers served her a much worse turn by making her completely vulnerable to Bannie and Michael. They had her believing, among other unhappy things, that a lion lived in the housing of the air-raid siren atop the cafeteria. And when the Civilian Defense truck came to check the mechanism and let the siren growl briefly, Dismey fled the room, white-eyed and gasping, too frightened to scream. She sat, wet-faced and rigid, half the afternoon in spite of all my attempts to reassure her.

Then one day I found her crying out by the sidewalk, when she should have been in class. Tears were falling without a sound as she rubbed with trembling desperation at the sidewalk.

"What's the matter, Dismey?" I asked, squatting down by her, the better to see. "What are you doing?"

"My mama," she choked out, "I hurt my mama!"

"What do you mean?" I asked, bewildered.

"I stepped on a crack," she sobbed. "I didn't mean to but Bannie pushed me. And now my mama's back is busted! Can you fix a busted back? Does it cost very much?"

"Oh, Dismey, honey!" I cried, torn between pity and exasperation. "I told you not to believe Bannie. 'Step on a crack and break your mother's back' isn't for true! It's just a singing thing the children like to say. It isn't really so!"

I finally persuaded Dismey to leave the sidewalk, but she visibly worried all the rest of the day and shot out of the door at dismissal time as though she couldn't wait to get home to reassure herself.

Well, school went on and we switched from fairy tales to the Oz books, and at story time every day I sat knee-deep in a sea of wondering faces and experienced again with them my own enchantment when I was first exposed to the stories. And Dismey so firmly believed in every word I read that Michael and Bannie had her terror-stricken and fugitive every time a dust devil whirled across the playground. I finally had to take a decisive hand in the affair when I found Michael struggling with a silently desperate Dismey, trying to pry her frenzied hands loose from the playground fence so the whirlwind could pick *her* up and blow *her* over the Deadly Desert and into the hands of the Wicked Witch of the West.

Michael found his levi's not impervious to a ping-pong paddle, which was the ultimate in physical punishment in our room. He also found not to his liking the Isolation outside the room, sitting forlornly on the steps by our door for half a day, but the worst was the corporal punishment he and Bannie had visited upon them. They were forbidden to play with each other for three days. The sight of their woebegone, drooping figures cast a blight over the whole playground, and even Dismey forgave them long before the time was up.

But her tender-heartedness left her only more vulnerable to the little devils when they finally slipped back into their old ways.

We finished the first of the Oz books and were racing delightedly into the first part of *The Magic of Oz,* and there it was! Right on page 19! We all looked at it solemnly. We wrote it on the board. We contemplated it with awe. *A real live magic word!* All we had to do now to work real magic was to learn how to pronounce the word.

Therein lay the difficulty. We considered the word. PYRZQXGL. We analyzed it. We knew all the letters in it, but there were no vowels except 'and sometimes Y.' How could you sound out a word with no vowels and no place to divide it into syllables? Surely a word that long would have more than one syllable!

"We'll have to be careful even trying to say it, though," I warned. "Because if you do find the right way to pronounce it, you can—well, here it tells you—'. . . transform anyone into beast, bird or fish, or anything else, and back again, once you know how to pronounce the mystical word.'"

"You could even change yourself. Wouldn't it be fun to be a bird for a while? But that's what you have to watch carefully. Birds can talk in the Land of Oz, but can they talk here?"

The solemn consensus was no, except for parakeets and myna birds.

"So if you changed yourself into a bird, you couldn't ever change yourself back. You'd have to stay a bird unless someone else said the magic word for you. So you'd better be careful if you learn the way to say it."

"How *do* you say it, teacher?" asked Donna.

"I've never found out," I sighed. "I'll have to spell it every time I come to it in the story because I can't say it. Maybe someday I'll learn it. *Then* when it's Quiet Time, I'll turn you all into Easter Eggs, and we'll have a really quiet Quiet Time!"

Laughing, the children returned to their seats and we prepared for our afternoon work. But first, most of the children bent studiously to the task of copying PYRZQXGL from the board to take the word home to see if anyone could help them with it. It was all as usual, the laughing, half-belief of the most of the children in the wonderful possibilities of the word, and the solemn intensity of Dismey, bent over a piece of paper, carefully copying, her mouth moving to the letters.

The affair of Bannie and Michael versus Dismey went on and on. I consulted with the boys' parents, but we couldn't figure out anything to bring the matter to a halt. There seemed to be an irresistible compulsion that urged the boys on in spite of everything we could do. Sometimes you get things like that, a clash of personalities—or sometimes a meshing of personalities that is inexplicable. I tried to attack it from Dismey's angle, insisting that she check with me on everything the boys tried to put over on her before she believed, but Dismey was too simple a child to recognize the subtlety with which the boys worked on occasion. And I tried ignoring the whole situation, thinking perhaps I was making it a situation by my recognition of it. A sobbing Dismey in my arms a couple of times convinced me of its reality.

Then there came yesterday. It was a raw blistery day, bone-chilling in spite of a cloudless sky, a day that didn't invite much playing outdoors after lunch. We told the children to run and romp for fifteen minutes after we left the cafeteria and then to come back indoors for the rest of the noon period. I shivered in my sweater and coat, blinking against the flood of sunlight that only made the cold, swirling winds across the grounds feel even colder. The children, screaming with excitement and release, swirled with the winds, to and fro, in a mad game of tag that consisted in whacking anyone handy and running off madly in all directions shrieking, "You're it, had a fit, and can't get over it!"

It didn't take long for the vitality of some of our submarginals to run short, and when I saw Treesa and Hannery huddling in the angle of the building, shaking in their cracked, oversized shoes as they hugged their tattered sweaters about them, I blew the whistle that called the class in-doors.

The clamor and noise finally settled down to the happy hum of Quiet Time, and I sighed and re-laxed, taking a quick census of the room, automat-ically deducting the absentees of the day. I straightened and checked again.

"Where's Dismey?" I asked. There was a long silence. "Does anyone know where Dismey is?"

"She went to the restroom with me," said Donna. She's afraid to go alone. She thinks a dragon lives down in the furnace room and she's scared to go by the steps by herself."

"She wuz play tag weez us," said Hannery, with his perennial sniff.

"Maybe she go'd to beeg playgroun'," sug-gested Treesa. "We don' s'pose to go to beeg playgroun'," she added virtuously.

Then I heard Bannie's high, embarrassed gig-gle.

"Bannie and Michael, come here."

They stood before me, a picture of innocence. "Where is Dismey?" I asked. They exchanged side-glances. Michael's shoulders rose and fell. Bannie looked at his thumb, dry of, lo, these many weeks, and popped it into his mouth.

"Michael," I said, taking hold of his shoul-ders, my fingers biting. "Where is Dismey?"

"We don't know," he whined, suddenly afraid. "We thought she was in here. We were just playing tag."

"What did you do to Dismey?" I asked, won-dering wildly if they had finally killed her.

"We—we—" Michael dissolved into fright-ened tears before the sternness of my face and the lash of my words.

"We didn't do nothing," cried Bannie, taking his thumb out of his mouth, suddenly brave for Michael. "We just put a rock on her shadow."

"A rock on her shadow?" My hands dropped from Michael's shoulders.

"Yeth." Bannie's courage evaporated and his thumb went back into his mouth. "We told her she couldn't move."

"Sit down," I commanded, shoving the two from me as I stood. "All of you remember the rules for when I'm out of the room," I reminded the class. "I'll be right back."

The playground was empty except for the crumpled papers circling in an eddy around the trash can. I hurried over to the jungle gym. No Dismey. I turned the corner of the Old Building and there she was, straining and struggling, her feet digging into the ground, the dirt scuffed up over her ragged shoes, her whole self pulling desperately away from the small rock that lay on her shadow. I saw—or thought I saw—the shadow itself curl up around her knobby, chapped ankles.

"Dismey!" I cried. "Dismey!"

"Teacher!" she sobbed. "Oh, teacher!"

I had my arms around her, trying to warm her stiff little hands in mine, trembling to her shiver-ing, wincing to the shriveled blue lips that shook with her crying.

"But, Dismey, honey!" I cried. "It isn't so! You could have come back to the room anytime! A rock can't hold your shadow! It isn't true!"

*But I had to move that rock* before I could pick her up to carry her back to the room.

It was a subdued, worried room the rest of the day. Bannie and Michael lost all interest in working. They sat apprehensively in their chairs, waiting for lightning to strike. I didn't say any-thing to them. I had nothing left to say. I had said and re-said everything I could ever think of. I had done what I knew to do, and it hadn't worked. Not even a trip into the office to interview Mr. Beasley had subdued them more than half a day. I couldn't even think straight about the matter any more. I had reached the point where I believed that I felt the tug of a tethered shadow. I had found it necessary to move a rock before I could lift a child. I was out of my depth—but complete-ly. And I was chilled to realize that not only Dis-mey but I—an adult—was entrapped in this believing bit. What might happen next? A feeling that must have been psychic indigestion kept me swallowing all afternoon.

In the warmth of the room, Dismey soon stopped shivering and went quietly about her work, but her eyes slid past the boys or looked through them. Donna swished her brief skirts up to the supply table for paper for Dismey, because the boys sat between her and the table. It looked as though the iron had finally entered Dismey's soul, and I hoped hopelessly that she had finally got wise to the little monsters.

The unnaturally subdued restraint lasted until dismissal time. I had the quietest-most industrious room in my experience—but it wasn't a happy one.

At Put-away Time, Michael and Bannie put their chairs up on the table *quietly*—without being told to. They *walked* to the coat closet. They lingered by the door until they saw that I had no word for them—or smile—or even frown. They scuffled slowly off to the bus gate. Dismey scurried out of the room as if she were the guilty party and had no word or smile for *me,* and I scuffled off slowly to bus duty.

Children bounce back amazingly. The next day—oh, lordy! that's today!—started off normally enough. We worked well all this morning—though at the tops of our voices. Michael and Bannie had the devilish light flickering in their eyes again. Dismey neither noticed them nor ignored them. She had a small smile that turned up the corner of her mouth a little. She played happily with Donna and I blessed the good night's sleep I'd had for my return to calmness. I hoped—oh, how I hoped this morning—that the boys had finally decided to find something besides Dismey to occupy their energies.

Lunchtime passed and the mild temperatures out-of-doors let us relax into a full-time play period. Afternoon recess came and went. The tide of children flowed across the floor to pool around my feet for story time.

"Bannie," I said automatically, "I don't want you sitting my—" Then I felt a huge sinking inside of me. My eyes flew to Dismey. She returned my look, completely at ease and relaxed, the small smile still bending her mouth.

"Where's Bannie and Michael?" I asked casually, feeling insanely that this was yesterday again.

"They tol' me they wuz go to beeg playgroun'," sniffed Hannery. "They alla time sneak up there."

"Yeh, yeh," said Treesa. "They go'd to beeg playgroun' but they comed back. They go'd Old Building and slided on steps. Ain' s'posed to slide on steps," she added virtuously.

"Maybe they didn't hear the bell," suggested Donna. "When you play by the Old Building, sometimes you don't."

I looked at Dismey. She looked back. Her small, pointed tongue circled the smile and then disappeared for the automatic swallow. I looked away, uncomfortable.

"Well, they'll miss out on the story, then," I said. "And because they've been late twice this week, they'll have to be in Isolation for twice as long as they are late." I checked my watch to time the boys and began to read. I didn't hear a word I read. I suppose I paraphrased the story as I usually do, bringing it down to first grade level. I suppose I skipped over the discursive passages that had little interest for my children, but I have no way of knowing. I was busy trying to hold down that psychic indigestion again, the feeling that something terribly wrong had to be put to rights.

After the group went back to their seats and became immersed in their work. I called Dismey quietly up to my desk.

"Where are Michael and Bannie?" I asked her.

She flushed and twisted her thin shoulders. "Out on the playground," she said.

"Why didn't they come when the bell rang?" I asked.

"They couldn't hear the bell ring." The little smile lifted the corners of her mouth. I shivered.

"Why not?" Dismey looked at me without expression. She looked down at the desk and followed her finger as it rubbed back and forth on the edge. "Dismey," I urged. "Why couldn't they hear the bell?"

"'Cause I changed them," she said, her chin lifting a little. "I changed them into rocks."

"Changed them?" I asked blankly. "Into rocks?"

"Yes," said Dismey. "They're mean. They're awfully mean. I changed them." The little smile curled briefly again.

"How did you do it?" I asked. "What did you do?"

"I learned the magic word," she said proudly. "I can say it right. You know, the one you read to us. That PYRZQXGL." Her voice fluttered and hissed through a sound that raised the short hairs on the back of my neck and all down both my arms.

"And it worked!" I cried incredulously.

"Why sure," she said. "You said it would. It's a magic word. You read it in the book. Mama told me how to say it. She said how come they put words like that in kids' books. They get away with anything nowadays. That's not a word for kids. But she told me how to say it anyway. See?" She picked up the stapler from my desk. "Be a baby rabbit—PYRZQXGL!" She sputtered the word at it.

And there was a tiny gray bunny nosing inquisitively at my blotter!

"Be what you were before," said Dismey. "PYRZQXGL!" The bunny started slightly and the stapler fell over on its side. I picked it up. It felt warm. I dropped it.

"But—but—" I took a deep breath. "Where are the boys, Dismey? Do you know?"

"I guess so," she said, frowning a little. "I guess I remember."

"Go get them," I said. "Bring them to me."

She looked at me quietly for a moment, her jaw muscles tensing, then said, "Okay, teacher."

So I sent her, heaven help me! And she came back, heaven help us all! She came back and put three little rocks on the corner of my desk.

"I guess these is them," she said. "Two of them are, anyway. I couldn't remember exactly which ones they was, so I brought an extra one."

We looked at the rocks.

"They're scared," she said. "I turned them into *scared* rocks."

"Do rocks know?" I asked. "Can rocks be scared?"

Dismey considered, head tilted. "I don't know." The small smile came back. "But if they can—they are."

And there they lie, on my green blotter, in the middle of my battered old desk, in front of my crowded room—three rocks, roughly the size of marbles—and two of them are Michael and Bannie.

And time is running out fast—fast! I can't say the magic word. Nobody can say the magic word except Dismey—and her mother.

Of course I could take them to Mr. Beasley in the office and say, "Here are two of my boys. Remember? They're the ones that kept picking on the little girl in my room. She turned them into rocks because they were mean. What shall we do?"

Or I could take them to the boys' parents and say, "One of these is your boy. Which one resembles Bannie the most? Take your choice."

I've been looking down at my quiet hands for fifteen minutes now, but the rising murmur in the room and the rustle of movement tell me that it's past time to change activities. I've got to do something—and soon.

Looking back over the whole affair, I see only one possible course of action. I'm going to take a page from Dismey's own book. I'm going to be the believingest teacher there ever was. I believe—I believe implicitly that Dismey will mind me—she'll do as she is told. I believe, I believe, I believe—

"Dismey, come here, please." Here comes the obedient child, up to my desk. "It's almost time to go home, Dismey," I tell her. "Here, take the rocks and go outside by the door. Turn them back into Michael and Bannie again."

"I don't want to." It's not refusal! It's not refusal! It's just a statement.

"I know you don't. But the bell will be ringing soon, and we don't want to make them miss the bus. Mr. Beasley gets very annoyed when we miss the bus."

"But they're awfully mean." Her eyes are hurt and angry.

"Yes, I know they were, and I'm going to use the paddle on them. But they've been rocks a long time—scared rocks. They know now that you can be mean back at them, so they'll probably let you alone and not bother you any more. Go on, take them outside." She's looking at me intently.

"Remember, your mama said mind the teacher." Her jaws tighten.

The three rocks click together in her hand. She is going out the door. It swings shut jerkily behind her.

Now I am waiting for the doorknob to turn again. *I believe, I believe, I believe—*

# The Anything Box

## ZENNA HENDERSON

I suppose it was about the second week of school that I noticed Sue-lynn particularly. Of course, I'd noticed her name before and checked her out automatically for maturity and ability and probable performance the way most teachers do with their students during the first weeks of school. She had checked out mature and capable and no worry as to performance as I had pigeonholed her—setting aside for the moment the little nudge that said, "Too quiet"—with my other no-worrys until the fluster and flurry of the first days had died down a little.

I remember my noticing day. I had collapsed into my chair for a brief respite from guiding hot little hands through the intricacies of keeping a crayola within reasonable bounds and the room was full of the relaxed, happy hum of a pleased class as they walked away, not realizing that they were rubbing "blue" into their memories as well as onto their papers. I was meditating on how individual personalities were beginning to emerge among the thirty-five or so heterogeneous first graders I had, when I noticed Sue-lynn—really noticed her—for the first time.

She had finished her paper—far ahead of the others as usual—and was sitting at her table facing me. She had her thumbs touching in front of her on the table and her fingers curving as though they held something between them—something large enough to keep her fingertips apart and angular enough to bend her fingers as if for corners. It was something pleasant that she held—pleasant and precious. You could tell that by the softness of her hold. She was leaning forward a little, her lower ribs pressed against the table, and she was looking completely absorbed, at the table between her hands. Her face was relaxed and happy. Her mouth curved in a tender half-smile, and as I watched, her lashes lifted and she looked at me with a warm share-the-pleasure look. Then her eyes blinked and the shutters came down inside them. Her hand flicked into the desk and out. She pressed her thumbs to her forefingers and rubbed them slowly together. Then she laid one hand over the other on the table and looked down at them with the air of complete denial and ignorance children can assume so devastatingly.

The incident caught my fancy and I began to notice Sue-lynn. As I consciously watched her, I saw that she spent most of her free time staring at the table between her hands, much too unobtrusively to catch my busy attention. She hurried through even the funnest of fun papers and then lost herself in looking. When Davie pushed her down at recess, and blood streamed out of her knee to her ankle, she took her bandages and her tear-smudged face to that comfort she had so readily—if you'll pardon the expression—at hand, and emerged minutes later, serene and dry-eyed. I think Davie pushed her down because of her Looking. I know the day before he had come up to me, red faced and squirming.

"Teacher," he blurted. "She Looks!"

"Who looks?" I asked absently, checking the vocabulary list in my book, wondering how on earth I'd missed *where,* one of those annoying *wh* words that throw the children for a loss.

"Sue-lynn. She Looks and Looks!"

"At you?" I asked.

"Well—" He rubbed a forefinger below his nose, leaving a clean streak on his upper lip, accepted the proffered tissue and put it in his pocket. "She looks at her desk and tell lies. She says she can see—"

"Can see what?" My curiosity picked up its ears.

"Anything," said Davie. "It's her Anything Box. She can see anything she wants to."

"Does it hurt you for her to Look?"

"Well," he squirmed. Then he burst out: "She says she saw me with a dog biting me because I took her pencil—she said." He started a pell-mell verbal retreat. "She *thinks* I took her pencil. I only found—" His eyes dropped. "I'll give it back."

"I hope so," I smiled. "If you don't want her to look at you, then don't do things like that."

"Durn girls," he muttered and clomped back to his seat.

So I think he pushed her down the next day to get back at her for the dog-bite.

Several times after that I wandered to the back of the room, casually in her vicinity, but always she either saw or felt me coming and the quick sketch of her hand disposed of the evidence. Only once I thought I caught a glimmer of something—but her thumb and forefinger brushed in sunlight, and it must have been just that.

Children don't retreat for no reason at all, and, though Sue-lynn did not follow any overt pattern of withdrawal, I started to wonder about her. I watched her on the playground, to see how she tracked there. That only confused me more.

She had a very regular pattern. When the avalanche of children first descended at recess, she avalanched along with them and nothing in the shrieking, running, dodging mass resolved itself into a withdrawn Sue-lynn. But after ten minutes or so, she emerged from the crowd, tousle-haired, rosy-cheeked, smutched with dust, one shoelace dangling and, through some alchemy that I coveted for myself, she suddenly became untousled, undusty and unsmutched. And there she was, serene and composed on the narrow little step at the side of the flight of stairs just where they disappeared into the base of the pseudo-Corinthian column that graced Our Door and her cupped hands received whatever they received and her absorption in what she saw became so complete that the bell came as a shock every time.

And each time, before she joined the rush to Our Door, her hand would sketch a gesture to her pocket, if she had one, or to the tiny ledge that extended between the hedge and the building. Apparently she always had to put the Anything Box away, but never had to go back to get it.

I was so intrigued by her putting whatever it was on the ledge that once I actually went over and felt along the grimy little outset. I sheepishly followed my children into the hall, wiping the dust from my fingertips, and Sue-lynn's eyes brimmed amusement at me without her mouth's smiling. Her hands mischievously squared in front of her and her thumbs caressed a solidness as the line of children swept into the room.

I smiled too because she was so pleased with having outwitted me. This seemed to be such a gay withdrawal that I let my worry die down. Better this manifestation than any number of other ones that I could name.

Someday, perhaps, I'll learn to keep my mouth shut. I wish I had before that long afternoon when we primary teachers worked together in a heavy cloud of ditto fumes, the acrid smell of India ink, drifting cigarette smoke and the constant current of chatter, and I let Alpha get me started on what to do with our behavior problems. She was all steamed up about the usual rowdy loudness of her boys and the eternal clack of her girls, and I—bless my stupidity—gave her Sue-lynn as an example of what should be our deepest concern rather than the outbursts from our active ones.

"You mean she just sits and looks at nothing?" Alpha's voice grated into her questioning.

"Well, I can't see anything," I admitted. "But apparently she can."

"But that's having hallucinations!" Her voice went up a notch. "I read a book once—"

"Yes," Marlene leaned across the desk to flick ashes into the ashtray. "So we have heard and heard and heard."

"Well!" sniffed Alpha. "It's better than *never* reading a book."

"We're waiting," Marlene leaked smoke from her nostrils, "for the day when you read another book. This one must have been uncommonly long."

"Oh, I don't know." Alpha's forehead wrinkled with concentration. "It was only about—" Then she reddened and turned her face angrily away from Marlene.

"Apropos of *our* discussion—" she said pointedly. "It sounds to me like that child has a deep personality disturbance. Maybe even a psychotic—whatever—" Her eyes glistened faintly as she turned the thought over.

"Oh, I don't know," I said, surprised into echoing her words at my sudden need to defend Sue-lynn. "There's something about her. She doesn't have that apprehensive, hunched-shoulder, don't-hit-me-again air about her that so many withdrawn children have." And I thought achingly of one of mine from last year that Alpha had now and was verbally bludgeoning back into silence after all my work with him. "She seems to have a happy, adjusted personality, only with this odd little—*plus.*"

"Well, I'd be worried if she were mine," said Alpha. "I'm glad all my kids are so normal." She sighed complacently. "I guess I really haven't anything to kick about. I seldom ever have problem children except wigglers and yakkers, and a holler and a smack can straighten them out."

Marlene caught my eye mockingly, tallying Alpha's class with me, and I turned away with a sigh. To be so happy—well, I suppose ignorance does help.

"You'd better do something about that girl." Alpha shrilled as she left the room. "She'll probably get worse and worse as time goes on. Deteriorating, I think the book said."

I had known Alpha a long time and I thought I knew how much of her talk to discount, but I began to worry about Sue-lynn. Maybe this *was* a disturbance that was more fundamental than the usual run-of-the-mill that I had met up with. Maybe a child *can* smile a soft, contented smile and still have little maggots of madness flourishing somewhere inside.

Or, by gorry! I said to myself defiantly, maybe she *does* have an Anything Box. Maybe she *is* looking at something precious. Who am I to say no to anything like that?

An Anything Box! What could you see in an Anything Box? Heart's desire? I felt my own heart lurch—just a little—the next time Sue-lynn's

hands curved. I breathed deeply to hold me in my chair. If it was *her* Anything Box, I wouldn't be able to see my heart's desire in it. Or would I? I propped my cheek up on my hand and doddled aimlessly on my time-schedule sheet. How on earth, I wondered—not for the first time—do I manage to get myself off on these tangents?

Then I felt a small presence at my elbow and turned to meet Sue-lynn's wide eyes.

"Teacher?" The word was hardly more than a breath.

"Yes?" I could tell that for some reason Sue-lynn was loving me dearly at the moment. Maybe because her group had gone into new books that morning. Maybe because I had noticed her new dress, the ruffles of which made her feel very feminine and lovable, or maybe just because the late autumn sun lay so golden across her desk. Anyway, she was loving me to overflowing, and since, unlike most of the children, she had no casual hugs or easy moist kisses, she was bringing her love to me in her encompassing hands.

"See my box, teacher? It's my Anything Box."

"Oh, my!" I said, "May I hold it?"

After all, I have held—tenderly or apprehensively or bravely—tiger magic, live rattlesnakes, dragon's teeth, poor little dead butterflies and two ears and a nose that dropped off Sojie one cold morning—none of which I could see any more than I could see the Anything Box. But I took the squareness from her carefully, my tenderness showing in my fingers and my face.

And I received weight and substance and actuality!

I almost let it slip out of my surprised fingers, but Sue-lynn's apprehensive breath helped me catch it and I curved my fingers around the precious warmness and looked down, down, past a faint shimmering, down into Sue-lynn's Anything Box.

*I was running barefoot through the whispering grass. The swirl of my skirts caught the daisies as I rounded the gnarled appletree at the corner. The warm wind lay along each of my cheeks and*

*chuckled in my ears. My heart outstripped my fly-*
*ing feet and melted with a rush of delight into*
*warmness as his arms—*

I closed my eyes and swallowed hard, my
palms tight against the Anything Box. "It's beautiful" I whispered. "It's wonderful, Sue-lynn.
Where did you get it?"

Her hands took it back hastily. "It's mine,"
she said defiantly. "It's mine."

"Of course," I said. "Be careful now. Don't
drop it."

She smiled faintly as she sketched a motion
to her pocket. "I won't." She patted the pocket on
her way back to her seat.

Next day she was afraid to look at me at first
for fear I might say something or look something
or in some way remind her of what must seem like
a betrayal to her now, but after I only smiled my
usual smile, with no added secret knowledge, she
relaxed.

A night or so later when I leaned over my
moon-drenched window sill and let the shadow of
my hair hide my face from such ebullient glory, I
remembered about the Anything Box. Could I
make one for myself? Could I square off this aching waiting, this out-reaching, this silent cry inside me, and make it into an Anything Box? I
freed my hands and brought them together thumb
to thumb, framing a part of the horizon's darkness
between my upright forefingers. I stared into the
empty square until my eyes watered. I sighed, and
laughed a little, and let my hands frame my face
as I leaned out into the night. To have magic so
near—to feel it tingle off my fingertips and then to
be so bound that I couldn't receive it. I turned
away from the window—turning my back on
brightness.

It wasn't long after this that Alpha succeeded
in putting sharp points of worry back in my
thought of Sue-lynn. We had ground duty together, and one morning when we shivered while the
kids ran themselves rosy in the crisp air, she
sizzed in my ear.

"Which one is it? The abnormal one, I
mean."

"I don't have any abnormal children," I said,
my voice sharpening before the sentence ended
because I suddenly realized whom she meant.

"Well, I call it abnormal to stare at nothing."
You could almost taste the acid in her words.
"Who is it?"

"Sue-lynn," I said reluctantly. "She's playing
on the bars now."

Alpha surveyed the upside-down Sue-lynn,
whose brief skirts were belled down from her bare
pink legs and half covered her face as she swung
from one of the bars by her knees. Alpha clutched
her wizened blue hands together and breathed on
them. "She looks normal enough," she said.

"She *is* normal!" I snapped.

"*Well,* bite my head off!" cried Alpha.
"You're the one that said she wasn't, not me—or
is it 'not I'? I never could remember. Not me? Not
I?"

The bell saved Alpha from a horrible end. I
never knew a person so serenely unaware of es-
sentials and so sensitive to trivia. But she had succeeded in making me worry about Sue-lynn again,
and the worry exploded into distress a few days
later.

Sue-lynn came to school sleepy-eyed and
quiet. She didn't finish any of her work and she
fell asleep during rest time. I cussed TV and
drive-ins and assumed a night's sleep would put it
right. But next day Sue-lynn burst into tears and
slapped Davie clear off his chair.

"Why Sue-lynn!" I gathered Davie up in all
his astonishment and took Sue-lynn's hand. She
jerked it away from me and flung herself at Davie
again. She got two handfuls of his hair and had
him out of my grasp before I knew it. She threw
him bodily against the wall with a flip of her
hands, then doubled up her fists and pressed them
into her streaming eyes. In the shocked silence of
the room, she stumbled over to Isolation and, seating herself, back to the class, on the little chair,
she leaned her head into the corner and sobbed
quietly in big gulping sobs.

"What on earth goes on?" I asked the stupe-
fied Davie who sat spraddle-legged on the floor

fingering a detached tuft of hair. "What did you do?"

"I only said 'Robber Daughter,'" said Davie. "It said so in the paper. My mamma said her daddy's a robber. They put him in jail cause he robbered a gas station." His bewildered face was trying to decide whether or not to cry. Everything had happened so fast that he didn't know yet if he was hurt.

"It isn't nice to call names," I said weakly. "Get back into your seat. I'll take care of Sue-lynn later."

He got up and sat gingerly down in his chair, rubbing his ruffled hair, wanting to make more of a production of the situation but not knowing how. He twisted his face experimentally to see if he had tears available and had none.

"Durn girls," he muttered and tried to shake his fingers free of a wisp of hair.

I kept my eye on Sue-lynn for the next half hour as I busied myself with the class. Her sobs soon stopped and her rigid shoulders relaxed. Her hands were softly in her lap and I knew she was taking comfort in her Anything Box. We had our talk together later, but she was so completely sealed off from me by her misery that there was no communication between us. She sat quietly watching me as I talked, her hands trembling in her lap. It shakes the heart, somehow, to see the hands of a little child quiver like that.

That afternoon I looked up from my reading group, startled, as though by a cry, to catch Sue-lynn's frightened eyes. She looked around bewildered and then down at her hands again—her empty hands. Then she darted to the Isolation corner and reached under the chair. She went back to her seat slowly, her hands squared to an unseen weight. For the first time, apparently, she had had to go get the Anything Box. It troubled me with a vague unease for the rest of the afternoon.

Through the days that followed while the trial hung fire, I had Sue-lynn in attendance bodily, but that was all. She sank into her Anything Box at every opportunity. And always, if she had put it away somewhere, she had to go back for it. She roused more and more reluctantly from these waking dreams, and there finally came a day when I had to shake her to waken her.

I went to her mother, but she couldn't or wouldn't understand me, and made me feel like a frivolous gossip-monger taking her mind away from her husband, despite the fact that I didn't even mention him—or maybe because I didn't mention him.

"If she's being a bad girl, spank her," she finally said, wearily shifting the weight of a whining baby from one hip to another and pushing her tousled hair off her forehead. "Whatever you do is all right by me. My worrier is all used up. I haven't got any left for the kids right now."

Well, Sue-lynn's father was found guilty and sentenced to the State Penitentiary and school was less than an hour old the next day when Davie came up, clumsily a-tiptoe, braving my wrath for interrupting a reading group, and whispered hoarsely, "Sue-lynn's asleep with her eyes open again, Teacher."

We went back to the table and Davie slid into his chair next to a completely unaware Sue-lynn. He poked her with a warning finger. "I told you I'd tell on you."

And before our horrified eyes, she toppled, as rigidly as a doll, sideways off the chair. The thud of her landing relaxed her and she lay limp on the green asphalt tile—a thin paper-doll of a girl, one hand still clenched open around something. I pried her fingers loose and almost wept to feel enchantment dissolve under my heavy touch. I carried her down to the nurse's room and we worked over her with wet towels and prayer and she finally opened her eyes.

"Teacher," she whispered weakly.

"Yes, Sue-lynn." I took her cold hands in mine.

"Teacher, I almost got in my Anything Box."

"No," I answered. "You couldn't. You're too big."

"Daddy's there," she said. "And where we used to live."

I took a long, long look at her wan face. I hope it was genuine concern for her that prompted my next words. I hope it wasn't envy or the memory of the niggling nagging of Alpha's voice that put firmness in my voice as I went on. "That's playlike," I said. "Just for fun."

Her hands jerked protestingly in mine. "Your Anything Box is just for fun. It's like Davie's cowpony that he keeps in his desk or Sojie's jet plane, or when the big bear chases all of you at recess. It's fun-for-play, but it's not for real. You mustn't think it's for real. It's only play."

"No!" she denied. "*No!*" she cried frantically and, hunching herself up on the cot, peering through her tear-swollen eyes, she scrabbled under the pillow and down beneath the rough blanket that covered her.

"Where is it?" she cried. "Where is it? Give it back to me, Teacher!"

She flung herself toward me and pulled open both my clenched hands.

"Where did you put it? Where did you put it?"

"There is no Anything Box," I said flatly, trying to hold her to me and feeling my heart breaking along with hers.

"You took it!" she sobbed. "You took it away from me!" And she wrenched herself out of my arms.

"Can't you give it back to her?" whispered the nurse. "If it makes her feel so bad? Whatever it is—"

"It's just imagination," I said, almost sullenly. "I can't give her back something that doesn't exist."

Too young! I thought bitterly. Too young to learn that heart's desire is only play-like.

Of course the doctor found nothing wrong. Her mother dismissed the matter as a fainting spell and Sue-lynn came back to class next day, thin and listless, staring blankly out the window, her hands palm down on the desk. I swore by the pale hollow of her cheek that never, *never* again would I take any belief from anyone without replacing it

with something better. What had I given Sue-lynn? What had she better than I had taken from her? How did I know but that her Anything Box was on purpose to tide her over rough spots in her life like this? And what now, now that I had taken it from her?

Well, after a time she began to work again, and later, to play. She came back to smiles, but not to laughter. She puttered along quite satisfactorily except that she was a candle blown out. The flame was gone wherever the brightness of belief goes. And she had no more sharing smiles for me, no overflowing love to bring to me. And her shoulder shrugged subtly away from my touch.

Then one day I suddenly realized that Sue-lynn was searching our classroom. Stealthily, casually, day by day she was searching, covering every inch of the room. She went through every puzzle box, every lump of clay, every shelf and cupboard, every box and bag. Methodically she checked behind every row of books and in every child's desk until finally, after almost a week, she had been through everything in the place except my desk. Then she began to materialize suddenly at my elbow every time I opened a drawer. And her eyes would probe quickly and sharply before I slid it shut again. But if I tried to intercept her looks, they slid away and she had some legitimate errand that had brought her up to the vicinity of the desk.

She believes it again, I thought hopefully. She won't accept the fact that her Anything Box is gone. She wants it again.

But it *is* gone, I thought drearily. It's really-for-true gone.

My head was heavy from troubled sleep, and sorrow was a weariness in all my movements. Waiting is sometimes a burden almost too heavy to carry. While my children hummed happily over their fun stuff, I brooded silently out the window until I managed a laugh at myself. It was a shaky laugh that threatened to dissolve into something else, so I brisked back to my desk.

As good time as any to throw out useless things, I thought, and to see if I can find that colored chalk I put away so carefully. I plunged my hands into the wilderness of the bottom right-hand drawer of my desk. It was deep with a huge accumulation of anything—just anything—that might need a temporary hiding place. I knelt to pull out leftover Jack Frost pictures, and a broken bean shooter, a chewed red ribbon, a roll of cap-gun ammunition, one striped sock, six Numbers papers, a rubber dagger, a copy of *The Gospel According to St. Luke,* a miniature coal shovel, patterns for jack-o'-lanterns, and a pink plastic pelican. I retrieved my Irish linen hankie I thought lost forever and Sojie's report card that he had told me solemnly had blown out of his hand and landed on a jet and broke the sound barrier so loud that it busted all to flitters. Under the welter of miscellany, I felt a squareness. Oh, happy! I thought, this *is* where I put the colored chalk! I cascaded papers off both sides of my lifting hands and shook the box free.

*We were together again. Outside, the world was an enchanted wilderness of white, the wind shouting softly through the windows, tapping wet, white fingers against the warm light. Inside all the worry and waiting, the apartness and loneliness were over and forgotten, their hugeness dwindled by the comfort of a shoulder, the warmth of clasping hands—and nowhere, nowhere was the fear of parting, nowhere the need to do without again. This was the happy ending. This was—*

This was Sue-lynn's Anything Box!

My racing heart slowed as the dream faded— and rushed again at the realization. I had it here! In my junk drawer! It had been here all the time!

I stood up shakily, concealing the invisible box in the flare of my skirts. I sat down and put the box carefully in the center of my desk, covering the top of it with my palms lest I should drown again in delight. I looked at Sue-lynn. She was finishing her fun paper, competently but unjoyously. Now would come her patient sitting with quiet hands until told to do something else.

Alpha would approve. And very possibly, I thought, Alpha would, for once in her limited life, be right. We may need "hallucinations" to keep us going—all of us but the Alphas—but when we go so far as to try to force ourselves, physically, into the Never-never land of heart's desire....

I remembered Sue-lynn's thin rigid body toppling doll-like off its chair. Out of her deep need she had found—or created?—who could tell?— something too dangerous for a child. I could so easily bring the brimming happiness back to her eyes—but at what possible price!

No, I had a duty to protect Sue-lynn. Only maturity—the maturity born of the sorrow and loneliness that Sue-lynn was only beginning to know—could be trusted to use an Anything Box safely and wisely.

My heart thudded as I began to move my hands, letting the palms slip down from top to shape the sides of—

I had moved them back again before I really saw, and I have now learned almost to forget that glimpse of what heart's desire is like when won at the cost of another's heart.

I sat there at the desk trembling and breathless, my palms moist, feeling as if I had been on a long journey away from the little schoolroom. Perhaps I had. Perhaps I had been shown all the kingdoms of the world in a moment of time.

"Sue-lynn," I called. "Will you come up here when you're through?"

She nodded unsmilingly and snipped off the last paper from the edge of Mistress Mary's dress. Without another look at her handiwork, she carried the scissors safely to the scissors box, crumpled the scraps of paper in her hand and came up to the waste basket by the desk.

"I have something for you, Sue-lynn," I said, uncovering the box.

Her eyes dropped to the desk top. She looked indifferently up at me. "I did my fun paper already."

"Did you like it?"

"Yes," It was a flat lie.

"Good," I lied right back. "But look here." I squared my hands around the Anything Box.

She took a deep breath and the whole of her little body stiffened.

"I found it," I said hastily, fearing anger. "I found it in the bottom drawer."

She leaned her chest against my desk, her hands caught tightly between, her eyes intent on the box, her face white with the aching want you see on children's faces pressed to Christmas windows.

"Can I have it?" she whispered.

"It's yours," I said, holding it out.

Still she leaned against her hands, her eyes searching my face. "Can I have it?" she asked again.

"Yes!" I was impatient with this anticlimax. "But—"

Her eyes flickered. She had sensed my reservation before I had. "But you must never try to get in it again."

"O.K.," she said, the word coming out on a long relieved sigh. "O.K., Teacher."

She took the box and tucked it lovingly into her small pocket. She turned from the desk and started back to her table. My mouth quirked with a small smile. It seemed to me that everything about her had suddenly turned upward—even the ends of her straight taffy-colored hair. The subtle flame about her that made her Sue-lynn was there again. She scarcely touched the floor as she walked.

I sighed heavily and traced on the desk top with my finger a probable size for an Anything Box. What would Sue-lynn choose to see first? How like a drink after a drought it would seem to her.

I was startled as a small figure materialized at my elbow. It was Sue-lynn, her fingers carefully squared before her.

"Teacher," she said softly, all the flat emptiness gone from her voice. "Any time you want to take my Anything Box, you just say so."

I groped through my astonishment and incredulity for words. She couldn't possibly have had time to look into the Box yet.

"Why, thank you, Sue-lynn," I managed. "Thanks a lot. I would like very much to borrow it sometime."

"Would you like it now?" she asked, proffering it.

"No, thank you," I said, around the lump in my throat. "I've had a turn already. You go ahead."

"O.K.," she murmured. Then—"Teacher?"

"Yes?"

Shyly she leaned against me, her cheek on my shoulder. She looked up at me with her warm, unshuttered eyes, then both arms were suddenly around my neck in a brief awkward embrace.

"Watch out!" I whispered laughing into the collar of her blue dress. "You'll lose it again!"

"No I won't," she laughed back, patting the flat pocket of her dress. "Not ever, ever again!"

# Kindergarten

## JAMES GUNN

*First day—*

Teacher told my parent that I am the slowest youngster in my class, but today I made a star in the third quadrant of kindergarten.

Teacher was surprised. Teacher tried to hide it and said the solar phoenix reaction is artistic, but is it practical?

I don't care. I think it's pretty.

*Second day—*

Today I made planets: four big ones, two middle sized ones, and three little ones. Teacher laughed and said why did I make so many when all but three were too hot or too cold to support life and the big ones were too massive and poisonous for any use at all.

Teacher doesn't understand. There is more to creation than mere usefulness.

The rings around the sixth planet are beautiful.

*Third day—*

Today I created life. I begin to understand why my people place creation above all else.

I have heard philosophers discussing the purpose of existence, but I thought it was merely age. Before today joy was enough: to have fun with the other kids, to speed through endless space, to explode some unstable star into a nova, to flee before the outrage of some adult—this would fill eternity.

Now I know better. Life must have a function.

Teacher was right: only two of the middle-sized planets and one of the little ones were suitable for life. I made life for all three, but only on the third planet from the sun was it really successful.

I have given it only one function: survive!

*Fourth day—*

The third planet has absorbed all my interest. The soupy seas are churning with life.

Today I introduced a second function: multiply!

The forms developing in the seas are increasingly complex.

The kids are calling me to come and play, but I'm not going.

This is more fun.

*Fifth day—*

Time after time I stranded sea creatures on the land and kept them alive long past the time when they should have died. At last I succeeded. Some of them have adapted.

I was right. The sea is definitely an inhibiting factor.

The success of the land creatures is pleasing.

*Sixth day—*

Everything I did before today was nothing. Today I created intelligence.

I added a third function: know!

Out of a minor primate has developed a fabulous creature. It has two legs and walks upright and looks around it with curious eyes. It has weak hands and an insignificant brain, but it is conquering all things. Most of all, it is conquering its environment.

It has even begun speculating about me!

*Seventh day—*

Today there is no school.

After the pangs and labors of creation, it is fun to play again. It is like escaping the gravitational field of a white dwarf and regaining the dissipated coma.

Teacher talked to my parent again today. Teacher said I had developed remarkably in the last few days but my creation was hopelessly warped and inconsistent. Moreover, it was potentially dangerous.

Teacher said it would have to be destroyed.

**295**

My parent objected, saying that the solar phoenix reaction in the sun would lead the dangerous life form on the third planet to develop a thermonuclear reaction of its own. With the functions I had given that life form, the problem would take care of itself.

It wasn't my parent's responsibility Teacher said, and Teacher couldn't take that chance.

I didn't hear who won the argument. I drifted away, feeling funny.

I don't care, really. I'm tired of the old thing anyway. I'll make a better one.

But it was the first thing I ever made, and you can't help feeling a kind of sentimental attachment.

If anyone sees a great comet plunging toward the sun, it isn't me.

*Eighth day—*

# CHAPTER 10

## LIFE AND DEATH

Donald Barthelme, "The School"
María T. Solari, "Death and Transfiguration of a Teacher"
Charles Baxter, "Gryphon"
Marjorie Marks, "Death in the Fifth Grade"

Life and death may seem like an odd topic to address through stories about school teaching but the complexity of human experience is perhaps never more keenly perceived than at those times when death must be faced. Each of these stories touches upon encounters with death in school classrooms, exploring human emotions concerning life and death among children and adults.

In "The School" by David Barthelme, an elementary school teacher named Edgar recounts a year in the life of his classroom: sad, unsuccessful attempts to nurture plants and animals, and tragedies involving classmates, and parents, and grandparents. As a result, the students have begun to ask questions that Edgar finds difficult to answer.

*One day, we had a discussion in class. They asked me, where did they go? The trees, the salamander, the tropical fish, . . . the poppas and the mommas . . . And I said, I don't know, I don't know. And they said, who knows? and I said, nobody knows. And they said, is death that which gives meaning to life? and I said, no, life is that which gives meaning to life.*

Marjorie Marks, in "Death in the Fifth Grade," explores a teacher's struggle with her own beliefs about death and how they might affect her students. The classroom mothers have asked Miss Steineck to explain a classmate's death to the other children. She worries about how to approach the topic and decides to tell an emotional story about a death from her childhood which highlights the notion that death does not mean we have to forget those we loved.

The surrealistic "Death and Transfiguration of a Teacher" by María Solari is a satirical study of a different type of death: the intentional murder of ideas by those who find them discomforting or inconvenient. A poetry teacher in a wealthy girls school in South America tries to explain the magical power of poetry to her students who despise the teacher and her ideas.

*She often talked about poetry. She tried to explain the magical power of poetic utterance. Something like the supreme effort of the poet to rise above the maddening crowd and to create. Somewhere in the back of the classroom a girl started going meeeooow, smothering the poetry of the impassioned rhapsodist. The laughter sharpened in tone. The class became a single giant cat, glaring at the teacher with piercing, bloodshot eyes.*

In a frenzy of spite, the girls decide to free themselves from the influence of this teacher through a bizarre ritual resulting in a shallow, selfish victory for the girls and the school.

In Charles Baxter's "Gryphon" the topic of death slips into a fourth-grade classroom through the antics of an unusual substitute teacher: Miss Ferenczi bends the curriculum, rewrites history, ignores basic principles of mathematics, and regales the students with tales of the occult, mythology, mysticism, exotic, distant places beyond rural America— even death. The tales seem unbelievable but with a small kernel of truth in them that leaves the students uncertain. The students struggle in discussions amongst themselves to discern whether Miss Ferenczi is telling the truth all the time, some of the time, or none of the time. They are interested and puzzled by the way reality and fantasy seem to mix in her tales.

Just before Christmas, as a reward, Miss Ferenczi abandons their regularly scheduled activities in favor of making predictions with tarot cards. The class seems only mildly interested until Wayne Razmer picks his five cards. "Well Wayne," she said, "you will undergo a great metamorphosis, a change, before you become an adult." The story moves to a rapid conclusion and Miss Ferenczi discovers the school's tolerance of her classroom predictions and antics has ended.

Each of the stories in this chapter is about the tensions between life and death in school classrooms. These tensions are most obvious in "The School," and "Death in the Fifth Grade." These stories are unblinking explorations of life and death: The deep wonder and awe, the mournful and mysterious. Both stories reflect a constant struggle to ensure that death does not reduce life to irrelevance; both grapple with the mystery and tragedy of death. The explorations of life and death tensions are, perhaps, less obvious and more symbolic in "Death and Transfiguration of a Teacher" and "Gryphon."

# The School

## DONALD BARTHELME

Well, we had all these children out planting trees, see, because we figured that...that was part of their education, to see how, you know, the root systems...and also the sense of responsibility, taking care of things, being individually responsible. You know what I mean. And the trees all died. They were orange trees. I don't know why they died, they just died. Something wrong with the soil possibly or maybe the stuff we got from the nursery wasn't the best. We complained about it. So we've got thirty kids there, each kid had his or her own little tree to plant, and we've got these thirty dead trees. All these kids looking at these little brown sticks, it was depressing.

It wouldn't have been so bad except that just a couple of weeks before the thing with the trees, the snakes all died. But I think that the snakes— well, the reason that the snakes kicked off was that...you remember, the boiler was shut off for four days because of the strike, and that was explicable. It was something you could explain to the kids because of the strike. I mean, none of their parents would let them cross the picket line and they knew there was a strike going on and what it meant. So when things got started up again and we found the snakes they weren't too disturbed.

With the herb gardens it was probably a case of overwatering, and at least now they know not to overwater. The children were very conscientious with the herb gardens and some of them probably...you know, slipped them a little extra water when we weren't looking. Or maybe... well, I don't like to think about sabotage, although it did occur to us. I mean, it was something that crossed our minds. We were thinking that way probably because before that the gerbils had died, and the white mice had died, and the salamander...well, now they know not to carry them around in plastic bags.

Of course we *expected* the tropical fish to die, that was no surprise. Those numbers, you look at

them crooked and they're belly-up on the surface. But the lesson plan called for a tropical-fish input at that point, there was nothing we could do, it happens every year, you just have to hurry past it.

We weren't even supposed to have a puppy.

We weren't even supposed to have one, it was just a puppy the Murdoch girl found under a Gristede's truck one day and she was afraid the truck would run over it when the driver had finished making his delivery, so she stuck it in her knapsack and brought it to school with her. So we had this puppy. As soon as I saw the puppy I thought, Oh Christ, I bet it will live for about two weeks and then...And that's what it did. It wasn't supposed to be in the classroom at all, there's some kind of regulation about it, but you can't tell them they can't have a puppy when the puppy is already there, right in front of them, running around on the floor and yap yap yapping. They named it Edgar—that is, they named it after me. They had a lot of fun running after it and yelling, "Here, Edgar! Nice Edgar!" Then they'd laugh like hell. They enjoyed the ambiguity. I enjoyed it myself. I don't mind being kidded. They made a little house for it in the supply closet and all that. I don't know what it died of. Distemper, I guess. It probably hadn't had any shots. I got it out of there before the kids got to school. I checked the supply closet each morning, routinely, because I knew what was going to happen. I gave it to the custodian.

And then there was this Korean orphan that the class adopted through the Help the Children program, all the kids brought in a quarter a month, that was the idea. It was an unfortunate thing, the kid's name was Kim and maybe we adopted him too late or something. The cause of death was not stated in the letter we got, they suggested we adopt another child instead and sent us some interesting case histories, but we didn't have the heart. The class took it pretty hard, they began (I think; nobody ever said anything to me directly) to feel that maybe there was something wrong with the school. But I don't think there's anything wrong with the school, particularly, I've seen better and I've seen worse. It was just a run of bad luck. We had an extraordinary number of parents passing away, for instance. There were I think two heart attacks and two suicides, one drowning, and four killed together in a car accident. One stroke. And we had the usual heavy mortality rate among the grandparents, or maybe it was heavier this year, it seemed so. And finally the tragedy.

The tragedy occurred when Matthew Wein and Tony Mavrogordo were playing over where they're excavating for the new federal office building. There were all these big wooden beams stacked, you know, at the edge of the excavation. There's a court case coming out of that, the parents are claiming that the beams were poorly stacked. I don't know what's true and what's not. It's been a strange year.

I forgot to mention Billy Brandt's father, who was knifed fatally when he grappled with a masked intruder in his home.

One day, we had a discussion in class. They asked me, where did they go? The trees, the salamander, the tropical fish, Edgar, the poppas and mommas, Matthew and Tony, where did they go? And I said, I don't know, I don't know. And they said, who knows? and I said, nobody knows. And

they said, is death that which gives meaning to life? and I said, no, life is that which gives meaning to life. Then they said, but isn't death, considered as a fundamental datum, the means by which the taken-for-granted mundanity of the everyday may be transcended in the direction of—

I said, yes, maybe.

They said, we don't like it.

I said, that's sound.

They said, it's a bloody shame!

I said, it is.

They said, will you make love now with Helen (our teaching assistant) so that we can see how it is done? We know you like Helen.

I do like Helen but I said that I would not.

We've heard so much about it, they said, but we've never seen it.

I said I would be fired and that it was never, or almost never, done as a demonstration. Helen looked out of the window.

They said, please, please make love with Helen, we require an assertion of value, we are frightened.

I said that they shouldn't be frightened (although I am often frightened) and there was value everywhere. Helen came and embraced me. I kissed her a few times on the brow. We held each other. The children were excited. Then there was a knock on the door. I opened the door, and the new gerbil walked in. The children cheered wildly.

# Death and Transfiguration of a Teacher

## MARÍA T. SOLARI

The teacher was dead; she had been cut up by the girls who, after killing her, cannibalistically disposed of her remains. The teacher was a poet endowed with great sensitivity and a romantic temperament, having started writing at twenty, although her career was now over at thirty-five. They were going over the scene of the crime. All the students presumed guilty. They were interrogating the top student in the class:

"Now please tell us everything from the start..."

The girl, a young thing with a blank expression on her face, grabbed one foot and sardonically exclaimed:

"Here."

"What's that supposed to mean? What are you doing with your foot? Get to the point!"

"I mean, I started on her foot. I took off her sock and bit into the heel."

"You can't be serious!"

The principal was nonplussed. Actually, all that was left were the gnawed-on bones. They left a little sign on the macabre residue: "Anatomy Lesson," it said.

One of the murdered teacher's poems went:

*Oh, bittersweet youth,*
  *object of my abject toil...*

And nothing else. She had published only one book, entitled *Destiny*. She was timid in conversation and at times could not seem to express herself. When she got frustrated during the torture of her classes, she turned red and her mouth trembled. But she was incapable of raising her voice. And the classroom noise of the students' uninterrupted chattering seemed to envelop, disorient and paralyze her. She often talked about poetry. She tried to explain the magical power of poetic utterance. Something like the supreme effort of the poet to rise above the maddening crowd and to

create. Somewhere in the back of the classroom a girl started going meeeeeooow, smothering the poetry of the impassioned rhapsodist. The laughter sharpened in tone. The class became a single giant cat, glaring at the teacher with piercing, bloodshot eyes. Four girls in the front row were singing some pop tune that went:

*When I love you*
*from the bottom of my heart*
*my brains go*
*suddenly into knots...*

The teacher left the room, crestfallen. Looking out at the empty schoolyard, she thought about her Calvary, about poets no longer having any place in this world. Why make teachers cover poets and poetry? It was laughable, and cruel to boot. A little bird swooped down and daintily snatched up a crumb from the gutter. The school's dog wagged his tail as she passed by, and without realizing it she glanced at him tenderly. At least he was sincere. The principal had called her to the office. When she went in, she couldn't help staring at a row of stuffed animals neatly lined up in an open cabinet. She remembered how the day before the principal had ordered them taken out into the sun to keep down the moths. The glass-eyed rabbit and the hawk with one wing stretched out got to sun themselves all morning. She felt the school was lifeless, and the principal just another stuffed animal.

"You don't seem to appreciate how serious the situation is. Your class is a madhouse, I've noticed it when I go by. The students don't respect you; you don't know how to make them respect you. You don't understand the principle of authority. You've just got to face them down and use a firm tone of voice—and make them afraid of you. You can manage them only if they fear you. But what do you do? You talk about poetry, sweetness and light, subtleties that they'll never understand

and they don't care about! Stick to those dates, yes, dates! For example: this poet was born in 1506 and died of tuberculosis in 1526! Therefore, he lived twenty years, wrote twenty books and a dictionary of poetry. Never made a red cent, nobody gave a damn about his books! The first was Illusion, the last, Desperation. Women wanted nothing to do with him, but now he's a great poet. That's all, enough for them to learn and then get on with the next writer!"

She left the office and her spirit seemed to mope along behind her, but at least it wasn't stuffed.

The day of the crime started normally enough. As she entered the classroom a student gave her a bouquet of red roses. Totally unheard of. Some others arranged them in a vase and placed them on the lectern. One girl got up and recited one of Bécquer's poems from beginning to end, the one that starts with "The dark swallows will return." And then, you could have heard a pin drop. One of them—the one that had recited the poem—suddenly came forward and plunged the knife into her before she knew what was happening. She died with a beatific smile on her face and then they simply ate her up. Laughter was everywhere and spring was in the air, as befit the month of October. Later they went home and no one was hungry, although some complained about upset stomachs. A few threw up, but they were mostly calm. Sensitive to the deceased's poetic inclinations, they buried the bones next to a rosebush, but the dog—who was always hungry—dug them up. And when the principal was notified, she did not know what to make of them, since they did not match any of the bones in her collection. When the teacher did not show up the following day—she had never missed a class—the principal began to suspect something was wrong. Her suspicions were confirmed after questioning the class. There was no accounting for it; this had never happened before at her school. She tried to blame it on the noxious influence of television, but the psychologist she brought in felt that there was more to it: perhaps some of the girls in the class had a congenital predisposition to crime. She called an emergency meeting of the P.T.A. to discuss what should be done, whether to go public or adopt an attitude of prudent silence. More than one father during that long session embarked on a rambling disquisition on how damaging it would be to interrupt or perhaps even end his daughter's studies. Other, more draconian parents noted that the girls' sense of right and wrong would suffer if it were not made clear what they had done stepped out of line. Around midnight the sterner ones prevailed; they voted and it was decided to call in the authorities. But who would go to the police with the news? This duty fell to the gardener because, after all, he was the one who found the bones (and the dog chewing on them). So off he went. The police seemed more upset than anyone else. The whole thing was blown up in the press and newspapers sold like hotcakes, although after a while things quieted down and it was all conveniently forgotten. Some of the fathers had a lot of pull and reached an understanding with the court. Money changed hands, classes resumed and the girls did very well in their finals, and 99% of the class passed. The jury admitted that they were very bright. The principal decided to screen all prospective teachers for poetic tendencies, so as to avoid a repetition of this disagreeable and most inconvenient event. She found a taxidermist with literary inclinations to fill the recently vacated position and keep her supplied with a steady stream of new specimens as well. She even felt a twinge of regret, reflecting on the lost opportunity to stuff the slain Lit teacher and label her "Poet," for an example to all the students: a dangerous breed, an egregious flaw in the Lord's creation. Later on, she and the new teacher started a Taxidermy Club which, to her surprise, proved very popular with the student body, including many of those involved in the incident of the previous year. Not only with the girl with the knife—very bright and a lot of personality, by the way—but also with the best student in the class, who—she knew—had nothing to do with it except for the cannibalism part.

# Gryphon

## CHARLES BAXTER

On Wednesday afternoon, between the geography lesson on ancient Egypt's hand-operated irrigation system and an art project that involved drawing a model city next to a mountain, our fourth-grade teacher, Mr. Hibler, developed a cough. This cough began with a series of muffled throat-clearings and progressed to propulsive noises contained within Mr. Hibler's closed mouth. "Listen to him," Carol Peterson whispered to me. "He's gonna blow up." Mr. Hibler's laughter—dazed and infrequent—sounded a bit like his cough, but as we worked on our model cities we would look up, thinking he was enjoying a joke, and see Mr. Hibler's face turning red, his cheeks puffed out. This was not laughter. Twice he bent over, and his loose tie, like a plumb line, hung down straight from his neck as he exploded himself into a Kleenex. He would excuse himself, then go on coughing. "I'll bet you a dime," Carol Peterson whispered, "we get a substitute tomorrow."

Carol sat at the desk in front of mine and was a bad person—when she thought no one was looking she would blow her nose on notebook paper, then crumple it up and throw it into the wastebasket—but at times of crisis she spoke the truth. I knew I'd lose the dime.

"No deal," I said.

When Mr. Hibler stood us in formation at the door just prior to the final bell, he was almost incapable of speech. "I'm sorry, boys and girls," he said. "I seem to be coming down with something."

"I hope you feel better tomorrow, Mr. Hibler," Bobby Kryzanowicz, the faultless brown-noser, said, and I heard Carol Peterson's evil giggle. Then Mr. Hibler opened the door and we walked out to the buses, a clique of us starting noisily to hawk and raugh as soon as we thought we were a few feet beyond Mr. Hibler's earshot.

Since Five Oaks was a rural community, and in Michigan, the supply of substitute teachers was limited to the town's unemployed community college graduates, a pool of about four mothers. These ladies fluttered, provided easeful class days, and nervously covered material we had mastered weeks earlier. Therefore it was a surprise when a woman we had never seen came into the class the next day, carrying a purple purse, a checkerboard lunchbox, and a few books. She put the books on one side of Mr. Hibler's desk and the lunchbox on the other, next to the Voice of Music phonograph. Three of us in the back of the room were playing with Heever, the chameleon that lived in a terrarium and on one of the plastic drapes, when she walked in.

She clapped her hands at us. "Little boys," she said, "why are you bent over together like that?" She didn't wait for us to answer. "Are you tormenting an animal? Put it back. Please sit down at your desks. I want no caba's this time of the day." We just stared at her. "Boys," she repeated, "I asked you to sit down."

I put the chameleon in his terrarium and felt my way to my desk, never taking my eyes off the woman. With white and green chalk, she had started to draw a tree on the left side of the blackboard. She didn't look usual. Furthermore, her tree was outsized, disproportionate, for some reason.

"This room needs a tree," she said, with one line drawing the suggestion of a leaf. "A large, leafy, shady, deciduous . . . oak."

Her fine, light hair had been done up in what I would learn years later was called a chignon, and she wore gold-rimmed glasses whose lenses seemed to have the faintest blue tint. Harold Knardahl, who sat across from me, whispered, "Mars," I nodded slowly, savoring the imminent weirdness of the day. The substitute drew another branch with an extravagant arm gesture, then turned around and said, "Good morning. I don't believe I said good morning to all of you yet."

Facing us, she was no special age—an adult is an adult—but her face had two prominent lines, descending vertically from the sides of her mouth to her chin. I knew where I had seen those lines before: *Pinocchio.* They were marionette lines. "You may stare at me," she said to us, as a few more kids from the last bus came into the room, their eyes fixed on her, "for a few more seconds, until the bell rings. Then I will permit no more staring. Looking I will permit. Staring, no. It is impolite to stare, and a sign of bad breeding. You cannot make a social effort while staring."

Harold Knardahl did not glance at me, or nudge, but I heard him whisper "Mars" again, trying to get more mileage out of his single joke with the kids who had just come in.

When everyone was seated, the substitute teacher finished her tree, put down her chalk fastidiously on the phonograph, brushed her hands, and faced us. "Good morning," she said. "I am Miss Ferenczi, your teacher for the day. I am fairly new to your community, and I don't believe any of you know me. I will therefore start by telling you a story about myself."

While we settled back, she launched into her tale. She said her grandfather had been a Hungarian prince; her mother had been born in some place called Flanders, had been a pianist, and had played concerts for people Miss Ferenczi referred to as "crowned heads." She gave us a knowing look. "Grieg," she said, "the Norwegian master, wrote a concerto for piano that was..."—she paused—"my mother's triumph at her debut concert in London." Her eyes searched the ceiling. Our eyes followed. Nothing up there but ceiling tile. "For reasons that I shall not go into, my family's fortunes took us to Detroit, then north to dreadful Saginaw, and now here I am in Five Oaks, as your substitute teacher, for today, Thursday, October the eleventh. I believe it will be a good day: all the forecasts coincide. We shall start with your reading lesson. Take out your reading book. I believe it is called *Broad Horizons,* or something along those lines."

Jeannie Vermeesch raised her hand. Miss Ferenczi nodded at her. "Mr. Hibler always starts the day with the Pledge of Allegiance," Jeannie whined.

"Oh, does he? In that case," Miss Ferenczi said, "you must know it *very* well by now, and we certainly need not spend our time on it. No, no allegiance-pledging on the premises today, by my reckoning. Not with so much sunlight coming into the room. A pledge does not suit my mood." She glanced at her watch. "Time *is* flying. Take out *Broad Horizons.*"

She disappointed us by giving us an ordinary lesson, complete with vocabulary and drills, comprehension questions, and recitation. She didn't seem to care for the material, however. She sighed every few minutes and rubbed her glasses with a frilly handkerchief that she withdrew, magician-style, from her left sleeve.

After reading we moved on to arithmetic. It was my favorite time of the morning, when the lazy autumn sunlight dazzled its way through ribbons of clouds past the windows on the east side of the classroom and crept across the linoleum floor. On the playground the first group of children, the kindergartners, were running on the quack grass just beyond the monkey bars. We were doing multiplication tables. Miss Ferenczi had made John Wazny stand up at his desk in the front row. He was supposed to go through the tables of six. From where I was sitting, I could smell the Vitalis soaked into John's plastered hair. He was doing fine until he came to six times eleven and six times twelve. "Six times eleven," he said, "is sixty-eight. Six times twelve is..." He put his fingers to his head, quickly and secretly sniffed his fingertips, and said, "...seventy-two." Then he sat down.

"Fine," Miss Ferenczi said. "Well, now. That was very good."

"Miss Ferenczi!" One of the Eddy twins was waving her hand desperately in the air. "Miss Ferenczi! Miss Ferenczi!"

"Yes?"

"John said that six times eleven is sixty-eight and you said he was right!"

"*Did* I?" She gazed at the class with a jolly look breaking across her marionette's face. "Did I say that? Well, what *is* six times eleven?"

"It's sixty-six!"

She nodded. "Yes. So it is. But, and I know some people will not entirely agree with me, at some times it is sixty-eight."

"When? When is it sixty-eight?"

We were all waiting.

"In higher mathematics, which you children do not yet understand, six times eleven can be considered to be sixty-eight." She laughed through her nose. "In higher mathematics numbers are...more fluid. The only thing a number does is contain a certain amount of something. Think of water. A cup is not the only way to measure a certain amount of water, is it?" We were staring, shaking our heads. "You could use saucepans or thimbles. In either case, the water *would be the same.* Perhaps," she started again, "it would be better for you to think that six times eleven is sixty-eight only when I am in the room."

"Why is it sixty-eight," Mark Poole asked, "when you're in the room?"

"Because it's more interesting that way," she said, smiling very rapidly behind her blue-tinted glasses. "Besides, I'm your substitute teacher, am I not?" We all nodded. "Well, then, think of six times eleven equals sixty-eight as a substitute fact."

"A substitute fact?"

"Yes." Then she looked at us carefully. "Do you think," she asked, "that anyone is going to be hurt by a substitute fact?"

We looked back at her.

"Will the plants on the windowsill be hurt?" We glanced at them. There were sensitive plants thriving in a green plastic tray, and several wilted ferns in small clay pots. "Your dogs and cats, or you moms and dads?" She waited. "So," she concluded, "what's the problem?"

"But it's wrong," Janice Weber said, "isn't it?"

"What's your name, young lady?"

"Janice Weber."

"And you think it's wrong, Janice?"

"I was just asking."

"Well, all right. You were just asking. I think we've spent enough time on this matter by now, don't you, class? You are free to think what you like. When your teacher, Mr. Hibler, returns, six times eleven will be sixty-six again, you can rest assured. And it will be that for the rest of your lives in Five Oaks. Too bad, eh?" She raised her eyebrows and glinted herself at us. "But for now, it wasn't. So much for that. Let us go on to your assigned problems for today, as painstakingly outlined, I see, in Mr. Hibler's lesson plan. Take out a sheet of paper and write your names on the upper left-hand corner."

For the next half hour we did the rest of our arithmetic problems. We handed them in and then went on to spelling, my worst subject. Spelling always came before lunch. We were taking spelling dictation and looking at the clock. "Thorough," Miss Ferenczi said. "Boundary." She walked in the aisles between the desks, holding the spelling book open and looking down at our papers. "Balcony." I clutched my pencil. Somehow, the way she said those words, they seemed foreign, mis-voweled and mis-consonanted. I stared down at what I had spelled. *Balconie.* I turned the pencil upside down and erased my mistake. *Balconey.* That looked better, but still incorrect. I cursed the world of spelling and tried erasing it again and saw the paper beginning to wear away. *Balkony.* Suddenly I felt a hand on my shoulder.

"I don't like that word either," Miss Ferenczi whispered, bent over, her mouth near my ear. "It's ugly. My feeling is, if you don't like a word, you don't have to use it." She straightened up, leaving behind a slight odor of Clorets.

At lunchtime we went out to get our trays of sloppy joes, peaches in heavy syrup, coconut cookies, and milk, and brought them back to the classroom, where Miss Ferenczi was sitting at the desk, eating a brown sticky thing she had un-wrapped from tightly rubber-banded waxed paper. "Miss Ferenczi," I said, raising my hand. "You don't have to eat with us. You can eat with the other teachers. There's a teachers' lounge," I end-ed up, "next to the principal's office."

"No, thank you," she said. "I prefer it here."

"We've got a room monitor," I said. "Mrs. Eddy." I pointed to where Mrs. Eddy, Joyce and Judy's mother, sat silently at the back of the room, doing her knitting.

"That's fine," Miss Ferenczi said. "But I shall continue to eat here, with you children. I prefer it," she repeated.

"How come?" Wayne Razmer asked without raising his hand.

"I talked to the other teachers before class this morning," Miss Ferenczi said, biting into her brown food. "There was a great rattling of the words for the fewness of the ideas. I didn't care for their brand of hilarity. I don't like ditto-ma-chine jokes."

"Oh," Wayne said.

"What's that you're eating?" Maxine Sylvest-er asked, twitching her nose. "Is it food?"

"It most certainly *is* food. It's a stuffed fig. I had to drive almost down to Detroit to get it. I also brought some smoked sturgeon. And this," she said, "is raw spinach, cleaned this morning."

"Why're you eating raw spinach?" Maxine asked.

"It's good for you," Miss Ferenczi said. "More stimulating than soda pop or smelling salts." I bit into my sloppy joe and stared blankly out the window. An almost invisible moon was faintly silvered in the daytime autumn sky. "As far as food is concerned," Miss Ferenczi was saying, "you have to shuffle the pack. Mix it up. Too many people eat . . . well, never mind."

"Miss Ferenczi," Carol Peterson said, "what are we going to do this afternoon?"

"Well," she said, looking down at Mr. Hibler's lesson plan, "I see that your teacher, Mr. Hibler, has you scheduled for a unit on the Egyptians." Carol

groaned. "Yessss," Miss Ferenczi continued, "that is what we will do: the Egyptians. A remarkable people. Almost as remarkable as the Americans. But not quite." She lowered her head, did her quick smile, and went back to eating her spinach.

After noon recess we came back into the class-room and saw that Miss Ferenczi had drawn a pyramid on the blackboard close to her oak tree. Some of us who had been playing baseball were messing around in the back of the room, dropping the bats and gloves into the playground box, and Ray Schontzeler had just slugged me when I heard Miss Ferenczi's high-pitched voice, quaver-ing with emotion. "Boys," she said, "come to or-der right this minute and take your seats. I do not wish to waste a minute of class time. Take out your geography books." We trudged to our desks and, still sweating, pulled out *Distant Lands and Their People.* "Turn to page forty-two." She wait-ed for thirty seconds, then looked over at Kelly Munger. "Young man," she said, "why are you still fossicking in your desk?"

Kelly looked as if his foot had been stepped on. "Why am I what?"

"Why are you . . . burrowing in your desk like that?"

"I'm lookin' for the book, Miss Ferenczi."

Bobby Kryzanowicz, the faultless brown nos-er who sat in the first row by choice, softly said, "His name is Kelly Munger. He can't ever find his stuff. He always does that."

"I don't care what his name is, especially af-ter lunch," Miss Ferenczi said. "*Where is your book?*"

"I just found it." Kelly was peering into his desk and with both hands pulled at the book, shoveling along in front of it several pencils and crayons, which fell into his lap and then to the floor.

"I hate a mess," Miss Ferenczi said. "I hate a mess in a desk or a mind. It's . . . unsanitary. You wouldn't want your house at home to look like your desk at school, now, would you?" She didn't wait for an answer. "I should think not. A house at home should be as neat as human hands can make it. What were we talking about? Egypt. Page forty-two. I note from Mr. Hibler's lesson plan that you have been discussing the modes of Egyptian irrigation. Interesting, in my view, but not so interesting as what we are about to cover. The pyramids, and Egyptian slave labor. A plus on one side, a minus on the other." We had our books open to page forty-two, where there was a picture of a pyramid, but Miss Ferenczi wasn't looking at the book. Instead, she was staring at some object just outside the window.

"Pyramids," Miss Ferenczi said, still looking past the window. "I want you to think about pyramids. And what was inside. The bodies of the pharaohs, of course, and their attendant treasures. Scrolls. Perhaps," Miss Ferenczi said, her face gleeful but unsmiling, "these scrolls were novels for the pharaohs, helping them to pass the time in their long voyage through the centuries. But then, I am joking." I was looking at the lines on Miss Ferenczi's skin. "Pyramids," Miss Ferenczi went on, "were the repositories of special cosmic powers. The nature of a pyramid is to guide cosmic energy forces into a concentrated point. The Egyptians knew that; we have generally forgotten it. Did you know," she asked, walking to the side of the room so that she was standing by the coat closet, "that George Washington had Egyptian blood, from his grandmother? Certain features of the Constitution of the United States are notable for their Egyptian ideas."

Without glancing down at the book, she began to talk about the movement of souls in Egyptian religion. She said that when people die, their souls return to Earth in the form of carpenter ants or walnut trees, depending on how they behaved—"well or ill"—in life. She said that the Egyptians believed that people act the way they do because of magnetism produced by tidal forces in the solar system, forces produced by the sun and by its "planetary ally," Jupiter. Jupiter, she said, was a planet, as we had been told, but had "certain properties of stars." She was speaking very fast. She said that the Egyptians were great

explorers and conquerors. She said that the greatest of all the conquerors, Genghis Khan, had had forty horses and forty young women killed on the site of his grave. We listened. No one tried to stop her. "I myself have been in Egypt," she said "and have witnessed much dust and many brutalities." She said that an old man in Egypt who worked for a circus had personally shown her an animal in a cage, a monster, half bird and half lion. She said that this monster was called a gryphon and that she had heard about them but never seen them until she traveled to the outskirts of Cairo. She wrote the word out on the blackboard in large capital letters; GRYPHON. She said that Egyptian astronomers had discovered the planet Saturn but had not seen its rings. She said that the Egyptians were the first to discover that dogs, when they are ill, will not drink from rivers, but wait for rain, and hold their jaws open to catch it.

"She lies."

We were on the school bus home. I was sitting next to Carl Whiteside, who had bad breath and a huge collection of marbles. We were arguing. Carl thought she was lying. I said she wasn't, probably.

"I didn't believe that stuff about the bird," Carl said, "and what she told us about the pyramids? I didn't believe that, either. She didn't know what she was talking about."

"Oh yeah?" I had liked her. She was strange. I thought I could nail him. "If she was lying," I said, "what'd she say that was a lie?"

"Six times eleven isn't sixty-eight. It isn't ever. It's sixty-six, I know for a fact."

"She said so. She admitted it. What else did she lie about?"

"I don't know," he said. "Stuff."

"What stuff?::

"Well." He swung his legs back and forth. "You ever see an animal that was half lion and half bird?" He crossed his arms. "It sounded real fakey to me."

"It could happen," I said. I had to improvise, to outrage him. "I read in this newspaper my mom bought in the IGA about this scientist, this mad scientist in the Swiss Alps, and he's been putting genes and chromosomes and stuff together in test tubes, and he combined a human being and a hamster." I waited, for effect. "It's called a humster."

"You never." Carl was staring at me, his mouth open, his terrible bad breath making its way toward me. "What newspaper was it?"

"*The National Enquirer,*" I said, "that they sell next to the cash registers." When I saw his look of recognition, I knew I had him. "And this mad scientist," I said, "his name was, um, Dr. Frankenbush." I realized belatedly that this name was a mistake and waited for Carl to notice its resemblance to the name of the other famous mad master of permutations, but he only sat there.

"A man and a hamster?" He was staring at me, squinting, his mouth opening in distaste. "Jeez. What'd it look like?"

When the bus reached my stop, I took off down our dirt road and ran up through the backyard, kicking the tire swing for good luck. I dropped my books on the back steps so I could hug and kiss our dog, Mr. Selby. Then I hurried inside. I could smell brussels sprouts cooking, my unfavorite vegetable. My mother was washing other vegetables in the kitchen sink, and my baby brother was hollering in his yellow playpen on the kitchen floor.

"Hi, Mom," I said, hopping around the playpen to kiss her. "Guess what?"

"I have no idea."

"We had this substitute today, Miss Ferenczi, and I'd never seen her before, and she had all these stories and ideas and stuff."

"Well. That's good." My mother looked out the window in front of the sink, her eyes on the pine woods west of our house. That time of the afternoon her skin always looked so white to me. Strangers always said my mother looked like Betty Crocker, framed by the giant spoon on the side of the Bisquick box. "Listen, Tommy," she said. "Would you please go upstairs and pick your clothes off the floor in the bathroom, and then go

outside to the shed and put the shovel and ax away that your father left outside this morning?"

"She said that six times eleven was sometimes sixty-eight!" I said. "And she said she once saw a monster that was half lion and half bird." I waited. "In Egypt."

"Did you hear me?" my mother asked, raising her arm to wipe her forehead with the back of her hand. "You have chores to do."

"I know," I said. "I was just telling you about the substitute."

"It's very interesting," my mother said, quickly glancing down at me, "and we can talk about it later when your father gets home. But right now you have some work to do."

"Okay, Mom." I took a cookie out of the jar on the counter and was about to go outside when I had a thought. I ran into the living room, pulled out a dictionary next to the TV stand, and opened it to the Gs. After five minutes I found it. *Gryphon:* variant of griffin. *Griffin:* "a fabulous beast with the head and wings of an eagle and the body of a lion." Fabulous was right. I shouted with triumph and ran outside to put my father's tools in their proper places.

Miss Ferenczi was back the next day, slightly altered. She had pulled her hair down and twisted it into pigtails, with red rubber bands holding them tight one inch from the ends. She was wearing a green blouse and pink scarf, making her difficult to look at for a full class day. This time there was no pretense of doing a reading lesson or moving on to arithmetic. As soon as the bell rang, she simply began to talk.

She talked for forty minutes straight. There seemed to be less connection between her ideas, but the ideas themselves were, as the dictionary would say, fabulous. She said she had heard of a huge jewel, in what she called the antipodes, that was so brilliant that when light shone into it at a certain angle it would blind whoever was looking at its center. She said the biggest diamond in the world was cursed and had killed everyone who owned it, and that by a trick of fate it was called the Hope Diamond. Diamonds, are magic, she said, and this is why women wear them on their fingers, as a sign of the magic of womanhood. Men have strength, Miss Ferenczi said, but no true magic. That is why men fall in love with women but women do not fall in love with men: they just love being loved. George Washington had died because of a mistake he made about a diamond. Washington was not the first *true* President, but she didn't say who was. In some places in the world, she said, men and women still live in the trees and eat monkeys for breakfast. Their doctors are magicians. At the bottom of the sea are creatures thin as pancakes who have never been studied by scientists because when you take them up to air, the fish explode.

There was not a sound in the classroom, except for Miss Ferenczi's voice, and Donna DeShano's coughing. No one even went to the bathroom.

Beethoven, she said, had not been deaf; it was a trick to make himself famous, and it worked. As she talked, Miss Ferenczi's pigtails swung back and forth. There are trees in the world, she said, that eat meat: their leaves are sticky and close up on bugs like hands. She lifted her hands, and brought them together, palm to palm. Venus, which most people think is the next closest planet to the sun, is not always closer, and besides, it is the planet of greatest mystery because of its thick cloud cover. "I know what lies underneath those clouds," Miss Ferenczi said, and waited. After the silence, she said, "Angels. Angels live under those clouds." She said that angels were not invisible to everyone and were in fact smarter than most people. They did not dress in robes as was often claimed but instead wore formal evening clothes, as if they were about to attend a concert. Often angels *do* attend concerts and sit in the aisles, where, she said, most people pay no attention to them. She said the most terrible angel had the shape of the Sphinx. "There is no running away from that one," she said. She said that unquenchable fires burn just under the surface of the earth in Ohio, and that the baby Mozart fainted dead away in his cradle when he first heard the sound of a trumpet. She said that

someone named Narzim al Harrardim was the greatest writer who ever lived. She said that planets control behavior, and anyone conceived during a solar eclipse would be born with webbed feet.

"I know you children like to hear these things," she said, "these secrets, and that is why I am telling you all this." We nodded. It was better than doing comprehension questions for the readings in *Broad Horizons*.

"I will tell you one more story," she said, "and then we will have to do arithmetic." She leaned over, and her voice grew soft,. "There is no death," she said. "You must never be afraid. Never. That which is, cannot die. It will change into different earthly and unearthly elements, but I know this as sure as I stand here in front of you, and I swear it: you must not be afraid. I have seen this truth with these eyes. I know it because in a dream God kissed me. Here." And she pointed with her right index finger to the side of her head, below the mouth where the vertical lines were carved into her skin.

Absentmindedly we all did our arithmetic problems. At recess the class was out on the playground, but no one was playing. We were all standing in small groups, talking about Miss Ferenczi. We didn't know if she was crazy, or what. I looked out beyond the playground, at the rusted cars piled in a small heap behind a clump of sumac, and I wanted to see shapes there, approaching me.

On the way home, Carl sat next to me again. He didn't say much and I didn't either. At last he turned to me. "You know what she said about the leaves that close up on bugs.?"

"Huh?"

"The leaves," Carl insisted. "The meat-eating plants. I know it's true. I saw it on television. The leaves have this icky glue that the plants have got smeared all over them and the insects can't get off 'cause they're stuck. I saw it." He seemed demoralized. "She's tellin' the truth."

"Yeah."

"You think she's seen all those angels?"

I shrugged.

"I don't think she has," Carl informed me. "I think she made that part up."

"There's a tree," I suddenly said. I was looking out the window at the farms along County Road 11. I knew every barn, every broken windmill, every fence every anhydrous ammonia tank, by heart. "There's a tree that's . . . that I've seen . . ."

"Don't you try to do it," Carl said. "You'll just sound like a jerk."

I kissed my mother. She was standing in front of the stove. "How was your day?" she asked.

'Fine."

"Did you have Miss Ferenczi again?"

"Yeah."

"Well?"

"She was fine. Mom," I asked, "can I go to my room?"

"No," she said, "not until you've gone out to the vegetable garden and picked me a few tomatoes." She glanced at the sky. "I think it's going to rain. Skedaddle and do it now. Then you come back inside and watch your brother for a few minutes while I go upstairs. I need to clean up before dinner." She looked down at me. "You're looking a little pale, Tommy." She touched the back of her hand to my forehead and I felt her diamond ring against my skin. "Do you feel all right?"

"I'm fine," I said, and went out to pick the tomatoes.

Coughing mutedly, Mr. Hibler was back the next day, slipping lozenges into his mouth when his back was turned at forty-five-minute intervals and asking us how much of his prepared lesson plan Miss Ferenczi had followed. Edith Atwater took the responsibility for the class of explaining to Mr. Hibler that the substitute hadn't always done exactly what he, Mr. Hibler, would have done, but we had worked hard even though she talked a lot. About what? he asked. All kinds of things, Edith said. I sort of forgot. To our relief, Mr. Hibler seemed not at all interested in what Miss Ferenczi

had said to fill the day. He probably thought it was woman's talk: unserious and not suited for school. It was enough that he had a pile of arithmetic problems from us to correct.

For the next month, the sumac turned a distracting red in the field, and the sun traveled toward the southern sky, so that its rays reached Mr. Hibler's Halloween display on the bulletin board in the back of the room, fading the pumpkin head scarecrow from orange to tan. Every three days I measured how much farther the sun had moved toward the southern horizon by making small marks with my black Crayola on the north wall, ant-sized marks only I knew were there.

And then in early December, four days after the first permanent snowfall, she appeared again in our classroom. The minute she came in the door, I felt my heart begin to pound. Once again she was different: this time, her hair hung straight down and seemed hardly to have been combed. She hadn't brought her lunchbox with her, but she was carrying what seemed to be a small box. She greeted all of us and talked about the weather. Donna DeShano had to remind her to take her overcoat off.

When the bell to start the day finally rang, Miss Ferenczi looked out at all of us and said, "Children, I have enjoyed your company in the past, and today I am going to reward you." She held up the small box. "Do you know what this is?" She waited. "Of course you don't. It is a Tarot pack."

Edith Atwater raised her hand. "What's a Tarot pack, Miss Ferenczi?"

"It is used to tell fortunes," she said, "And that is what I shall do this morning. I shall tell your fortunes, as I have been taught to do."

"What's fortune?" Bobby Kryzanowicz asked.

"The future, young man. I shall tell you what your future will be. I don't do your whole future, of course. I shall have to limit myself to the five-card system, the wands, cups, swords, pentacles, and the higher arcanes. Now who wants to be first?"

There was a long silence. Then Carol Peterson raised her hand.

"All right," Miss Ferenczi said. She divided the pack into five smaller packs and walked back to Carol's desk, in front of mine. "Pick one card from each one of these packs," she said. I saw that Carol had a four of cups and a six of swords, but I couldn't see the other cards. Miss Ferenczi studied the cards on Carol's desk for minute. "Not bad," she said. "I do not see much higher education. Probably an early marriage. Many children. There's something bleak and dreary here, but I can't tell what. Perhaps just the tasks of a housewife life. I think you'll do very well, for the most part." She smiled at Carol, a smile with a certain lack of interest. "Who wants to be next?"

Carl Whiteside raised his hand slowly.

"Yes," Miss Ferenczi said, "let's do a boy." She walked over to where Carl sat. After he picked his five cards, she gazed at them for a long time. "Travel," she said. "Much distant travel. You might go into the army. Not too much romantic interest here. A later marriage, if at all. But the Sun in your major arcana, that's a very good card." She giggled. "You'll have a happy life."

Next I raised my hand. She told me my future. She did the same with Bobby Kryzanowicz, Kelly Munger, Edith Atwater, and Kim Foor. Then she came to Wayne Razmer. He picked his five cards, and I could see that the Death card was one of them.

"What's your name?" Miss Ferenczi asked.

"Wayne."

"Well, Wayne," she said, "you will undergo a great metamorphosis, a change, before you become an adult. Your earthly elements will no doubt leap higher, because you seem to be a sweet boy. This card, this nine of swords, tells me of suffering and desolation. And this ten of wands, well, that's a heavy load."

"What about this one?" Wayne pointed at the Death card.

"It means, my sweet, that you will die soon." She gathered up the cards. We were all looking at Wayne. "But do not fear," she said. "It is not real-ly death. Just change. Out of your earthly shape." She put the cards on Mr. Hibler's desk. "And now, lets's do some arithmetic."

At lunchtime Wayne went to Mr. Faegre, the principal, and informed him of what Miss Ferenczi had done. During the noon recess, we saw Miss Ferenczi drive out of the parking lot in her rusting green Rambler American. I stood under the slide, listening to the other kids coasting down and landing in the little depressive bowls at the bottom. I was kicking stones and tugging at my hair right up to the moment when I saw Wayne come out to the playground. He smiled, the dead fool, and with the fingers of his right hand he was showing everyone how he had told on Miss Ferenczi.

I made my way toward Wayne, pushing myself past two girls from another class. He was watching me with his little pinhead eyes.

"You told," I shouted at him. "She was just kidding."

"She shouldn't have," he shouted back. "We were supposed to be doing arithmetic."

"She just scared you," I said. "You're a chicken. You're a chicken, Wayne. You are. Scared of a little card," I singsonged.

Wayne fell at me, his two fists hammering down on my nose. I gave him a good one in the stomach and then I tried for his head. Aiming my fist, I saw that he was crying. I slugged him.

"She was right," I yelled. "She was always right! She told the truth!" Other kids were whooping. "You were just scared that's all!"

And then large hands pulled at us, and it was my turn to speak to Mr. Feagre.

In the afternoon Miss Ferenczi was gone, and my nose was stuffed with cotton clotted with blood, and my lip had swelled, and our class had been combined with Mrs. Mantei's sixth-grade class for a crowded afternoon science unit on insect life in ditches and swamps. I knew where Mrs. Mantei lived: she had a new house trailer just down the road from us, at the Clearwater Park. She was no mystery. Somehow she and Mr. Bodine, the other fourth-grade teacher, had managed to fit forty-five desks into the room. Kelly Munger asked if Miss Ferenczi had been arrested, and Mrs. Mantei said no, of course not. All that afternoon, until the buses came to pick us up, we learned about field crickets and two-striped grasshoppers, water bugs, cicadas, mosquitoes, flies, and moths. We learned about insects' hard outer shell, the exoskeleton, and the usual parts of the mouth, including the labrum, mandible, maxilla, and glossa. We learned about compound eyes, and the four-stage metamorphosis from egg to larva to pupa to adult. We learned something, but not much, about mat-

ing. Mrs. Mantei drew, very skillfully, the internal anatomy of the grasshopper on the blackboard. We learned about the dance of the honeybee, directing other bees in the hive to pollen. We found out about which insects were pests to man, and which were not. On lined white pieces of paper we made lists of insects we might actually see, then a list of insects too small to be clearly visible, such as fleas; Mrs. Mantei said that our assignment would be to memorize these lists for the next day, when Mr. Hibler would certainly return and test us on our knowledge.

# Death in the Fifth Grade

## MARJORIE MARKS

As soon as the first bell rang and the children took their places, Miss Steineck knew that they knew. Hardly any of the twenty-six looked at her as they said good morning.

The grade mother had called her up the evening before. "I've telephoned all the Fifth Grade mothers," she said. "They promised to keep it from the children tonight. We all agreed it would be better if you told them. You've had so much experience and besides, they're so fond of you. You'll do it, won't you?"

Miss Steineck had said she would. Although she dreaded the ordeal, she recognized its assignment as a tribute. It was true, the children were fond of her, even though sometimes they succumbed to the temptation of drawing caricatures of her with exaggerated pince-nez and a very long neck, which they labeled "Miss Stiffneck." Still, she nearly always got results with children, because she respected them and was honest with them. That's what she told the mothers when they asked her. But of course in every class there were some she defied anyone to reach. "The doltish dregs," she called them in her thoughts. But even these, she felt, were not unkindly disposed toward her.

She had lain awake most of the night trying to think of a way to tell them. "You know, Norma has been very ill," she planned to begin and would go on to say that if she had lived she probably would never have been able to move about or have fun again. They would understand that it was better for her to die than to be an invalid all her life. They must have felt, as she did herself, that Norma was someone apart, especially marked by joy and grace.

All—even the doltish dregs—sat still as stones while, with exaggerated deliberateness, she checked the roll book. She was conscious, meanwhile, of Rosanne, synthetic sorrow on her fat face, dabbing at her eyes. Undoubtedly it was she who had told the others.

Quietly Miss Steineck shut the roll book and squared her shoulders. "You know, Norma has been very, very ill," she said. That was the way she had planned. So far, so good. The bell rang. There was a little flutter through the class. Evie and Carolyn exchanged nervous glances over Norma's empty desk. Miss Steineck wished now that she'd had the janitor take it away before school. She had debated during the night the wisdom of this and decided it would be less of a shock this way. But now, her sensibilities heightened by this situation, its emptiness accused her.

Jane, the youngest in the class, who hadn't much sense, piped up from the front row, "We all know she's dead, Miss Steineck, you don't need to tell us."

A snicker which was half a shudder passed through the group.

Rosanne mouthed sanctimoniously, lifting her eyes for approval from the teacher, "You mustn't say she's dead. She's gone to heaven to be an angel. That's what my mother says. It's true, isn't it, Miss Steineck?"

The eyes of all twenty-six implored her for an answer. But how could she answer? She had left heaven behind with high button boots for Sunday and a dime inside her glove for the collection. How could she tell them what she really believed—that Norma, the vivid, the golden-haired, the pink-cheeked, the winner of races, the gayest, the fairest in games, was not an angel fluttering about the Throne but simply had ceased to exist?

She couldn't say that, but she had to say something. Without knowing she was beginning, she said, "When I was a little girl, we lived on a farm and I had a pet crow. He was my special friend. Whenever I whistled outside the house he would come and I would feed him. He'd sit on my hand or my shoulder and when I took a walk he'd flutter along beside me. His name was Timmie and I loved him very much."

She looked at the class. No one had moved except Rosanne, hitching about in her seat. Apparently she thought an animal story too babyish for the fifth grade. Miss Steineck looked at the others. They were waiting quietly, their eyes still unwaveringly upon her. She went on. "I used to talk to Timmie and he would answer me. He was my friend for a whole summer. When winter came I put crumbs out for him and left a window open in the tool-shed for him to fly in when it got too cold outside. But one morning, the coldest I could remember, when I whistled for Timmie he didn't come. I whistled and whistled till my lips were sore. Finally at the end of the day, my father found him. He was lying at the edge of the woods, frozen stiff. His wings were spread out as though he'd tried to come when I called him. How I cried. For days and days. I felt I'd never be happy again. I knew I'd never forget the way poor Timmie looked with his body all stiff and his eyes not seeing. I asked the minister on Sunday if there was a heaven for crows and he laughed and said he'd never heard of one. Then I felt worse than ever."

She paused and cleared her throat. Nobody said anything. For an instant she felt panicky, seeing how scornful Rosanne was looking, but she went on. "Well, for weeks and weeks I cried myself to sleep. My parents tried their best to comfort me. My father promised me a parrot, but I wouldn't let him buy one. Nothing could take Timmie's place. I kept seeing him in my dreams, all stiff and dead in the snow.

"But one night," said Miss Steineck slowly, because she was seeing it as she spoke, "a wonderful thing happened. I dreamed that it was spring and all the leaves and flowers were budding. I stood in the freshly planted garden and called Timmie. He came right away. How his feathers glistened! I'd never seen him look so handsome. He perched on my hand and cocked his head and spoke to me in his hoarse voice. 'Why don't you remember me this way?' he

asked and began to fly, around and around, up and up, in wonderful patterns and circles that got bigger and bigger until finally he flew so high that I couldn't see him any more. Then I woke up. But I wasn't sad now, because even though Timmie was dead, I was happy remembering him and the way he flapped his wings and how beautiful he was."

She surveyed the class. Nobody was looking at her. Nobody registered any reaction at all except Rosanne, who muttered sullenly, "I don't see what a silly crow has to do with Norma." There was a sort of assenting growl from a few of the doltish dregs, and then silence.

"I've made a fool of myself," Miss Steineck thought desperately. "I've failed them when they needed me most. Whatever possessed me to make such an exhibition of myself?" She felt the tight clamp of her pince-nez on her nose, as she always did when she was upset, and she knew that a red spot had appeared at the base of her neck. Rosanne was staring at it. She felt old and ugly and futile—Miss Stiffneck to the life.

The bell rang. "First period, Art," said Miss Steineck in her crispest voice. There was the rattle and bang of desk lids going up, the clatter of pencils and crayons being set out. The children were making as much noise as they could, to annoy her. Well, she deserved it. She had been an idiot.

Like a drill sergeant, she snapped out her orders. "Quiet, please. We'll have free work." (She felt capable of nothing else.) "Draw anything you like, using crayons. Plan to finish by the end of the period and sign your name in full in the lower right hand corner with the date." They set to work, while she made ferocious corrections with red pencil on the arithmetic homework papers.

As she marked automatically her C's and X's, she imagined the evening ahead of her, punctuated by indignant telephone calls from the mothers. Tomorrow, she knew, she would be summoned to the principal's office and be raked over the coals as she had been once before at the time of the great mumblety-peg war. "I can't imagine what you thought you were accomplishing by such unorthodox procedure," he would say sadly. "If it should happen again—" This was the threat of dismissal. Well, she certainly wouldn't blame him for wanting to replace her with a younger person, one with sensible ideas.

The bell rang. "Quietly, less noise, *please*," she sang out with a knife edge in her voice. Noisily they piled their drawings on her desk, noisily collected their equipment for history with Mr. MacVey in Room 103. Like hoodlums they scrambled for first place in line, brushing ruthlessly against a crayon landscape by Norma, which fluttered to the floor and was trampled on.

Carolyn said admiringly to Evie, who'd made first place, "Now that Norma isn't here, I guess you'll have a chance to win some races."

"I guess so," Evie giggled and Rosanne cried out in shocked tones, "It's awful to say such a thing." For once Miss Steineck agreed with her.

"The class may go now," she said, quietly icy. "Less noise, *please*." Regardless, they trampled up the corridor, William as usual making a noise like a muted saxophone.

Miss Steineck, smoothing Norma's crumpled drawing against her breast, gazed after them. "Cold-blooded little brats," she raged to herself. "I should know by this time it never pays to open your heart to them. I'll never be fooled into it again, never." She laughed aloud in self-derision as she picked up the drawings to transfer them to the side table.

Then her eyes were arrested by the topmost. It was a picture of a child with bright yellow hair, skipping rope in a field of brilliant flowers. Norma had loved to skip rope. Breathing hard, she turned to the next. This was Evie's. Evie did not draw well, but it was easy to see what she meant to convey—a group of children racing and far in advance of the others one girl with bright pink cheeks and yellow hair streaming behind her.

Miss Steineck sat down and went over the pictures one by one, skipping quickly over the products of the doltish dregs (the usual pretty-ladies by the girls and airplanes and boats by the boys). Her heart hammered at her thin ribs. For all the other pictures were about Norma; each was different; each about Norma doing one of the things she liked best—climbing, swimming, throwing a ball. There were two exceptions. One was William's—he was the best in drawing. He had done a large crow with wings spread wide against a vivid sunset sky. The other was Rosanne's—a minutely elaborate wreath of purple flowers, with Sinserest Simpathy printed beneath in neat black letters. Miss Steineck took pleasure in marking it with a large red X.Sp.

She laid the papers on the table. And then, to her own amazement, she found herself with her head on her desk, crying as she had not cried since Timmie died.

# APPENDIX

Editing this anthology fell naturally into four tasks. First, search for stories, second, read and analyze the stories, third, select the stories and fourth, get permission to use the stories. We began our search with stories from approximately the 1940s to 1994. We examined *Psychological Abstracts, Psychological Index, Reader's Guide to Periodical Literature, Short Story Index, Fiction Catalogue, Book Review Digest, Fiction Catalog, Fiction Index, Books in Print,* Library of Congress, anthologies, small press collections, research studies, dissertations and any serendipitous information that we happened upon (e.g., newspapers, magazine articles). For example, we discovered one article through an obituary reference in the New York Times. From these sources about 2000 stories were located. (Three assistants, graduate students in Anthropology and English as well as an interlibrary-loan librarian, helped in searching and obtaining the stories.) Each story was read by the editors. In the final analysis, we found approximately 100 stories that met our requirements. Length and availability considerations reduced that number to 51. Concerning length, several of the stories were simply too long for an anthology or would have required lengthy contextualizing excerpts or narration to make sense. Concerning availability, we were unable to get a publisher's permission to print or, in some cases, to afford the cost of the permission to print some stories.

# NOTES ON THE AUTHORS

Adedjouma, Davida (b. 1956)

Born in Chicago, Illinois, Davida Kilgore Adedjouma attended Macalester College and the University of Chicago. Her currently published work includes the poetry collection *The Palm of My Heart* (1996). "The Day We Discovered We Were Black" appeared in *Last Summer* (1988), a book of short stories.

Asimov, Isaac (1920–1992)

Born in Petrovichi (in the former Soviet Union) and died on April 6, 1992. Isaac Asimov was one of America's most prolific fiction and nonfiction writers; he is considered by many to have advanced science fiction from the realm of pulp fiction to a respected genre in its own right. He won five Hugo Awards in science fiction. In 1979, Asimov wrote an autobiography entitled *In Memory Yet Green* (1979). "The Fun They Had" appeared in *The Best of Isaac Asimov* (1974).

Barthelme, Donald (1931–1989)

Born in Philadelphia, Pennsylvania, Donald Barthelme was a regular contributor to *The New Yorker.* He was primarily a writer of short fiction. His collection of short stories entitled *Sixty Stories* won wide acclaim. He also authored and illustrated a children's literature story that won the National Book Award, *The Slightly Irregular Fire Engine or the Hithering Thithering Djinn* (1972.). "The School" appeared in *Amateurs* (1976).

Baxter, Charles (b. 1947)

Born in Minneapolis, Minnesota, Charles Baxter attended Macalester College (B.A., 1969) and SUNY at Buffalo (Ph.D., 1974). His works include the novel *Shadow Play* (1993), the short story collection *A Relative Stranger* (1990) and *Imaginary Paintings and Other Poems* (1990). Recent awards include the Reader's Digest Foundation Fellowship (1992) and the Lawrence Foundation Award (1991). "Gryphon" appeared in *Through the Safety Net* (1985) and was adapted for public television in 1988.

Berlin, Lucia (b. 1936)

Born in Juneau, Alaska, Lucia Berlin spent most of her early childhood in Montana, Idaho, Arizona, Texas and Kentucky because her father was a mining engineer. She spent her teenage years in Chile. She completed graduate and undergraduate programs at the University of New Mexico. For a while she taught Spanish at a catholic school in Albuquerque, New Mexico and this experience played a role in the writing of "El Tim." Her works include *Manual for Cleaning Women* (1977), *Angel's Laundromat* (1981), *Phantom Pain* (1984), *Safe and Sound* (1988) and *Homesick* (1990). "El Tim" appeared in *Homesick.*

Blaise, Clark (b. 1940)

Born in Fargo, North Dakota, of Canadian parents, Clarke Blaise attended Denison University (B.A., 1961) and the University of Iowa (M.F.A., 1964). "How I Became a Jew" appeared in *Making It New,* edited by John Metcalf (1992).

Bonosky, Phillip (b. 1916)

Born in Duquesne, Pennsylvania, Phillip Bonosky attended Wilson Teachers College (Washington, D.C.) and has worked as a writer most of his adult life. "The First Robin in the World" appeared in *A Bird in Her Hair* (1987).

Calisher, Hortense (b. 1911)

Born in New York City, Hortense Calisher attended Barnard College (A. B., 1932). She is a past president of PEN and the American Academy and Institute of Arts and Letters. Her writing appears in numerous anthologies and recent works include the novels *The Bobby-Soxer* (1986) and *Age* (1987) as well as *Saratoga, Hot* (1985), a collection of short stories. She has won four O. Henry Awards and is the author of an autobiography entitled *Herself* (1972). "A Wreath for Miss Totten" appeared in *In the Absence of Angels* (1951).

Chávez, Denise E. (b. 1948)

Born in Las Cruces, New Mexico, Denise Chávez attended New Mexico State University (B.A., 1971), Trinity University (M.F.A., 1974), and the University of New Mexico (M.A., M.F.A., 1984). Chávez won the Steele Jones Fiction Award in 1986 for *The Last of the Menu Girls,* a collection of short stories that contains "Space is a Solid: Kari Lee."

Clarke, John Henrik (b. 1915)

Born in Union Springs, Alabama, John Clarke attended New York University, the New School for Social Research, and Pacific Western University. In 1968 he was coordinator and special consultant to CBS-TV for the television series *Black Heritage.* Clarke began teaching at Hunter College (CUNY) in 1970 and gained emeritus rank in 1985. "The Boy Who Painted Christ Black" appeared in *Prejudice: 20 Tales of Oppression and Liberation,* edited by Charles Larson (1971).

Díaz Alfaro, Abelardo (b. 1919)

Born in Caguas, Puerto Rico, Abelardo Díaz Alfaro attended Inter-American University and worked as a social worker in rural Puerto Rican communities. He became a screenwriter for the Puerto Rican Department of Education's radio station, and during ten years of writing produced over 2,000 scripts. "Peyo Mercé: English Teacher" appeared in *Cuentos: An Anthology of Short Stories from Puerto Rico,* edited by Kal Wagenheim (1978).

Ellin, Stanley (1916–1986)

Born in Brooklyn, New York, Stanley Ellin attended Brooklyn College (B.A., 1936). He was a teacher and dairy farmer before turning to a new vocation as a mystery and crime writer. He wrote thirteen novels, the most recent of which was *Very Old Money* (1985), and four collections of short stories, the most recent of which was *The Specialty of the House and Other Stories* (1979). His short stories have appeared in numerous anthologies. "Robert" appeared in *Terrors, Torments and Traumas,* edited by Helen Hoke (1978).

Gropman, Donald S. (b. 1936)

Born in Boston, Massachusetts, Donald Gropman attended Brandeis University (B.A., 1956) and San Francisco State University (M.A., 1962). He has been a private investigator, college teacher, civil rights activist, anti-poverty worker, and an education and editorial consultant. His books include *Say It Ain't So, Joe,* the biography of Shoeless Joe Jackson, for which he was named a Knight of Mark Twain by the *Mark Twain Journal* for his contribution to American biography. "The Heart of This or That Man" appeared in *Adolescence in Literature,* edited by Thomas Gregory (1978).

Gunn, James E. (b. 1923)

Born in Kansas City, Missouri, James Gunn attended the University of Kansas (B.S., 1947, M.A., 1951). He won the Hugo Award for science fiction in 1983. "Kindergarten" appeared in *Young Extraterrestrials,* edited by Isaac Asimov, Martin Greenberg, and Charles Waugh (1984).

Hassler, Jon F. (b. 1933)

Born in Minneapolis, Minnesota, Jon Hassler attended St. John's University (B.A.., 1955) and the University of North Dakota (M.A.,1960). He was a high school and community college English teacher in Minnesota. The excerpt used in the anthology is from his novel *Staggerford* (1974).

Henderson, Zenna (1917–1983)

Born in Tucson, Arizona, Zenna Henderson attended Arizona State University (B.A., 1940; M.A., 1954). She was a classroom teacher in Arizona, in the Department of Defense Schools in France and at Seaside (a tuberculosis sanatorium for children in Arizona). "You Know What, Teacher?" and "The Believing Child" appeared in *Holding Wonder* (1971), an American Library Association Notable Book. "The Anything Box" appeared in *The Golden Road,* edited by Damon Knight (1973).

Hsiang, Lao

Lao Hsiang is a pseudonym for Wang Hsiang-ch'en, a writer best known in China for his humorous essays. He was born and brought up in the country and for several years wrote about rural education in Tinghsien. During this period he wrote "A Country Boy Withdraws from School." The story appeared in *Contemporary Chinese Stories,* translated by Chi-Hen Wang (1944).

James, Brian (b. 1892)

John Tierney (pseudonym Brian James) was born near Mudgee in Western New South Wales, Australia. He was a schoolteacher and one of Australia's finest short story writers—his depiction of the Australian bush and its people are especially compelling. He also wrote novels and stories about schoolteaching (*Hopeton High* and *The Advancement of Spencer Button*). "Untimely Aid" appeared in *Australian Short Stories: Second Series* (1963).

Jones, Edward P. (b. 1950)

Edward P. Jones attended the College of the Holy Cross (Worcester, Massachusetts) and the University of Virginia. "The First Day," appeared in *Lost in the City* (1992), his first work which profiles the lives of African Americans in Washington, D.C., in fourteen short stories. The collection was nominated for the 1992 National Book Award.

Loewenstein, Andrea Freud (b. 1949)

Born in Boston, Massachusetts, Andrea Freud Loewenstein attended Clark University, University of Wisconsin, and Sussex University in England.

Her recent works include *This Place* (1984) and *Engulfing Women and Loathsome Jews* (1993). "Awards" appeared in *The Worry Girl: Stories from a Childhood* (1992). For all of her adult life Loewenstein has been a teacher. She is one of the great-granddaughters of Sigmund Freud.

MacMahon, Bryan (b. 1909)

Born in Listowel, Ireland, Bryan MacMahon attended St. Michael's College and St. Patrick's College (1921–1930). He was a classroom teacher and school principal in Ireland. "The Windows of Wonder" appeared in *The Red Petticoat* (1955).

MacLaverty, Bernard (b. 1942)

Born in Belfast, Northern Ireland, Bernard MacLaverty attended Queens University (Belfast), (B.A., 1970). He was a classroom teacher from 1975 to 1981 in Scotland. He wrote several novels and collections of short stories as well as radio plays, teleplays, and screenplays. "The Exercise" appeared in *Secrets and Other Stories* (1977).

(Marks) Bitker, Marjorie (1901–1990)

Born in New York City, Marjorie Bitker (Marks is a married name) attended Barnard College (B.A., 1921) and Columbia University (M.A., 1922). Her works include the novels *Gold of the Evening* (1975) and *A Different Flame* (1976) as well as stories that have been published in *The New Yorker* and *Reader's Digest.* "Death in the Fifth Grade" appeared in *Time to Be Young,* edited by Whit Burnett (1945).

Martínez-Serros, Hugo (b. 1930)

Born in the south side of Chicago in 1930, Hugo Martínez-Serros attended the University of Chicago (B.A.,1951) and Northwestern University (Ph.D., literature). He taught at several universities including Lawrence University in Appleton, Wisconsin. He published his first stories in 1980 and his first collection, *The Last Laugh and Other Stories* (including "Her" and "Ricardo's War") followed in 1988.

Milburn, George (1906–1966)

George Milburn was born in Coweta, Oklahoma. A screenwriter during his lifetime he also contributed fiction to *Harper's* and *The New Yorker.* "Revenge" appeared in *No More Trumpets and Other Stories* (1933, reprinted in 1970).

Mohr, Nicholasa (b. 1935)

Born in New York City, Nicholasa Mohr attended the Art Student's League (1953–1956), the Brooklyn Museum of Art School (1959–1966), and the Pratt Center for Contemporary Printmaking (1966–1969). She has been a printmaker, painter, and lecturer in creative writing and Puerto Rican studies. Her first novel of adolescent fiction, *Nilda* won wide acclaim. "The Wrong Lunch Line" appeared in *Puerto Rican Writers at Home in the USA,* edited by Faythe Turner, 1991.

Moose, Ruth (b. 1938)

Born in Albemarle, North Carolina, Ruth Moose attended the University of North Carolina. She has contributed more than one hundred of her works to magazines and newspapers, including *Good Housekeeping, New York Times, Woman's Day, Mother Earth News* and *House and Garden.* "Rules and Secrets" appeared in *Dreaming in Color* (1989).

Narayan, R. K. (b. 1906)

Born in Madras, India, R. K. Narayan graduated from the University of Mysore in 1930. He is one of India's best-known authors in the English language and was awarded the National Prize of the Indian Literary Academy in 1958. His numerous stories and novels include *The World of Nagaraj* (1990) and *Under the Banyan Tree and Other Stories* (1985). "Father's Help" appeared in *Malgudi Days* (1982); Malgudi is a fictional village that appears in many of Narayan's stories.

Nicol, Abioseh (1924–1994)

Davidson Nicol (Abioseh is a pseudonym) was born in Freetown, Sierra Leone. He attended Christ's College in Cambridge, England (B.A.,

1946; M. D., 1958). Nicol held medical positions in England and Sierra Leone. Switching to a career in diplomacy, he held positions with UNESCO, the World Health Organization, and the World Federation of United Nations. Although most of his adult life was dedicated to medicine and diplomacy, he was also a prolific short story writer. "As the Night the Day" appeared in *Short Stories from Around the World,* edited by Lee A. Jacobus (1976).

O'Donovan, Joan

"Little Brown Jesus" appeared in *Shadows on the Wall* (1960).

Packer, Barbara

"The Blue Eagle" appeared in *Mademoiselle Prize Stories 1951–1975* (1976). Barbara Packer graduated from Stanford University (1968).

Patchett, Ann (b. 1963)

Born in Los Angeles, California, Ann Patchett attended Sarah Lawrence College (B.A., 1984) and the University of Iowa (M. F. A., 1987). Recent works include *The Patron Saint of Liars* (1992) and *Taft* (1994). "All Little Colored Children Should Play the Harmonica" appeared in *20 under 30,* edited by Debra Spark (1986).

Patton, Frances Gray (b. 1906)

Born in Raleigh, North Carolina, Frances Gray Patton attended Duke University and the University of North Carolina. Perhaps her most famous work is *Good Morning, Miss Dove* (1955) which was also made into a movie. In addition, she wrote three collections of short stories, *The Finer Things in Life* (1951), *A Piece of Luck* (1955), and *Twenty-Eight Stories* (1969)—the source of "Grade 5B and the Well-fed Rat."

Primoff, Joanne

Joanne Primoff (Shatraw) attended Syracuse University (B.A., 1951). "Discipline" appeared in *Mademoiselle Prize Stories 1951–1975* (1976).

Rodríguez, Abraham, Jr. (b. 1961)

"The Boy Without a Flag" appeared in *The Boy Without a Flag: Tales of the South Bronx* (1992).

Sharp, Paula (b. 1957)

Born in San Diego, California, Paula Sharp attended Dartmouth College (B.A., 1979) and Columbia University (J.D., 1985). She is a public defender in New York City. Her recent works include the novel *The Woman Who Was Not All There* (1988) and *The Imposter* (1991) in which the story "Books" appeared.

Saroyan, William (1908–1981)

Born in Fresno, California, William Saroyan attended school until he was 15 and then dropped out. He held a series of odd jobs such as grocery clerk, vineyard worker, postal employee, and office manager until he gained attention as a writer and playwright in the 1930s. In 1940 he won the Drama Critics Circle Award and the Pulitzer Prize for *The Time of Your Life*. In 1943 he won an Academy Award for the screenplay *The Human Comedy*. "Citizens of Third Grade" appeared in *The Saroyan Special* (1970).

Spencer, Elizabeth (b. 1921)

Born in Carrollton, Mississippi, Elizabeth Spencer attended Belhaven College (B.A., 1942) and Vanderbilt University (M.A., 1943). "The Bufords" appeared in *The Stories of Elizabeth Spencer* (1981). Her recent work includes *Jack of Diamonds and Other Stories* (1988). She has contributed stories to periodicals such as *Redbook, The New Yorker, The Southern Review, The Texas Quarterly* and *The Atlantic*.

Silverberg, Frances (b. 1916)

Born in Baltimore, Maryland, Frances Silverberg attended New York University. "Rebecca" was her first published story and appeared in *American Scene: New Voices*, edited by Don Wolfe (1963).

Stack, Eddie

"Limbo" appeared in *The West: Stories From Ireland* (1989).

Schor, Lynda (b. 1938)

Born in Brooklyn, New York, Lynda Schor attended Cooper Union (B.F.A., 1959) and the New School for Social Research. Her written works include *Appetites,* (1975) and reviews in periodicals such as *Ms., Village Voice,* and *Redbook*. "Class Outing" appeared in *True Love & Real Romance* (1979).

Solari, María Teresa

María Solari is a Peruvian author whose recent works include *Mi Amiga Paquina,* a collection of three short stories (1988). "Death and Transfiguration of a Teacher" appeared in *Short Stories by Latin American Women: The Magic and the Real,* edited by Celia Correas de Zapata (1990).

Vroman, Mary Elizabeth (1923–1967)

Born in Buffalo, New York, Mary Vroman attended Alabama State University. She taught in Alabama, Illinois and New York public schools for over twenty years. Later she became the music and art coordinator for the New York City Board of Education. In 1952, Vroman won the Christopher Award for "See How They Run." The story was made into a movie *(Bright Road)* and she wrote the screenplay. As a result, she became the first African American woman member of the Screen Writers Guild. "See How They Run" appeared in *Ladies Home Journal* (June 1951).

Wilson, Jacqueline (b. 1945)

Born in Bath, England, Jacqueline Wilson attended Carshalton Technical College. Her career has spanned journalism and freelance magazine writing. She is also the author of several novels and radio plays. "The Boy Who Couldn't Read" appeared in *Winter's Crimes 10*, edited by Hilary Watson (1979).

Yates, Richard (1926–1992)

Born in Yonkers, New York, Richard Yates authored several novels including *Cold Springs Harbor* (1986), his last. He also wrote two collections of short stories, *Eleven Kinds of Loneliness* (1962) and *Liars in Love* (1981). He was a writer for his entire adult life; in 1963 he served as speech writer for Attorney General Robert Kennedy. His book entitled *Revolutionary Road* (1961) won a National Book Award nomination. "Fun with a Stranger" and "Doctor Jack-o'-Lantern" appeared in *Eleven Kinds of Loneliness.*

Zavos, Spiro B. (b. 1937)

"Class Wars" appeared in *Faith of Our Fathers* (1982).

**Note:** A diligent effort was made to locate the original source of the stories collected in this anthology. When unable to find the original, we have cited the publication that we were able to obtain. Also, every effort was made to obtain complete information on each author. In a few cases, we were unable to locate information and welcome help from our readers.

**Credits**

Davida Adedjouma, "The Day We Discovered We Were Black." © 1988 Davida Kilgore, © 1991 Davida Adedjouma. Used by permission of the author.

Diaz Alfaro, "Peyo Merce" (translated by Pedro Juan Soto) from *Cuentos* edited by Kal Wagenheim, 1978. Reprinted by permission of the author.

Isaac Asimov, "The Fun They Had" from *Earth is Room Enough* by Isaac Asimov. Copyright © 1957 by Isaac Asimov. Used by permission of Doubleday, a division of Bantam Doubleday Dell Publishing Group, Inc.

Donald Barthelme, "The School" from *Amateurs* by Donald Barthelme. © 1976 by Donald Barthelme, reprinted with permission of Wylie, Aitken, & Stone, Inc.

Charles Baxter, "Gryphon" from *Through the Safety Net* by Charles Baxter. Copyright © 1985 by Charles Baxter. Used by permission of Viking Penguin, a division of Penguin Books USA Inc.

Lucia Berlin, "El Tim," Copyright © 1990 by Lucia Berlin. Reprinted from *Home Sick: New & Selected Stories* with the permission of Black Sparrow Press.

Clark Blaise, "How I Became a Jew" from *Tribal Justice,* © 1974 by Clark Blaise. Reprinted by permission of Doubleday-Canada Limited.

Phillip Bonosky, "The First Robin in the World" from *A Bird in Her Hair,* 1987, International Publishers Co., Inc. Reprinted by permission of the publisher.

Hortense Calisher, "A Wreath for Miss Totten" from *The Collected Short Stories of Hortense Calisher,* copyright 1951 by Hortense Calisher, published by Arbor House. Reprinted by permission of Donadio & Ashworth, Inc.

Denise Chavez, "Space Is a Solid" and "Kari Lee" are reprinted with permission from the publisher of *The Last of the Menu Girls* (Houston: Arte Publico Press—University of Houston, 1986).

John Henrick Clarke, "The Boy Who Painted Christ Black" from *Prejudice: 20 Tales of Oppression and Liberation,* edited by Charles Larson, published by The New American Library, 1971. Used by permission of John Henrick Clarke. First appeared in *Opportunity Magazine,* 1940.

Stanley Ellin, "Robert" from *The Blessing Method.* Reprinted by permission of Curtis Brown, Ltd. Copyright © 1958 by Stanley Ellin.

Donald Gropman, "The Heart of This or That Man" from *The Literary Review,* Autumn 1967, Vol. II, No. I. © 1967 by Donald Gropman. Used with permission of the author.

James Gunn, "Kindergarten," copyright 1970 by UPD Publishing Corp. Reprinted by permission of the author.

Jon Hassler, excerpt from *Staggerford,* Copyright © 1974, 1977 by Jon Hassler. Reprinted by permission of the Harriet Wasserman Literary Agency.

Zenna Henderson, "Anything Box." Copyright © 1956 by Zena Henderson, renewed 1984 by The Estate of Zenna Henderson; first appeared in *The Magazine of Fantasy and Science Fiction.* "The Believing Child." Copyright © 1970 by Zenna Henderson; first appeared in *The Magazine of Fantasy and Science Fiction.* "You Know What Teacher." Copyright © 1954, 1982 by Zenna Henderson; first appeared in *Ellery Queen Mystery Magazine.* Reprinted by permission of the author's Estate and the Estate's agent, Virginia Kidd.

Lao Hsiang, "A Country Boy Withdraws from School" from *Contemporary Chinese Stories,* translated by Chi-Chen Wang, 1944. © Columbia University Press, New York. Reprinted with permission of the publisher.

Brian James (pseudonym for John Tierney), "Untimely Aid" from *Australian Short Stories.* First published in *Quadrant,* Vol. 3, No. 1, Summer 1958–59, pp. 73–78. Copyright by the Estate of the late John Lawrence Tierney. Reprinted by permission of the Estate.

Edward Jones, "The First Day" from *Lost in the City* by Edward Jones. Copyright © 1992 by Edward P. Jones. By permission of William Morrow & Co., Inc.

Andrea Freud Loewenstein, "Awards," *The Worry Girl: Stories from a Childhood,* Firebrand Books, Ithaca, New York. Copyright © 1992 by Andrea Freud Loewenstein. Reprinted by permission.

Bernard MacLaverty, "The Exercise" from *Secrets and Other Stories* by Bernard MacLaverty. Copyright © 1977, 1979 by Bernard MacLaverty. Used by permission of Viking Penguin, a division of Penguin Books USA Inc., and Blackstaff Press, Inc.

Bryan MacMahon, "The Windows of Wonder," copyright 1953 by Bryan MacMahon, from *The Red Petticoat and Other Stories* by Bryan MacMahon. Used by permission of Dutton Signet, a division of Penguin Books USA Inc., and AP Watt Ltd.

Marjorie Marks (pseudonym for Marjorie Mayer), "Death in the Fifth Grade." Copyright 1939 by *Story Magazine.* Reprinted with permission of the Scholastic, Inc.

Hugo Martinez-Serros, "Her" and "Ricardo's War" are reprinted with permission from the publisher of *The Last Laugh and Other Stories* (Houston: Arte Publico Press—University of Houston, 1988).

George Milburn, excerpt from "Revenge" from *No More Trumpets.* Published 1933 by Harcourt Brace & Co., Inc. Copyright © 1933 by Harcourt Brace & Co., Inc. Reprinted by permission of John Hawkins & Associates, Inc.

Nicholosa Mohr, "The Wrong Lunch Line" from *El Bronx Remembered: A Novella and Stories* by Nicholosa Mohr. Copyright © 1975 by Nicholosa Mohr. Reprinted by permission of HarperCollins Publishers.

Ruth Moose, "Rules and Secrets" from *Dreaming in Color,* 1989. Reprinted by permission of August House Publishers, Inc.

R. K. Narayan, "Father's Help" from *Malgudi Days* by R. K. Narayan. Copyright © 1981 by R. K. Narayan. Used by permission Viking Penguin, a division of Penguin Books USA Inc.

Abioseh Nicol, "As the Night the Day" from *Modern African Prose,* edited by Richard Rieve. Reprinted by permission of Harold Ober Associates. Copyright 1964 by Abioseh Nicol.

Joan O'Donovan, "Little Brown Jesus" from *Shadows on the Wall* by Joan O'Donovan. Copyright © 1960, 1968 by Joan O'Donovan. By permission of William Morrow & Co., Inc.

Barbara Packer, "The Blue Angel." Courtesy *Mademoiselle Prize Stories 1951–1975.* Copyright 1967 by The Conde Nast Publications. Reprinted by permission of The Conde Nast Publications, Inc.

Ann Patchett, "All Little Colored Children Should Play the Harmonica." First published in *The Paris Review,* 1984. Copyright © 1984 by Ann Patchett. Reprinted by permission of International Creative Management, Inc.

Frances Gray Patton, "The Second Grade Mind" from *Twenty-Eight Stories* by Frances Gray Patton. Published by Dodd, Mead Co., New York, 1969. Copyright © 1969 Frances Gray Patton. Story originally published in *Colliers* Magazine. "Grade 5B and the Well Fed Rat" from *Harper's* Magazine, May 1946. Copyright © 1946 by Frances Gray Patton, © renewed 1974 by Frances Gray Patton. Reprinted by permission of Russell & Volkening as agents for the author.

Joanne Primoff, "Discipline." Courtesy *Mademoiselle Prize Stories 1951–1975.* Copyright © 1951 by Street and Smith Publications. Reprinted by permission of The Conde Nast Publications, Inc.

Abraham Rodriquez, Jr., "The Boy Without a Flag" was originally published in *The Boy Without a Flag* by Abraham Rodriquez, Jr. (Milkweed Editions, 1992). Copyright © 1992 by Abraham Rodriquez, Jr. Reprinted with permission from Milkweed Editions.

William Saroyan, "Citizens of the Third Grade." Reprinted by permission of the William Saroyan Foundation.

Lynda Schor, excerpt from "Class Outing" from *True Love & Real Romance* by Lynda Schor. Reprinted by permission of The Putnam Publishing Group. Copyright © 1979 by Lynda Schor.

Paula Sharp, "Books" from *The Impostor* by Paula Sharp. Reprinted by permission of HarperCollins Publishers, Inc. Copyright © 1991 by Paula Sharp.

Frances Silverberg, excerpt from "Rebecca By Any Other Name." From *American Scene: New Voices,* edited by Don M. Wolfe. Copyright © 1963 by Don M. Wolfe. Published by arrangement with Carol Publishing Group. A Lyle Stuart Book.

Maria Teresa Solari, "Death and Transfiguration of a Teacher" [edited by Correas de Zapata] is reprinted with permission of the publisher from *Short Stories by Latin American Women* (Houston: Arte Publico Press—University of Houston, 1990).

Elizabeth Spencer, "The Bufords," copyright © 1967 by Elizabeth Spencer. From *The Stories of Elizabeth Spencer.* Used by permission of Doubleday, a division of Bantam Doubleday Dell Publishing Group, Inc.

Eddie Stack, "Limbo" from *The West: Stories from Ireland,* 1989. Reprinted by permission of Elder Books.

Mary Elizabeth Vroman, "See How They Run," published in 1951 by *Colliers* Magazine. Copyright 1951 by Mary Elizabeth Vroman.

Jacqueline Wilson, "The Boy Who Couldn't Read," 1979. Reprinted by permission of Laurence Pollinger Limited as agent for the author.

Richard Yates, "Fun With a Stranger," copyright © 1955 by Richard Yates and "Doctor Jack-o-Lantern," copyright © 1962 by Richard Yates. Reprinted from *Eleven Kinds of Loneliness,* by permission of The Ned Leavitt Agency, on behalf of the author.

Spiro Zavos, "Class Wars" from *Faith of our Fathers,* published by University of Queensland Press, 1982. Reprinted by permission of University of Queensland Press.

# BIBLIOGRAPHY

Barone, T. "A Narrative of Enhanced Professionalism." *Educational Researcher* 21, no. 8 (1992):15–24.

Benjet, R. "Opening and Closing the Door." In *Images of Schoolteachers in Twentieth Century America,* edited by P. Joseph and G. Burnaford, 231–242. N.Y.: St. Martin's Press, 1994.

Bilken, S. "Good Morning, Miss Mundy: Fictional Portrayals of Young Female School Teachers." Paper presented at the annual meeting of the American Educational Research Association, San Francisco, California, April 1986.

Bower, E. *The Handicapped in Literature.* Denver: Love Publishing, 1980.

Briggs, F. "The Changing Concept of the Public School Teacher as Portrayed in American Novels: 1990–1960." Doctoral dissertation, University of North Carolina, Chapel Hill, 1962.

Britton, B., and A. Pellegrini, eds. *Narrative Thought and Narrative Language.* Hillsdale, N.J.: Erlbaum, 1990.

Brooks, C., and R. P. Warren. *Understanding Fiction.* New York: Appleton-Century-Croft, 1959.

Bruner, J. *Actual Minds, Possible Worlds.* Cambridge, MA.: Harvard University Press, 1986.

Bruner, J. "Narrative and Paradigmatic Modes of Thought. In *Learning and Teaching as Ways of Knowing* (84th yearbook of the National Society of the Study of Education), edited by E. Eisner, 97–115. Chicago: University of Chicago Press, 1985.

Cardarelli, A. "Teachers Under Cover: Promoting the Personal Reading of Teachers." *Reading Teacher* 45, no. 9 (1992): 664–668.

Carter, K. "The Place of Story in the Study of Teaching and Teacher Education." *Educational Researcher* 22, no. 1 (1993): 5–12, 18.

Charles, D. "The Stereotype of the Teacher in American Literature. *Educational Forum* 14, (1950): 299–305.

Ciolli, A. *The Teacher in Fiction.* Brooklyn, N.Y.: Brooklyn College Library, 1955.

Coles, R. *The Call of Stories.* Boston: Houghton-Mifflin, 1989.

Connelly, M., and J. Clandinin. "Stories of Experience and Narrative Inquiry." *Educational Researcher* 19, no. 5 (1990): 2–14.

Coser, L., ed. *Sociology through Literature.* Englewood Cliffs, N.J.: Prentice-Hall, 1963.

Deegan, D. *The Stereotype of the Single Woman in American Novels.* N.Y.: King's Crown Press, Columbia University, 1951.

Dietrich, R., and R. Sundell. *The Art of Fiction.* New York: Holt, Rinehart, Winston, 1978.

Duell, L., ed. *The Teacher's Treasure Chest.* Englewood Cliffs, N.J.: Prentice Hall, 1956.

Dyson, A., and C. Genishi. *The Need for Story.* Urbana, IL.: National Council of Teachers of English, 1994.

Eisner, E. *The Enlightened Eye.* New York: Macmillan, 1991.

Egan, K. *Teaching as Story Telling.* London: Routledge, 1988.

Elbaz, F. "Research on Teacher's Knowledge: The Evolution of a Discourse." *Journal of Curriculum Studies* 23, No. 1 (1991): 1–19.

Enger, M. "The Contemporary Images of the Teacher." Doctoral dissertation. Arizona State University, Tempe, 1974.

Fernández, R., ed. *Social Psychology through Literature.* New York: John Wiley, 1972.

Foff, A. "Scholars and Scapegoats." *The English Journal* 47, (1958): 118–126.

Fuess, C., and E. Basford, eds. *Unseen Harvests.* New York: Macmillan, 1947.

Furness, E. "The Image of the High School Teacher in American Literature. *Educational Forum* 24, (1960): 457–464.

Gregory, T. *Juvenile Delinquency in Literature.* New York: Longman, 1980.

Griffin, A. "A Portrait of the Woman Teacher in Twentieth Century Popular Magazines." Doctoral dissertation, Columbia University, New York, 1961.

Grumet, M. *Bitter Milk: Women and Teaching.* Amherst, MA.: University of Massachusetts Press, 1988.

Gudmundsdottir, S. "Story-maker, Story-teller: Narrative Structures in Curriculum." *Journal of Curriculum Studies* 23, (1991): 207–218.

Hansen-Krening, N. "Author of Color: A Multicultural Perspective." *Journal of Reading* 36, no. 2 (1992): 124–129.

Jackson, P. *Life in Classrooms.* New York: Holt, Rinehart & Winston, 1968.

Jones, H. "Some Aspects of an Occupational Stereotype: The American Public School Teacher." Doctoral dissertation, Claremont Graduate School, Claremont California, 1957.

Joseph, P., and G. Burnaford. *Images of Schoolteachers in Twentieth Century America.* New York: St. Martin's Press, 1994.

Kauffman, N. "An Analysis of the Teacher as Portrayed in Modern Juvenile Fiction." Doctoral dissertation, Columbia University, New York, 1962.

Landau, E., S. Epstein, and A. Stone. *Child Development Through Literature.* Englewood Cliffs, N.J.: Prentice-Hall, 1972.

Lass, A., and N. Tasman, eds. *Going to School: An Anthology of Prose about Teachers and Students.* New York: Mentor, 1980.

Le Guin, U. "The Stories We Agree to Tell." *New York Times Book Review,* 12 March 1995, 6.

Lightfoot, S. *The Good High School.* New York: Basic Books, 1983.

Lincoln, Y., and E. Guba. *Naturalistic Inquiry.* Beverly Hills: Sage, 1985.

Lortie, D. *School Teacher: A Sociological Study.* Chicago: University of Chicago Press, 1975.

Manke, M. "The Sentimental Image of the Rural Schoolteacher." In *Images of Schoolteachers in Twentieth Century America,* edited by P. Joseph and G. Burnaford, 243–257. New York: St. Martin's Press, 1994.

Martin, W. *Recent Theories of Narrative.* Ithaca, N.Y.: Cornell University Press, 1986.

Megroy, R. *Pedagogues are Human.* London: Rockcliff, 1950.

Miller, J. Hillis. "Narrative." In *Critical Terms for Literary Study,* edited by F. Lentricchia and T. McLaughlin, 66–79. Chicago: University of Chicago Press, 1990.

Mills, A. "The Image of the Teacher in the Nineteenth Century American Novel." Doctoral dissertation. Temple University, Philadelphia, 1977.

Mitchell, W. *On Narrative.* Chicago: University of Chicago Press, 1981.

Nissman, A. "An Investigation into the Image of the Teacher as Reflected in Selected American Short Stories Published between 1900–1964." Doctoral dissertation. Pennsylvania State University, University Park, 1965.

Noddings, N. "Stories in Dialogue: Caring and Interpersonal Reasoning." In *Stories Lives Tell: Narrative and Dialogue in Education* edited by C. Witherell and N. Noddings, 157–170. New York: Teachers College Press, 1991.

Polkinghorne, D. *Narrative Knowing and the Human Sciences.* New York: State University of New York Press, 1988.

Sarbin, T. "The Narrative as a Root Metaphor for Psychology." In *Narrative Psychology: The Storied Nature of Human Conduct,* edited by T. Sarbin, 3–21. New York: Praeger, 1986.

Scholes, R., and R. Kellogg. *The Nature of Narrative.* New York: Oxford University Press, 1966.

Silko, L. *Ceremony.* New York: Viking Press, 1977.

Smith, L., D. Thomas, and C. Nicholas. "Utilizing Literature as a Vehicle for Teaching about Multicultural Education in a Reading Methods Course." In *Inquiries in Literacy and Instruction,* edited by T. Raskinski and N. Padak, 162–170. Fifteenth Yearbook of the College Reading Association, Kent Ohio: College Reading Association, 1993.

Spradley, J., and G. McDonough, eds. *Anthropology through Literature.* Boston: Little, Brown and Co., 1973.

Tama, M., and K. Peterson. "Achieving Reflectivity through Literature." *Educational Leadership* 48, no. 6 (1991): 22–24.

Tiedt, I. Responding to the Call of Stories: Learning from Literary Case Studies. *Phi Delta Kappan* 73, no. 10 (1992): 802–805.

Tiedt, I., and S. Tiedt. "Unrequired Reading: An Annotated Bibliography for Teachers and School Administrators." Eugene, Oregon: Oregon State University Press, 1967.

Trabue, A. "An Analysis of Guidance Procedures Reflected in Student-teacher Relationships Portrayed in Selected Popular Fiction." Doctoral dissertation., University of North Carolina, Chapel Hill, 1962.

Valence, E. "The Public Curriculum of Orderly Images." *Educational Researcher* 24, no. 2 (1995): 4–13.

Vitz, P. "The Use of Stories in Moral Development." *American Psychologist* 45, no. 6 (1990): 709–720.

Walsh, W. *Autobiographical Literature and Educational Thought.* Cambridge: Leeds University Press, 1959.

Warren, R. *New and Selected Essays (Why Do We Read Fiction?).* New York: Random House, 1989.

# THE SUBJECT INDEX

Developing the subject index that follows was not an easy task. As we have already noted, the stories contained in this volume are not easy to categorize. Most of them would have fit easily in several of the ten sections so our decisions about where to place a story were subjective, guided only by our own interpretations.

Most of these stories are complex and weave various themes within them. Nonetheless, we believe the users of this book would benefit from a few guideposts through the density of the 51 stories included in the book. Stories within each section are keyed to a list of topics. We believe this will assist readers in their search for those topics that most interest them. In doing this we have added to a few additional categories such as setting, level and curricular area, as well as a few others which we think are salient but are not otherwise addressed in the book.

Our intention is to provide guideposts to your reading, not to limit it. The value of a given story is not determined by the topic but by the reader's response to the author's message. As Robert Coles points out: "... constructing a good reading list involves not so much matching student interest with author's subject matter ... as considering the degree of moral engagement a particular text seems able to make with any number of readers" (p. 190). Whether a story takes place in an urban or rural setting, or at an elementary or secondary school, is less important than the reader's response to the "writer's call."

# THE AUTHOR INDEX